# The Oligosaccharides

Scientific Editors: Ivan Ernest, D.Sc.

Jaromír Hebký, D.Sc.

Translated by Karel Mayer

Translation Editor: P. M. Williams

# The
# Oligosaccharides

JAROSLAV STANĚK, D.Sc., MILOSLAV ČERNÝ, D.Sc.,
JOSEF PACÁK, D.Sc.

ACADEMIC PRESS
NEW YORK AND LONDON

PUBLISHING HOUSE
OF THE CZECHOSLOVAK ACADEMY
OF SCIENCES • PRAGUE

1965

Academic Press Inc., 111 Fifth Avenue, New York, New York 10003

Library of Congress Catalog Card Number 64-18218

Copyright Ⓒ by Nakladatelství Československé akademie věd, Praha 1965

Translation Ⓒ by Karel Mayer 1965

Printed in Czechoslovakia

# Preface

Oligosaccharides do belong without doubt to very specific chapters of organic chemistry, as explained in our Preface to the English edition of Monosaccharides. It seemed to us advisable to subdivide the chemistry of saccharides into that of monosaccharides and oligosaccharides (polysaccharides will not appear as a third part, belonging to these two, mentioned above).

Writing a monograph on Oligosaccharides is a very attractive task, especially because such a book has never been written before. The latest monographs on saccharides reserved for the chemistry of oligosaccharides generally amount to two or three scores of pages. However, much may be deduced from the results obtained in the chemistry of oligosaccharides in last few years. The number of oligosaccharides that have been obtained both from natural materials and by synthetic methods, as well as the number of oligosaccharide derivatives, provide sufficient material for a substantial monograph. The results mentioned above are due to the well-known modern methods of isolation and identification, especially chromatographic methods; enzymic syntheses are particularly useful and they have already yielded many new substances.

The Czech edition of Oligosaccharides, issued early in 1962 and with references until 1960, was very well received. The English edition is a very great honour for us; however, after our preliminary negotiations with representatives of Academic Press, we decided against a direct translation and, with the aim of incorporating recent developments chose to produce a completely new edition.

The book is written using a system very similar to that used for Monosaccharides; compared with the Czech edition, this new edition, where necessary or helpful, is supplemented with new results and partly rearranged.

It is assumed, of course, that the reader knows the fundamental concepts not only of organic chemistry, but also of monosaccharides; reactions which are typical for monosaccharides are not explained again. The Tollens formulas have been omitted completely and replaced by the Haworth formulas, though these are sometimes more difficult for the reader. Various functional groups are represented by abbreviations currently employed, for instance *Ac*- (for acetyl), *Ms*- (for mesyl, i.e. methanesulphonyl), *Ts*- (for tosyl, i.e. *p*-toluenesulphonyl), *Tr*- (for trityl, i.e. triphenylmethyl), etc.

As to the nomenclature used, our manuscript has been adjusted to the usage of English literature according to the rules given in the *Journal of the Chemical Society (London) 1952*, 5108—5121 and *Journal of Organic Chemistry 28*, 281 (1963).

We trust that the contents of all important papers published before September 1962 has been considered; all important new data have been adjoined in October 1963 and June 1964 in the form of notes. Informations about papers, which were unintentionally omitted, will be very much appreciated; let us hope that they will be not very many.

Great care was devoted to references to reviews, especially in *Advances in Carbohydrate Chemistry, Quarterly Reviews, Angewandte Chemie* and other journals.

Chapters on the analytical chemistry of oligosaccharides have been prepared by Mr. M. Černý and Mr. J. Pacák. Their work was a very great help, as well as critical comments of unnamed colleagues. Mr. W. Walter, professor in Organic Chemistry, University of Hamburg, read the Czech Edition of Oligosaccharides very carefully and communicated to us some very important comments; his help is appreciated very much.

We are extremely indebted to Mr. I. Ernest and Mr. J. Hebký for their active participation as reviewers. They studied very thoroughly all the English manuscript in an extremely short period, having devoted all their free time to it, and called my attention to many minor inaccuracies. As well as this, they balanced all the delay almost from the period of translation.

Our work was greatly facilitated by the fact that the translator, Mr. K. Mayer, pointed out quite a number of possible improvements to certain passages in the text. Mr. P. M. Williams, Harrow, made the final, very thorough stylistic revision and drew our attention to many inconsistencies; we are very much indebted for his help.

Our thanks are due to the editorial staff of the Publishing House of the Czechoslovak Academy of Sciences as well as to the employees of the Knihtisk printing-works, who converted our manuscript into a book representing us well with its lay-out and graphic arrangement.

J. Staněk                                            *Prague, October 8, 1963*

# Contents

# I

# Nomenclature of Oligosaccharides

By definition,[1] an oligosaccharide is a compound which, on complete hydrolysis, gives one or more monosaccharides, in relatively small numbers per molecule (in contrast to the high-polymeric polysaccharides). The term oligosaccharides (from the Greek *oligos*, a few)[2] is applied to the whole group of these composite saccharides.

Most frequently encountered are the disaccharides, composed of two monosaccharide molecules, and the trisaccharides, containing three molecules; less common are tetrasaccharides, pentasaccharides and hexasaccharides, however, even higher oligosaccharides with a defined molecular weight are known. For this reason, substances of up to ten monosaccharide molecules are included into the group of oligosaccharides.

The cleavage products of oligosaccharides are most frequently hexoses and less usually pentoses. However, even some of their derivatives may be encountered, such as their *O*-methyl ethers, deoxy sugars, aminodeoxy sugars, anhydro sugars, as well as uronic acids and their *O*-methyl ethers.

In general, two types of oligosaccharide can be distinguished, namely nonreducing and reducing compounds. In the latter group, one hemiacetal hydroxyl group is preserved in the molecule and thus also its reducing power. In our further considerations, it will be advantageous to restrict the nomenclature to disaccharides and to simplify the case to a disaccharide composed of two D-glucose molecules; if the disaccharide were composed of two different monosaccharide molecules, the situation would be analogous, but the number of possible isomers would be larger. The same applies to trisaccharides, tetrasaccharides, etc.

A non-reducing disaccharide is derived by eliminating one water molecule from the hemiacetal hydroxyl groups of two molecules of a monosaccharide, for example, of D-glucose. The resultant substance has no free hemiacetal hydroxyl group and consequently also no reducing properties. Such a compound, corresponding to the general formula (I) is, according to the classification of sugar derivatives, in fact a double glycoside and, for this reason, substances of this type are also generally termed glycosyl aldosides or glycosyl ketosides (a less usual name, which, however, steadily appears in the German

*References see p. 22*

literature,[3] is Glycosidoaldoside or Glycosidoketoside; the first of both styles is more logical).

(I)

However, a disaccharide composed of two D-glucose molecules linked in this way can exist in three isomeric forms, in which both D-glucose units are bound together in the relations α, α; α, β; or β, β; according to this, there must and actually do exist three isomeric D-glucopyranosyl D-glucopyranosides (so-called trehaloses).

α-D-Glucopyranosyl α-D-glucopyranoside
Trehalose

α-D-Glucopyranosyl β-D-glucopyranoside
neo-Trehalose

β-D-Glucopyranosyl β-D-glucopyranoside
Isotrehalose

If two different monosaccharides are combined in this way, the situation is analogous, but there are four possible isomers, as can be demonstrated in, for example, D-glucopyranosyl D-fructofuranoside, i. e. of sucrose and its isomers.

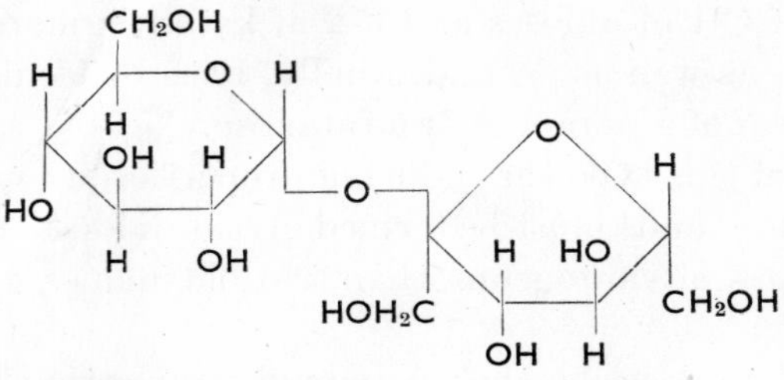

α-D-Glucopyranosyl α-D-fructofuranoside

α-D-Glucopyranosyl β-D-fructofuranoside

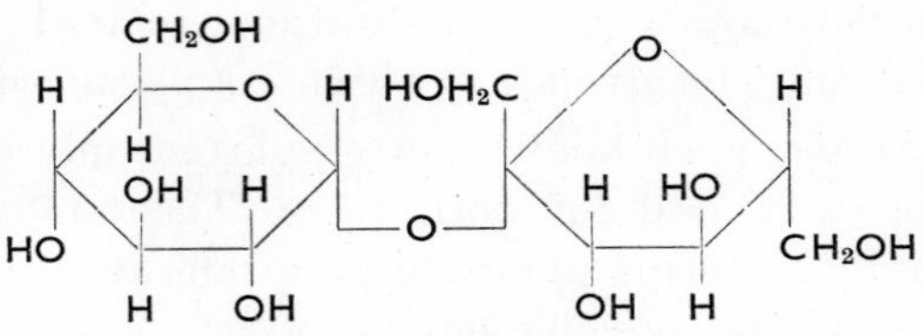

Sucrose (saccharose)

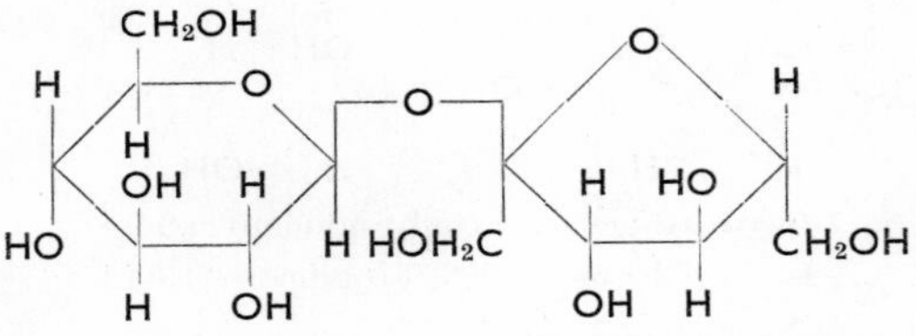

β-D-Glucopyranosyl α-D-fructofuranoside

Isosucrose

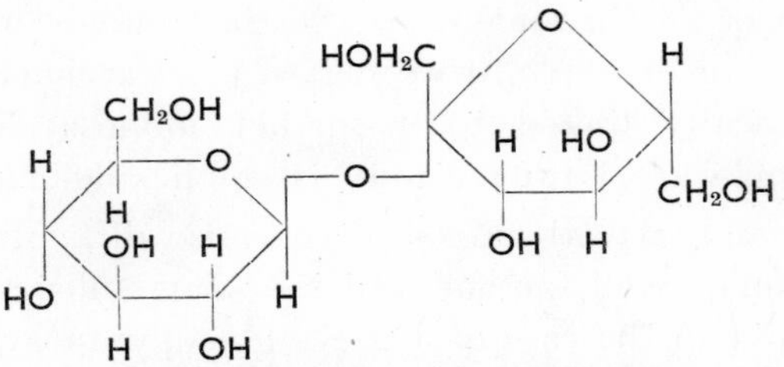

β-D-Glucopyranosyl β-D-fructofuranoside

References see p. 22

Reducing disaccharides are in principle *O*-substituted derivatives of a monosaccharide to which another monosaccharide is bound by a glycosidic linkage. Even two molecules of one and the same monosaccharide may give rise to a large number of reducing disaccharides, for the glycosidically bound monosaccharide may be linked to any hydroxyl group of the other monosaccharide (except that at C-1 of aldoses and C-2 of ketoses); moreover, the glycosidic bond may be α- as well as β-, and, finally, both molecules bound together may exist in the form of a pyranose or a furanose.

In substances of this type the reducing properties are preserved and, consequently, these compounds must be termed glycosylaldoses or glycosylketoses. This is likewise more advantageous than the old names glycosidoaldoses or glycosidoketoses.[3,4]

The term used to describe the compound in question must be based on that of the monosaccharide whose reducing function has been preserved and this name must be preceded by that of the substituting monosaccharide, also indicating the respective anomeric configuration. In both parts the state of the ring arrangement must be given (i.e. whether a pyranose or a furanose).

According to the older methods,[5] now employed only exceptionally,[3] the numerical indication was used for both rings. The now generally adopted system[1] sets out from the terms pyranose or furanose. Thus, maltose can be defined by the following two possible names:

4-*O*-α-D-Glucopyranosyl-D-glucopyranose
4-[α-D-Glucosido⟨1,5⟩]-D-glucose⟨1,5⟩

Another method, formerly also applied,[6] according to which maltose was termed 4-D-glucose-α-D-glucopyranoside, has fallen into disuse.

Many disaccharides have trivial names, of course, and the same applies to higher oligosaccharides. In some cases, this fact may be utilized for creating new denominations, for example, if we regard a trisaccharide as a known disaccharide glycosidically linked to a further monosaccharide (see later). A systematic nomenclature, however, must be applicable in all cases.

On the other hand, trivial names often cause difficulties if one or more denominations are employed for one and the same substance. For example, there is no uniformity in the case of 3-*O*-α-D-glucopyranosyl-D-glucose, which is termed nigerose as well as sakébiose. Similarly, some authors use the name amylobiose for maltose, and another term, dextranbiose, may be introduced for isomaltose (in the last two cases, analogous names of all four types are employed for higher oligosaccharides).

* * *

The naming of trisaccharides and higher oligosaccharides requires a certain modification of this nomenclature. In the case of trisaccharides, the molecule may always be divided into a disaccharide with either one (reducing trisaccharide) or two (non-reducing trisaccharide) glycosidic linkages; a further glycosidic linkage attaches the third constituent of the molecule, in this case a monosaccharide. A name of similar type, such as 4-$O$-$\alpha$-D-glucopyranosyl-6-$O$-$\alpha$-D-glucopyranosyl-D-glucose, would not be unambiguous; for branched oligosaccharides are known to occur where, for instance, a D-glucose molecule is substituted in two positions by glycosidically bound monosaccharides. The above-mentioned term would not indicate whether the three glucose units are arranged in line or branched. A more exact application of such a nomenclature would probably require the introduction of various brackets etc. and thus lead to a very complicated and cumbersome system.

The generally adopted method[1] is based on the principle that, in the description of the composition of an oligosaccharide, an arrow shall be used to connect those numbers that indicate the carbon atoms, one from each of the two monosaccharide molecules, which are linked by an oxygen atom, regardless of whether a single (reducing oligosaccharide) or a twofold (non-reducing oligosaccharide) glycosidic bond is concerned.

According to this, there are two possible names for a non-reducing trisaccharide, such as raffinose.

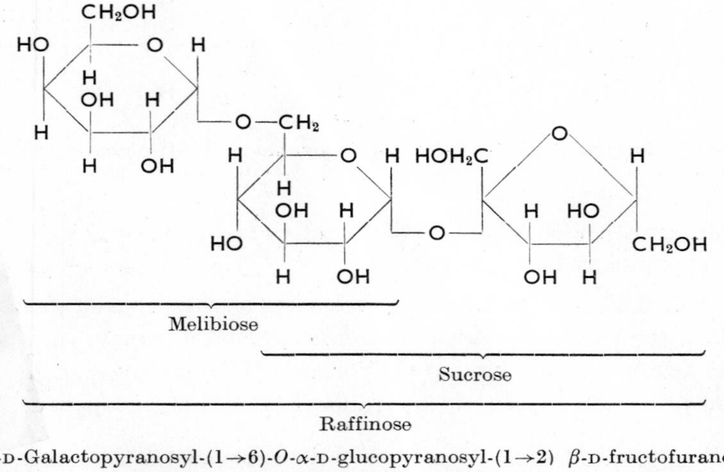

$O$-$\alpha$-D-Galactopyranosyl-$(1\rightarrow6)$-$O$-$\alpha$-D-glucopyranosyl-$(1\rightarrow2)$ $\beta$-D-fructofuranoside
$O$-$\beta$-D-Fructofuranosyl-$(2\rightarrow1)$-$O$-$\alpha$-D-glucopyranosyl-$(6\rightarrow1)$ $\alpha$-D-galactopyranoside

*References see p. 22*

Moreover, no objections can be raised against defining raffinose as α-me-libiosyl β-D-fructofuranoside, since this compound is in fact a non-reducing trisaccharide in which the carbonyl groups of the disaccharide melibiose and the monosaccharide D-fructose are linked glycosidically.

According to this conception, it will not be difficult to form a correct name for the non-reducing trisaccharide gentianose (α-gentiobiosyl β-D-fructofura-noside).

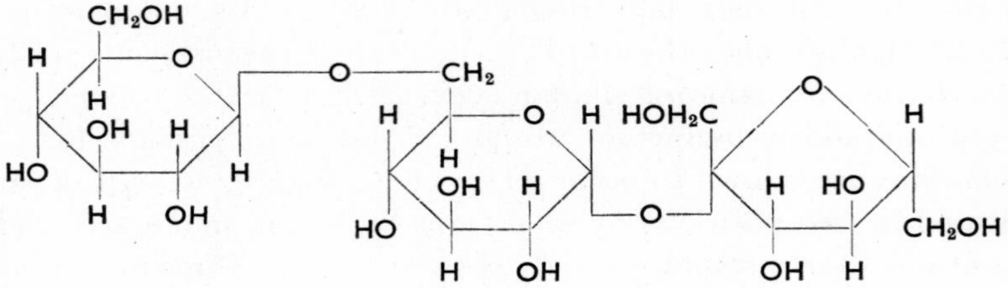

Gentianose

O-β-D-Glucopyranosyl-(1→6)-O-α-D-glucopyranosyl-(1→2)  β-D-fructofuranoside
O-β-D-Fructofuranosyl-(2→1)-O-α-D-glucopyranosyl-(6→1)  β-D-glucopyranoside

Names for reducing trisaccharides can be created in a very similar way. Maltotriose, which also could be termed 4-O-α-maltosyl-D-glucopyranose, is quite exactly and unambiguously defined as

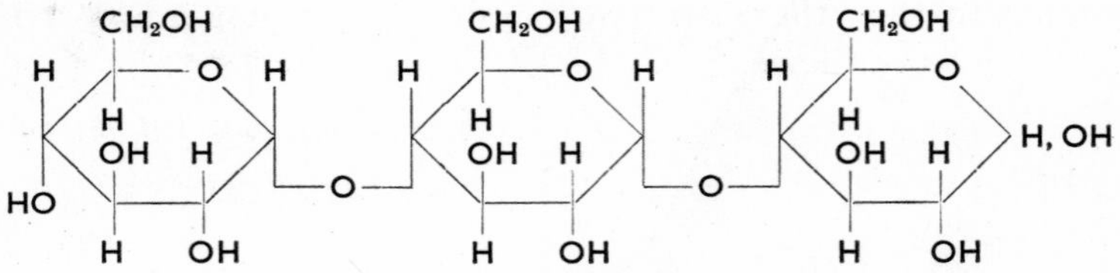

Maltotriose

O-α-D-Glucopyranosyl-(1→4)-O-α-D-glucopyranosyl-(1→4)-D-glucopyranose

Extending this system, it is not difficult to formulate an exact systematic name for the pentasaccharide verbascose.

This method can also be applied to branched oligosaccharides*; in this case, however, the branched part of the molecule is given in square brackets. Thus, the branched trisaccharide having the formula (II) must be written as O-α-D-glucopyranosyl-(1→4)-O-[α-D-glucopyranosyl-(1→6)]-D-glucopyranose; here it

---

* The term branched oligosaccharide has been recommended independently by R. de Souza and I. J. Goldstein, Tetrahedron Letters *1964*, 1215.

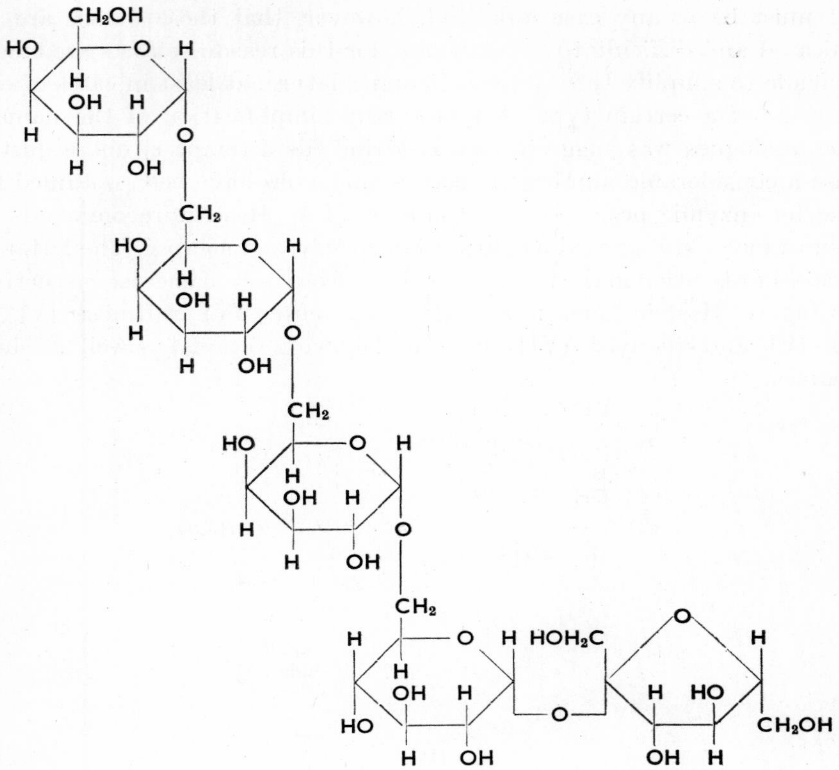

Verbascose

$O$-α-D-Galactopyranosyl-$(1\rightarrow6)$-$O$-α-D-galactopyranosyl-$(1\rightarrow6)$-$O$-α-D-**galactopyranosyl-$(1\rightarrow6)$**-$O$-α-D-glucopyranosyl-$(1\rightarrow2)$ β-D-fructofuranoside

is possible to employ also the simpler denomination 4,6-di-$O$-α-D-glucopyranosyl-D-glucopyranose.[2]

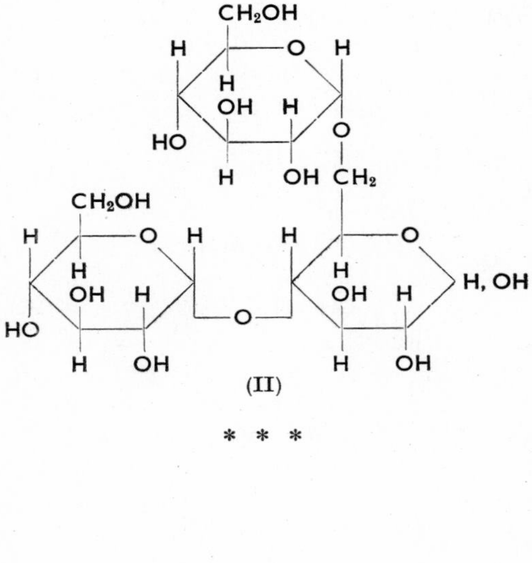

(II)

* * *

*References see p. 22*

It must be in any case admitted, however, that these names are very complicated and difficult to set out and, for this reason, efforts are steadily being made to simplify this system of nomenclature, at least in cases of oligosaccharides of a certain type. A noteworthy simplification of the names of sucrose analogues was suggested by Hestrin;[7] his attempt is not unjustified because a considerable number of sucrose analogues have been obtained from sucrose by enzymic processes (see Chapter VI.5). Hestrin recommends that such substances be regarded as glycosyl derivatives of sucrose. The letters[F] or [G] indicate substitution in the fructose or the glucose unit of sucrose respectively. According to Hestrin, melezitose (III), planteose (IV), raffinose (V), *neo*-kestose (VI) and stachyose (VII) have the following rational as well as shortened names.

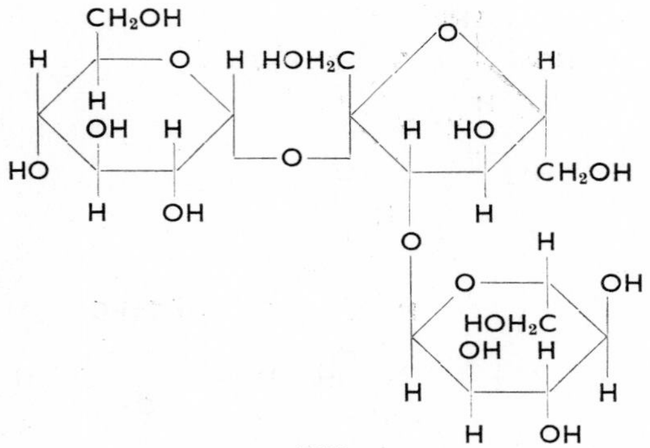

(III)
Melezitose

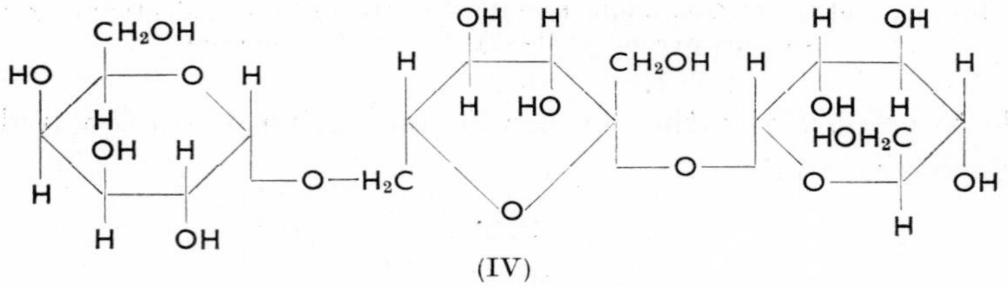

(IV)
Planteose

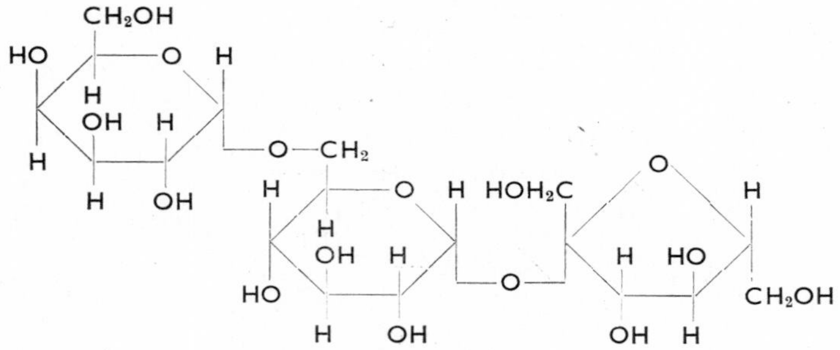

(V)
Raffinose

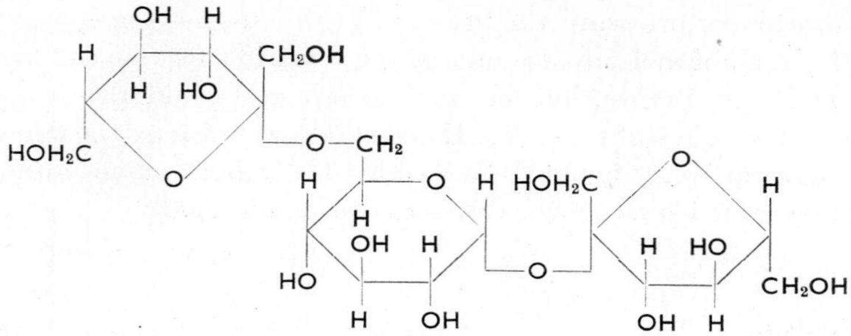

(VI)

*neo*-Kestose

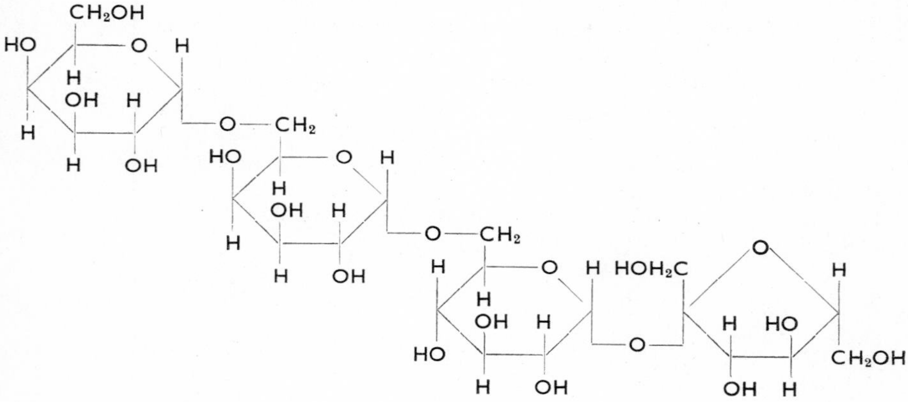

(VII)

Stachyose

## Table I

Oligosaccharide Nomenclature

| Oligosaccharide | Rational Name | Designation According to Hestrin[7] |
|---|---|---|
| Melezitose | *O*-α-D-glucopyranosyl-(-1→3)-*O*-β-D-fructofurano-syl-(2→1) α-D-glucopyranoside | 3$^F$-α-glucosylsucrose |
| Planteose | *O*-α-D-galactopyranosyl-(1→6)-*O*-β-D-fructofura-nosyl-(2→1) α-D-glucopyranoside | 6$^F$-α-galactosylsucrose |
| Raffinose | *O*-α-D-galactopyranosyl-(1→6)-*O*-α-D-glucopyra-nosyl-(1→2) β-D-fructofuranoside | 6$^G$-α-galactosylsucrose |
| *neo*-Kestose | *O*-β-D-fructofuranosyl-(2→6)-*O*-α-D-glucopyrano-syl-(1→2) β-D-fructofuranoside | 6$^G$-β-fructosylsucrose |
| Stachyose | *O*-α-D-galactopyranosyl-(1→6)-*O*-α-D-galactopy-ranosyl-(1→6)-*O*-α-D-glucopyranosyl-(1→2) β-D-fructofuranoside | 6$^G$-α-galactobiosyl-sucrose |

*References see p. 22*

This shortening of terms, though very ingenious, has one great disadvantage. The formula of melezitose could be regarded in this case as that of a glucosyl derivative of sucrose, but the same compound could also be considered as a glucosyl derivative of turanose. If somebody were to use the denomination $1^F$-D-glucosylturanose, it is not to be expected that both names formed in this way would be regarded as identical without profound study.

### REFERENCES

1. J. Chem. Soc. *1952*, 5120; J. Org. Chem. *28*, 281 (1963).
2. B. Helferich, E. Bohn, and S. Winkler, Ber. *63*, 989 (1930).
3. F. Micheel, *Chemie der Zucker und Polysaccharide*, Akad. Verlagsges., Leipzig 1956, p. 229.
4. J. F. Bates, *Polarimetry, Saccharimetry and the Sugars*, National Bureau of Standards, Washington 1942, p. 459.
5. M. Bergmann, Ber. *58*, 2647 (1925).
6. W. Pigman and R. M. Goepp, *Chemistry of the Carbohydrates*, Acad. Press, New York 1948, p. 437.
7. S. Hestrin, D. S. Feingold, and G. Avigad, Biochem. J. *64*, 340 (1956).

# II

# Derivation of Oligosaccharide Formulas

In the monosaccharide series it is often possible to obtain a clearer survey by means of acyclic formulas, although they usually do not correspond to the actual state of the molecule. This method is not at all applicable to the group of oligosaccharides, since the non-reducing portion of the oligosaccharide molecule is always exactly fixed in the form of a pyranose or a furanose with definite anomeric configuration. The reducing part of the molecule has as a rule the form of a pyranose, in particular in the case of aldoses; however, even here there are known furanoses in which the non-reducing part of the molecule of the oligosaccharide is bound just to the C-5 carbon atom. If the reducing portion of the oligosaccharide molecule is D-fructose, it is usually linked as fructopyranose (for example, leucrose, see Chapter XII, 1, F).

The structure of oligosaccharides can be represented only by cyclic formulas, either in the Tollens or in the Haworth modifications. The former are well suited for indicating the structure of cellobiose (4-*O*-β-D-glucopyranosyl-D-

(I)                                                         (II)

glucose, I), but less appropriate to the structure of maltose (4-*O*-α-D-glucopy-
ranosyl-D-glucose, II).  The application of the Tollens formulas to the series of
non-reducing oligosacharides involves considerable difficulties, as is evident
from the formula of trehalose (α-D-glucopyranosyl α-D-glucopyranoside, III).

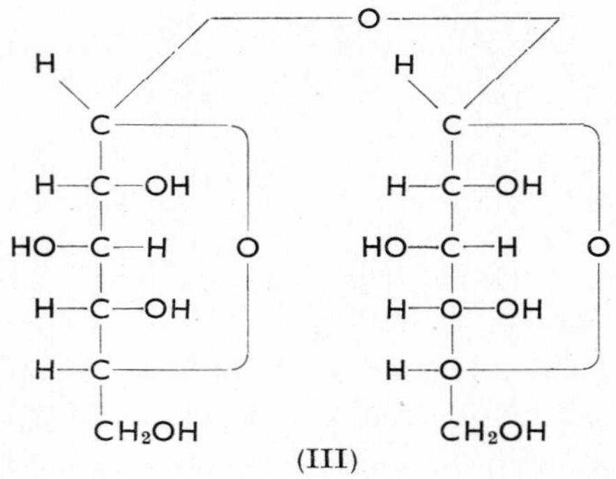

(III)

The Haworth formulas are applicable without exception. The formula of
maltose (IV) is the simplest solution in this respect; the formula of cellobiose
must be expressed with a shift of the non-reducing portion of the molecule
(formula V) or with a partial rotation of the ring in the reducing part (formula
VI), in order to satisfy the requirement of the β-bond in the glycosidic linkage.

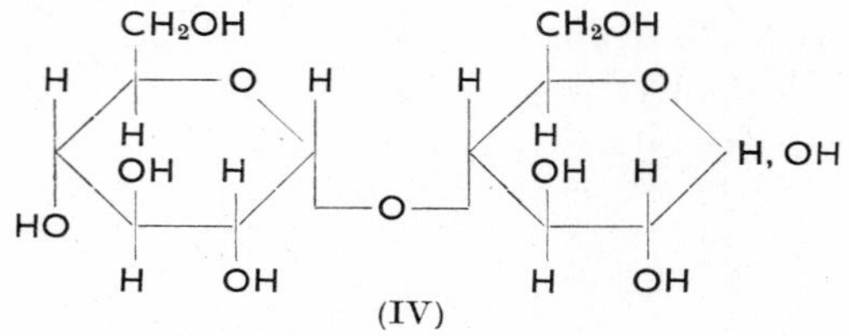

(IV)

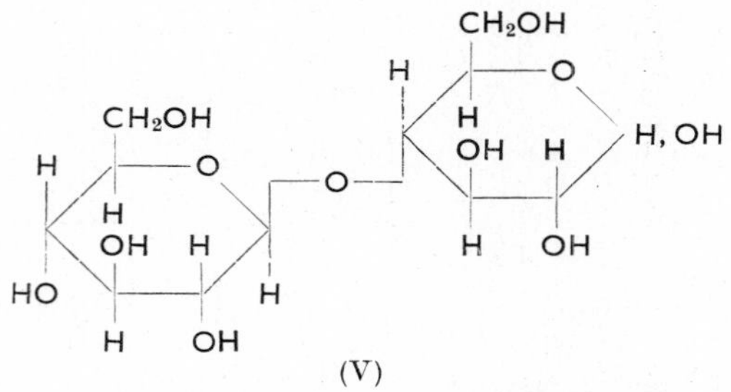

(V)

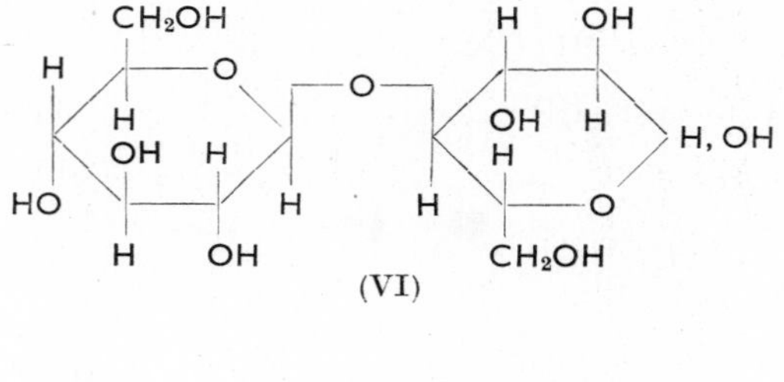

(VI)

As far as non-reducing oligosaccharides are concerned, the formula of a part of the molecule must nearly always be turned around to bring the correct apex of the ring into position at the glycosidic linkage (see formula VII, trehalose), and turning part of the formula will be inevitable in various other cases.

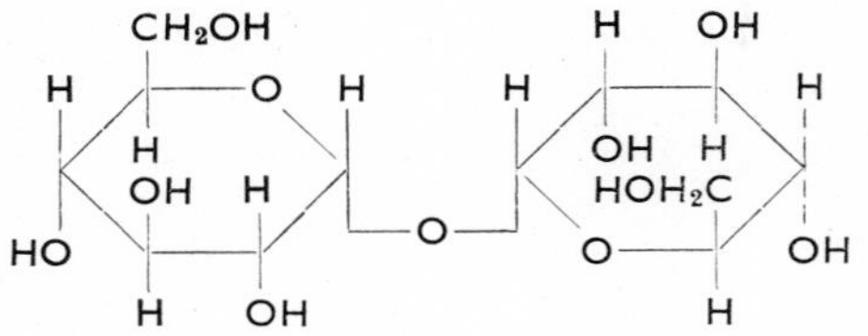

(VII)

In principle it must be borne in mind that all the formulas [(VIII a) to (VIII e)] correspond to D-glucose and any of them can be applied according to requirements; depending on the known mutual position of the hydroxyl groups, the formula of any other aldose can also be rotated into the required state.

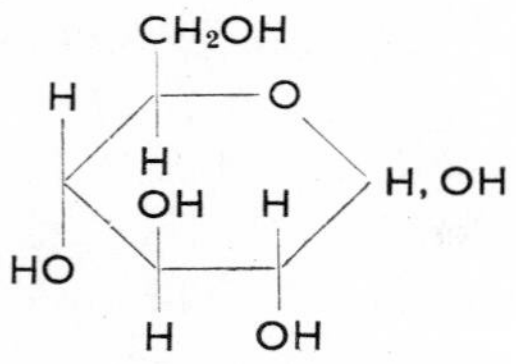

(VIIIa)

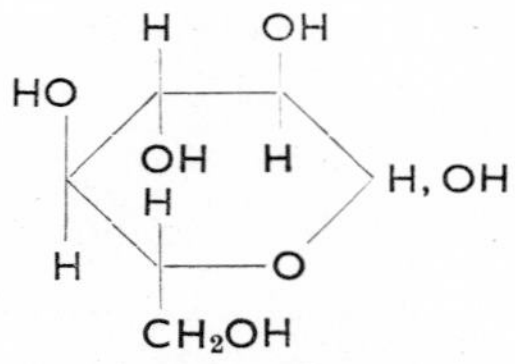

(VIIIb)

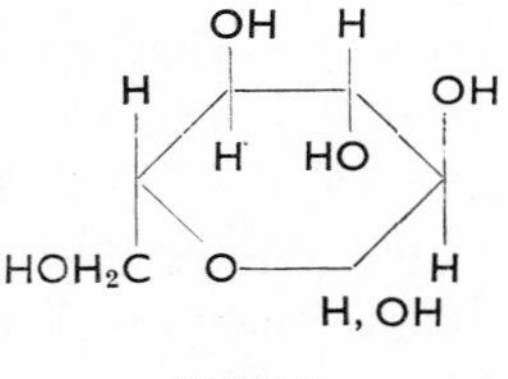

(VIIIc)

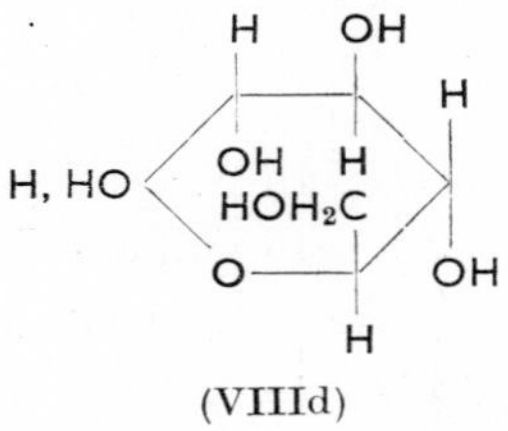

(VIIId)

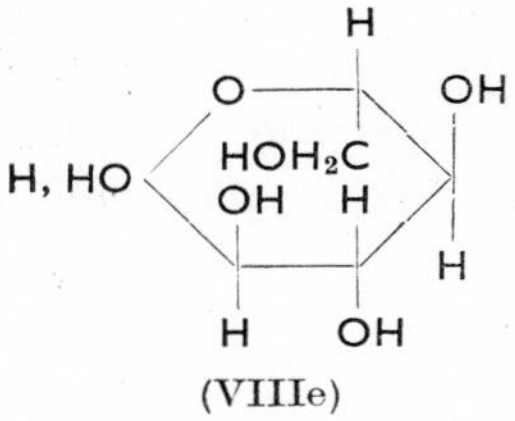

(VIIIe)

# III

# Constitution of Oligosaccharides *

The first task in ascertaining the constitution of oligosaccharides is the identification of the monosaccharide or monosaccharides of which the oligosaccharide molecule is composed. This is effected either by acid or by enzymic hydrolysis; more recent papers describe also the cleavage of oligosaccharides, such as sucrose, on ion exchangers.[1-4] The identification of the cleavage products by means of chromatography on paper[5,6] presents no difficulty.

The hydrolysis products, however, offer little information as to the type of linkage between the monosaccharide molecules in the molecule of the oligosaccharide. Only in the case of non-reducing disaccharides may this problem be solved by hydrolysis, and there still remains the question of whether $\alpha$- or $\beta$-linkages are concerned.

In the case of reducing oligosaccharides it is possible to determine indirectly which of the monosaccharides is not glycosidically bound, i. e. to identify the terminal, reducing portion of the oligosaccharide. The first step required is the oxidation of the reducing oligosaccharide to the corresponding aldonic acid in the oligosaccharide series, whereupon this acid is subjected to hydrolysis. The constitution of lactose (I) was established[7] by oxidizing this substance to lactobionic acid lactone (II), which on hydrolysis yielded a molecule of D-galactose (III) and a molecule of D-gluconic lactone (IV). According to this, lactose must be D-galactosyl-D-glucose and not D-glucosyl-D-galactose.

Elucidating the constitution of higher oligosacharides (trisaccharides, tetrasaccharides, etc.) may be facilitated even by partial hydrolysis, which can be carried out likewise either by acids or by enzymic action (see also Chapter VI, 5). Acid hydrolysis of the trisaccharide melezitose (V) leads to two D-glucose molecules and one D-fructose molecule.[8] Partial hydrolysis of the same trisaccharide yields D-glucose and the disaccharide turanose (3-O-$\alpha$-D-glucopyranosyl-D-fructose).[9] Since melezitose is a non-reducing trisaccharide, the type of the linkage between turanose and D-glucose is clear, therefore, apart from the arrangement at C-1 of both combined parts of the trisaccharide.

---

* For a review see R. W. Bailey and J. B. Pridham, Advances in Carbohydrate Chem. *17*, 121 (1962).

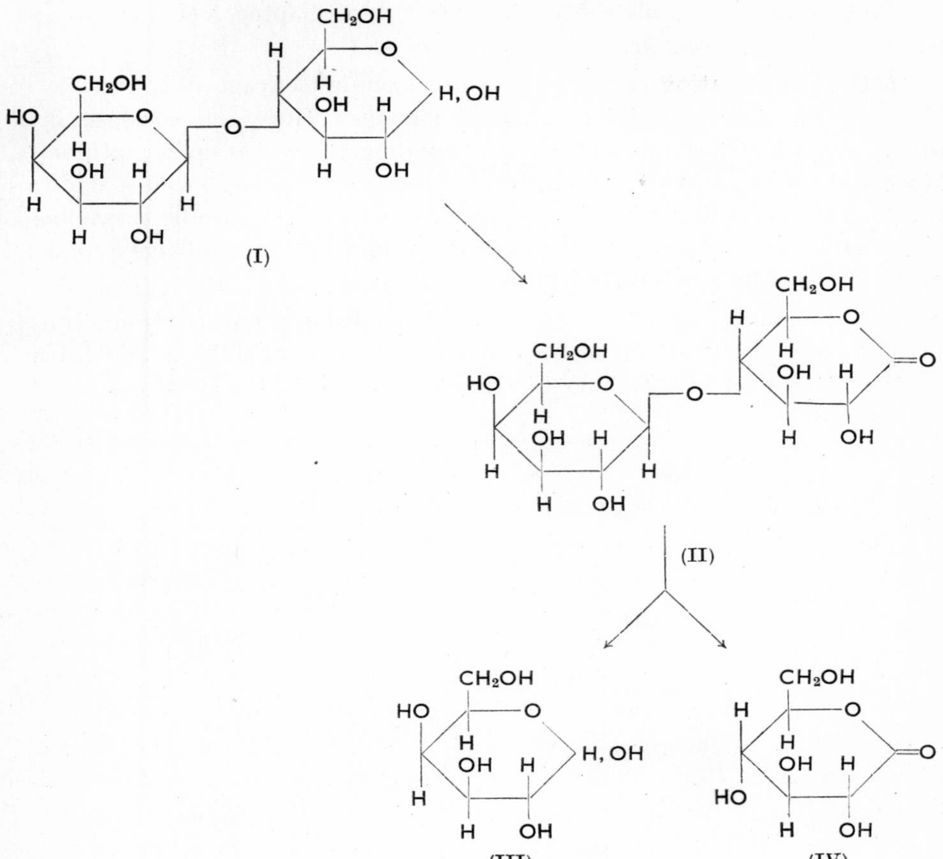

(I)

(II)

(III)          (IV)

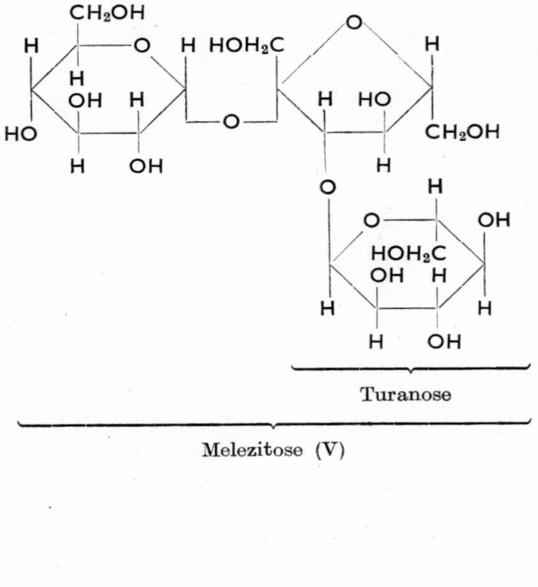

Turanose

Melezitose (V)

References see p. 29

Many similar cases have been described (see Chapter XII, for example with regard to raffinose, planteose and verbascose).

In the investigation of the course of enzymic cleavage it is possible to utilize also the stereoselectivity of various enzymes. Thus, $\alpha$-glucosidases split maltose, manninotriose and melezitose, while $\beta$-glucosidases split gentiobiose, lactose and cellobiose. In the hydrolysis of reducing oligosaccharides, additional information is offered by the change of the values of specific rotations; a decrease of these values during the hydrolysis indicates an $\alpha$-linkage and, conversely, rising values are characteristic of a $\beta$-linkage.

Partial enzymic hydrolysis, too, may be utilized in constitution studies. Since, for example, yeast invertase splits raffinose into melibiose and D-fructose, the latter must here be linked in the same way as in the sucrose molecule.

These applications, too, have been dealt with in several papers (see Chapter XII, for example concerning gentianose, sucrose, planteose, raffinose and stachyose).

\* \* \*

If the monosaccharides of which the oligosaccharide is composed are known, there remain the following points to be determined.

1. The positions of the hydroxyl groups where the monosaccharide molecules are linked together.

2. Whether the monosaccharide molecules are contained in the oligosaccharide molecule in the form of pyranoses or of furanoses.

3. The stereochemistry at the anomeric carbon atoms, i.e. whether α-linkages or β-linkages are present.

The solution of these tasks is undertaken mainly by two methods, i.e. methylation analysis and oxidative degradation either with periodic acid[10] or with lead tetra-acetate,[11] apart from some other procedures which have been employed in individual cases and are of minor importance.

### REFERENCES

1. K. Täufel and K. S. Grunert, Arch. Pharm. *294*, 439 (1961).
2. K. J. Steinbach, K. S. Grunert, and K. Täufel, Nahrung *5*, 617 (1961).
3. K. Täufel and K. S. Grunert, Nahrung *6*, 93 (1962).
4. M. Abdel-Akher, Alexandria J. Agr. Research *6*, No. 2, 13 (1958); Chem. Abstr. *56*, 11681 (1962).
5. J. Staněk, M. Černý, J. Kocourek, and J. Pacák, *The Monosaccharides*, Acad. Press, New York 1963, p. 927.
6. E. Lederer, *Chromatographie en Chimie Organique et Biologique*, Vol. II, Masson et Cie, Paris 1960, p. 1, Chapter by R. Dedonder.
7. E. Fischer and J. Meyer, Ber. *22*, 361 (1889).
8. G. Tanret, Bull. soc. chim. France (3) *35*, 817 (1906).
9. C. S. Hudson and E. Pacsu, J. Am. Chem. Soc. *52*, 2522 (1930).
10. J. M. Bobbitt, Advances in Carbohydrate Chem. *11*, 1 (1956).
11. A. S. Perlin, Advances in Carbohydrate Chem. *14*, 9 (1959).

## 1. METHYLATION ANALYSIS

This method is based upon complete methylation of the oligosaccharide, hydrolysis of the per-O-methyl ether obtained and separation and identification of the hydrolysis products. Methylation of oligosaccharides can be effected by any of the known methods,[1] such as the Purdie method, i.e. methylation by means of methyl iodide in the presence of silver oxide, according to Haworth with dimethyl sulphate in a solution of sodium hydroxide or by the Muskat method, i.e. with methyl iodide in liquid ammonia in the presence of dissolved sodium. The best results are obtained by a combination of the last two methods.

If, after permethylation and hydrolysis, an unsubstituted hydroxyl group is found at C-2, C-3 or C-6 of the aldohexose molecule, the place is directly indicated where the second molecule was attached. Detection of a free hydroxyl group at C-4 or C-5 is not unambiguous; a reducing 1→4 disaccharide, in which the reducing aldohexose has the structure of the pyranose (I), and a reducing 1→5 disaccharide, in which the reducing aldohexose has the structure of the furanose (II), yield on permethylation and hydrolysis the same 2,3,6-tri-*O*-methyl ether of aldohexose (III):

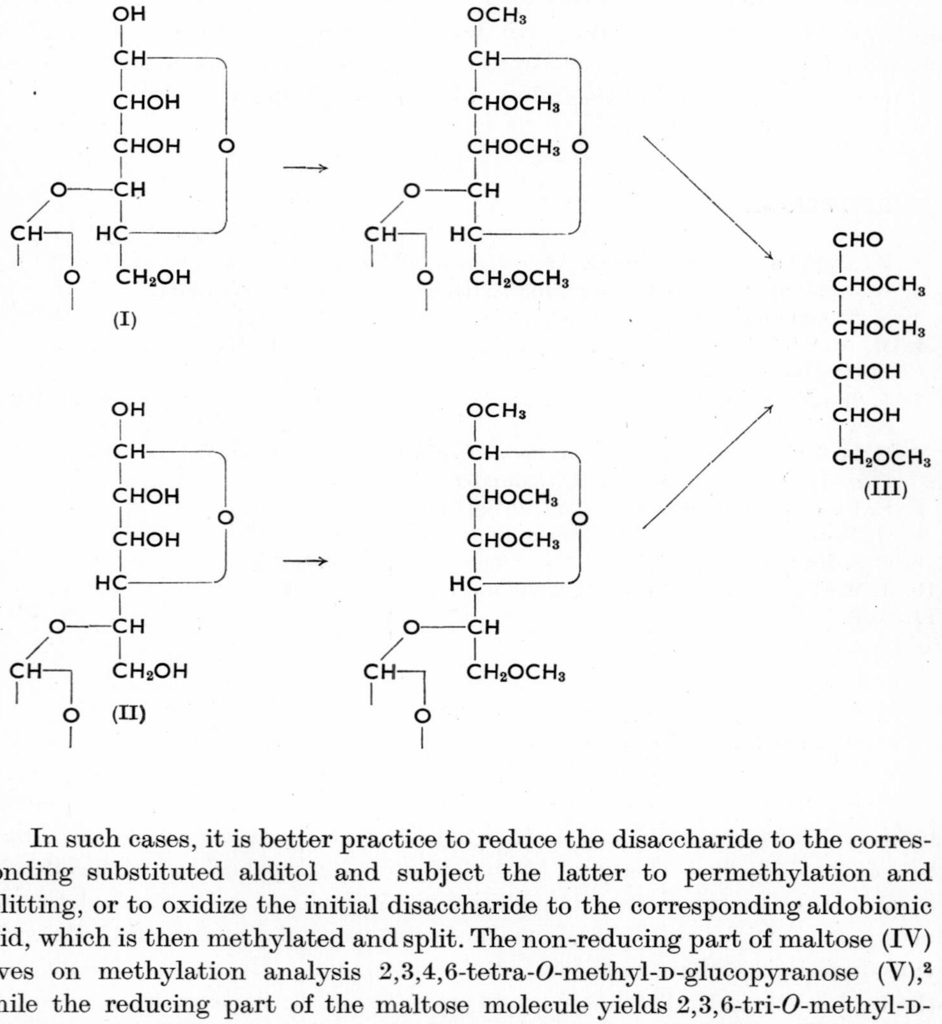

In such cases, it is better practice to reduce the disaccharide to the corresponding substituted alditol and subject the latter to permethylation and splitting, or to oxidize the initial disaccharide to the corresponding aldobionic acid, which is then methylated and split. The non-reducing part of maltose (IV) gives on methylation analysis 2,3,4,6-tetra-*O*-methyl-D-glucopyranose (V),[2] while the reducing part of the maltose molecule yields 2,3,6-tri-*O*-methyl-D-glucopyranose (VI), which does not offer much useful information. If maltose is first reduced to maltitol (VII) and the latter then methylated and split, 1,2,3,5,6-penta-*O*-methyl-D-glucitol (VIII) is obtained besides 2,3,4,6-tetra-*O*-methyl-D-glucose. Oxidation of maltose to maltobionic acid (IX) and hydrolysis of the permethyl derivative of this acid gives besides 2,3,4,6-tetra-*O*-methyl-D-glucose (V) also 2,3,5,6-tetra-*O*-methyl-D-gluconic γ-lactone (X):

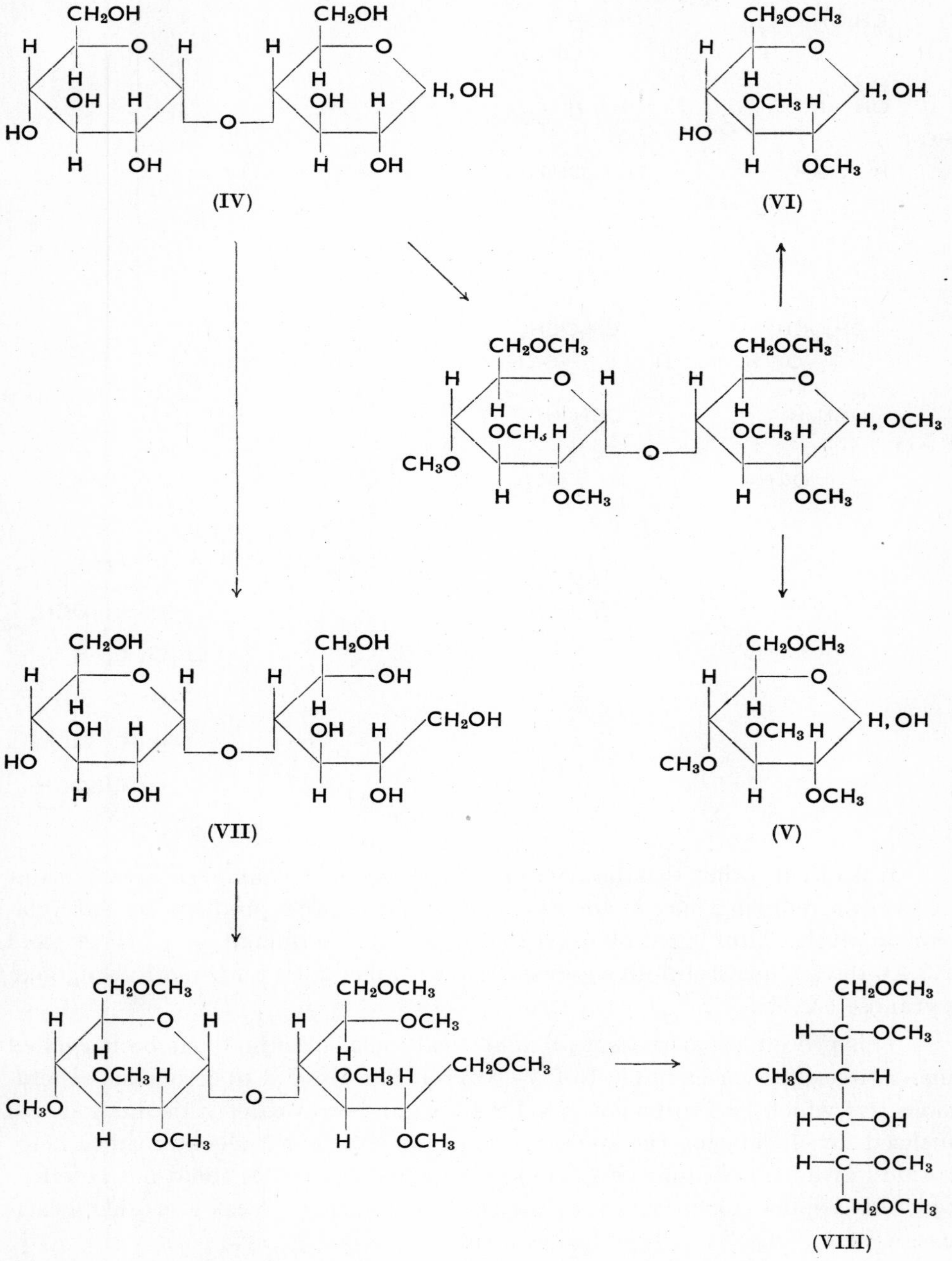

(IV)

(VI)

(VII)

(V)

(VIII)

*References see p. 34*

(IV)

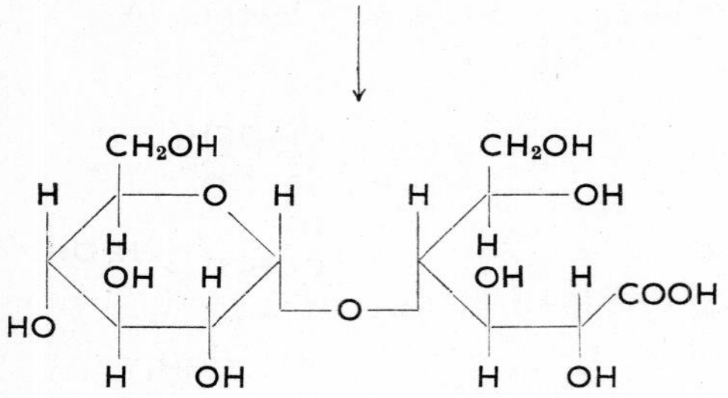

(IX)

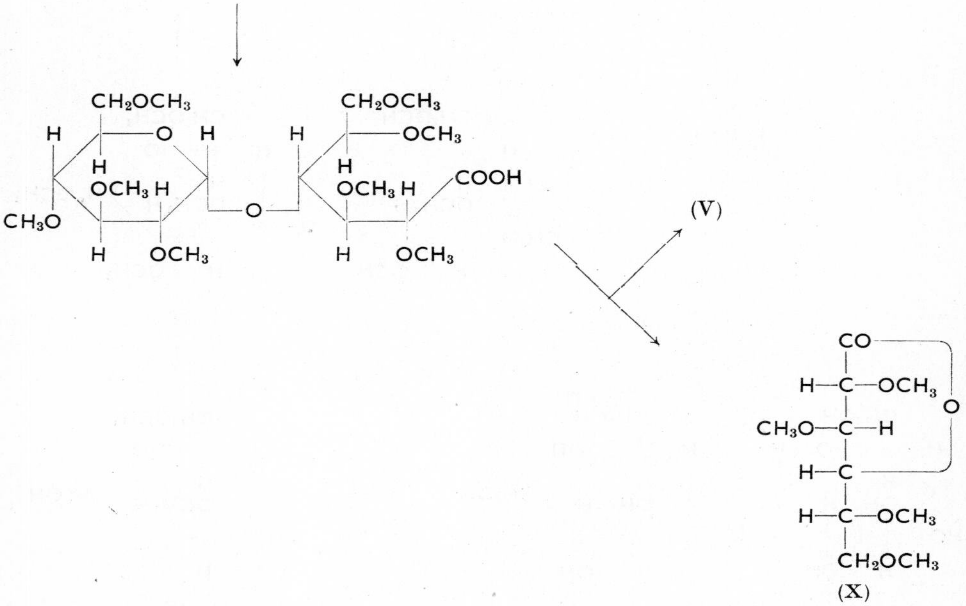

(V)

(X)

It is obvious that two disaccharides differing in the anomeric arrangement of the non-reducing part of the molecule give the same products by methylation analysis. Thus, gentiobiose (XI)[3,4] as well as isomaltose (XII)[5,6] yield 2,3,4,6-tetra-*O*-methyl-D-glucopyranose (V) and 2,3,4-tri-*O*-methyl-D-glucopyranose (XIII).

This procedure, at present an analytical routine method, has been applied many times (see for example Ref. 7—16) but has also led to erroneous conclusions,[13,14] which had to be corrected.[12] In a number of cases, this method was utilized for elucidating the constitution of oligosaccharides contained in heterosides, although the splitting-off of these oligosaccharides could not be effected; this applies, for instance, to the sugar component of the glycoside asiaticoside[17] etc.

(XI)

(V)

(XIII)

(XII)

**REFERENCES**

1. J. Staněk, M. Černý, J. Kocourek, and J. Pacák, *The Monosaccharides,* Acad. Press, New York 1963, p. 300.
2. W. N. Haworth, J. V. Loach, and C. W. Long, J. Chem. Soc. *1927*, 3146.
3. W. Charlton, W. N. Haworth, and L. Hickinbottom, J. Chem. Soc. *1927*, 1527.
4. W. N. Haworth and B. Wylam, J. Chem. Soc. *123*, 3120 (1923).
5. A. Georg, Compt. rend. soc. phys. et hist. nat. Genève *47*, 94 (1930).
6. M. L. Wolfrom, L. W. Georges, and I. L. Miller, J. Am. Chem. Soc. *71*, 125 (1949).
7. W. N. Haworth and S. Peat, J. Chem. Soc. *1926*, 3094.
8. W. N. Haworth, C. W. Long, and J. H. G. Plant, J. Chem. Soc. *1927*, 2809.
9. I. Levin and C. B. Purves, Advances in Carbohydrate Chem. *4*, 1 (1949).
10. H. Schlubach and K. Maurer, Ber. *58*, 1179 (1925).
11. J. M. Sugihara and M. L. Wolfrom, J. Am. Chem. Soc. *71*, 3357 (1949).
12. R. A. Laidlaw and C. B. Wylam, J. Chem. Soc. *1953*, 567.
13. M. Onuki, Proc. Imp. Acad. Tokyo *8*, 496 (1932).
14. M. Onuki, Sci. Papers Inst. Phys. Chem. Research Tokyo *20*, 201 (1933).
15. R. Kuhn, I. Löw, and H. Trischmann, Chem. Ber. *90*, 203 (1957).
16. C. N. Turton, A. Bebbington, S. Dixon, and E. Pascu, J. Am. Chem. Soc. *77*, 2565 (1955).
17. J. Polonsky, E. Sach, and E. Lederer, Bull. soc. chim. France *1959*, 880.

## 2. DEGRADATION OF OLIGOSACCHARIDES WITH PERIODIC ACID *

Periodic acid is an agent of great importance in the investigation of the structure not only of monosaccharides[1] but also of oligosaccharides. The first study in this respect was concerned with the course of oxidation of trehalose (I),[2] whereby the known finding was confirmed[3,4] that both glucose units in the trehalose molecule exist in the form of pyranoses. This is obvious from the consumption of 4 moles of periodic acid[2,5] and the formation of 2 molecules of formic acid, regardless of whether the oxidation is carried out with periodic acid or its potassium salt. The tetraldehyde (II) obtained in this way was converted by mild oxidation into the corresponding tetracarboxylic acid (III):

In the course of a further exhaustive study,[6] the oxidation of trehalose and *neo*-trehalose was investigated by measuring the evolution of carbon dioxide; it is interesting to note that the latter compound is oxidized more rapidly.

In the case of sucrose, too, the structure derived earlier was confirmed by the result from the oxidation with periodic acid.[7-9] The consumption of 3 moles of periodic acid[5,8,10] and the formation of one molecule of formic acid

---

* For a review see R. W. Bailey and J. B. Pridham, Advances in Carbohydrate Chem. *17*, 125 (1962).

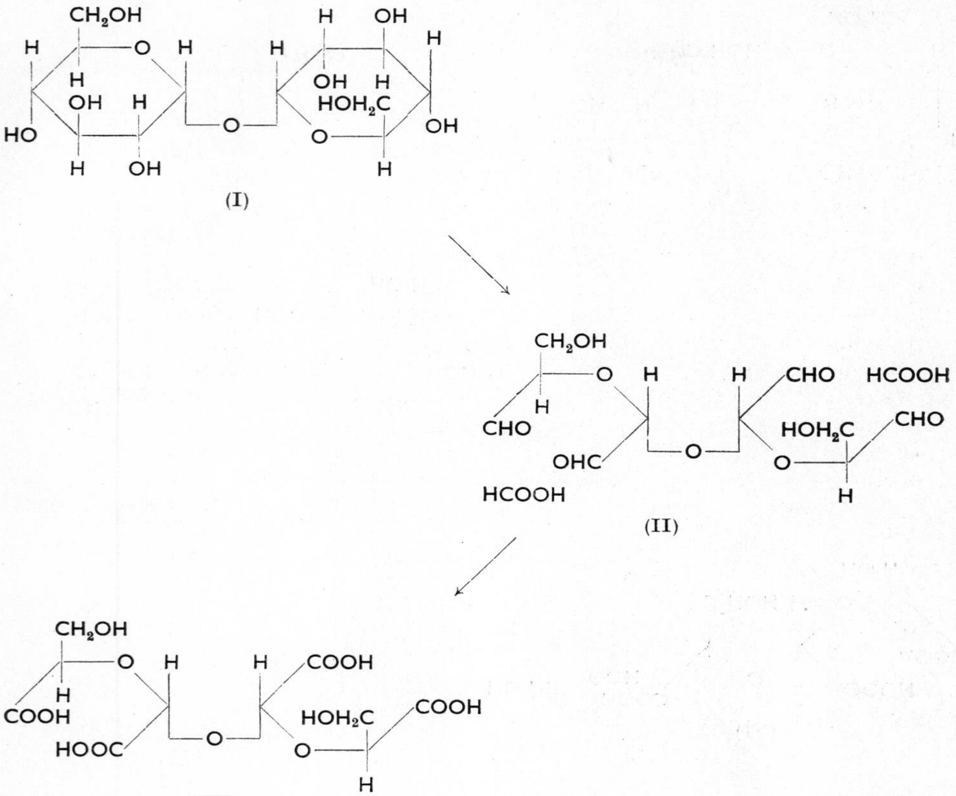

(I)

(II)

(III)

prove that the oxidation of sucrose (IV) proceeds with the formation of the tetraldehyde (V). This was further confirmed by oxidation of the tetraldehyde (V) with bromine water and hydrolysis of the tetracarboxylic acid (VI) obtained in this way. The resultant substances, i. e. hydroxypyruvic acid, D-glyceric acid and glyoxylic acid correspond to the structure (VI) for the tetracarboxylic acid and thus also to (V) for the tetraldehyde.

The tetraldehyde (V) produced by oxidation of sucrose is interesting because in its reaction with phenylhydrazine it is not possible to detect the presence of all four aldehydic groups as would correspond to the given formula, but only of two such groups.[11] A similar phenomenon was observed in the case of trehalose where two of the four aldehydic groups were found, and in the case of raffinose where three of the six assumed aldehydic groups were proved.[12]

The original assumption that the oxidation product of sucrose, the so-called oxysucrose, has the structure (VII)[13] was corrected[11] by the proof that oxysucrose has the character of a double hemiacetal (VIII). This is evident

*References see p. 43*

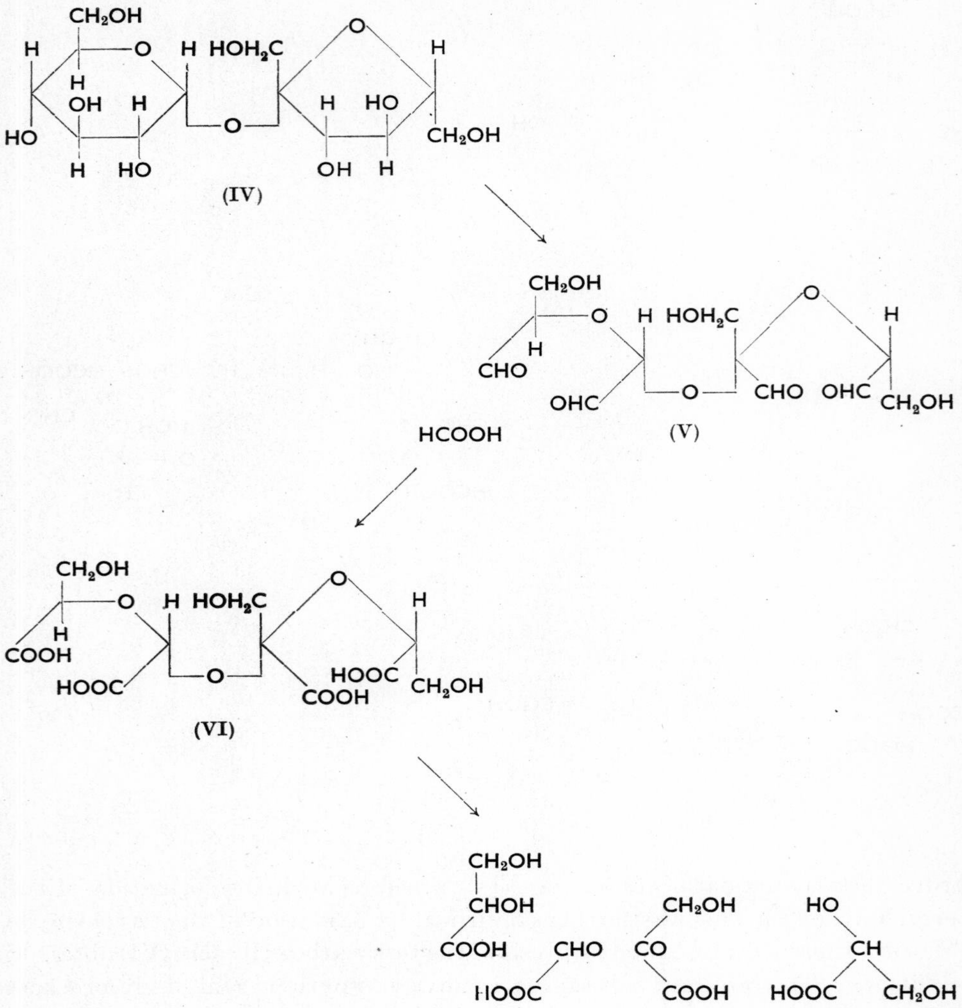

CH₂OH ... H O H HOH₂C ... O ... H
H
OH H H HO
HO CH₂OH
H HO OH H
**(IV)**

CH₂OH ... O H HOH₂C ... O ... H
H
CHO
OHC CHO OHC CH₂OH
OH H
HCOOH **(V)**

CH₂OH ... O H HOH₂C ... O ... H
H
COOH
HOOC O HOOC CH₂OH
COOH
**(VI)**

CH₂OH
CHOH CH₂OH HO
COOH CHO CO CH
HOOC COOH HOOC CH₂OH

from the **formation** of the double phenylhydrazone (IX) which, as a true Schiff base, **reacts with** benzenediazonium chloride with the formation of a bright red **formazan** derivative (X).

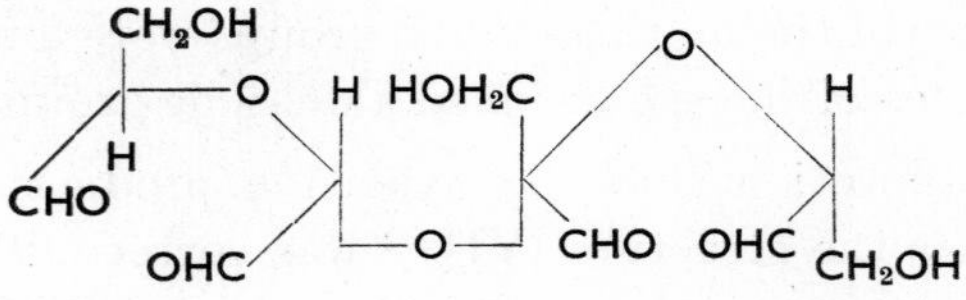

CH₂OH ... O H HOH₂C ... O ... H
H
CHO
OHC CHO OHC CH₂OH
**(V)**

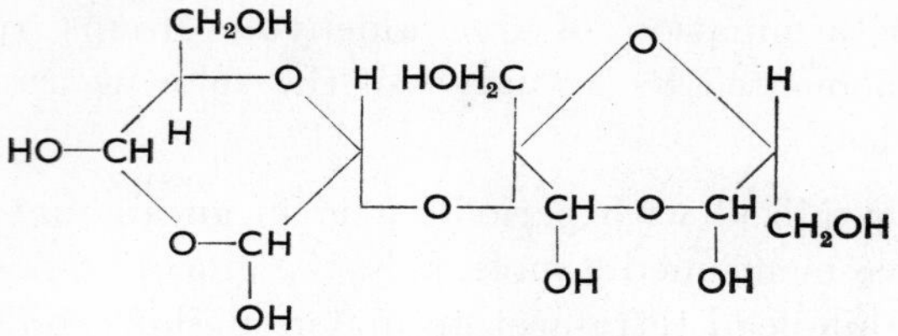

(VII)

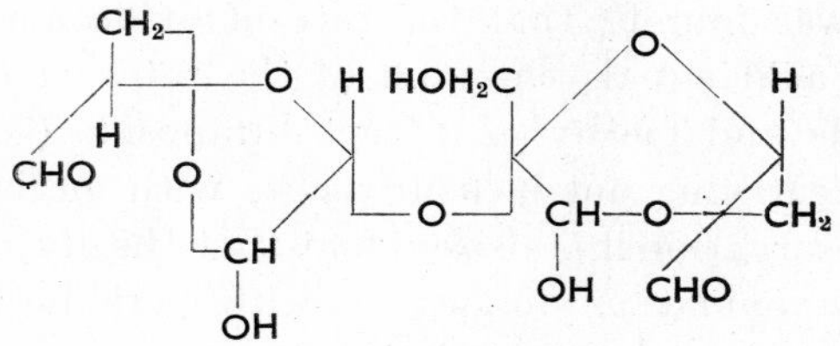

(VIII)

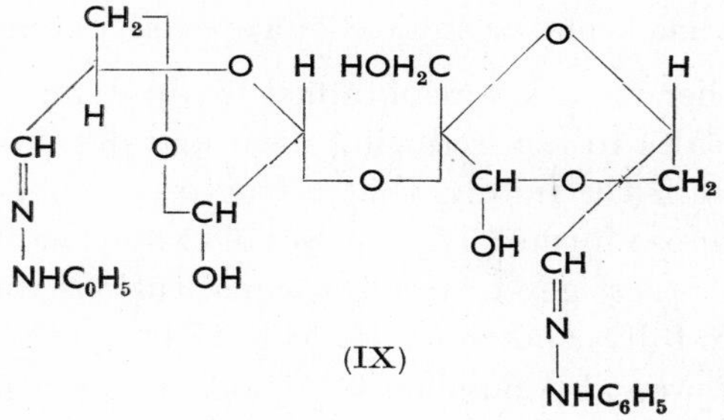

(IX)

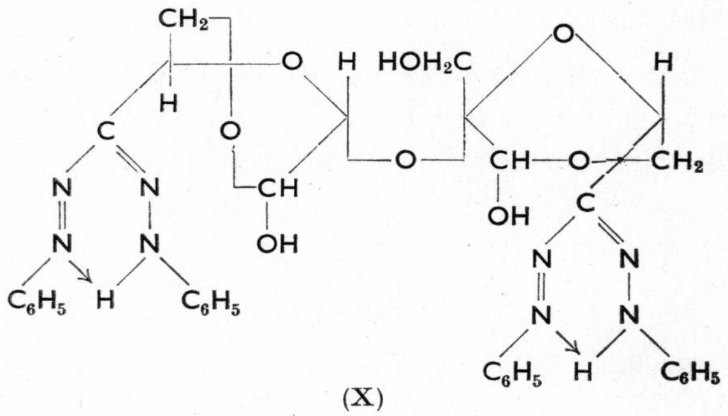

(X)

This explanation has been accepted, although it was pointed out[14] that so far the presence of two aldehydic groups in the molecule of the so-called oxysucrose has not been proved spectroscopically.

A French paper[15] presents a study of the infra-red spectra of crystalline forms of the polyaldehydes obtained from sucrose, raffinose and melibiose, and

*References see p. 43*

further of the determination of free aldehydic groups and crystal water; this work is supplemented by a study[16] of the colorimetric determination of these polyaldehydes.

If sucrose is oxidized with periodic acid in an amount corresponding to less than the above-mentioned 3 molecules, the glucopyranose part is affected preferentially,[17] while lead tetra-acetate under similar conditions attacks preferentially the fructofuranose unit of the sucrose molecule.[17]

Moreover, it was found[18] that the rate of oxidation of sucrose with an excess of periodic acid equals the sum of the rates of oxidation of methyl α-D-glucopyranoside and methyl α-D-fructofuranoside (the investigators had no opportunity of carrying out measurements with methyl β-D-fructofuranoside). From this observation it is also evident that the glycosidic linkage proper is not split in the oxidation of sucrose with periodic acid; the oxidation with lead tetra-acetate proceeds here in the same way.

The formation of rubazonic acid in the reaction of so-called oxysucrose with phenylhydrazine has been the subject of a special, extensive study.[19]

A number of further results were obtained by applying the oxidation with periodic acid and its salts to non-reducing disaccharides, nowadays a routine method. Of significance is the finding that D-fructose is contained in the melezitose molecule in furanose form.[20] The courses of oxidation of raffinose[21,22] and stachyose[23] were also investigated and the constitutions already established by other methods were fully confirmed. By oxidation of raffinose and stachyose with periodic acid[24] it was also possible to attack preferentially the galactose units, which are the only components with *cis*-arrangement of the hydroxyl groups in the entire molecule of these oligosaccharides.

Of interest also is the extent to which the oxidation of sucrose and raffinose with sodium periodate is influenced by temperature. This was investigated by ascertaining the consumption of sodium periodate[24], which is given in the following table in moles of $NaIO_4$ per mole of oligosaccharide.

**Table II**

Consumption of Sodium Periodate by Sucrose and Raffinose

| Time | Sucrose | | Raffinose |
|---|---|---|---|
| | 0°C | 25°C | 0°C |
| 15 Minutes | 0·13 moles | 0·38 moles | — |
| 30 Minutes | 0·31 moles | 0·66 moles | 0·94 moles |
| 60 Minutes | 0·72 moles | 1·24 moles | 1·30 moles |
| 100 Minutes | — | — | 1·85 moles |

From this table it is evident that the rate of the reaction is strongly influenced by temperature. The rate of oxidation of these oligosaccharides was also studied by following the amount of formic acid produced with time.[25]

**Table III**

The Rate of Oxidation of Several Oligosaccharides according to the Amount of Formic Acid Produced

| Time (hours) | 24 | 48 | 96 | 144 | 216 | 288 | 336 |
|---|---|---|---|---|---|---|---|
| Sucrose | 18% | 25% | 49% | 61% | 80% | 92% | 98% |
| Raffinose | 21% | 47% | 57% | 78% | 99% | 99% | 99% |

\* \* \*

In the series of reducing oligosaccharides, periodate titration was employed[23,26,27] for determining the structure of melibiose and manninotriose. Here it was found that in the oxidation of a reducing disaccharide, periodate attacks first the [C-1, C-2]-diol grouping of the reducing part, whereby the opinion was refuted[28] that the oxidation proceeds preferentially between carbon atoms C-2 and C-3. A very interesting finding[5,8,25] is that the oxidation of a reducing disaccharide always proceeds faster than the oxidation of a non-reducing disaccharide; however, considerable differences exist in this respect even between individual reducing disaccharides. Ahlborg[29] has found that reducing disaccharides with 1→4 linkages (lactose, maltose, cellobiose) are oxidized at the same rate as but more strongly than reducing disaccharides with 1→6 linkages (such as melibiose).

It is clear that the rate of oxidation of a reducing oligosaccharide is strongly influenced and retarded by its conversion into the corresponding glycoside, since in this case the fast oxidation between C-1 and C-2 of the reducing part does not take place.[30]

The course of oxidation of reducing oligosaccharides with periodic acid and its salts has been the subject of a number of papers and was studied on maltose,[5,10,25,28,31–35] cellobiose,[5,28,33,34,36–38] lactose,[5,10,25,28,33,36,39,40] melibiose,[5,10,26,32,33] turanose,[5,36] and others.[5,33,34] It was found throughout that the rate of oxidation of reducing oligosaccharides is retarded in the course of the reaction.[5,25,28,34–36] The oxidation of lactose and maltose with periodic acid proceeds in principle at the same rate.[5,28] The oxidation of maltose and lactose with potassium periodate proceeds much more slowly, but again at equal rate.[25] It has been reported[36] that within the first 24 hours the oxidation with periodic acid proceeds approximately four times faster than with potassium

*References see p. 43*

periodate. In the same paper it was stated[36] that oxidation of lactose with periodic acid is completed within 96 hours, whereas oxidation with potassium periodate requires not less than 336 hours for completion.[25]

The oxidation of cellobiose (XI)[37] proceeds via the intermediate products (XII—XVII) up to the formation of formaldehyde, formic acid and carbon dioxide. An analogous scheme is presented for the oxidation of turanose.[36]

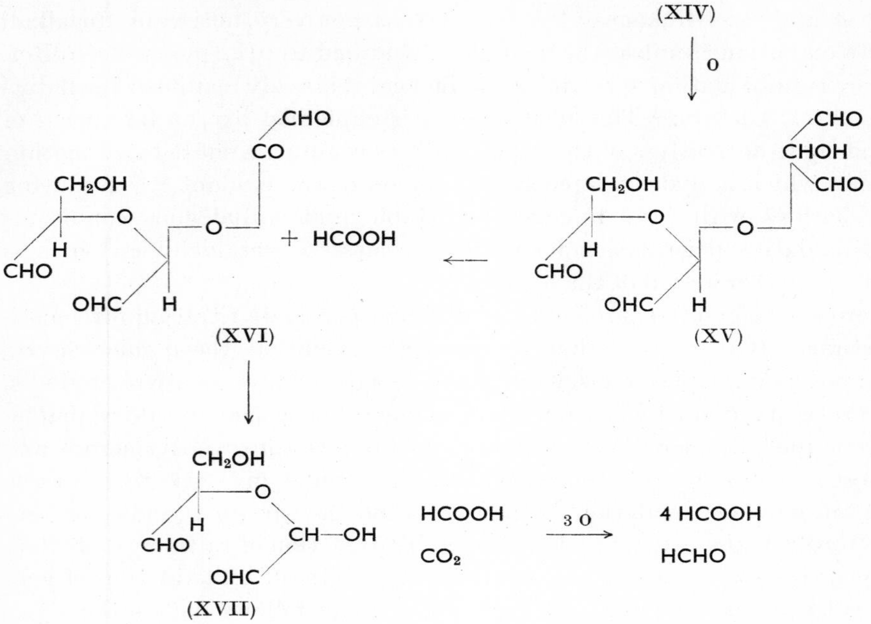

(XIV)

↓ O

CH₂OH ... CHO / CO ... + HCOOH ... ← ... CH₂OH ... CHO / CHOH / CHO

(XVI) ... (XV)

↓

(XVII)

HCOOH
$CO_2$   →₃ₒ   4 HCOOH
HCHO

Lactose has been oxidized with periodic acid[39] to tetraldehyde (XIV) which, after conversion into the corresponding tetracarboxylic acid (oxidation with bromine water) and hydrolysis, yielded a mixture of tartronic, glyoxylic and glyceric acids; this is in full agreement with the suggested and assumed structures of the intermediate products.

The kinetics of the oxidation of lactose with periodic acid has been followed by M. Guernet, Bull. soc. chim. biol. 45, 537 (1936). The first product of lactose degradation has been found to be 3-O-β-D-galactopyranosyl-D-arabinose mono-O-formate; further degradation of this compound yields 3-O-β-D-galactopyranosyl-D-arabinose, 2-O-β-D-galactopyranosyl-D-erythrose mono-O-formate, 2-O-β-D-galactopyranosyl-D-erythrose and a tetraldehyde (XIV).

The course of the oxidation of oligosaccharides with periodates is reported to be accelerated by addition of sodium chloride.[31,35] The influence of the pH value has also been investigated;[32] periodate oxidation proceeds faster in an acid medium.

However, the scheme of oxidative degradation of cellobiose (XI), proceeding via the intermediate products (XII—XVII) and yielding very simple compounds, is not in full agreement with the principles according to which oxidation of vicinal diols should take place and be terminated at the compound (XIV); the further course is already anomalous, leading to higher consumption of periodic acid and decomposition of the entire molecule. This so-called overoxidation is a characteristic phenomenon for reducing oligosaccharides with

*References see p. 43*

1→2, 1→3 and 1→4 linkages.[5,33,36,37,41-43] It is not very noticeable in alkali periodate oxidation,[36] unless the medium is acidified to pH 3—4 (see also Ref. 29), whereas in oxidation with free periodic acid it already manifests itself during the first 24 hours.[36] This phenomenon is explained by the formation of malonaldehyde derivatives of the type (XIV), containing a substituted methylene group which is hydroxylated by the action of the oxidant.[33,37] Reducing oligosaccharides with 1→6 linkages are stable under analogous conditions because oxidative degradation leads in this case to acetaldehyde, which is resistant to further action of the oxidant.[5,33]

There is still another possibility of utilizing periodate titration for constitution studies. It is known[44] that, on periodate oxidation, the D-galactopyranosides and the D-glucopyranosides of the same aglycon give identical products, a dextrorotatory dialdehyde from the α-isomers and a laevorotatory dialdehyde from the β-isomers. As raffinose is 6-O-D-galactopyranosylsucrose and gentianose is 6-O-D-glucopyranosylsucrose, they might give rise to the same product on periodate oxidation, if they both had the same glycosidic configuration. However, the hexaldehyde obtained by oxidation of raffinose is dextrorotatory ($[\alpha]_D$ +45.6°), while the hexaldehyde produced by oxidation of gentianose is laevorotatory ($[\alpha]_D$ —33.1°).[22] From this it follows that in these two cases the substituting glycosyl remainders must be linked in different ways to the -6- position of sucrose.

This method of structure correlation was successfully applied even quite recently.[45] Methyl β-lactoside (XVIII) as well as methyl β-cellobioside (XIX) yield by periodic acid oxidation the same tetraldehyde (XX). The unoxidized parts of both compounds must have the same configuration:

Many similar methods of structure correlation are known.[41,46]

Polyaldehydes obtained from melibiose, lactose, sucrose, raffinose and stachyose can be used for quantitative determinations; pink coloration which arises after the action of $\beta$-naphthylamine and thymol in phosphoric acid can be determined spectrophotometrically, as described by A. Jurado-Soler, M. Guernet, and P. Malangeau, Bull. soc. chim. France *1963*, 2119.

Oxidation with periodic acid and its salts has often been applied in the oligosaccharide series for most varied structure studies, such as determination of the structure of 6-*O*-$\alpha$-D-galactopyranosyl-D-galactose obtained by reversion (see Chapter VI, 4),[47] of maltopentaose[48] and of the by-products formed in the synthesis of lactose according to Koenigs-Knorr (see Chapter VI, 1).[49] This procedure has also been employed in the series of alditols derived from oligosaccharides.[50,51] A recent investigation was also concerned with the relationship between the rate of periodic acid oxidation and the degree of polymerization in the series of oligosaccharides of the maltose type.[52]

Periodic acid oxidation of sessilifolan, see Chap. IX, has been used for structure elucidation by T. Sasaki and M. Mikami, J. Pharm. Soc. Japan (Yakugaku Zasshi) *82*, 1520 (1962); Chem. Abstr. *59*, 5245 (1963).

### REFERENCES

1. J. M. Bobbitt, Advances in Carbohydrate Chem. *11*, 1 (1956).
2. E. L. Jackson and C. S. Hudson, J. Am. Chem. Soc. *61*, 1530 (1939).
3. H. H. Schlubach and K. Maurer, Ber. *58*, 1178 (1925).
4. H. Bredereck, Ber. *63*, 959 (1930).
5. K. Takiura and K. Koizumi, Chem. Pharm. Bull. (Tokyo) *10*, 134 (1962).
6. R. U. Lemieux and H. F. Bauer, Can. J. Chem. *32*, 340 (1954).
7. P. Fleury and J. Courtois, Compt. rend. *216*, 65 (1943).
8. P. Fleury and J. Courtois, Bull. soc. chim. France (5) *10*, 245 (1943).
9. P. Fleury and J. Courtois, Bull. soc. chim. France (5) *12*, 548 (1945).
10. M. Guernet, Bull. soc. chim. France *1961*, 1752.
11. L. Mester and E. Móczár, Chem. & Ind. (London) *1957*, 764.
12. S. Akiya, S. Okui, and S. Suzuki, J. Pharm. Soc. Japan (Yakugaku Zasshi) *72*, 891 (1952); Chem. Abstr. *47*, 7447 (1953).
13. V. C. Barry and P. W. D. Mitchell, J. Chem. Soc. *1954*, 4022.
14. V. C. Barry and P. W. D. Mitchell, Chem. & Ind. (London) *1957*, 1045.
15. M. Guernet and A. J. Soler, Compt. rend. *254*, 2985 (1962).
16. A. J. Soler and M. Guernet, Compt. rend. *254*, 2586 (1962).
17. A. K. Mitra and A. S. Perlin, Can. J. Chem. *37*, 2047 (1959).
18. R. C. Hockett and M. Zief, J. Am. Chem. Soc. *72*, 2130 (1950).
19. V. C. Barry, J. E. McCormick, G. Henseke, P. Brosche, I. Demuth, U. Müller, H. Engelmann, and G. Crawack, Ann. *648*, 96 (1961).
20. N. K. Richtmyer and C. S. Hudson, J. Org. Chem. *11*, 610 (1946).
21. J. E. Courtois and A. Wickström, Bull. soc. chim. biol. *32*, 759 (1950).
22. H. Hérissey, A. Wickström, and J. E. Courtois, Bull. soc. chim. biol. *33*, 642 (1951).

23. H. Hérissey, A. Wickström, and J. E. Courtois, Bull. soc. chim. biol. *34*, 856 (1952).

24. A. K. Mitra and A. S. Perlin, Can. J. Chem. *35*, 1079 (1957).

25. M. Černý and J. Staněk, Monatsh. Chem. *90*, 159 (1959).

26. J. E. Courtois, A. Wickström, and P. Le Dizet, Bull. soc. chim. biol. *34*, 1121 (1952); Chem. Abstr. *48*, 3268 (1954).

27. J. E. Courtois, A. Wickström, and P. Le Dizet, Bull. soc. chim. biol. *35*, 1111 (1953); Chem. Abstr. *49*, 3831 (1955).

28. J. E. Courtois and M. Ramet, Bull. soc. chim. biol. *29*, 240 (1947).

29. K. Ahlborg, Svensk Kem. Tidskr. *54*, 205 (1942); Chem. Abstr. *38*, 4254 (1944).

30. W. Z. Hassid, M. Doudoroff, A. L. Potter, and H. A. Barker, J. Am. Chem. Soc. *70*, 306 (1948).

31. A. L. Potter and W. Z. Hassid, J. Am. Chem. Soc. *70*, 3488 (1948).

32. G. Neumüller and E. Vasseur, Arkiv Kemi, *5*, 235 (1953); Chem. Abstr. *48*, 1283 (1954).

33. L. Hough and M. B. Perry, Chem. & Ind. (London) *1956*, 768.

34. G. O. Aspinall and R. J. Ferrier, Chem. & Ind. (London) *1957*, 1216.

35. D. J. Manners and A. R. Archibald, J. Chem. Soc. *1957*, 2205.

36. W. G. Wright, J. Chem. Soc. *1957*, 1913.

37. F. S. H. Head and G. Hughes, J. Chem. Soc. *1954*, 603.

38. F. S. H. Head, Chem. & Ind. (London) *1958*, 38.

39. J. E. Courtois, Bull. soc. chim. biol. *29*, 248 (1947).

40. M. Guernet, Bull. soc. chim. France *1961*, 2272.

41. A. J. Charlson and A. S. Perlin, Can. J. Chem. *34*, 1804 (1956).

42. R. W. Bailey, S. A. Barker, E. J. Bourne, P. M. Grant, and M. Stacey, J. Chem. Soc. *1958*, 1895.

43. J. K. N. Jones and P. E. Reid, Can. J. Chem. *38*, 944 (1960).

44. E. L. Jackson and C. S. Hudson, J. Am. Chem. Soc. *59*, 994 (1937).

45. J. K. Hamilton, G. W. Huffman, and F. Smith, J. Am. Chem. Soc. *81*, 2176 (1959).

46. P. A. J. Gorin and A. S. Perlin, Can. J. Chem. *37*, 1930 (1959).

47. C. N. Turton, A. Bebbington, S. Dixon, and E. Pacsu, J. Am. Chem. Soc. *77*, 2565 (1955).

48. R. L. Whistler and J. H. Duffy, J. Am. Chem. Soc. *77*, 1017 (1955).

49. E. J. C. Curtiss and J. K. N. Jones, Can. J. Chem. *37*, 358 (1959).

50. L. Hough, B. M. Woods, and M. B. Perry, Chem. & Ind. (London) *1957*, 1100.

51. M. Cantley, L. Hough, and A. O. Pittet, Chem. & Ind. (London) *1959*, 1253.

52. K. Takiura and K. Koizumi, Chem. Pharm. Bull. (Tokyo) *10*, 140 (1962).

## 4. DEGRADATION OF OLIGOSACCHARIDES BY LEAD TETRA-ACETATE*

Althought it has been known for some time that oligosaccharides, in particular maltose and lactose, are oxidized with the consumption of 3 moles of lead tetra-acetate,[1] oxidations of further oligosaccharides with lead tetra-acetate[2] were carried out comparatively late without any essential contribution to the elucidation of the structure of the substances in question.

---

* For a review see A. S. Perlin, Advances in Carbohydrate Chem. *14*, 9 (1959).

As far as non-reducing oligosaccharides are concerned, the oxidation of sucrose by the action of lead tetra-acetate[3] proceeds in a similar way to the oxidation with potassium periodate. In this case, too, the rate of oxidation is the sum of the rates of oxidation of methyl α-D-glucopyranoside and methyl α-D-fructofuranoside (which some investigators employed instead of the corresponding β-anomer).[3] If a smaller amount of lead tetra-acetate is used,[4] the fructofuranose system of the sucrose molecule is preferentially oxidized between C-3 and C-4. Here appears a great difference in comparison with the course of oxidation by the action of periodate, which attacks preferentially the glucopyranose system of the sucrose molecule.[4]

Mild oxidation of raffinose with lead tetra-acetate destroys the galacto-pyranose system in the molecule, so that, on mild alkaline hydrolysis, sucrose can be isolated.[5]

In the series of reducing disaccharides it was found by Ahlborg[6] that lead tetra-acetate oxidation of oligosaccharides with 1→4 and 1→6 linkages proceeds at different rates, whereas no differences were observed in the oxidation with potassium periodate.[7] This problem was very thoroughly investigated by Perlin,[7] who pointed out the interesting phenomenon that in the series of reducing disaccharides containing D-glucose, the rate of oxidation decreases in the order 1→6 disaccharide (isomaltose), 1→3 disaccharide (laminaribiose) and 1→4 disaccharide (maltose). In the last case, the oxidation proceeds approximately at the same rate as that of methyl α-D-glucopyranoside, and from this it can be derived that in the maltose molecule only the non-reducing part is oxidized.

Perlin concluded from these findings[7] that the total consumption of lead tetra-acetate in the oxidation of a reducing disaccharide containing D-glucose would always be the sum of the consumptions for the methyl glycoside of the monosaccharide corresponding to the non-reducing part of the oligosaccharide molecule and for the methyl ether of the monosaccharide corresponding to the reducing part of the oligosaccharide molecule. On the basis of these considerations, he then placed, according to the rate of oxidation, reducing disaccharides containing 1→2 linkages between those with 1→6 and with 1→3 linkages.

A relation similar to that derived for the rate of oxidation of a reducing disaccharide containing two D-glucose molecules also applies to other disaccharides containing both hexoses and pentoses.[7] Perlin further derived from these relations that ,,galactobiose" isolated from *Acacia pycnantha* gum[7,8] must contain 1→3 linkages. Basing his studies upon similar relations, Wickström[9] found that the structure of the reducing disaccharide obtained by partial hydrolysis of the trisaccharide umbelliferose corresponds to 2-*O*-α-D-galacto-pyranosyl-D-glucose. Recently it was also found[10] that galactobiose isolated after hydrolysis of α-cellulose from white birch wood (*Betula papyrifera*)

*References see p. 49*

belongs among 1→4 disaccharides with a β-glycosidic linkage and that the substance in question is 4-*O*-β-D-galactopyranosyl-D-galactose.

These relations can also be applied to higher oligosaccharides,[11] the only exception being those oligosaccharides that contain in the middle unit of the bound monosaccharide a 2,3-*trans*-glycol grouping in the neighbourhood of the glycosidically linked hydroxyl group at C-4. Such a glycol grouping is obviously very stable in oxidation with lead tetra-acetate, and in the oligosaccharide series of the maltose type it can be observed that the consumption of the oxidant is almost constant. Obviously, only the end-monosaccharide units are oxidized:

**Table IV**

Lead Tetra-acetate Consumption by Maltose-type Oligosaccharides

| Oligosaccharide | Lead Tetra-acetate Consumed by Compound |
|:---:|:---:|
| Maltose | 5·2 moles |
| Maltotriose | 5·4 moles |
| Maltotetraose | 3·9 moles |
| Maltopentaose | 5·0 moles |
| Maltohexaose | 5·7 moles |

In the case of maltohexaose only it was found, by comparison with the oxidant consumption for maltose, that one of the middle glucose units is also oxidized by lead tetra-acetate. The anomalous value of the consumption of the oxidant in the case of maltotetraose may be explained by the hygroscopic nature of the material under investigation, or by insufficient purity.

Similar conditions were observed in the series of oligosaccharides containing a cellobiose or xylobiose grouping.[11] This method was also applied[12] to oligosaccharides containing D-mannose, further in the series of aldobiouronic acids, and for partial shortening of the molecule of a reducing disaccharide in its reducing part.

The oxidation of a reducing oligosaccharide with lead tetra-acetate obviously first attacks the reducing part of the molecule and first of all the glycol grouping between C-1 and C-2. Consequently, controlled oxidation of a reducing disaccharide permits the degradation of, for example, maltose (I) to 2-*O*-α-D-glucopyranosyl-D-erythrose (II); this substance, on reduction to 2-*O*-α-D-glucopyranosyl-D-erythritol (III), is converted by further oxidation with lead tetra-acetate into 2-*O*-α-D-glucopyranosyl-L-glyceraldehyde (IV), which in turn can be reduced to 2-*O*-α-D-glucopyranosylglycerol (V).[13]

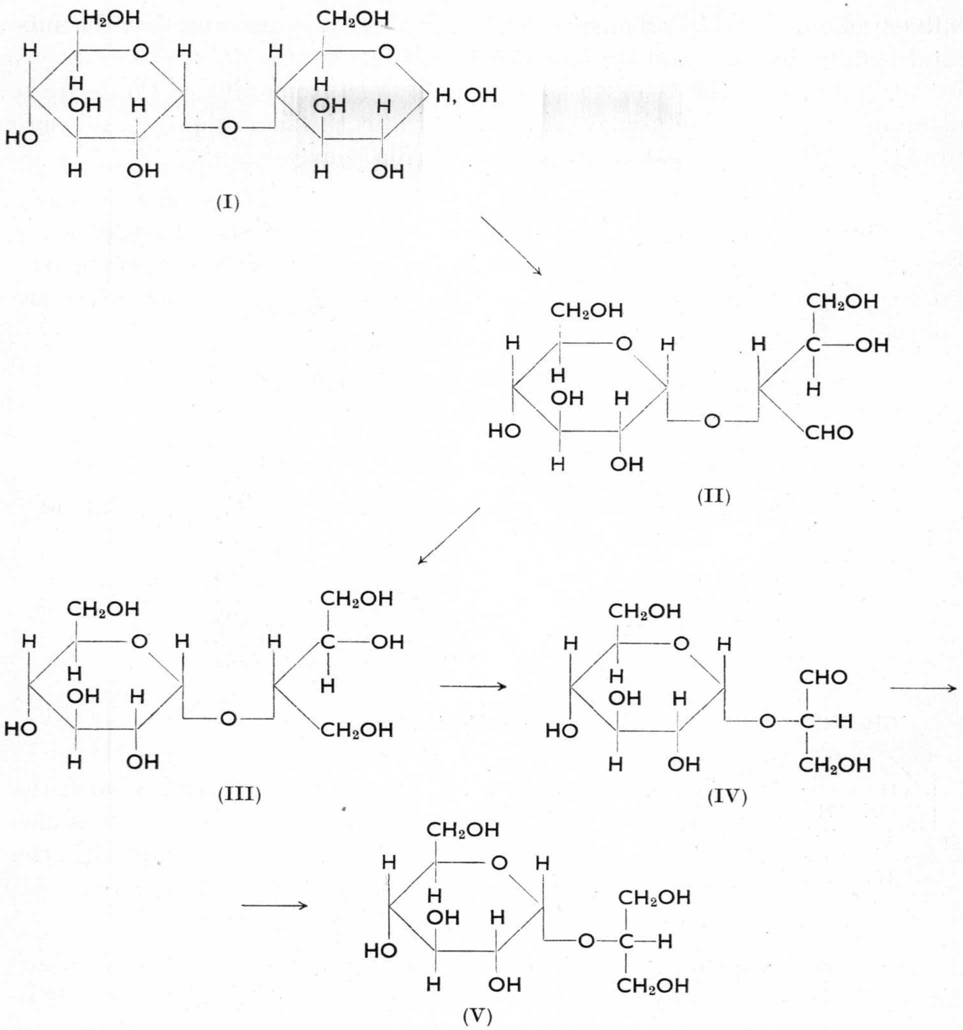

(I)

(II)

(III) → (IV) →

→ (V)

Perlin prepared a large number of substances of this type[13,14] and thus obtained a series of glycosides[13] containing glycerol as aglycon, and the values of the specific rotations of these substances were utilized for classifying various oligosaccharides from plant gums.[14]

The values of the specific rotations of the oxidation products formed from disaccharides by the action of lead tetra-acetate may also be utilized for classification purposes.[15] It may be assumed that the molecule is decomposed, with the exception of a remainder containing those two of the former asymmetric carbon atoms that are bound glycosidically. In the case of 1→6 disaccharides, the situation is clear, the specific rotation of the oxidation product is then

influenced only by the carbon atom of the original glycosidically bound hemiacetal hydroxyl group, and the oxidation products obtained from disaccharides
with α-linkages of the 1→6 series [melibiose (VI), isomaltose (VII), 6-*O*-α-D-
mannopyranosyl-D-mannose (VIII)] must exhibit the same rotation, differing
from the analogous β, 1→6 reducing disaccharide (gentiobiose, IX):

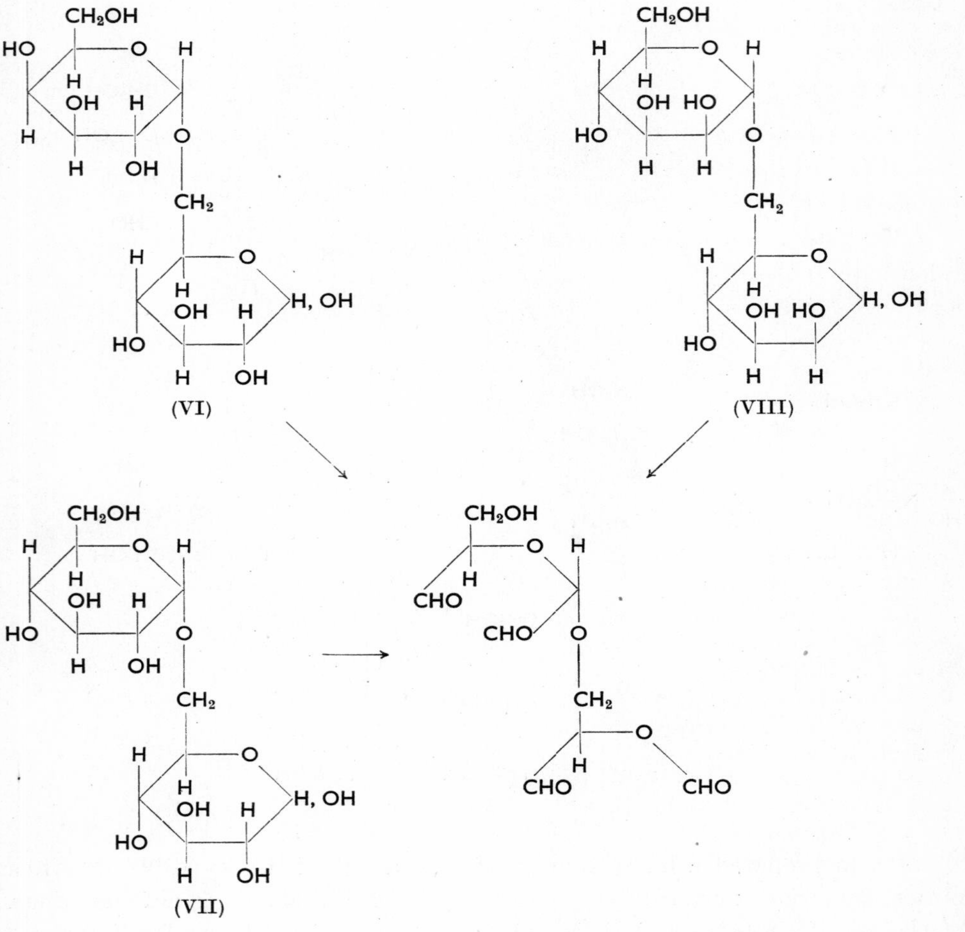

(VI)          (VIII)

(VII)          (X)

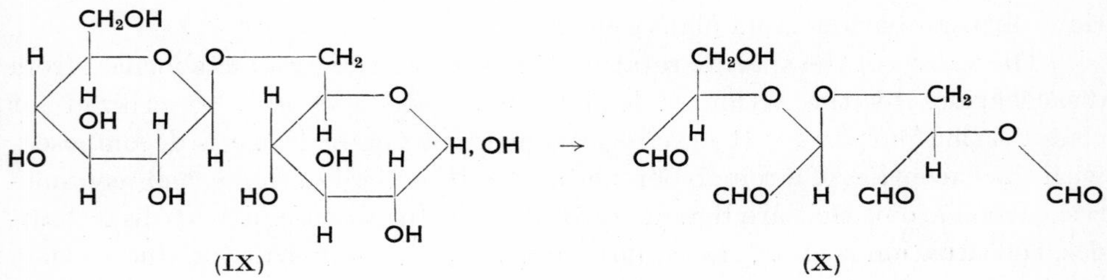

(IX)

**Table V**

Specific Rotations of the Products Obtained by the Action of Lead Tetra-acetate
on Oligosaccharides

| Oligosaccharide | $[\alpha]_D$ Disaccharide | $[\alpha]_D$ Oxidation Product |
|---|---|---|
| Melibiose | +129° | + 79° |
| Isomaltose | + 98° | + 85° |
| 6-O-α-D-Mannopyranosyl-D-mannose | + 50° | + 88° |
| Gentiobiose | + 8° | −109° |

The results of later investigations in which the structures of oligosaccharides, already established by other methods, were confirmed in all cases are in full agreement with the preceding conclusions.[16-19]

The rate of oxidation of reducing oligosaccharides with lead tetra-acetate in a medium of acetic acid is strongly catalysed by the presence of potassium acetate;[2,7,12] the course of this „potassium acetate-catalysed reaction" is explained by the assumption that in the presence of potassium acetate the formyl esters are hydrolysed more quickly, whereby a faster and more profound oxidation is effected.

## REFERENCES

1. R. Criegee, Ann. *495*, 211 (1932).
2. A. S. Perlin, Advances in Carbohydrate Chem. *14*, 9 (1959).
3. R. C. Hockett and M. Zief, J. Am. Chem. Soc. *72*, 2130 (1950).
4. A. K. Mitra and A. S. Perlin, Can. J. Chem. *37*, 2047 (1959).
5. A. K. Mitra and A. S. Perlin, Can. J. Chem. *35*, 1079 (1957).
6. K. Ahlborg, Svensk Kem. Tidskr. *54*, 205 (1942); Chem. Abstr. *38*, 4254 (1944).
7. A. S. Perlin, Anal. Chem. *27*, 396 (1955).
8. E. L. Hirst and A. S. Perlin, J. Chem. Soc. *1954*, 2622.
9. A. Wickström, Acta Chem. Scand. *11*, 1473 (1957).
10. J. K. Gillham, A. S. Perlin, and T. E. Timell, Can. J. Chem. *36*, 1741 (1958).
11. A. S. Perlin and A. R. Lansdown, Can. J. Chem. *34*, 451 (1956).
12. A. J. Charlson and A. S. Perlin, Can. J. Chem. *34*, 1200 (1956).
13. A. J. Charlson, P. A. J. Gorin, and A. S. Perlin, Can J. Chem. *34*, 1811 (1956).
14. A. J. Charlson, P. A. J. Gorin, and A. S. Perlin, Can. J. Chem. *35*, 365 (1957).
15. A. J. Charlson and A. S. Perlin, Can. J. Chem. *34*, 1804 (1956).
16. B. O. Lindgren, Acta Chem. Scand. *11*, 1365 (1957).
17. J. H. Pazur, C. L. Tipton, T. Budovich, and J. M. Marsh, J. Am. Chem. Soc. *80*, 119 (1958).
18. C. P. J. Glaudemans and T. E. Timell, J. Am. Chem. Soc. *80*, 941 (1958).
19. J. K. N. Jones and W. H. Nicholson, J. Chem. Soc. *1958*, 27.

# IV

# Conformation of Oligosaccharides

Although the conformation of the tetrahydropyran ring in the monosaccharide series is well established,[1] comparatively little work has so far been undertaken in adapting and developing these considerations in the oligosaccharide group. A few papers[2-4] have been concerned with the problem of cuprammonium complexes of oligosaccharides and their derivatives, such as sucrose,[3,4] methyl $\beta$-cellobioside,[2] methyl $\beta$-maltoside[2] and di-D-fructopyranose 1,2'-2,1'-dianhydride.[3,4]

There is no doubt that the opinions about the conformation of pyranoses as accepted for the monosaccharides can be applied in their full extent to the oligosaccharide series, and the possible conformation of the reducing and non-reducing glucose units in cellobiose and maltose are discussed in the light of these results.[2] It is concluded that in cellobiose both glucose units have the *C1* conformation, whilst in maltose, the reducing glucose unit is probably *C1* and the non-reducing unit may be in or near a skew conformation lying intermediate between the *B1* and *3B* boat forms[2] (for details about these forms see Ref. 1).

The conformation of oligosacharides has been studied via nuclear magnetic resonance, see V. S. R. Rao and J. F. Foster, J. Phys. Chem. *67*, 951 (1963); J. M. van der Veen, J. Org. Chem. *28*, 564 (1963).

## REFERENCES

1. J. Staněk, M. Černý, J. Kocourek, and J. Pacák, *The Monosaccharides*, Acad. Press, New York 1963, p. 60.
2. R. Bentley, J. Am. Chem. Soc. *81*, 1952 (1959).
3. E. J. McDonald, J. Org. Chem. *25*, 111 (1960).
4. R. E. Reeves and P. Bragg, J. Org. Chem. *26*, 3487 (1961).

# V

# Numerical Relations of the Values of Rotations in the Oligosaccharide Series

The first attempt to ascertain the numerical relationships cf the rotations in the oligosaccharide series was undertaken by Hudson.[1-4] He applied the rule employed for monosaccharides[5] to the group of oligosaccharides in such a way that he divided the molecular rotation of a disaccharide into 3 parts:

A. Partial rotation of one monosaccharide unit shortened by C-1.
B. Partial rotation of C-1 separated from part A.
C. Partial rotation of the remainder of the disaccharide molecule.

Thus, the molecular rotation of sucrose (I) is composed of:

A. Part G, i.e. D-glucose less C-1.
B. Part A', i.e. C-1 of the glucose unit.
C. Part F, i.e. D-fructose.

(I)

From this follows that

$$[M]_{suc} = G + A' + F.$$

Similarly, the molecular rotation of raffinose (II) can be divided into 3 components, of which A' and F are identical with the analogous components of sucrose, while the third part, $[M]_{mel}$, stems from the melibiose unit in raffinose (II), shortened by C-1.

*References see p. 58*

4*

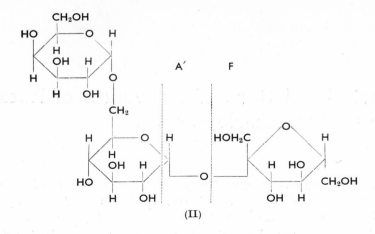

(II)

Hence

$$[M]_{raf} = [M]_{mel} + A' + F .$$

Subtraction of the molecular rotation of sucrose from that of raffinose then gives the expression.

$$[M]_{raf} - [M]_{suc} = [M]_{mel} + A' + F - G - A' - F$$

or

$$[M]_{raf} - [M]_{suc} = [M]_{mel} - G$$

and hence

$$[M]_{mel} = [M]_{raf} - [M]_{suc} + G .$$

This relation can be solved numerically since the corresponding data are known,

$$[M]_{suc} = +227°,$$
$$[M]_{raf} = +625°,$$

and G is given by half the sum of the molecular rotations of α- and β-D-glucose, i.e. $+119°$.

The value for $[M]_{mel}$ would thus be $+517°$, however, Hudson introduces here a certain adjustment[4] by adding to or subtracting from the calculated value the value A from the monosaccharide series, defined as the difference of the molecular rotations of α- and β-D-glucose because melibiose, too, may occur as α- or as β-anomer. The value A amounts to $\pm 85°$, so that the following results are obtained for

$[M]$ of the α-anomer of melibiose: $+517° + 85° = +602°,$

$[M]$ of the β-anomer of melibiose: $+517° - 85° = +432°.$

Now it is easy to calculate the values of the specific rotations of both anomers of melibiose from the above data, and it is interesting that this calculation is in good agreement with results determined later.

### Table VI

Calculated and Observed Rotations of Melibiose Anomers

|  | $[\alpha]_D$ | | References |
| | Calculated | Observed | |
| --- | --- | --- | --- |
| $\alpha$-Melibiose | $+176°$ | $+163°$ | 6 |
| $\beta$-Melibiose | $+126°$ | $+122°$ | 7 |

In a similar way, Hudson calculated the rotations of other reducing oligosaccharides, such as gentiobiose,[2,4] maltose,[3,4] maltotriose,[3] manninotriose[2] and others.[4]

In the series of non-reducing oligosaccharides, Hudson[2] first solved the problem of the three possible trehaloses. With regard to Hudson's rules for the monosaccharide series and their application to oligosaccharides,[2] the molecular rotations of these trehaloses would be given by the following expressions:

$[M]$ of $\alpha,\alpha$-trehalose: $G + A + A + G = 2\,G + 2\,A$

$[M]$ of $\alpha,\beta$-trehalose: $G + A - A + G = 2\,G$

$[M]$ of $\beta,\beta$-trehalose: $G - A - A + G = 2\,G - 2\,A$

The term 2 G in these equations is identical with the value 2 B in the monosaccharide series, which means that it is equal to the sum of the molecular rotations of $\alpha$- and of $\beta$-D-glucose, i. e. 238°. This value would at the same time be the value $[M]$ for $\alpha,\beta$-trehalose (unknown at that time), whose specific rotation $[\alpha]_D$ would thus amount to $+70°$ (the calculation agrees very accurately with the actual value, see Table IX on p. 58).

Natural trehalose ($\alpha,\alpha$), known at that time, has a $[\alpha]_D$ value of $+197°$, corresponding to a $[M]$ of $+674°$; Hudson correctly assumed that the substance in question must be $\alpha,\alpha$-trehalose. However, the value 2 A which he calculated on this basis from the known value of molecular rotation of $\alpha,\alpha$-trehalose according to the relation

$$674° = 238° + 2\,A,$$
$$2\,A = +426°$$

is quite different from the value 2 A employed by Hudson in the monosaccharide series[5]; this latter value may be considered as constant, at least in a certain, rather limited range.

On the basis of the 2 A value obtained in this way, Hudson calculated also the $[M]$ value for $\beta,\beta$-trehalose and found $-198°$, corresponding to $[\alpha]_D =$

$= -58°$, which in this case, too, differs from the specific rotation of the substance prepared later (see Table IX on p. 58). Nevertheless, it cannot be denied that, on the basis of his Isorotation Rules, Hudson determined very accurately the constitution of the natural trehalose known at that time.

Just as in the monosaccharide series, Hudson extended the validity of his rules in the oligosaccharide series also to glycosides,[8-10] per-$O$-acetyl derivatives,[2] and Purves after him to thioglycosides from the oligosaccharide group.[11-13]

A relatively large amount of work was expended in calculating the rotations of sucrose and its possible isomers. No special attention will be given here to Pictet's work,[14] concerned with calculations of the rotations of „Sucrose C" and „Sucrose D", since obviously neither of these substances was a sufficiently pure compound (see Chapters VI and XII). Shortly afterwards, Hudson determined with certainty by his calculations that the structure of sucrose corresponds to a combined system of $\alpha$-D-glucose and $\beta$-D-fructose.[4]

In course of time these rules were utilized by numerous investigators for calculating the rotations and also characterizing the structures of various substances. The structure of melibiose was exactly calculated to correspond to 6-$O$-$\alpha$-D-galactopyranosyl-D-glucose.[15] The character of the glycosidic linkage in 2-$O$-$\beta$-D-xylopyranosyl-L-arabinose was elucidated.[16] An agreement was found in calculations of the rotations of per-$O$-acetyl derivatives of some di-[17] and trisaccharides.[18] Finally, these rules were applied to some anhydro derivatives from the oligosaccharide series,[19] to glycosyl derivatives of compounds in the inositol group,[20] to glycosyl derivatives of glycerol,[21-23] and to carboxylic acids formed from reducing disaccharides by addition of hydrogen cyanide and hydrolysis.[24]

In the series of non-reducing D-galactopyranosyl D-galactopyranosides, Bredereck obtained very good results in his calculations of rotations.[25]

On the basis of Hudson's rules, a number of useful variations were proposed. For example, it may be assumed that if two oligosaccharides differ only in a certain part of their molecules, their values of molecular rotation will also be in a certain relation. Expressing according to the generally valid equation (see p. 51) the molecular rotation of sucrose (I) by the relation

$$[M]_1 = [M]_g + A' + F$$

(I)

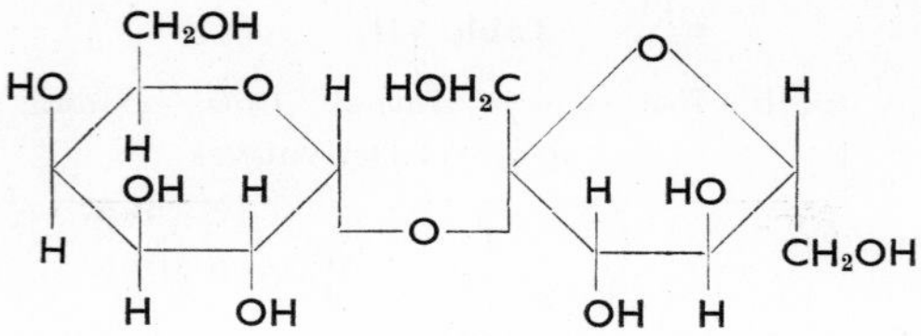

(III)

and the molecular rotation of so-called galsucrose (i.e. $\alpha$-D-galactopyranosyl $\beta$-D-fructofuranoside, III) by the relation

$$[M]_2 = [M]_{gal} + A' + F$$

and subtracting the second equation from the first one gives

$$[M]_1 - [M]_2 = [M]_g - [M]_{gal} + A' - A' + F - F ,$$

or

$$[M]_1 - [M]_2 = [M]_g - [M]_{gal} ,$$

and hence

$$[M]_2 = [M]_1 - [M]_g + [M]_{gal} ,$$

where $[M]_2$ is the molecular rotation of galsucrose, $[M]_1$ is the molecular rotation of sucrose, $[M]_g$ is the molecular rotation of methyl $\alpha$-D-glucopyranoside, and $[M]_{gal}$ is the molecular rotation of methyl $\alpha$-D-galactopyranoside.

This method was applied by a group of investigators,[26-28] who obtained very good results for non-reducing disaccharides [26,27] and trisaccharides.[28] In the case of $\alpha$-D-xylopyranosyl $\beta$-D-fructofuranoside, the arrangement of both anomeric carbon atoms was correctly predicted.[26] Another paper[27] presented a satisfactory calculation of the theoretical value $[M]$ for galsucrose (III), amounting to 294°, in agreement with the experimentally determined value of 279°. Furthermore, the theoretical value $[M]$ for the so-called lactsucrose (4-$O$-$\beta$-D-galactopyranosylsucrose) of 315°, agrees well with the experimental value of 297°.[28]

A recent paper by S. Fukui, R. M. Hochster, R. Durbin, E. E. Grebner, and D. S. Feingold, Bull. Res. Council Israel *11* A, 262 (1963) communicates good results of molecular rotation calculations for an oxidation product of sucrose, namely $\alpha$-D-*ribo*-hexopyranosyl-3-ulose $\beta$-D-fructofuranoside.

An analogous relationship was also discovered in the series of reducing disaccharides; it was found[29] that the difference in the specific rotations of the mutually corresponding -$O$-$\beta$-D-glucosyl and -$O$-$\beta$-D-galactosyl derivatives appears to be a constant, and it is very interesting to note that this circumstance occurs also in the values of the specific rotations of the equilibrium states, see Table VII.

*References see p. 58*

**Table VII**

Differences in Specific Rotations of Mutually Corresponding D-Glucosyl
and D-Galactosyl Derivatives

|  | $[\alpha]_D$ equilibr. | Δ |
|---|---|---|
| 3-*O*-β-D-Galactopyranosyl-D-glucose | $+41 \cdot 2°$ | |
| 3-*O*-β-D-Glucopyranosyl-D-glucose | $+20 \cdot 8°$ | $20 \cdot 4$ |
| 4-*O*-β-D-Galactopyranosyl-D-glucose | $+54 \cdot 9°$ | |
| 4-*O*-β-D-Glucopyranosyl-D-glucose | $+32 \cdot 2°$ | $19 \cdot 7$ |
| 6-*O*-β-D-Galactopyranosyl-D-glucose | $+30 \cdot 7°$ | |
| 6-*O*-β-D-Glucopyranosyl-D-glucose | $+ 9 \cdot 6°$ | $20 \cdot 9$ |

The structure of a tetrasaccharide containing L-arabinose and D-xylose has been dealt with in a paper by H. R. Goldschmid and A. S. Perlin, Can. J. Chem. *41*, 2272 (1963); Isorotation Rules were successfully used.

The method of epimeric differences was also applied in several cases.[18,30-33] According to quite an analogous consideration, on the basis of which the calculation of galsucrose was derived (see p. 55), it may be assumed that it is possible to calculate the value $[M]$ of *epi*-gentiobiose (6-*O*-β-D-glucopyranosyl-D-mannose) from the value $[M]$ of gentiobiose by means of the relation

$$[M]_{epigent} = [M]_{gent} - [M]_g + [M]_{man} \, ,$$

where $[M]_{epigent}$ is the molecular rotation of *epi*-gentiobiose, $[M]_{gent}$ is the molecular rotation of gentiobiose, $[M]_g$ is the molecular rotation of D-glucose, and $[M]_{man}$ is the molecular rotation of D-mannose, of course, always of the analogous anomers.[31] The values obtained by this method were generally quite satisfactory,[18,31-33] although there were a few exceptions.[30]

The mentioned Isorotation Rules were successfully applied for characterizing a number of varied compounds, such as the trisaccharide Y from laminarin,[34] or some higher oligosaccharides composed of D-galactose.[35] A good result was also obtained in the calculation of the molecular rotation of 3-*O*-α-isomaltosyl-D-glucose.[36]

* * *

Another interesting method for ascertaining the numerical relations between the rotation values of oligosaccharides was introduced by Klages and Niemann,[37] and later by Wolfrom and Shafizadeh.[38] The first of these investigators[37] found that the value of molecular rotation of sucrose (α-D-glucopyranosyl β-D-fructofuranoside) agrees well with the sum of the molecular rotations of methyl α-D-glucopyranoside and methyl β-D-fructofuranoside, as well as the value of the molecular rotation of isosucrose (β-D-glucopyranosyl α-D-fructo-furanoside) equals the sum of the values of molecular rotations of methyl β-D-glucopyranoside and methyl α-D-fructofuranoside. The calculation was influenced by an error in the value of $[M]$ for methyl α-D-fructofuranoside.

Wolfrom and Shafizadeh[38] started from the assumption that the values of molecular rotations of isomeric sucroses are composed of 4 parts, namely the constants G and F (corresponding to the glucose less C-1 and the fructose less C-2 residues respectively, and the variables A and B (corresponding to C-1 or C-2 of glucose or fructose respectively, with the sign according to the anomeric configuration). The expression is in principle identical with that introduced by Hudson[2] for trehalose, but Wolfrom replaced the values A and B of glucose or fructose respectively by the values of the molecular rotations of the corresponding methyl glycosides. According to this, the molecular rotation of non-reducing disaccharides is equal to the sum of the molecular rotations of the methyl glycosides of both corresponding components. If one of these glycosides is regarded as an aglycon, this rule is in full agreement with the rule formulated by Klyne[39] for the calculation of the values of molecular rotation of glycosides with an optically active aglycon.

The results of the calculation of the molecular rotations of sucrose and its isomers are in good agreement with the values so far known (see Table VIII).[38]

### Table VIII

Molecular Rotations of Isomeric Sucroses

| D-Glucopyranosyl   D-fructofuranoside | $[M]_D$ | |
|:---:|:---:|:---:|
| | Calculated | Found |
| α, α | +486° | |
| α, β | +215° | +227° |
| β, α | +117° | +116° |
| β, β | −154° | |

Very satisfactory results were also obtained in the calculation of the values of the molecular rotations of octa-O-acetyl derivatives of sucrose and its isomers.[37,38]

Shortly afterwards it was found that the rotation values of isomeric trehaloses ascertained in this way using the values of methyl D-glucopyranosides are more accurate throughout[40] than those determined by Hudson.

**Table IX**

Specific Rotations of Isomeric Trehaloses

|  | $[\alpha]_D$ | |
|---|---|---|
|  | Calculated | Found |
| $\alpha,\alpha$-Trehalose | $+180 \cdot 5°$ | $+178°$ |
| $\alpha,\beta,$-Trehalose (*neo*-trehalose) | $+ 70 \cdot 8°$ | $+ 70°$ |
| $\beta,\beta$-Trehalose (isotrehalose) | $- 58°$ | $- 41 \cdot 5°$ |

An equally good agreement was also found by means of this method for *O*-acetyl derivatives of isomeric trehaloses.[40]

This procedure can also be employed[41] for calculating the molecular rotations of non-reducing trisaccharides from the values of the methyl glycosides of the corresponding mono- and disaccharides, as demonstrated by the examples of gentianose, raffinose and melezitose; the same also applies to the undeca-*O*-acetyl derivatives of these substances.[41]

\* \* \*

The last rule applied in the series of homologous oligosaccharides was formulated by Freudenberg.[42,43] It has been employed several times.[44-48] This rule states that in a polymeric homologous series, if the linkages are identical, $[M]_n$ plotted against $n(n\text{-}1)$ yields straight line, where $[M]$ is the molecular rotation and $n$ is the degree of polymerization. The validity of this rule was confirmed in the series: cellobiose, cellotriose, cellotetraose;[42-44,46,47] isomaltose, isomaltotriose, etc.;[45] and xylobiose, xylotriose, etc.[48]

**REFERENCES**

1. C. S. Hudson, X. Conférence de l'Union Internationale de Chimie, Liège *1930*.
2. C. S. Hudson, J. Am. Chem. Soc. *38*, 1566 (1916).
3. C. S. Hudson, H. Pringsheim, and J. Leibowitz, J. Am. Chem. Soc. *48*, 288 (1926).
4. C. S. Hudson, J. Am. Chem. Soc. *52*, 1707 (1930).
5. J. Staněk, M. Černý, J. Kocourek and J. Pacák, *The Monosaccharides*, Acad. Press, New York 1963.
6. P. Witonsky and F. Smith, J. Org. Chem. *24*, 124 (1959).
7. F. J. Bates, *Polarimetry, Saccharimetry and the Sugars*, National Bureau of Standards, Washington 1942, p. 474.
8. C. S. Hudson and R. Sayre, J. Am. Chem. Soc. *38*, 1867 (1916).
9. C. S. Hudson, J. Am. Chem. Soc. *47*, 268 (1925).
10. C. S. Hudson, J. Am. Chem. Soc. *47*, 872 (1925).
11. C. B. Purves, J. Am. Chem. Soc. *51*, 3619 (1929).

12. C. B. Purves, J. Am. Chem. Soc. *51*, 3627 (1929)
13. C. B. Purves, J. Am. Chem. Soc. *51*, 3631 (1929).
14. A. Pictet and H. Vogel, Helv. Chim. Acta *11*, 905 (1928).
15. W. Charlton, W. N. Haworth, and W. J. Hickinbottom, J. Chem. Soc. *1927*, 1527.
16. G. O. Aspinall and R. J. Ferrier, J. Chem. Soc. *1958*, 1501.
17. M. L. Wolfrom, L. W. Georges, and I. L. Miller, J. Am. Chem. Soc. *71*, 125 (1949).
18. S. H. Nichols, W. L. Evans, and W. D. McDowell, J. Am. Chem. Soc. *62*, 1754 (1940).
19. H. G. Fletcher, L. H. Koehler, and C. S. Hudson, J. Am. Chem. Soc. *71*, 3679 (1949).
20. S. Umezawa and Y. Ito, Bull. Chem. Soc. Japan *34*, 1540 (1961).
21. A. J. Charlson, P. A. J. Gorin, and A. S. Perlin, Can. J. Chem. *34*, 1811 (1956).
22. A. J. Charlson, P. A. J. Gorin, and A. S. Perlin, Can. J. Chem. *35*, 365 (1957).
23. P. A. J. Gorin and J. F. T. Spencer, Can. J. Chem. *37*, 499 (1959).
24. M. Uenaka, Scient. Papers Osaka Univ., *1951*, No. 24, 7.
25. H. Bredereck, G. Höschele, and K. Ruck, Chem. Ber. *86*, 1277 (1953).
26. G. Avigad, D. S. Feingold, and S. Hestrin, Biochim. et Biophys. Acta *20*, 129 (1956).
27. D. S. Feingold, G. Avigad, and S. Hestrin, J. Biol. Chem. *224*, 295 (1957).
28. G. Avigad, J. Biol. Chem. *229*, 121 (1957).
29. R. Kuhn and H. H. Baer, Chem. Ber. *87*, 1560 (1954).
30. W. N. Haworth and E. L. Hirst, J. Chem. Soc. *1930*, 2631.
31. J. Dauben and W. L. Evans, J. Am. Chem. Soc. *60*, 886 (1938).
32. D. D. Reynolds and W. L. Evans, J. Am. Chem. Soc. *62*, 66 (1940).
33. E. A. Talley, D. D. Reynolds, and W. L. Evans, J. Am. Chem. Soc. *65*, 575 (1943).
34. J. R. Turvey and J. M. Evans, J. Chem. Soc. *1960*, 2366.
35. F. May and H. Weinland, Hoppe-Seyler's Z. physiol. Chem. *305*, 207 (1956).
36. A. Sato and H. Ono, Chem. & Ind. (London) *1962*, 1536.
37. F. Klages and R. Niemann, Ann. *529*, 185 (1937).
38. M. L. Wolfrom and F. Shafizadeh, J. Org. Chem. *21*, 88 (1956).
39. J. Klyne, Biochem. J. *47*, XLI (1950).
40. J. Staněk, Nature *179*, 97 (1957).
41. J. Staněk, Chemie und Biochemie der Solanum-Alkaloide, Vorträge und Diskussionsbeiträge des Internationalen Symposiums der Deutschen Akademie der Landwirtschaftswissenchaften, Berlin 1959, p. 117.
42. K. Freudenberg, K. Friedrich, and I. Bumann, Ann. *494*, 41 (1932).
43. K. Freudenberg, *Tannin, Cellulose und Lignin*, Springer, Berlin *1933*, p. 104.
44. E. E. Dickey and M. L. Wolfrom, J. Am. Chem. Soc. *71*, 825 (1949).
45. J. H. Pazur and D. French, J. Biol. Chem. *196*, 265 (1952).
46. R. L. Whistler and C. C. Tu, J. Am. Chem. Soc. *74*, 4334 (1952).
47. M. L. Wolfrom and J. C. Dacons, J. Am. Chem. Soc. *74*, 5331 (1952).
48. C. T. Bishop, Can. J. Chem. *33*, 1073 (1955).

# VI

# Synthesis of Oligosaccharides*

The synthesis of oligosaccharides[1,2] has already been elaborated to a considerable extent using existing methods; however, with regard to the number of possible isomers there are still many unutilized possibilities. In principle, the synthesis of oligosaccharides can be effected in the following ways.

1. From lower components; in the case of disaccharides, this would be the synthesis from two monosaccharide molecules.

2. By lengthening or shortening the carbon chain of one monosaccharide unit in the oligosaccharide molecule.[3]

3. By changing the structure of one of the monosaccharide units in the oligosaccharide molecule.

Quite an independent field is the biochemical oligosaccharide synthesis, which comprises several types of varied reactions (see Chapter VI, 5).

## 1. SYNTHESIS OF OLIGOSACCHARIDES FROM LOWER CONSTITUENTS (USUALLY FROM MONOSACCHARIDES)

Among this group of reactions belong, in the simplest cases, those processes in which two monosaccharide molecules, or molecules of substituted monosaccharides, are connected by a hemiacetal linkage; this reaction may involve the elimination of a molecule of water or of hydrogen halide generally. Oligosaccharide derivatives formation from anhydromonosaccharide derivatives and monosaccharide derivatives proceeds without formation of other simple compounds at all, of course.

### A. SYNTHESIS OF DISACCHARIDES BY ELIMINATION OF A WATER MOLECULE FROM TWO MONOSACCHARIDE MOLECULES

#### a) Synthesis of non-reducing disaccharides
#### Trehalose

The first successful experiment for synthesizing a disaccharide by combining two monosaccharide molecules with simultaneous elimination of water

* For reviews see W. L. Evans, D. D. Reynolds, and E. A. Talley, Advances in Carbohydrate Chem. 6, 27 (1951); M. G. Blair and W. Pigman, Angew. Chem. 69, 422 (1959).

was Fischer's synthesis of isotrehalose (i.e. $\beta,\beta$-trehalose).[4] Heating of 2,3,4,6-tetra-$O$-acetyl-$\beta$-D-glucopyranose (I) in the presence of phoshorus pentoxide gave rise to octa-$O$-acetylisotrehalose (II), though in a yield of only 2%.

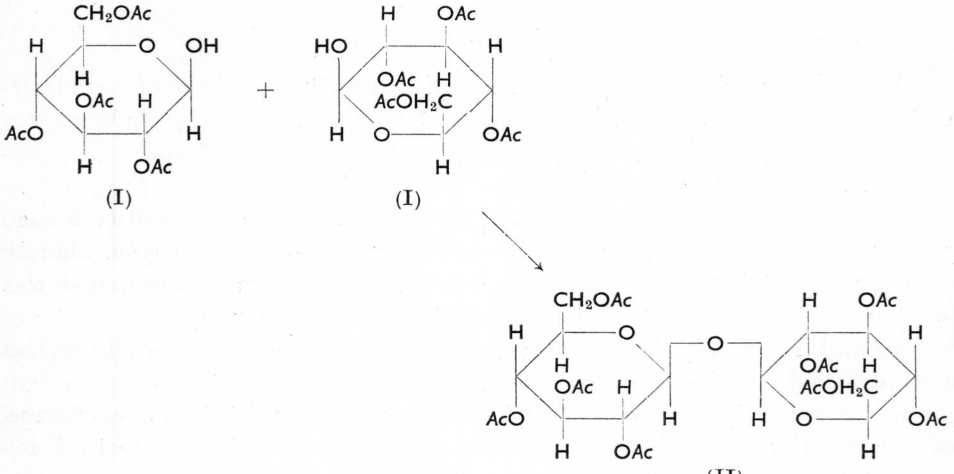

(II)

In their attempts to prepare in this way $\alpha,\alpha$-trehalose, other investigators[5] carried out similar reactions in the presence of acid catalysts, but without significant success. From the values of specific rotations of the reaction products they concluded that they had prepared *neo*-trehalose (i. e. $\alpha,\beta$-trehalose); this opinion was also shared by other workers.[6] However, the products obtained in this way were mixtures which contained about 30% of octa-$O$-acetyl derivatives of reducing disaccharides besides 20% of octa-$O$-acetyltrehalose, as proved much later by Bredereck.[7]

The octa-$O$-acetyl derivative of *neo*-trehalose, i. e. $\alpha,\beta$-trehalose, has been prepared by Vogel[8] from 2,3,4,6-tetra-$O$-acetyl-$\beta$-D-glucopyranose by heating in the presence of phosphorus pentoxide or zinc chloride. Bredereck investigated this reaction very thoroughly[7] and found that heating of 2,3,4,6-tetra-$O$-acetyl-$\beta$-D-glucopyranose in the presence of zinc chloride leads to a mixture of octa-$O$-acetyl derivatives of *neo*-trehalose and isotrehalose (i. e. $\alpha,\beta$-trehalose and $\beta,\beta$-trehalose), whereas in the presence of potassium bisulphate only the latter of these substances is formed, and this in a yield of about 10%. Analogously, 2,3,4,6-tetra-$O$-acetyl-$\beta$-D-galactopyranose gave in the presence of zinc chloride a crystalline octa-$O$-acetyl derivative of $\alpha$-D-galactopyranosyl $\alpha$-D-galactopyranoside, while the syrupy mixture of other isomeric non-reducing disaccharides, containing D-galactose, did not crystallize at all.[7] After acetylation it was possible to isolate from it $\beta$-D-galactopyranosyl $\beta$-D-galactopyranoside [7]

*References see p. 90*

From 2,3,4,6-tetra-*O*-acetyl-α-D-glucopyranose, too, only the octa-*O*-acetyl derivative of *neo*-trehalose was produced by the dehydrating action of phosphorus pentoxide.[9]

### Sucrose

Pictet reported in 1928 the synthesis of sucrose[10] in the form of its octa-*O*-acetyl derivative, prepared by heating 2,3,4,6-tetra-*O*-acetyl-β-D-glucopyranose with 1,3,4,6-tetra-*O*-acetyl-β-D-fructofuranose in chloroform in the presence of zinc chloride. In a further communication[11] he added that the reaction of the same organic components in the presence of phosphorus pentoxide also gives rise to the isomers of the corresponding octa-*O*-acetylsucrose. Shortly afterwards, Pictet's sucrose synthesis was unfavourably criticized and it was pointed out that in this way other products, corresponding to isosucrose,[12] are formed and that this synthesis is not reproducible at all.[13] Pictet then published more detailed data,[14] but soon it was safely proved[15] that the only reaction product is the octa-*O*-acetyl derivative of isosucrose, and this was confirmed later.[16] Even by chromatographic methods it was not possible to detect a trace of sucrose among the reaction products.[17]

A new reaction belonging to this type has been described by J. A. Zderic, Experientia *20*, 48 (1964). 1-*O*-Acetyl-2,3,5-tri-*O*-benzoyl-β-D-ribofuranose, when treated in benzene with boron trifluoride, yielded β-D-ribofuranosyl β-D-ribofuranoside hexa-*O*-benzoate.

### b) Synthesis of reducing disaccharides

According to a very early work[18] the method of which, however, is not reproducible, lactose should be formed by heating a mixture of D-glucose and D-galactose. Neither is it possible to reproduce later methods,[19,20] according to which maltose should be formed by heating a mixture of α-D-glucose and β-D-glucose in the presence of zinc chloride up to a temperature of 150—160°C in a vacuum of 14 mm Hg; maltose, claimed to have been isolated in the form of its octa-*O*-acetyl derivative, should be produced in a yield of up to 10%. Similarly, lactose should be formed by heating a mixture of β-D-glucose and β-D-galactose.[20]

These thermal condensations are not likely to be successfully realized; far better results, however, were obtained by heating monosaccharides in an acid aqueous solution. This process, termed reversion, will be dealt with in a separate chapter (see Chapter VI,4).

An actual chemical synthesis of a reducing disaccharide by combination of two monosaccharide molecules with simultaneous elimination of water was carried out by Gakhokidze.[21-25] In his first paper,[21] this writer reported that heating 2,3,4,6-tetra-$O$-acetyl-$\beta$-D-glucopyranose (I) and 1,3,4,6-tetra-$O$-acetyl-D-glucopyranose (III) yields the octa-$O$-acetyl derivative of sophorose (i. e. 2-$O$-$\beta$-D-glucopyranosyl-D-glucose, IV):[21],[22]

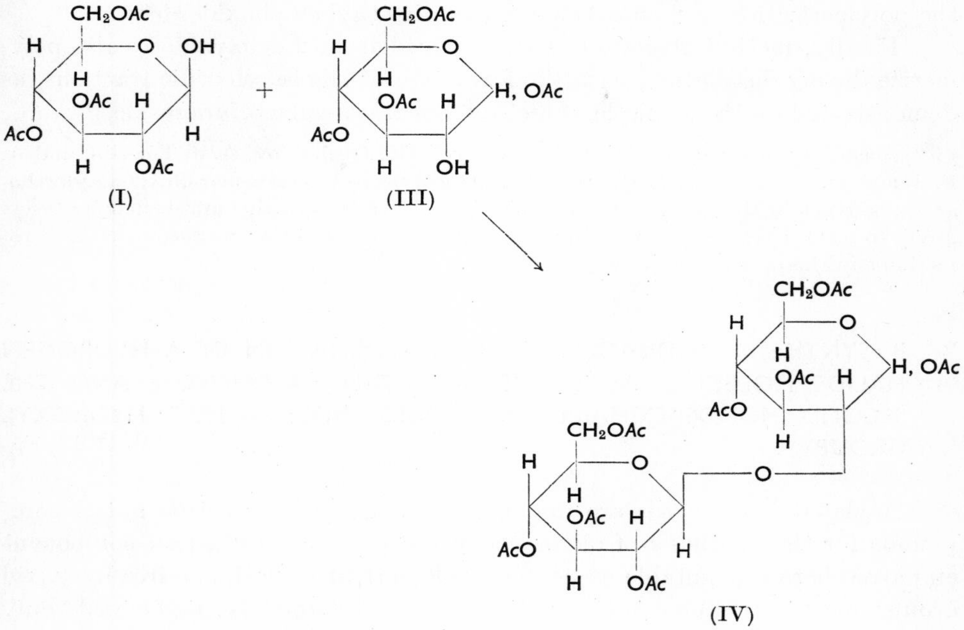

(I)    (III)

(IV)

In a similar way, Gakhokidze prepared 2-$O$-$\beta$-D-galactopyranosyl-D-galactose,[23] and by the reaction of 2,3,4,6-tetra-$O$-acetyl-$\beta$-D-glucopyranose with 1,2-$O$-isopropylidene-4,6-$O$-benzylidene-D-glucopyranose he then also obtained the correspondingly substituted derivative of laminaribiose (i.e. 3-$O$-$\beta$-D-glucopyranosyl-D-glucose).[22]

The further two works are only applications of the described procedures to additional syntheses, i. e. of 2-$O$-$\beta$-D-glucopyranosyl-D-galactose[24] and 2-$O$-$\beta$-D-mannopyranosyl-D-mannose.[25] According to a recent paper,[26] 1,2,3,4-tetra-$O$-acetyl-$\beta$-D-glucopyranose, on heating in the presence of $p$-toluenesulphonic acid, yields oligosaccharides of the 1—6′ series; among the seven oligosaccharides obtained were identified gentiobiose, gentiotriose and gentiotetraose. A similar reaction in the presence of zinc chloride leads to products of the polysaccharide type.

On the other hand, 1,3,4,6-tetra-$O$-acetyl-$\beta$-D-glucopyranose can be converted in the presence of zinc chloride into sophorose and kojibiose in the ratio 3 : 1 besides a simultaneously produced trisaccharide, while 1,2,3,6-tetra-$O$-acetyl-$\beta$-D-glucopyranose yields a mixture of cellobiose and maltose in the ratio 3 : 1.[26]

*References see p. 90*

Some other types of reactions are also known, according to which oligo-saccharides, or rather non-specific fractions of oligosaccharide character, can be obtained from monosaccharides. Thus, higher oligosaccharides are formed by the action of thionyl chloride on monosaccharides,[27] and other papers describe the polymerization of monosaccharides in dimethyl sulphoxide.[28,29]

Finally, methyl glycofuranosides derived from 2-deoxyaldoses also poly-merize during distillation, with the formation of oligosaccharidic fractions, as demonstrated on the example of methyl 2-deoxy-D-galactofuranoside.[30]

According to a recent communication by N. K. Kochetkov, A. J. Khorlin, and A. F. Bochkov, Tetrahedron Letters *1964*, 289, acetylated monosaccharide 1,2-alkylortho-acetates react with suitable monosaccharide derivatives with unprotected hydroxyl group to form derivatives of reducing disaccharides. The reaction proceeds well in nitro-methane in the presence of mercuric bromide.

## B. SYNTHESIS OF DISACCHARIDES BY ELIMINATION OF A HYDROGEN HALIDE MOLECULE FROM THE ACYLATED HALOGENOSE AND THE SECOND MONOSACCHARIDE MOLECULE WITH A FREE HYDROXYL GROUP

Acylated halogenoses are undoubtedly sufficiently reactive initial com-pounds for the synthesis of oligosaccharides; the second reaction component employed here is a suitable monosaccharide derivative with one free hydroxyl group, since it was found that usually the reaction proceeds satisfactorily only when the other hydroxyl groups are blocked, although there are actually rare cases where the action could be effected in the presence of a larger number of free hydroxyl groups. It is necessary, however, to select an appropriate agent for neutralizing the hydrogen halide formed in the reaction.

Sodium hydroxide is not a suitable reagent for binding hydrogen halide. The first paper in this respect is the study by Fischer and Armstrong,[31] who in-vestigated the course of the reaction of 2,3,4,6-tetra-O-acetyl-α-D-glucopy-ranosyl bromide with D-glucose in ethanolic solution in the presence of one equivalent of sodium hydroxide. They believed to have prepared melibiose, or its derivatives. After analogous experiments with 2,3,4,6-tetra-O-acetyl-α-D-glucopyranosyl bromide and D-galactose, as well as with 2,3,4,6-tetra-O-acetyl-α-D-galactopyranosyl bromide and D-galactose, they arrived at the conclusion that the primary alcoholic group of the unsubstituted aldohexose reacts pre-ferentially in any case.

Other investigators who studied these reactions more thoroughly[32,33] proved by methylation analysis that Fischer[31] had in no case succeeded in preparing melibiose. They assumed, at first with doubts,[32] that the substance in question could be lactose and this was confirmed with certainty in a later paper.[33] A more advantageous procedure in this respect would be the reaction of an acylated halogenose with a partially substituted monosaccharide. In fact, the reaction of 2,3,4,6-tetra-$O$-acetyl-$\alpha$-D-glucopyranosyl bromide (V) with the sodium salt of 1,2,3,4-tetra-$O$-acetyl-$\beta$-D-glucopyranose (VI) leads to the octa-$O$-acetyl derivative of gentiobiose (VII) in a yield of 80%:[34]

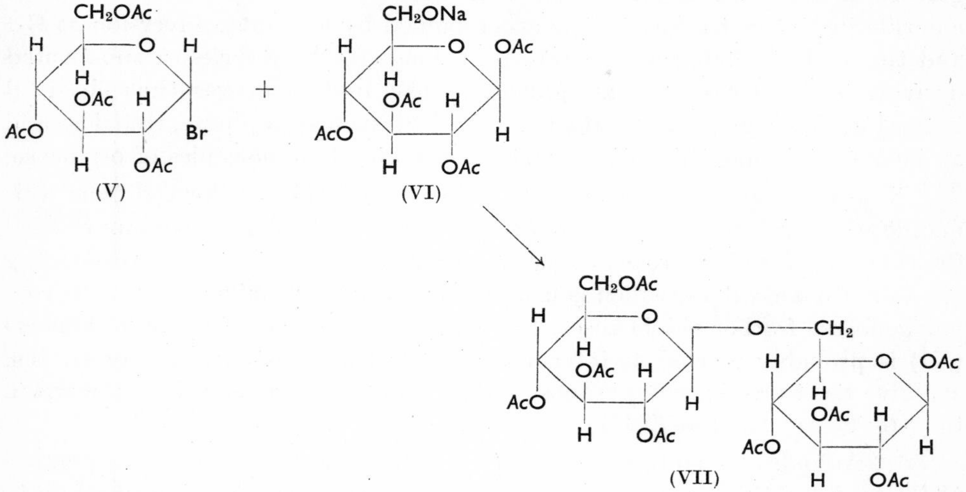

It is interesting to note that in some cases the reaction could also be carried out with a secondary alcoholic group; thus the octa-$O$-acetyl derivative of cellobiose (IX) has been obtained from 2,3,4,6-tetra-$O$-acetyl-$\alpha$-D-glucopyranosyl bromide (V) and the sodium salt of 1,2,3,6-tetra-$O$-acetyl-$\beta$-D-glucopyranose (VIII):[34]

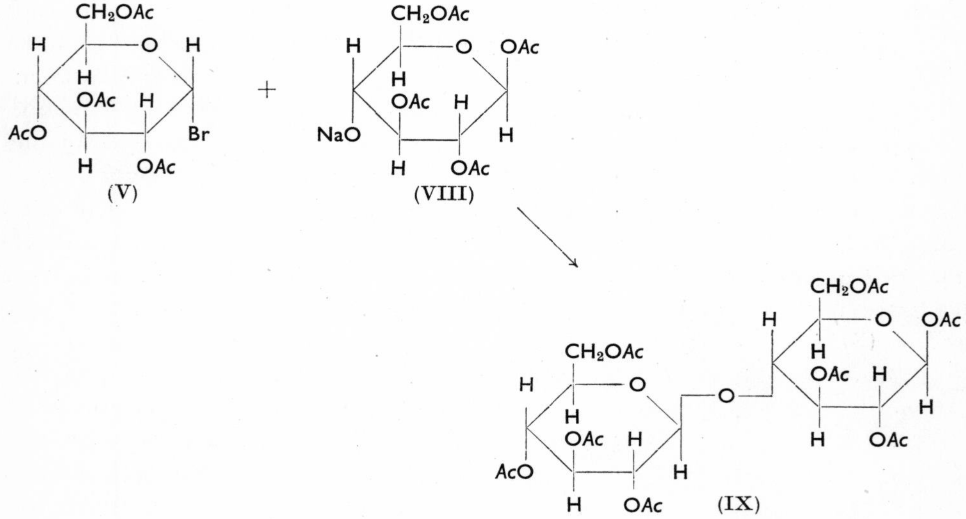

*References see p. 90*

5 — The Oligosaccharides

Unsuccessful, however, was an attempt to synthesize octa-$O$-acetyl-lactose from 2,3,4,6-tetra-$O$-acetyl-α-D-galactosyl bromide and the sodium salt of 1,2,3,6-tetra-$O$-acetyl-D-glucose.[9]

On the other hand, the sodium salt of 1,2:5,6-di-$O$-isopropylidene-α-D-glucofuranose could be condensed with 3,4,6-tri-$O$-acetyl-β-D-glucopyranosyl chloride.[35,36] Since the reaction is accompanied by a Walden inversion at C-1 and the acylated halogenose employed belongs to the β-series, a substituted derivative of nigerose (3-$O$-α-D-glucopyranosyl-D-glucose) was thus obtained in good yield, although by-products are formed, such as kojibiose, trehalose and an incompletely identified disaccharide containing two molecules of D-glucose.

Non-reducing disaccharides, containing D-mannose, are formed from α-D-mannopyranosyl fluoride in alkaline solution.[37] This α-D-mannopyranosyl fluoride (X), for steric reasons, cannot be converted into the corresponding 1,6-anhydro derivative, which is usually formed under similar conditions from halogenoses of other aldohexoses. In this case, 1,2-anhydro-D-mannopyranose (XI) is probably formed as intermediate, and this substance, on hydrolysis, can give rise to α-D-mannopyranose (XII), which in turn may be anomerized to β-D-mannopyranose (XIII).

1,2-Anhydro-D-mannopyranose (XI) reacts with α-D-mannopyranose (XII) to form the non-reducing α-D-mannopyranosyl α-D-mannopyranoside (XIV), as well the reaction of the compounds (XI) and (XIII) gives α-D-mannopyranosyl β-D-mannopyranoside (XV); furthermore, one of these non-reducing disaccharides reacts with 1,2-anhydro-D-mannose to form a non-reducing trisaccharide.

(XI)  +  (XII)  $\longrightarrow$

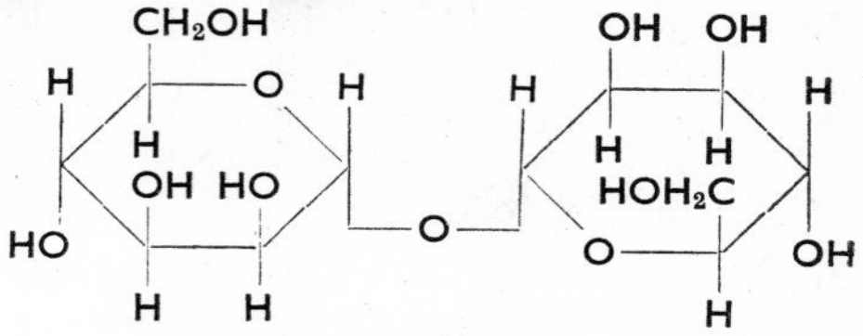

(XIV)

(XI)  +  (XIII)  $\longrightarrow$

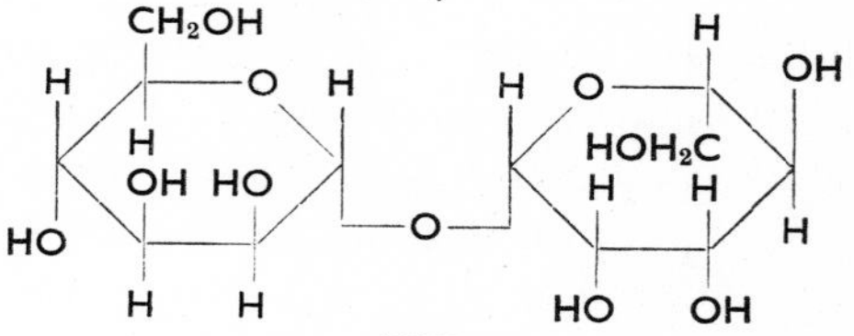

(XV)

Among the reactions of this type we may also include attempts to obtain per-$O$-acetylated derivatives of non-reducing disaccharides by the action of sodium on acetylated halogenoses of monosaccharides in the melt.[9] 2,3,4,6-Tetra-$O$-acetyl-α-D-glucopyranosyl fluoride gives under these conditions the octa-$O$-acetyl derivative of *neo*-trehalose; 2,3,4,6-tetra-$O$-acetyl-α-D-galacto-pyranosyl bromide, on treatment with sodium in the presence of air, yields the octa-$O$-acetyl derivative of α-D-galactopyranosyl β-D-galactopyranoside (if such a reaction is carried out under nitrogen, no peracetyl derivative of a non-reducing disaccharide is formed). No disaccharide at all could be prepared in this way from 2,3,4,6-tetra-$O$-acetyl-α-D-glucopyranosyl bromide.

From the cases here described, which probably represent a complete enu-meration of the reactions carried out with alkali metals and their compounds, it is obvious that this method cannot be regarded as generally applicable. As already pointed out, the only method usable without restriction for con-version of acylated halogenoses is that of Koenigs and Knorr and some of its modifications.

### a) The Koenigs-Knorr synthesis

This method is based in principle on the action of acylated, usually acety-lated, halogenoses on alcohols in general.[38] Koenigs and Knorr themselves attempted to apply this method, elaborated for the preparation of glycosides, to the preparation of disaccharides also; however, they did not find a suitable solvent.[38]

The acylated halogenoses usually employed for this purpose are the bro-mides, which are easily obtainable, sufficiently stable and contain a sufficiently reactive bromine atom. Unstable acylated iodides or not very reactive chlorides were used only in rare cases. The fluorine atom is not reactive at all under the conditions of the Koenigs-Knorr synthesis,[9,39] and the same applies to halogen atoms linked to other carbon atoms of the monosaccharide molecule. For example, in the molecule of 2,3,4-tri-*O*-acetyl-6-bromo-6-deoxy-α-D-glucopyranosyl bromide it is only the bromine atom at C-1 that can participate in the Koenigs-Knorr reaction.[40]

The other component in the Koenigs-Knorr reaction must be a monosaccharide derivative substituted so that just one hydroxyl group remains free, and here the reaction occurs. No general conclusions can be drawn from only a small number of successful applications of the Koenigs-Knorr reaction taking place unambiguously at one hydroxyl group in the presence of another free hydroxyl group.[41,42] Monosaccharide derivatives under consideration for this purpose are compounds with an unsubstituted hemiacetal hydroxyl group or substances with a free primary alcoholic group (in this case, the starting materials are trityl ethers, which are acetylated, whereupon the trityl group is removed from the products obtained by mild hydrolysis in acid solution[43]), or other partially acylated compounds. Various isopropylidene derivatives[44] may also be used to advantage, as well as various derivatives of monosaccharide glycosides.

The reagent binding the liberated hydrogen halide is most frequently silver oxide[4,39,41,42,45-66] or silver carbonate;[7,67-71] the Koenigs-Knorr reaction proceeds in this case almost exclusively with Walden inversion at C-1 of the reacting acylated halogenose. If tertiary organic bases, in particular quinoline,[72] are employed for binding the hydrogen halide, the reaction proceeds without Walden inversion and thus converts acylated halogenoses of the α-series into disaccharides with α-linkage. No general conclusions, however, can be drawn from this one work, since other investigators did not succeed in carrying out the Koenigs-Knorr reaction in quinoline without Walden inversion.[65]

Some new syntheses of reducing oligosaccharides using the Koenigs-Knorr procedure have been described in papers by P. A. Finan and C. D. Warren, J. Chem. Soc. *1963*, 5229; J. K. N. Jones and P. E. Reid, Can J. Chem. *41*, 2382 (1963); A. Klemer and F. Gundlach, Chem. Ber. *96*, 1765 (1963); N. Yamaoka, T. Fujita, M. Kusaka, and K. Aso, J. Agr. Chem. Soc. Japan *38*, 5 (1964).

The use of mercury salts, in particular mercuric cyanide,[55,57,73-90] leads to mixtures of both expected anomers, however, the reaction can be controlled so as to obtain in satisfactory yield the disaccharide with the same configuration as that of the initial acylated halogenose, i.e. to conduct the reaction without Walden inversion.[87] The action of mercuric cyanide on 2,3,4,6-tetra-*O*-acetyl-α-D-galactopyranosyl bromide gives 2,3,4,6-tetra-*O*-acetyl-β-D-galactopyranosyl cyanide as by-product.[85,86,88,89]

All three possible isomeric D-xylopyranosyl D-xylopyranosides have been prepared [see B. Helferich and W. Ost, Chem. Ber. *95*, 2616 (1962)] by the action of 2,3,4-tri-*O*-acetyl-α-D-xylopyranosyl bromide on anomers of 2,3,4-tri-*O*-acetyl-D-xylose using mercuric cyanide and mercuric bromide for binding the hydrogen halide and acetonitrile as solvent. A new failure of this reaction has been reported by I. J. Goldstein and W. J. Whelan, J. Chem. Soc. *1963*, 4264; 2,3,4,6-tetra-*O*-acetyl-α-D-glucopyranosyl bromide and 1,2:3,4-di-*O*-isopropylidene-D-galactose yield not the expected derivative of 6-*O*-α-D-glucopyranosyl-D-galactose, but only a derivative of 6-*O*-β-D-glucopyranosyl-D-galactose.

The reaction of 2,3,4,6-tetra-*O*-acetyl-α-D-glucopyranosyl bromide with 1,3,4,6-tetra-*O*-acetates of α-D-glucopyranose and α-D-galactopyranose [see B. Helferich and J. Zirner, Chem. Ber. *95*, 2604 (1962)] using mercuric cyanide gives rise to derivatives of 2-*O*-α-D-glucopyranosyl-D-glucose and 2-*O*-α-D-glucopyranosyl-D-galactose. The analogous reaction of 2,3,4,6-tetra-*O*-acetyl-α-D-galactopyranosyl bromide with 1,3,4,6-tetra-*O*-acetyl-α-D-glucopyranose yields the expected derivative of 2-*O*-α-D-galactopyranosyl-D-glucose, however, 2,3,4,6-tetra-*O*-acetyl-α-D-galactopyranosyl bromide and 2,3,4,6-tetra-*O*-acetyl-β-D-galactopyranose gives rise to derivatives of both 2-*O*-α-D-galactopyranosyl-D-galactose and 2-*O*-β-D-galactopyranosyl-D-galactose.

The action of silver perchlorate, employed quite recently,[91] gives also rise to mixtures of both anomers. Zinc oxide has so far been used for this reaction in one case only.[92]

Of late, quite new possibilities for syntheses were described by Bredereck.[93–95] 1,2,3,4-Tetra-*O*-acetyl-6-*O*-trityl-β-D-glucopyranose (XVI) reacts with 2,3,4,6-tetra-*O*-acetyl-α-D-glucopyranosyl bromide (V) in the presence of silver perchlorate in nitromethane to form octa-*O*-acetylgentiobiose (XVII) with a yield of 60%:

In order to explain this reaction, the authors assumed that silver perchlorate reacts with 2,3,4,6-tetra-$O$-acetyl-$\alpha$-D-glucopyranosyl bromide to form an unstable perchlorate (XVIII) which, in nitromethane, dissociates into the perchlorate anion and the corresponding cation (XIX), the latter being added to the electron pair of the oxygen atom in the triphenylmethoxy group with the formation of the cation (XX). This oxonium cation is likewise unstable and splits off the triphenylmethyl cation (which combines with the perchlorate anion into a salt) with the formation of a substance containing a glycosidic C—O—C linkage (XXI).

CH₂OAc ... structures (XVIII), (XIX), (XX), (XXI)

The reactions of acylated halogenoses with 1,2,3,4-tetra-$O$-acetyl-6-$O$-trityl derivatives of aldohexoses have been followed very carefully in more recent papers, see H. Bredereck, A. Wagner, D. Geissel, and H. Ott, Chem. Ber. *95*, 3064 (1962); H. Bredereck, A. Wagner, D. Geissel, P. Gross, U. Hutten, and H. Ott, Chem. Ber. *95*, 3056 (1962).

The reaction of an acylated halogenose with the appropriate component is usually carried out in solution; however, a condensation using silver carbonate and no solvent has also been described.[7] The reaction with silver oxide is as a rule performed mainly in chloroform,[41,42,50,51,53,54,59-61] or benzene.[63] The reaction in the presence of silver carbonate is also carried out in chloroform,[7] methylene chloride,[70] or benzene,[68,69] while with mercuric cyanide, benzene[90] or acetone[77] may be employed, but an especially advantageous solvent is nitromethane,[55,78,79,87,88] which is also used for the reaction in the presence of silver perchlorate.

Neutralization of the liberated hydrogen halide with silver oxide or silver carbonate exerts an unfavourable influence on the proceeding reaction by forming the water which hydrolyses the acylated halogenose. For this reason, water-binding agents are added, such as anhydrous sodium sulphate, anhydrous copper sulphate,[96,97] or anhydrous calcium chloride.[47,98] In some cases, the yield of the reaction could be considerably increased in this way,[99,100] even from 0·25 up to 25%. Widespread use is made of an addition of Drierite (anhydrous calcium sulphate)[48,58,71,101-104] and of a small amount of iodine.[46-48] Both these desiccants are almost universally employed in the Koenigs-Knorr synthesis,[7, 41,42,50,52-54,56,58-61,63-65,68-71] and glass beads,[50,56,58] too, are added to the reaction mixture. In the synthesis of gentiobiose from 2,3,4,6-tetra-$O$-acetyl-$\alpha$-D-glucopyranosyl bromide and 1,2,3,4-tetra-$O$-acetyl-D-glucopyranose, the yield of the reaction was increased from 23%[46] to 52%[47] by the use of anhydrous calcium chloride and iodine, and further up to 74%[48] by means of Drierite and iodine.

Magnesium perchlorate,[9] too, may be employed as desiccant; however, great care is required as the reaction is carried out at higher temperature and there is a risk of explosion.[105,106] In some cases, the synthesis was carried out successfully with removal of the produced water by azeotropic distillation[107,108] and also under these conditions the reaction was advantageously influenced by the addition of iodine.[47,49,109-112] In general, iodine facilitates the formation of oligosaccharides in cases where acylated halogenoses of suitable configurations might preferentially yield an orthoester.

All these reactions obviously lead to oligosaccharide derivatives with various blocking groups, which must be removed. This usually involves no difficulties; acyloxy groups can be hydrolysed in alkaline solution,[7,41,42,52-54, 58-61,64,68-70,78,84,87,95,113-118] or in a weakly acid medium;[119] screening isopropylidene groups, too, can be eliminated hydrolytically in acid solution,[21,36,41,68, 69,84,120,121] or on ion exchangers[56,58] without attacking the glycosidic linkage proper in the oligosaccharide. Acids are also suited for hydrolytic removal of the blocking ethylidene[54] or benzylidene group;[59] the latter can also be eliminated by hydrolysis. The synthesis of an oligosaccharide from a monosaccharide methyl glycoside obviously leads to the methyl glycoside of a reducing oligosaccharide. The screening glycosidic methyl group can be hydrolytically eliminated by heating with 10% formic acid to 90°C;[41] even under these conditions the glycosidic linkage of the oligosaccharide is not affected. Screening benzyl groups are always eliminated by hydrogenolysis.[42,71,90*]

From the stereochemical point of view it must be taken into account that the Koenigs-Knorr synthesis proceeds with Walden inversion at C-1 of the acylated halogenose,[122-126] and since the majority of acylated halogenoses of D-aldoses belongs to the $\alpha$-series, this method leads in most cases to compounds with $\beta$-configuration. In general it can be stated that only when quinoline[72] or mercury salts[55,57,73-90] are employed for binding the hydrogen halide formed may this reaction be expected to proceed without Walden inversion or with the

---

* See also P. A. Finan and C. D. Warren, J. Chem. Soc. *1963*, 5229.

*References see p. 90*

formation of both possible anomers. If silver oxide is used, Walden inversion must always be taken into account, especially in the case of acylated halogenoses with D-configuration of the acyloxy group at C-2. It has been reported[127] that 3,4,6-tri-O-acetyl-2-(2,4-dinitrophenylamino)-2-deoxy-α-D-glucopyranosyl bromide reacts with 1,2:3,4-di-O-isopropylidene-D-galactopyranose in the presence of silver carbonate exclusively with the formation of the β-anomer (in a yield of 30%), whereas the reaction of the same organic components in a mixture of chloroform and pyridine leads to a product containing 30% of the α-anomer and 15% of the β-anomer.

Considerable difficulties were formerly encountered in the Koenigs-Knorr reaction of acylated halogenoses of aldohexoses of the D-series with an L-acyloxy group at C-2; since this acyloxy group is in *trans*-position to the halogen atom at C-1, the conditions are here given for the formation of ortho-esters[123] (see Chapter XVII). For example, the reaction of 2,3,4,6-tetra-O-acetyl-α-D-mannopyranosyl bromide (XXII) with 1,2,3,4-tetra-O-acetyl-β-D-gluco-pyranose (XXIII) yields besides the expected disaccharide also a mixture of two diastereoisomeric substances of orthoester structure (XXIV):[111]

Interesting stereochemical phenomena in the Koenigs-Knorr reaction, especially with the use of 2,3,4,6-tetra-O-acetyl-α-D-mannopyranosyl bromide, were in recent years observed by Canadian investigators. In their first paper on this subject[57] they proved that the disaccharides formerly prepared from 2,3,4,6-tetra-O-acetyl-α-D-mannopyranosyl bromide[111] are formed without Walden inversion at C-1. Consequently, these substances must be regarded as 6-*O*-α-D-mannopyranosyl derivatives[57] and not as 6-*O*-β-D-mannopyranosyl derivatives.[111] In connection with this problem, the Canadian investigators were also concerned with other factors influencing the course of the Koenigs-Knorr reaction,[63] in particular the reaction of the acylated halogenoses with silver oxide; the fast reaction of these two substances leads to undesirable products, especially to 2,3,4,6-tetra-*O*-acetyl derivatives of aldohexoses.

Decomposition of 2,3,4,6-tetra-*O*-acetyl-α-D-mannopyranosyl bromide in the presence of silver oxide has been followed carefully by C. S. Giam, H. R. Goldschmid, and A. S. Perlin, Can. Chem. *41*, 3074 (1963); a trisaccharide orthoester is one of the products formed. It contains three units of D-mannose linked together through the functional groups of a molecule of acetoacetic acid.

The steric course of the Koenigs-Knorr reaction of 2,3,4,6-tetra-*O*-substituted derivatives of α-D-mannopyranosyl bromide was investigated in a further work[64] with interesting results. Of the substances employed, 2,3,4,6-tetra-*O*-benzoyl, 3,4,6-tri-*O*-acetyl and 3,4,6-tri-*O*-acetyl-2-*O*-benzyl derivatives react without Walden inversion, while 4,6-di-*O*-acetyl-2,3-di-*O*-carbonyl-α-D-mannopyranosyl bromide reacts with 1,2,3,4-tetra-*O*-acetyl-β-D-glucopyranose with Walden inversion and formation of a derivative of 6-*O*-β-D-mannopyranosyl-D-glucose.

Further stereochemical studies were concerned with 2-substituted derivatives of 3,5-di-*O*-benzoyl-α-L-arabinofuranosyl bromide and 3,5-di-*O*-benzoyl-β-D-ribofuranosyl bromide.[66] In both these acylated halogenoses the halogen atom is in the *trans*-position to the substituting group at C-2, and the formation of orthoesters is possible in both cases. The reaction is strongly influenced by the nature of the substitutent at C-2 and can be controlled so as to proceed either without or with Walden inversion; the formation of orthoesters can also be prevented by appropriate selection of this substituent.

The preparation of *O*-α-D-glucosyl derivatives by the Koenigs-Knorr reaction entails starting acylated halogenoses of the β-series. The possibilities here are limited as some substances suited for this purpose are not easily obtainable, such as 3,4,6-tri-*O*-acetyl-β-D-glucopyranosyl chloride or its 2-*O*-trichloroacetyl derivative. Quite recently, the corresponding 2-*O*-nitrate and silver perchlorate were also recommended for this purpose.[91]

According to a communication by M. L. Wolfrom, A. Thompson, and D. R. Lineback, J. Org. Chem. *28*, 860 (1963), the reaction of 3,4,6-tri-*O*-acetyl-2-*O*-nitro-β-D-glucopyranosyl chloride with 1,3,4,6-tetra-*O*-acetyl-β-D-glucopyranose proceeds with Walden inversion giving rise to a derivative of kojibiose (2-*O*-α-D-glucopyranosyl-D-glucose).

Some other syntheses with 3,4,6-tri-*O*-acetyl-2-*O*-nitro-β-D-glucopyranosyl chloride have been described by R. de Souza and I. J. Goldstein, Tetrahedron Letters *1964*, 1215.

*References see p. 90*

### Synthesis of non-reducing disaccharides

The first, *de facto* unintentional synthesis of a non-reducing disaccharide was that of octa-$O$-acetylisotrehalose, obtained by Fischer[4] as a by-product in the preparation of 2,3,4,6-tetra-$O$-acetyl-$\beta$-D-glucopyranose from 2,3,4,6-tetra-$O$-acetyl-$\alpha$-D-glucopyranosyl bromide by the action of silver oxide in ether with a small admixture of water. The hydrolysis of 2,3,4,6-tetra-$O$-acetyl-$\alpha$-D-glucopyranosyl bromide (V) obviously proceeded with the formation of 2,3,4,6-tetra-$O$-acetyl-$\beta$-D-glucopyranose (I), and both these substances, on condensation, then yielded octa-$O$-acetylisotrehalose (II):

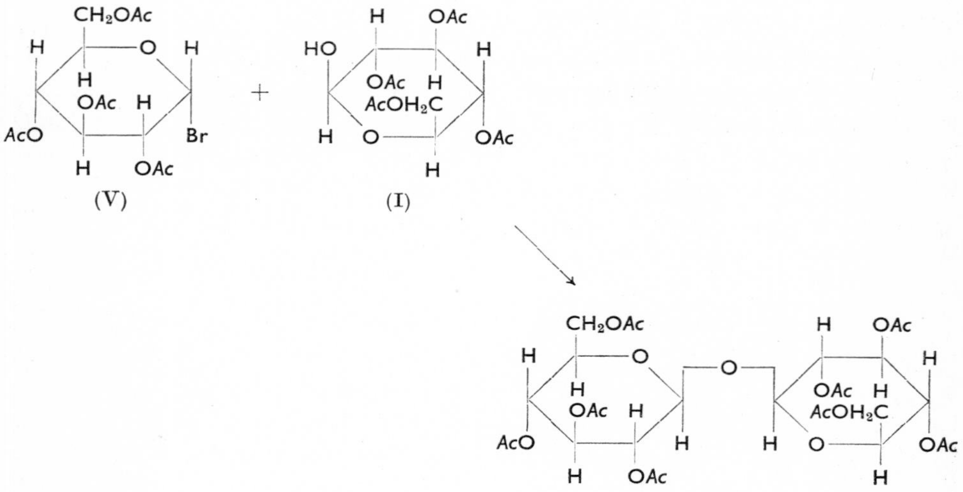

The yields were very low, about 1%, although the synthesis was later adjusted with the intention to prepare octa-$O$-acetylisotrehalose as main product.[109,128] By the use of iodine, silver oxide and Drierite the yield could be increased to about 10%.[7,49] No improvement was achieved by another variation of the condensation of 2,3,4,6-tetra-$O$-acetyl-$\alpha$-D-glucopyranosyl bromide with 2,3,4,6-tetra-$O$-acetyl-$\beta$-D-glucopyranose, i.e. heating these components in the melt, in the presence of silver oxide, since in this case the yield amounted to only 7%.[7]

Essentially higher yields, however, were obtained by the use of mercuric cyanide for binding the hydrogen halide; the reaction can be carried out in acetone[77] or in nitromethane.[78] The yields of octa-$O$-acetylisotrehalose are 9·7% in the first case[77] and 31·5% in the second case.[78] In both cases, octa-$O$-acetyl-*neo*-trehalose is formed as by-product, amounting to 18% in acetone[77] and to 9% in nitromethane.[78]

Analogously to these reactions, octa-$O$-acetyl-$\beta$-D-galactopyranosyl $\beta$-D-galactopyranoside was obtained in a yield of 15.5%[7] from 2,3,4,6-tetra-$O$-acetyl-$\alpha$-D-galactopyranosyl bromide and 2,3,4,6-tetra-$O$-acetyl-$\beta$-D-galacto-pyranose, and the same initial halogenose and 2,3,4,6-tetra-$O$-acetyl-$\beta$-D-glucopyranose were converted into octa-$O$-acetyl-$\beta$-D-galactopyranosyl $\alpha$-D-glucopyranoside.[78]

Helferich,[121] using mercuric cyanide in nitromethane, recently prepared a number of non-reducing disaccharides in the form of the corresponding per-$O$-acetyl derivatives in yields usually amounting to about 30%. The reactions were carried out between 2,3,4-tri-$O$-acetyl-$\alpha$-D-xylopyranosyl bromide and 2,3,4-tri-$O$-acetyl-$\beta$-D-xylopyranose, 2,3,4,6-tetra-$O$-acetyl-$\beta$-D-glucopyranose and 2,3,4,6-tetra-$O$-acetyl-$\beta$-D-galactopyranose respectively; further, with 2,3,4,6-tetra-$O$-acetyl-$\alpha$-D-galactopyranosyl bromide and either 2,3,4-tri-$O$-acetyl-$\beta$-D-xylopyranose or 2,3,4,6-tetra-$O$-acetyl-$\beta$-D-galactopyranose. The latter compound was also treated with 2,3,4,6-tetra-$O$-acetyl-$\alpha$-D-glucopyranosyl bromide.

For some more details on the syntheses of the isomeric D-xylopyranosyl D-xylopyranosides see B. Helferich and W. Ost, Chem. Ber. *95*, 2616 (1962).

Finally, the octa-$O$-acetyl derivative of isosucrose ($\beta$-D-glucopyranosyl $\alpha$-D-fructofuranoside, XXV),[7,129] too, was prepared on the one hand by condensing 2,3,4,6-tetra-$O$-acetyl-$\alpha$-D-glucopyranosyl bromide with 1,3,4,6-tetra-$O$-acetyl-$\alpha$-D-fructofuranose, and on the other hand by condensation of 1,3,4,6-tetra-$O$-acetyl-$\beta$-D-fructofuranosyl chloride with 2,3,4,6-tetra-$O$-acetyl-$\beta$-D-glucopyranose. The yields of the reactions were low,[7] in the first case 2%, in the second case 4%.

(XXV)

Helferich also prepared the 1,3,4,5,2',3',4',6'-octa-$O$-acetyl derivative of $\beta$-D-fructopyranosyl $\beta$-D-galactopyranoside by the action of 2,3,4,6-tetra-$O$-acetyl-$\alpha$-D-galactopyranosyl bromide on 1,3,4,5-tetra-$O$-acetyl-$\beta$-D-fructopyranose in nitromethane, in the presence of mercuric cyanide.[121]

The octa-$O$-acetyl derivative of a non-reducing disaccharide was also obtained as condensation product from 2,3,4,6-tetra-$O$-acetyl-$\alpha$-D-galactopyranosyl bromide and 1,3,4,6-tetra-$O$-acetyl-$\alpha$-D-glucopyranose in acetonitrile, in the presence of silver oxide and iodine.[60] This reaction must obviously invol-

*References see p. 90*

ve a re-arrangement of the acetyl groups in the glucose unit; according to the values of the specific rotation of the product, the investigators assume to have obtained β-D-galactopyranosyl β-D-glucopyranoside.

To the above reactions may be added, on the one hand, those already mentioned earlier, leading to acylated derivatives of non-reducing disaccharides by the action of sodium on acylated halogenoses of monosaccharides,[9] and, on the other hand, the reactions giving rise to non-reducing disaccharides, containing D-mannose, from α-D-mannopyranosyl fluoride in alkaline solution.[37]

### Synthesis of reducing disaccharides

#### Reaction of acylated halogenoses with a primary alcoholic group

The first substances synthesized in this group were gentiobiose and its derivatives. All the original syntheses were carried out by Helferich and associates.[39,45-47] The initial compound was in each case 2,3,4,6-tetra-O-acetyl-α-D-glucopyranosyl bromide (V); the other reaction component was a suitable D-glucopyranose derivative with an unsubstituted primary alcoholic group such as methyl 2,3,4-tri-O-benzoyl-α-D-glucopyranoside,[45] 2,3,4-tri-O-benzoyl-α-D-glucopyranosyl fluoride,[39] or 1,2,3,4-tetra-O-acetyl-β-D-glucopyranose (XXVI).[46,47] In principle it may be stated that, in the presence of silver oxide in chloroform, 2,3,4,6-tetra-O-acetyl-α-D-glucopyranosyl bromide (V) reacts with an appropriately substituted derivative of D-glucopyranose, such as (XXVI), with Walden inversion at C-1 and formation of the corresponding derivative of gentiobiose (XXVII).

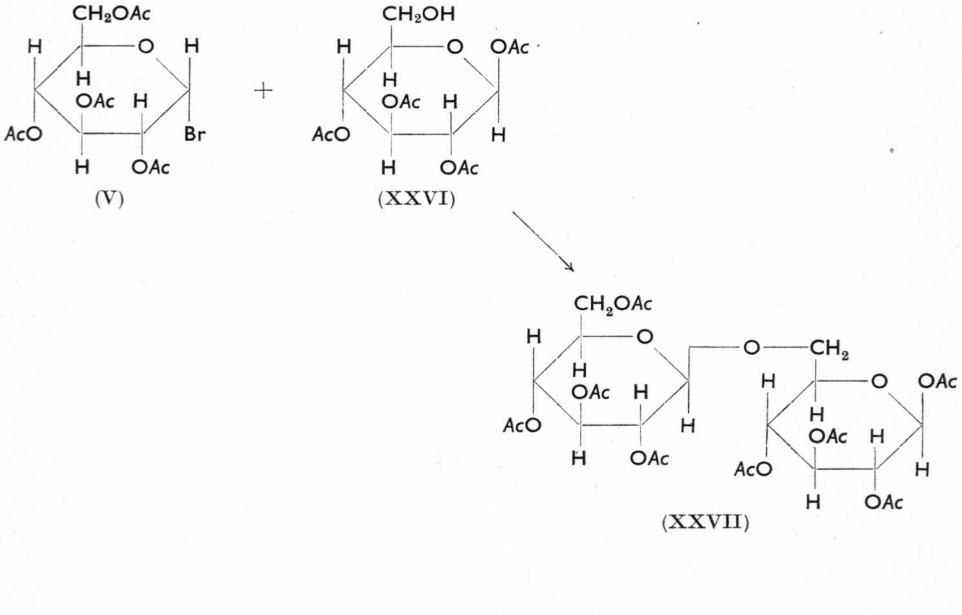

According to Helferich's original procedure,[46] the synthesis of octa-*O*-acetylgentiobiose afforded no satisfactory yield, only 23%; Helferich himself increased the yield to 52% by an addition of anhydrous calcium chloride;[47] other investigators then achieved further improvements[48] by carrying out the reaction with the use of silver oxide, Drierite and iodine, whereby the yield attained 74%.

It is interesting to note that the yield of the reaction with 1,2,3,4-tetra-*O*-acetyl-α-D-glucopyranose is lower.[112] The amorphous product reacts with 2,3,4,6-tetra-*O*-acetyl-α-D-glucopyranosyl bromide with a yield of 50%, while crystalline 1,2,3,4-tetra-*O*-acetyl-α-D-glucopyranose affords a yield of only 42%.

Further significant improvements were undoubtedly achieved by Bredereck's method[93-95] (see p. 69), according to which octa-*O*-acetylgentiobiose can be obtained by the reaction of 2,3,4,6-tetra-*O*-acetyl-α-D-glucopyranosyl bromide with 1,2,3,4-tetra-*O*-acetyl-6-*O*-trityl-β-D-glucopyranose.[93,94] This acylated halogenose can also be condensed with 6-*O*-trityl derivatives of other monosaccharides, such as D-mannose, whereby derivatives of *epi*-gentiobiose (i. e. 6-*O*-β-D-glucopyranosyl-D-mannose) can be obtained.[95]

Quite a lot of 6-*O*-glycosylaldohexoses have been prepared recently, see H. Bredereck, A. Wagner, D. Geissel, P. Gross, U. Hutten, and H. Ott, Chem. Ber. *95*, 3056 (1962); H. Bredereck, A. Wagner, B. Geissel, and H. Ott, Ber. *95*, 3064 (1962). The reaction conditions and components can be chosen so as to yield the 6-*O*-α derivatives.

Another variation is the method already mentioned (see p. 65), according to which octa-*O*-acetylgentiobiose is formed by the reaction of 2,3,4,6-tetra-*O*-acetyl-α-D-glucopyranosyl bromide with the sodium salt of 1,2,3,4-tetra-*O*-acetyl-β-D-glucopyranose.[34]

It is obvious that a larger number of similar reactions were carried out between acylated halogenoses and suitable aldose derivatives with an unsubstituted primary alcoholic group under the conditions of the Koenigs-Knorr synthesis. Substances prepared in this way are, for example derivatives of 6-*O*-β-D-glucopyranosyl-D-galactopyranose[41,44,130] and especially, derivatives of *allo*-lactose (i. e. 6-*O*-β-D-galactopyranosyl-D-glucose). A number of investigators[52,131,132] have utilized the reaction of 2,3,4,6-tetra-*O*-acetyl-α-D-galactopyranosyl bromide (XXVIII) with 1,2,3,4-tetra-*O*-acetyl-β-D-glucopyranose (XXVI) for the preparation of octa-*O*-acetyl-*allo*-lactose (XXIX), and it is interesting to note that this substance is produced as the main product even when the condensation of the reaction components is carried out in the presence of mercury salts.[133] Zemplén did not succeed in preparing the expected α-anomer, i. e. melibiose, by condensing 2,3,4,6-tetra-*O*-acetyl-α-D-galactopyranosyl bromide with 1,2,3,4-tetra-*O*-acetyl-β-D-glucopyranose in the presence of mercury salts.[134] Melibiose is obtainable in the form of its octa-*O*-acetyl derivative only by condensation of the mentioned initial materials in the presence of quinoline.[72]

*References see p. 90*

(XXVIII)                    (XXVI)

(XXIX)

According to a recent communication, see I. J. Goldstein and W. J. Whelan, J. Chem. Soc. *1963*, 4264, 2,3,4,6-tetra-$O$-acetyl-$\alpha$-D-glucopyranosyl bromide and 1,2:3,4-di-$O$-isopropylidene-D-galactopyranose yield in the presence of mercuric cyanide only a 6-$O$-$\beta$-D-glucopyranosyl-D-galactopyranose derivative.

Analogous condensations were carried out to prepare derivatives of other reducing oligosaccharides, such as 6-$O$-$\beta$-D-galactopyranosyl-D-galactose;[130] primeverose (i. e. 6-$O$-$\beta$-D-xylopyranosyl-D-glucose) has also been prepared in the form of its hepta-$O$-acetyl derivative by the reaction of 2,3,4-tri-$O$-acetyl-$\alpha$-D-xylopyranosyl bromide with 1,2,3,4-tetra-$O$-acetyl-$\beta$-D-glucopyranose.[121, 134-136] In this case it was found that even in the presence of mercury salts[135,136] only the substance mentioned and not its $\alpha$-anomer is formed.

Analogously, the reaction of 2,3,4-tri-$O$-acetyl-$\alpha$-D-xylopyranosyl bromide with 1,2:3,4-di-$O$-isopropylidene-D-galactose yielded the expected derivative of 6-$O$-$\beta$-D-xylopyranosyl-D-galactose,[41] and similar methods were employed for the preparation of further oligosaccharides or their derivatives; a derivative of vicianose (6-$O$-$\alpha$-L-arabinopyranosyl-D-glucose) is formed by the reaction of 2,3,4-tri-$O$-acetyl-$\beta$-L-arabinopyranosyl bromide with 1,2,3,4-tetra-$O$-acetyl-$\beta$-D-glucopyranose,[72] a derivative of 5-$O$-$\beta$-D-galactopyranosyl-L-arabinose results from the reaction of 2,3,4,6-tetra-$O$-acetyl-$\alpha$-D-galactopyranosyl bromide with ethyl 2,3-di-$O$-acetyl-$\alpha$-L-arabinofuranoside,[53] and a derivative of 1-$O$-$\beta$-D-glucopyranosyl-D-fructose is obtained in the reaction of 2,3,4,6-tetra-$O$-acetyl-$\alpha$-D-glucopyranosyl bromide with 2,3:4,5-di-$O$-isopropylidene-D-fructopyranose.[121]

For the synthesis of 5-$O$-$\beta$-D-glucopyranosyl-D-xylose see J. K. N. Jones and P. E. Reid, Can. J. Chem. *41*, 2382 (1963).

Of interest are observations concerning the behaviour of 2,3,4,6-tetra-*O*-acetyl-α-D-mannopyranosyl bromide. The first paper on this subject reports that Koenigs-Knorr reactions with this compound proceed with Walden inversion and thus yield 6-*O*-β-D-mannosyl derivatives,[111] and that the same applies to the reaction of 2,3:5,6-di-*O*-isopropylidene-α-D-mannofuranosyl chloride.[130] A revision of these results showed that the Koenigs-Knorr reactions of 2,3,4,6-tetra-*O*-acetyl-α-D-mannopyranosyl bromide and of an analogous compound derived from rhamnose proceed without Walden inversion;[57] this finding led to a correction of some data on the structure even of substances as well known as robinobiose and rutinose,[57] and also to a systematic investigation of the steric course of the Koenigs-Knorr reaction at C-1 of acylated halogenoses derived from D-mannose,[64] L-arabinose and D-ribose[66] (see p. 73).

In two cases it is reported[41,82] that the Koenigs-Knorr reaction can be carried out at the primary alcoholic group with the use of an acylated halogenose and an aldose derivative containing even more unsubstituted hydroxyl groups; according to this, the primary alcoholic hydroxyl group should always react preferentially, and thus a derivative of gentiobiose has been obtained by the reaction of 2,3,4,6-tetra-*O*-acetyl-α-D-glucopyranosyl bromide with 1,2-*O*-isopropylidene-D-glucofuranose.[82] The reaction of 2,3,4-tri-*O*-acetyl-α-D-xylopyranosyl bromide with an anomeric mixture of methyl L-arabinofuranosides also gives rise to a derivative of 5-*O*-β-D-xylopyranosyl-L-arabinofuranose.[41]

### Reactions of acylated halogenoses with a secondary alcoholic group

### In position 2

In the group of these reducing disaccharides, the reaction of 2,3,4,6-tetra-*O*-acetyl-α-D-glucopyranosyl bromide (V) with methyl 4,6-*O*-benzylidene-α-D-glucopyranoside (XXX) yields the corresponding derivative (XXXI) of sophorose (2-*O*-β-D-glucopyranosyl-D-glucose).[70,137,138] It is interesting to note that in this case the reaction takes place exclusively at C-2, although the hydroxyl group at C-3 is likewise unsubstituted, whereas the reaction of the corresponding benzyl 4,6-*O*-benzylidene-β-D-glucopyranoside proceeds at both free hydroxyl groups, thus giving rise to a mixture of 2-*O*-β- and 3-*O*-β-D-glucopyranosyl-D-glucose derivatives.[42,62] A similar reaction occurs with derivatives of methyl 4,6-*O*-benzylidene-β-D-glucopyranoside and 2,3,4,6-tetra-*O*-acetyl-α-D-glucopyranosyl bromide.[138a]

A new synthesis of sophorose and its derivatives from 2,3,4,6-tetra-*O*-acetyl-α-D-glucopyranosyl bromide and benzyl 3,5,6-tri-*O*-benzyl-α-D-glucofuranoside has been reported by P. A. Finan and C. D. Warren, J. Chem. Soc. *1963*, 5229.

The same acylated halogenose (V) and 1,3,4,6-tetra-*O*-acetyl-α-D-glucopyranose (XXXII) react to form octa-*O*-acetylsophorose (XXXIII)[21] while both these initial compounds in the presence of mercuric cyanide give octa-*O*-

acetylkojibiose (2-*O*-α-D-glucopyranosyl-D-glucose, XXXIV).[79],[81] The reaction can be exploited so as to yield derivatives of both kojibiose and sophorose.[138b],[138c]

Kojibiose derivatives can be obtained using 1,3,4,6-tetra-$O$-acetyl-$\beta$-D-glucopyranose and 3,4,6-tri-$O$-acetyl-2-$O$-nitro-$\beta$-D-glucopyranosyl chloride, see M. L. Wolfrom, A. Thompson, and D. R. Lineback, J. Org. Chem. *28*, 860 (1963).

The reaction of 2,3,4,6-tetra-$O$-acetyl-$\alpha$-D-galactopyranosyl bromide with 1,3,4,6-tetra-$O$-acetyl-$\alpha$-D-glucopyranose in the presence of mercuric cyanide in nitromethane leads to the substituted derivative of 2-$O$-$\alpha$-D-galactopyranosyl-D-glucose in a yield of 25%.[87]

The reaction of the same acylated halogenose as well as of 2,3,4,6-tetra-$O$-acetyl-$\alpha$-D-glucopyranosyl bromide with both 1,3,4,6-tetra-$O$-acetyl-D-glucopyranose and 1,3,4,6-tetra-$O$-acetyl-D-galactopyranose has been followed carefully in a paper by B. Helferich and J. Zirner, Chem. Ber. *95*, 2604 (1962).

There have also been described syntheses of reducing disaccharides of this series, containing pentoses, such as 2-$O$-$\beta$-D-glucopyranosyl-D-xylose[58] and 2-$O$-$\beta$-D-xylopyranosyl-L-arabinose.[139,140]

### In position 3

The first substance synthesized in this group of reducing disaccharides was laminaribiose (3-$O$-$\beta$-D-glucopyranosyl-D-glucose).[67,68] It is produced by the reaction of 2,3,4,6-tetra-$O$-acetyl-$\alpha$-D-glucopyranosyl bromide (V) with 1,2:5,6-di-$O$-isopropylidene-D-glucofuranose (XXXV) in the form of the corresponding derivative (XXXVI) in a yield of 4%,[67] which can be increased to 9.5%[68] by the use of Drierite and iodine in benzene.

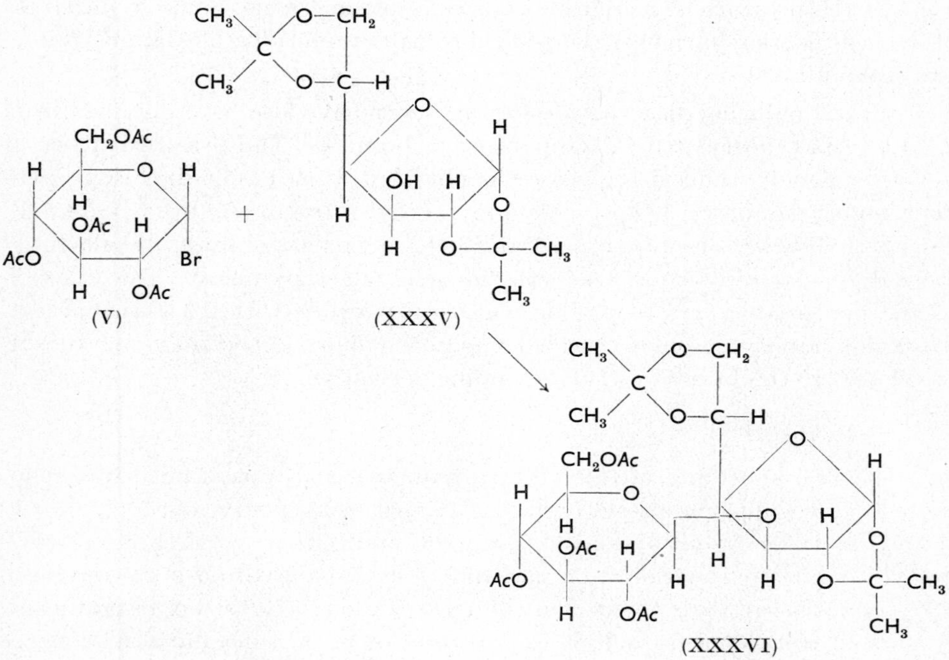

(V)          +          (XXXV)

(XXXVI)

*References see p. 90*

6 — The Oligosaccharides

The action of the same halogenose on 6-$O$-acetyl-1,2-$O$-isopropylidene-D-glucofuranose yields, after hydrolysis of the blocking groups, a relatively small amount of laminaribiose, approximately 2%;[67] a higher yield, up to 15%, is in this case obtained by the Koenigs-Knorr reaction at the other free hydroxyl group, i.e. in position -5-, |with the formation of 5-$O$-$\beta$-D-glucopyranosyl-D-glucose.[67] The reaction of 2,3,4,6 tetra-$O$-acetyl-$\alpha$-D-glucopyranosyl bromide with benzyl 4,6-$O$-benzylidene-$\beta$-D-glucopyranoside likewise proceeds not unambiguously with the formation of a derivative of 3-$O$-$\beta$-D-glucopyranosyl-D-glucose; it always takes place at the neighbouring hydroxyl group at C-2, besides the simultaneous formation of a trisaccharide at both free hydroxyl groups (but see p. 87).[42,62]

An attractive problem was the synthesis of the $\alpha$-anomer corresponding to laminaribiose, i.e. of nigerose (3-$O$-$\alpha$-D-glucopyranosyl-D-glucose). In its first synthesis, this substance could be prepared by the reaction of the sodium salt of 1,2:5,6-di-$O$-isopropylidene-D-glucofuranose with 3,4,6-tri-$O$-acetyl-$\beta$-D-glucopyranosyl chloride (as by-products are formed kojibiose, trehalose and other unidentified disaccharides).[35,36] More advantageous, however, is the procedure elaborated by certain Japanese investigators,[55,80,83,84] who have obtained nigerose (in the form of its derivatives, whose screening groups were subsequently removed) by the reaction of 2,3,4,6-tetra-$O$-acetyl-$\alpha$-D-glucopyranosyl bromide on the one hand with 1,2,4,6-tetra-$O$-acetyl-$\beta$-D-glucopyranose,[83] and, on the other, with 1,2:5,6-di-$O$-isopropylidene-D-glucofuranose,[55,80,84] in both cases in the presence of mercuric cyanide in nitromethane. Some by-products of the last reaction have been detected chromatographically, like laminaribiose, and isomaltose.[80]

Several reducing disaccharides of this series have also been obtained from 2,3,4,6-tetra-$O$-acetyl-$\alpha$-D-galactopyranosyl bromide. Thus, a derivative of 3-$O$-$\beta$-D-galactopyranosyl-D-glucose[69] is obtained from 1,2:5,6-di-$O$-isopropylidene-D-glucofuranose, 3-$O$-$\beta$-D-galactopyranosyl-D-fructose[69] from 1,2:4,5-di-$O$-isopropylidene-D-fructopyranose, and 3-$O$-$\beta$-D-galactopyranosyl-D-galactose[54] from 1,2-$O$-isopropylidene-4,6-$O$-ethylidene-D-galactopyranose. The reaction of an appropriately substituted derivative of D-xylose with 2,3,4-tri-$O$-acetyl-$\alpha$-D-xylopyranosyl bromide yielded rhodymenabiose (3-$O$-$\beta$-D-xylopyranosyl-D-xylose)[59] in the form of its corresponding derivative.

### In position 4

The first substance of this group whose synthesis was studied was cellobiose (4-$O$-$\beta$-D-glucopyranosyl-D-glucose). Experiments setting out from 2,3,4,6-tetra-$O$-acetyl-$\alpha$-D-glucopyranosyl bromide and either methyl 2,3,6-tri-$O$-acetyl-$\beta$-D-glucopyranoside[141] or derivatives of 1,6-anhydro-$\beta$-D-glucopyranose[142] accomplished their object, but the yield of the reactions was insignificant. A more advantageous procedure was the reaction of the same initial halogenose with the sodium salt of 1,2,3,6-tetra-$O$-acetyl-$\beta$-D-glucopyranose.[34] The failure of an attempt to prepare maltose by condensing 1,2,3,6-tetra-$O$-acetyl-$\beta$-D-glucopyranose with 2,3,4,6-tetra-$O$-acetyl-$\beta$-D-glucopyranosyl fluoride[9] must be ascribed to the non-reactivity of the fluorine atom.

Further syntheses were carried out with 2,3,4,6-tetra-$O$-acetyl-$\alpha$-D-glucopyranosyl bromide, for example, its reaction with 2,3-$O$-isopropylidene-D-mannosan yielded derivatives of *epi*-cellobiose (4-$O$-$\beta$-D-glucopyranosyl-D-mannose).[143,144]

Other experiments obviously were concerned with the synthesis of lactose. The first attempt to synthesize lactose by the reaction of 2,3,4,6-tetra-$O$-acetyl-$\alpha$-D-galactopyranosyl bromide with the sodium salt of 1,2,3,6-tetra-$O$-acetyl-$\beta$-D-glucopyranose was unsuccessful.[9] A satisfactory result, however, was obtained by the reaction of the same initial halogenose (XXVIII) with 2,3:5,6-di-$O$-isopropylidene-D-glucose diethyl acetal (XXXVII)[56] under the conditions of the Koenigs-Knorr synthesis. The expected lactose derivative (XXXVIII) is obtained in good yield.

(XXXVII)          (XXVIII)                    (XXXVIII)

Other investigators converted the same initial halogenose (XXVIII) and 2-$O$-acetyl-D-galactosan (XXXIX) into 4-$O$-(2,3,4,6-tetra-$O$-acetyl $\beta$-D-galactopyranosyl)-2-$O$-acetyl-D-galactosan (XL) and hydrolysed it to 4-$O$-$\beta$-D-galactopyranosyl-D-galactose (XLI).[52]

2,3,4,6-Tetra-$O$-acetyl-$\alpha$-D-galactopyranosyl bromide was condensed with 2,3-$O$-isopropylidene-D-mannosan to a derivative of *epi*-lactose (4-$O$-$\beta$-D-galactopyranosyl-D-mannose).[145,146] Xylobiose (4-$O$-$\beta$-D-xylopyranosyl-D-xylose) was recently synthesized in two cases from 2,3,4-tri-$O$-acetyl-$\alpha$-D-xylopyranosyl bromide and a suitable other component.[71,90]

The first synthesis in this group was the reaction of 2,3,4,6-tetra-$O$-methyl-$\alpha$-D-glucopyranosyl chloride with methyl 2,3,6-tri-$O$-methyl-$\beta$-D-glucopyranoside, which leads to methyl hepta-$O$-methyl-$\beta$-cellobioside.[147]

*References see p. 90*

6*

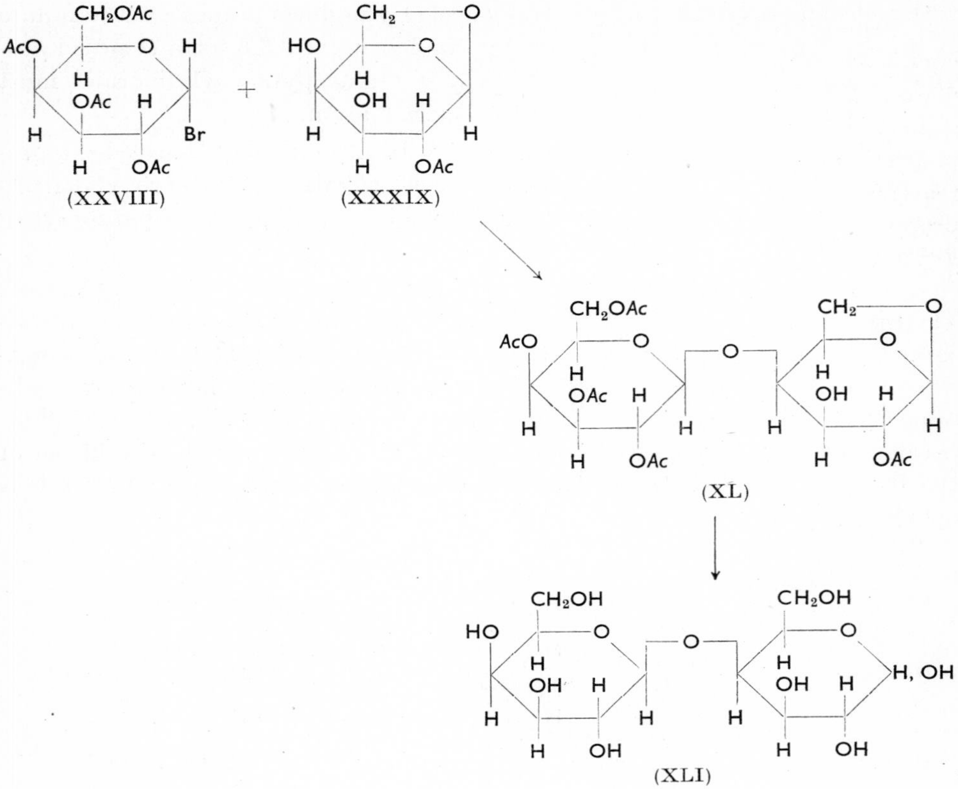

(XXVIII)   +   (XXXIX)

(XL)

(XLI)

Since, however, hydrolysis of the methyl groups could so far not be effected without destroying all the molecule, this reaction cannot be regarded as synthesis of a disaccharide.

### In position 5

Data concering this group are rather scarce. The reaction of 2,3,4,6-tetra-$O$-acetyl-$\alpha$-D-glucopyranosyl bromide with 1,2-$O$-isopropylidene-3,6-di-$O$-acetyl-D-glucofuranose yields the expected derivative of 5-$O$-$\beta$-D-glucopyranosyl-D-glucose;[67] a derivative of the same oligosaccharide can also be obtained by the reaction of the same acylated halogenose with 6-$O$-acetyl-1,2-$O$-isopropylidene-D-glucofuranose, besides the simultaneously produced 3-$O$-isomer.[67]

### Synthesis of trisaccharides and higher oligosaccharides

As far as non-reducing trisaccharides are concerned, mention can be made only of those containing D-mannose, formed as by-products from $\alpha$-D-mannopyranosyl fluoride in alkaline solution[37] (see p. 66).

The synthesis of reducing trisaccharides or tetrasaccharides under the conditions of the Koenigs-Knorr reaction has been described in a larger number of cases. [61,72,98,99,130,148-151] The initial compound is usually a per-O-acetylated halogenose derived from a reducing disaccharide, which is condensed with a suitable monosaccharide derivative containing one free hydroxyl group. For example, the reaction of hepta-O-acetyl-α-cellobiosyl bromide (XLII) and 1,2:3,4-di-O-isopropylidene-D-galactose (XLIII) gives rise to a substituted derivative of 6-O-β-cellobiosyl-D-galactose (XLIV):[130]

Tetrasaccharides may be prepared either from per-O-acetylated halogenoses of disaccharides by the reaction with a suitable disaccharide derivative,[72] or from the per-O-acetylated halogenose derived from a trisaccharide, in this case by the reaction with a suitable monosaccharide derivative.[148]

Bredereck's method (see p. 69, i. e. with the use of silver perchlorate), too, can be utilized for the preparation of trisaccharide derivatives;[95] and the reaction of a per-O-acetylated monosaccharide halogenose with a suitable disaccharide derivative can also be used for this purpose.[152]

Quite remarkable attention has recently been paid to the synthesis of branched trisaccharides.[42,50,62,65,93,152-154] On the basis of the known fact[155] that benzyl β-cellobioside reacts with benzaldehyde in the presence of zinc chloride to form a mono-O-benzylidene derivative containing the benzylidene group at C-4 and C-6 of the non-reducing part of the molecule, it was deduced[50] that

*References see p. 90*

methyl $\beta$-cellobioside (XLV) condensed with acetaldehyde gives the corresponding $O$-ethylidene derivative (XLVI). The trityl derivative (XLVII) obtained by tritylation can be acetylated to form the compound (XLVIII); the substance (XLIX) produced by detritylation reacts with 2,3,4,6-tetra-$O$-acetyl-$\alpha$-D-glucopyranosyl bromide (V) to form a branched trisaccharide derivative (L). The free reducing trisaccharide (LI) corresponding to this substance may be termed 6-$O$-$\beta$-D-glucopyranosylcellobiose or 4-$O$-$\beta$-6-$O$-$\beta$-di-D-glucopyranosyl-D-glucose.

(XLV)                          (XLVI)

(XLVII)                       (XLVIII)

(XLIX)                       (L)

(LI)

Other papers deal with the preparation of 6-*O*-β-D-glucopyranosylmaltose (4-*O*-α-6-*O*-β-di-D-glucopyranosyl-D-glucose) by the action of 2,3,4,6-tetra-*O*-acetyl-α-D-glucopyranosyl bromide on suitably substituted maltose derivatives,[65,153] as well as with the preparation of 3-*O*-β-6-*O*-β-di-D-glucopyranosyl-D-glucose from 2,3,4,6-tetra-*O*-acetyl-α-D-glucopyranosyl bromide and 1,2,4,2′, 3′,4′-hexa-*O*-acetyl-laminaribiose.[152] Since in the latter case the reaction can proceed either at any of the unsubstituted hydroxyl groups of the laminaribiose unit or at both these groups simultaneously, three reaction products may be formed, namely the mentioned branched trisaccharide, further a derivative of the un-branched 6-*O*-β-D-glucopyranosyl-laminaribiose (3-*O*-β-gentiobiosyl-D-glucose) and, finally, the branched tetrasaccharide 6-*O*-β-6′-*O*-β-di-D-glucopyranosyl-laminaribiose. All these three substances were actually isolated.[152]

The course of the reaction of 2,3,4,6-tetra-*O*-acetyl-α-D-glucopyranosyl bromide with benzyl 4,6-*O*-benzylidene-β-D-glucopyranoside is surprising.[42,62] This substance has unsubstituted hydroxyl groups at C-2 and C-3, so that the Koenigs-Knorr reaction may give rise to two disaccharides and a branched trisaccharide. It was convincingly demonstrated that, in fact, derivatives of 2-*O*-β-D-glucopyranosyl-D-glucose and 3-*O*-β-D-glucopyranosyl-D-glucose are formed in this way;[42,62] more difficult was the problem regarding the trisaccharide produced, because this compound is not 2-*O*-β-3-*O*-β-bis-D-glucopyranosyl-D-glucose, as originally assumed,[42] but 3-*O*-β-6-*O*-β-bis-D-glucopyranosyl-D-glucose.[62] Despite the addition of Drierite, the benzylidene group is hydrolytically split off by the simultaneously formed water, so that the Koenigs-Knorr reaction then proceeds in an unexpected way. The constitution of some other saccharide formed in this reaction has so far not been established.[42,62]

New syntheses of branched oligosaccharides have been described recently; e. g. the synthesis of 3,5-di-*O*-β-D-glucopyranosyl-D-xylose by J. K. N. Jones and P. E. Reid, Can.

J. Chem. *41*, 2382 (1963); the synthesis of 4,6-di-*O*-α-D-glucopyranosyl-D-glucose by R. de Souza and I. J. Goldstein, Tetrahedron Letters *1964*, 1215; and the synthesis of 6,6'-di-*O*-β-D-glucopyranosylmaltose by A. Klemer and F. Gundlach, Chem. Ber. *96*, 1765 (1963).

## C. SYNTHESIS BY THE ACTION OF MONOSACCHARIDE ANHYDRO DERIVATIVES UPON MONOSACCHARIDES OR THEIR DERIVATIVES

Attempts to synthesize disaccharides or oligosaccharides in general from anhydro derivatives of monosaccharides were started by Pictet,[156-158] who polymerized laevoglucosan (i. e. 1,6-anhydro-β-D-glucopyranose) by heating it to 140°C under a pressure of 15 mm Hg in the presence of zinc chloride; he named the product obtained dilaevoglucosan,[156,157] and in a further paper he reported that the hydrolysis of this dilaevoglucosan gives, among other substances, iso-maltose.[158]

It is probable that it was not possible by the classical methods of isolation to obtain lower oligosaccharides, and the substances produced by thermal polymerization of laevoglucosan were named polymers throughout,[159,160] although in some papers mention is made of fractions of tetrasaccharides and octasaccharides,[161] or of fractions of tri-, tetra- and heptasaccharides.[162]

Only with modern methods of isolation was it possible to obtain a clear survey of the complicated mixture of reaction products,[163] from which anhydro derivatives of di- and trisaccharides could be isolated in the form of their acetyl derivatives.

The polymerization of a mixture of both laevoglucosan and galactosan led to polymeric products.[164]

By far more concrete results have been obtained with the use of the so-called Brigl anhydride (i. e. 3,4,6-tri-*O*-acetyl-1,2-anhydro-D-glucose, LII). It is known[165] that this substance reacts with alcohols with opening of the anhydro ring and the formation of glycosides. Thus, 2,3,4,6-tetra-*O*-acetyl-β-D-glucopyranose (I) gives the hepta-*O*-acetyl derivative of *neo*-trehalose (LIII) in a yield of 11%:[166]

       (LII)                      (I)                               (LIII)

It may appear at the first glance that in this case a *cis* opening of the anhydro ring takes place; obviously, however, anomerization of 2,3,4,6-tetra-*O*-acetyl-β-D-glucopyranose sets in first and the anomer formed in this way is then converted into a *neo*-trehalose derivative by the reaction with the Brigl anhydride. This is also proved by a further paper[167] according to which anomerization of 2,3,4,6-tetra-*O*-acetyl-β-D-glucopyranose by boiling in ethanol led to a mixture of both anomeric forms of 2,3,4,6-tetra-*O*-acetyl-D-glucopyranose, containing 65% of the α-form. The reaction with the Brigl anhydride then led to a mixture of the hepta-*O*-acetyl derivative of trehalose and *neo*-trehalose.

The hepta-*O*-acetyl derivative of sucrose has also been prepared from the Brigl anhydride by heating with 1,3,4,6-tetra-*O*-acetyl-β-D-fructofuranose for 104 hours at 100°C in a sealed tube, but the yield of this reaction amounted to only 5.5%.[168,169]

This synthesis was also applied to the series of reducing disaccharides, and the hepta-*O*-acetyl derivative of maltose has been obtained in a yield of 8% from the Brigl anhydride and 1,2,3,6-tetra-*O*-acetyl-β-D-glucopyranose.[168,170] Other investigators utilized the reactivity of the Brigl anhydride for the preparation of derivatives of kojibiose (2-*O*-α-D-glucopyranosyl-D-glucose).[36] These syntheses were effected by heating to boiling the Brigl anhydride (LII) in a suitable solvent, such as butanol for 2—3 days. The opening of the 1,2-anhydro ring can proceed here in two ways and, in fact, derivatives of both trehalose (LIV) and kojibiose (LV) may be obtained in this way:

Another method of synthesizing disaccharides is based upon the utilization of 5,6-anhydro compounds of aldohexoses; their anhydro ring can be split by means of acylated halogenoses.[171–173] The 5,6-anhydro ring always opens so that the sugar remainder from the acylated halogenose is added to C-5, while the bromine atom is added to C-6, from where it can be removed by a suitable reducing procedure. Thus, 1,2-*O*-isopropylidene-5,6-anhydro-D-glucofuranose (LVI) reacts with 2,3,4,6-tetra-*O*-acetyl-α-D-glucopyranosyl bromide (V) to form the peracetyl derivative of 5-*O*-β-D-glucopyranosyl-6-bromo-6-deoxy-D-glucopyranose (LVII) which, on elimination of the bromine atom, yields the corresponding deoxy derivative (LVIII):

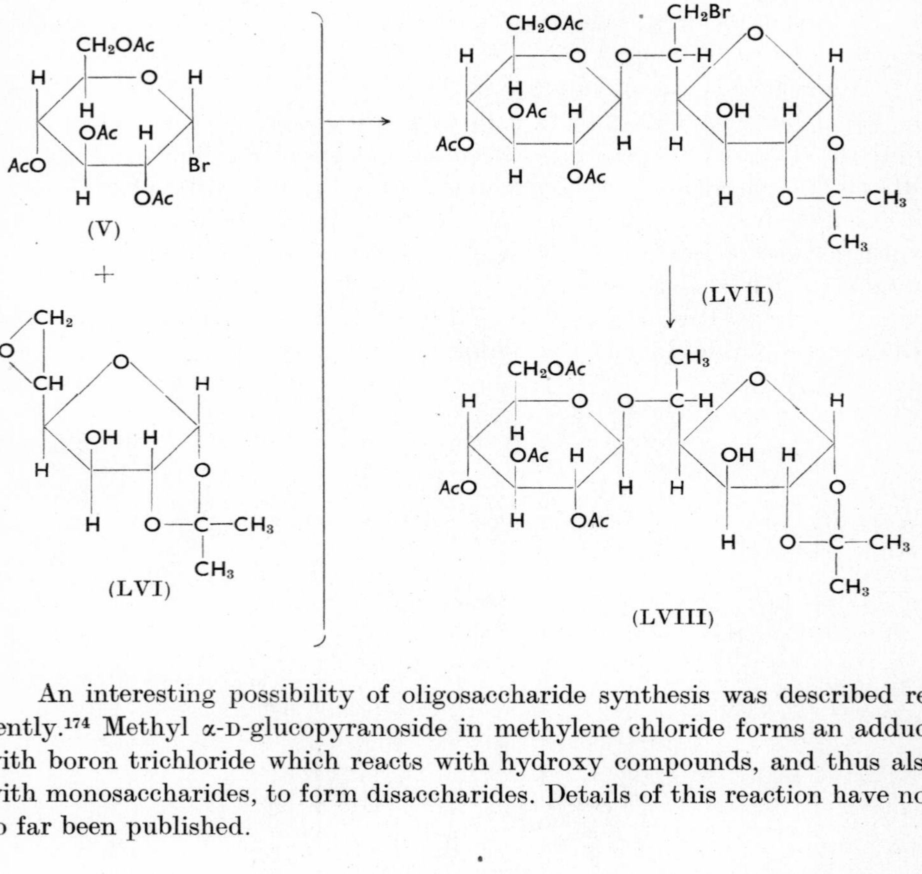

An interesting possibility of oligosaccharide synthesis was described recently.[174] Methyl α-D-glucopyranoside in methylene chloride forms an adduct with boron trichloride which reacts with hydroxy compounds, and thus also with monosaccharides, to form disaccharides. Details of this reaction have not so far been published.

**REFERENCES**

1. W. L. Evans, D. D. Reynolds, and E. A. Talley, Advances in Carbohydrate Chem. *6*, 26 (1951).
2. M. G. Blair and W. Pigman, Angew. Chem. *69*, 422 (1959).

3. J. Staněk, M. Černý, J. Kocourek, and J. Pacák, *The Monosaccharides*, Acad. Press, New York 1963.

4. E. Fischer and K. Delbrück, Ber. *42*, 2776 (1909).

5. H. H. Schlubach and K. Maurer, Ber. *58*, 1178 (1925).

6. F. Klages and R. Niemann, Ann. *529*, 185 (1937).

7. H. Bredereck, G. Höschele, and K. Ruck, Chem. Ber. *86*, 1277 (1953).

8. H. Vogel and H. Debowska-Kurnicka, Helv. Chim. Acta *11*, 910 (1928).

9. V. E. Sharp and M. Stacey, J. Chem. Soc. *1951*, 285.

10. A. Pictet and H. Vogel, Helv. Chim. Acta *11*, 436 (1928).

11. A. Pictet and H. Vogel, Helv. Chim. Acta *11*, 905 (1928).

12. J. C. Irvine, J. W. H. Oldham, and A. F. Skinner, J. Soc. Chem. Ind. *47*, 494 (1928).

13. G. Zemplén and A. Gerecs, Ber. *62*, 984 (1929).

14. A. Pictet and H. Vogel, Ber. *62*, 1418 (1929).

15. J. C. Irvine, J. W. H. Oldham, and A. F. Skinner, J. Am. Chem. Soc. *51*, 1279 (1929).

16. H. H. Schlubach and B. Middelhoff, An.. *550*, 134 (1942).

17. W. W. Binkley and M. L. Wolfrom, J. Am. Chem. Soc. *68*, 2171 (1946).

18. E. Demole, Ber. *12*, 1935 (1879).

19. A. Pictet and H. Vogel, Helv. Chim. Acta *10*, 588 (1927).

20. A. Pictet and H. Vogel, Helv. Chim. Acta *11*, 209 (1928).

21. A. M. Gakhokidze, Zhur. Obshcheĭ Khim. *11*, 117 (1941); Chem. Abstr. *35*, 5467 (1941).

22. A. M. Gakhokidze, Zhur. Obshcheĭ Khim. *16*, 1923 (1946); Chem. Abstr. *41*, 6210 (1947).

23. A. M. Gakhokidze, Trudy Tbilis. Uchitel. Inst. *2*, 146 (1941).

24. A. M. Gakhokidze and N. D. Kutidze, Zhur. Obshchei Khim. *22*, 139 (1952); Chem. Abstr. *46*, 11116 (1952).

25. A. M. Gakhokidze and N. D. Kutidze, Zhur. Obshchei Khim. *22*, 247 (1952); Chem. Abstr. *46*, 11117 (1952).

26. P. S. O'Colla, E. E. Lee, and D. McGrath, Chem. & Ind. (London) *1962*, 178.

27. P. W. Kent, Biochem. J. *55*, 361 (1953).

28. F. Micheel and W. Gresser, Chem. Ber. *91*, 1214 (1958).

29. F. Micheel and W. Gresser, Acta Chim. Acad. Sci. Hung. *18*, 437 (1959).

30. W. G. Overend, M. Shafizadeh, and M. Stacey, J. Chem. Soc. *1951*, 994.

31. E. Fischer and E. F. Armstrong, Ber. *35*, 3146 (1902).

32. H. H. Schlubach and W. Rauchenberger, Ber. *58*, 1184 (1925).

33. H. H. Schlubach and W. Rauchenberger, Ber. *59*, 2102 (1926).

34. V. E. Gilbert, F. Smith, and M. Stacey, J. Chem. Soc. *1946*, 622.

35. S. Haq and W. J. Whelan, Nature *178*, 1224 (1956).

36. S. Haq and W. J. Whelan, J. Chem. Soc. *1958*, 1342.

37. F. Micheel and D. Borrmann, Chem. Ber. *93*, 1143 (1960).

38. W. Koenigs and E. Knorr, Ber. *34*, 957 (1901).

39. B. Helferich, K. Bäuerlein, and F. Wiegand, Ann. *447*, 27 (1926).

40. B. Helferich and H. Collatz, Ber. *61*, 1640 (1928).

41. D. H. Ball and J. K. N. Jones, J. Chem. Soc. *1957*, 4871.

42. A. Klemer and K. Homberg, Chem. Ber. *93*, 1643 (1960).

43. B. Helferich, Advances in Carbohydrate Chem. *3*, 79 (1948).

44. K. Freudenberg, A. Noë, and F. Knopf, Ber. *60*, 239 (1927).

45. B. Helferich and J. Becker, Ann. *440*, 1 (1924).

46. B. Helferich and W. Klein, Ann. *450*, 219 (1926).

47. B. Helferich, E. Bohn, and S. Winkler, Ber. *63*, 989 (1930).

48. D. D. Reynolds and W. L. Evans, J. Am. Chem. Soc. *60*, 2559 (1938).
49. C. M. McCloskey, R. E. Pyle, and G. H. Coleman, J. Am. Chem. Soc. *66*, 349 (1944).
50. A. Klemer, Chem. Ber. *89*, 2583 (1956).
51. A. Z. Rogovin and L. I. Novikova, Referat. Zhurnal *1956*, No. 65038; Chem. Abstr. *53*, 5140 (1959).
52. H. Masamune and S. Kamiyama, Tôhoku J. Exptl. Med. *66*, 43 (1957); Chem. Abstr. *52*, 8974 (1958).
53. I. J. Goldstein, F. Smith, and H. C. Srivastava, J. Am. Chem. Soc. *79*, 3858 (1957).
54. D. H. Ball and J. K. N. Jones, J. Chem. Soc. *1958*, 905.
55. K. Matsuda, Chem. & Ind. (London) *1958*, 1627.
56. E. J. C. Curtis and J. K. N. Jones, Can. J. Chem. *37*, 358 (1959).
57. P. A. J. Gorin and A. S. Perlin, Can. J. Chem. *37*, 1930 (1959).
58. J. K. N. Jones and P. E. Reid, Can. J. Chem. *38*, 944 (1960).
59. E. J. C. Curtis and J. K. N. Jones, Can. J. Chem. *38*, 1305 (1960).
60. K. Wallenfels and J. Lehmann, Ann. *635*, 166 (1960).
61. S. Peat, W. J. Whelan, and J. M. Evans, J. Chem. Soc. *1960*, 175.
62. A. Klemer and K. Homberg, Chem. Ber. *94*, 2747 (1961).
63. H. R. Goldschmid and A. S. Perlin, Can. J. Chem. *39*, 2025 (1961).
64. P. A. J. Gorin and A. S. Perlin, Can. J. Chem. *39*, 2474 (1961).
65. I. J. Goldstein and B. Lindberg, Acta Chem. Scand. *16*, 383 (1962).
66. P. A. J. Gorin, Can. J. Chem. 40, 275 (1962).
67. K. Freudenberg and K. Oersten, Ann. 574, 37 (1951).
68. P. Bächli and E. G. V. Percival, J. Chem. Soc. *1952*, 1243.
69. R. Kuhn and H. H. Baer, Chem. Ber. *87*, 1560 (1954).
70. B. Coxon and H. G. Fletcher, J. Org. Chem. *26*, 2892 (1961).
71. G. O. Aspinall and K. M. Ross, J. Chem. Soc. *1961*, 3674.
72. B. Helferich and H. Bredereck, Ann. *465*, 166 (1928).
73. G. Zemplén and A. Gerecs, Ber. *63*, 2720 (1930).
74. G. Zemplén, Z. Bruckner, and A. Gerecs, Ber. *64*, 744 (1931).
75. G. Zemplén and A. Gerecs, Ber. *64*, 1545 (1931).
76. G. Zemplén and Z. Bruckner, Ber. *64*, 1852 (1931).
77. F. Micheel and K. Hagel, Chem. Ber. *85*, 1087 (1952).
78. B. Helferich and K. Weis, Chem. Ber. *89*, 314 (1956).
79. K. Matsuda, Nature *180*, 985 (1957).
80. K. Matsuda and T. Sekiguchi, J. Agr. Chem. Soc. Japan *33*, 309 (1959); Chem. Abstr. *58*, 5774 (1963).
81. K. Matsuda, J. Agr. Chem. Soc. Japan *33*, 714 (1959).
82. K. Matsuda and T. Sekiguchi, J. Agr. Chem. Soc. Japan *33*, 1154 (1959); Chem. Abstr *59*, 6494 (1963).
83. K. Matsuda, J. Agr. Chem. Soc. Japan *33*, 1156 (1959); Chem. Abstr *59*, 6495 (1963).
84. K. Matsuda and T. Sekiguchi, Tôhoku J. Agr. Research *9*, 263 (1959); Chem. Abstr. *53*, 21677 (1959).
85. J. Kocourek and N. Constantzas, Chem. listy *52*, 1629 (1958); Chem. Abstr. *53*, 1318 (1959).
86. J. Kocourek and N. Constantzas, Collection Czechoslov. Chem. Communs *24*, 1099 (1959).
87. J. Lehmann and D. Beck, Ann. *630*, 56 (1960).
88. B. Helferich and K. L. Bettin, Chem. Ber. *94*, 1159 (1961).
89. J. Kocourek, Chem. Ber. *94*, 3346 (1961).
90. D. V. Myhre and F. Smith, J. Org. Chem. *26*, 4609 (1961).

91. M. L. Wolfrom, A. B. Pittet, and I. C. Gillam, Proc. Natl. Acad. Sci. US *47*, 700 (1961); Chem. Abstr. *55*, 23352 (1961).
92. B. Helferich and W. Speicher, Ann. *579*, 106 (1953).
93. H. Bredereck, A. Wagner, and G. Faber, Angew. Chem. *69*, 438 (1957).
94. H. Bredereck, A. Wagner, G. Faber, H. Ott, and J. Rauther, Chem. Ber. *92*, 1135 (1959).
95. H. Bredereck, A. Wagner, H. Kuhn, and H. Ott, Chem. Ber. *93*, 1201 (1960).
96. P. A. Levene and M. L. Wolfrom, J. Biol. Chem. *78*, 525 (1928).
97. H. H. Schlubach and G. A. Schröter, Ber. *61*, 1216 (1928).
98. B. Helferich and R. Gootz, Ber. *64*, 109 (1931).
99. B. Helferich and W. Schäfer, Ann. *450*, 229 (1926).
100. B. Helferich and H. Bredereck, Ann. *465*, 166 (1928).
101. W. A. Hammond and J. R. Withrow, Ind. Eng. Chem. *25*, 653, 1112 (1933).
102. L. C. Kreider and W. L. Evans, J. Am. Chem. Soc. *57*, 229 (1935).
103. L. C. Kreider and W. L. Evans, J. Am. Chem. Soc. *58*, 797 (1936).
104. L. C. Kreider and W. L. Evans, J. Am. Chem. Soc. *58*, 1661 (1936).
105. M. J. Stross and G. B. Zimmerman, Ind. Eng. Chem., News Edition *17*, 70 (1939).
106. M. P. Bellis, Hexagon Alpha Chi Sigma *40*, 13 (1949); Chem. Abstr. *44*, 882 (1950).
107. Brit. Patent 584 062; Chem. Abstr. *41*, 3120 (1947).
108. U. S. Patent 2 479 761; Chem. Abstr. *44*, 1147 (1950).
109. H. H. Schlubach and W. S. Schetelig, Hoppe-Seyler's Z. physiol. Chem. *213*, 83 (1932).
110. C. W. Klingensmith and W. L. Evans, J. Am. Chem. Soc. *61*, 3012 (1939).
111. E. A. Talley, D. D. Reynolds, and W. L. Evans, J. Am. Chem. Soc. *65*, 575 (1943).
112. H. A. Hardy, J. Am. Chem. Soc. *69*, 518 (1947).
113. E. Fischer and M. Bergmann, Ber. *52*, 829 (1910).
114. G. Zemplén, Ber. *59*, 1254 (1926).
115. G. Zemplén, A. Gerecs, and L. Hadáczy, Ber. *69*, 1827 (1936).
116. W. A. Mitchell, J. Am. Chem. Soc. *63*, 3534 (1941).
117. Organic Syntheses, Coll. Vol. *2*, 122 (1943).
118. W. A. Bonner and W. L. Koehler, J. Am. Chem. Soc. *70*, 314 (1948).
119. J. Staněk and J. Černá, Tetrahedron Letters *1963*, 35.
120. K. Freudenberg, W. Dürr, and H. Hochstetter, Ber. *61*, 1735 (1928).
121. B. Helferich and R. Steinpreis, Chem. Ber. *91*, 1794 (1958).
122. C. S. Hudson and F. P. Phelps, J. Am. Chem. Soc. *46*, 2591 (1924).
123. E. Pascu, Advances in Carbohydrate Chem. *1*, 77 (1945).
124. W. L. Evans, D. D. Reynolds, and E. A. Talley, Advances in Carbohydrate Chem. *6*, 27 (1951).
125. R. U. Lemieux, Advances in Carbohydrate Chem. *9*, 1 (1954).
126. L. J. Haynes and F. H. Newth, Advances in Carbohydrate Chem. *10*, 207 (1955).
127. P. F. Lloyd and G. P. Roberts, Proc. Chem. Soc. *1960*, 250.
128. B. Helferich, L. Moog, and A. Jünger, Ber. *58*, 872 (1925).
129. J. C. Irvine, J. W. H. Oldham, and A. Skinner, J. Am. Chem. Soc. *51*, 1281 (1929).
130. K. Freudenberg, A. Wolf, E. Knopf, and S. H. Zaheer, Ber. *61*, 1743 (1928).
131. B. Helferich and H. Rauch, Ber. *59*, 2655 (1926).
132. B. Helferich and G. Sparmberg, Ber. *66*, 806 (1933).
133. G. Zemplén and R. Bognár, Acta Chem. Acad. Sci. Hung. *1*, 245 (1951); Chem. Abstr. *46*, 7053 (1952).
134. B. Helferich and H. Rauch, Ann. *455*, 168 (1927).
135. G. Zemplén and R. Bognár, Ber. *72*, 1160 (1939).

136. C. M. McCloskey and G. H. Coleman, J. Am. Chem. Soc. *65*, 1778 (1943).
137. K. Freudenberg and K. Soff, Ber. *69*, 1245 (1936).
138. K. Freudenberg, H. Knauber, and F. Cramer, Chem. Ber. *84*, 144 (1951).
138a. D. Beck, and K. Wallenfels, Ann. *655*, 173 (1962).
138b. K. Takiura and K. Koizumi, Chem. Pharm. Bull. (Tokyo) *10*, 134 (1962).
138c. K. Takiura and K. Koizumi, J. Pharm. Soc. Japan (Yakugaku Zasshi) *82*, 852 (1962).
139. G. O. Aspinall and R. J. Ferrier, Chem. & Ind. (London) *1957*, 819.
140. G. O. Aspinall and R. J. Ferrier, J. Chem. Soc. *1958*, 1501.
141. B. Helferich and H. Bredereck, Ber. *64*, 2411 (1931).
142. K. Freudenberg and W. Nagai, Ber. *66*, 27 (1933).
143. W. T. Haskins, R. M. Hann, and C. S. Hudson, J. Am. Chem. Soc. *63*, 1724 (1941).
144. W. T. Haskins, R. M. Hann, and C. S. Hudson, J. Am. Chem. Soc. *64*, 1281 (1942).
145. W. T. Haskins, R. M. Hann, and C. S. Hudson, J. Am. Chem. Soc. *64*, 1490 (1942).
146. W. T. Haskins, R. M. Hann, and C. S. Hudson, J. Am. Chem. Soc. *64*, 1853 (1942).
147. K. Freudenberg, C. C. Anderson, Y. Go, K. Friedrich, and N. K. Richtmyer, Ber. *63*, 1961 (1930).
148. G. Zemplén and A. Gerecs, Ber. *64*, 2458 (1931).
149. S. H. Nichols, W. L. Evans, and H. D. McDowell, J. Am. Chem. Soc. *62*, 1754 (1940).
150. E. A. Talley and W. L. Evans, J. Am. Chem. Soc. *65*, 573 (1943).
151. K. Freudenberg and W. Nagai, Ann. *494*, 63 (1932).
152. J. R. Turvey and J. M. Evans, J. Chem. Soc. *1960*, 2366.
153. A. Klemer, Angew. Chem. *69*, 638 (1957).
154. A. Klemer, Tetrahedron Letters *1960*, No. 22, 5.
155. K. Hess, H. Hammerstein, and W. Gramberg, Ber. *70*, 1134 (1937).
156. A. Pictet, Helv. Chim. Acta *1*, 226 (1918).
157. A. Pictet and J. H. Ross, Helv. Chim. Acta *5*, 876 (1922).
158. A. Georg and A. Pictet, Helv. Chim. Acta 9, 612 (1926).
159. J. da Silva Carvalho, W. Prins, and C. Schuerch, J. Am. Chem. Soc. *81*, 4054 (1959).
160. M. L. Wolfrom, A. Thompson, and R. B. Ward, J. Am. Chem. Soc. *81*, 4623 (1959).
161. H. Pringsheim and K. Schmalz, Ber. *55*, 3001 (1922).
162. J. C. Irvine and J. W. H. Oldham, J. Chem. Soc. *127*, 2903 (1925).
163. M. L. Wolfrom, A. Thompson, R. B. Ward, D. Horton, and R. H. Moore, J. Org. Chem. *26*, 4617 (1961).
164. I. J. Goldstein and B. Lindberg, Acta Chem. Scand. *16*, 387 (1962).
165. P. Brigl, Hoppe-Seyler's Z. physiol. Chem. *122*, 245 (1922).
166. W. N. Haworth and W. J. Hickinbottom, J. Chem. Soc. *1931*, 2847.
167. R. U. Lemieux and H. F. Bauer, Can. J. Chem. *32*, 340 (1954).
168. R. U. Lemieux and G. Huber, J. Am. Chem. Soc. *75*, 4118 (1953).
169. R. U. Lemieux and G. Huber, J. Am. Chem. Soc. *78*, 4117 (1956).
170. R. U. Lemieux, Can. J. Chem. *31*, 949 (1953).
171. K. Freudenberg, H. Toepffer, and S. H. Zaheer, Ber. *63*, 1966 (1930).
172. K. Freudenberg, H. Toepffer, and C. C. Andersen, Ber. *61*, 1750 (1938).
173. K. Freudenberg, H. Eich, C. Knoevenagel, and W. Westphal, Ber. *73*, 441 (1940).
174. T. G. Bonner, E. J. Bourne, and S. McNally, J. Chem. Soc. *1962*, 761.

## 2. OLIGOSACCHARIDE SYNTHESIS BY LENGTHENING OR SHORTENING THE CARBON CHAIN

### A. LENGTHENING OF THE CARBON CHAIN

The known addition of hydrogen cyanide to aldoses, which has been thoroughly elaborated in the monosaccharide series,* has been applied to oligosaccharides to a very limited extent only. The first papers on this subject from the past century[1,2] report that only syrups were obtained by the addition of hydrogen cyanide to lactose and maltose. It was much later that Hudson[3] succeeded in controlling the reaction; by the addition of hydrogen cyanide to lactose (I) and hydrolysis of the nitrile he produced crystalline 5-$O$-$\beta$-D-galactopyranosyl-D-$glycero$-D-$gulo$-heptonic acid (II).

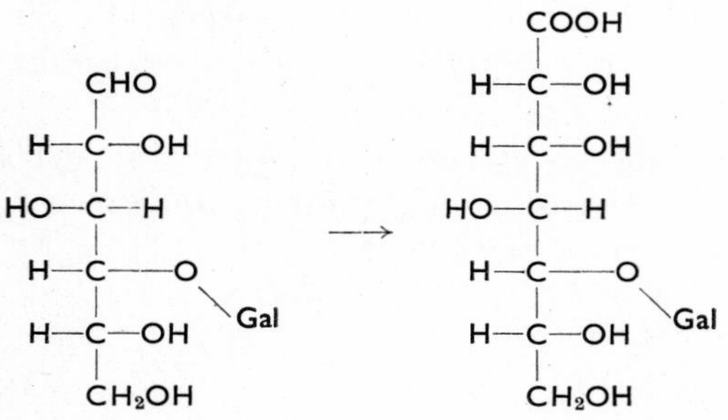

$$\text{(I)} \qquad\qquad \text{(II)}$$

A similar reaction has later also been carried out with maltose and cellobiose.[4,5]

The cyanohydrin synthesis is now mainly applied for the preparation of labelled oligosaccharides.[6,7] Isbell, using radioactive hydrogen cyanide with $^{14}$C, prepared in this way [1-$^{14}$C]-lactose from 3-$O$-$\beta$-D-galactopyranosyl-D-arabinose, and [1-$^{14}$C]-maltose from 3-$O$-$\alpha$-D-glucopyranosyl-D-arabinose.[7]

Nothing has so far been published in the available literature of the application of Sowden's nitromethane synthesis in the series of oligosaccharides.[8] **

### B. SHORTENING OF THE CARBON CHAIN

#### a) The Ruff method

This method, consisting of the conversion of an aldose into the corresponding aldonic acid and oxidation of the barium salt of this acid with hydrogen peroxide in the presence of trivalent iron salts, has found widespread use in

---

* For a review see C. S. Hudson, Advances in Carbohydrate Chem. *1*, 2 (1945).
** For a review see J. C. Sowden, Advances in Carbohydrate Chem. *6*, 291 (1951).

*References see p. 100*

the monosaccharide series. In the group of oligosaccharides, however, it has been applied a few times only, mainly for shortening lactose (I) via the corresponding lactobionic acid (III) to 3-$O$-$\beta$-D-galactopyranosyl-D-arabinose (IV).[9-11]

Gakhokidze prepared non-reducing disaccharides in this way.[12,13] For example, he converted 2-$O$-$\beta$-D-glucopyranosyl-D-galactose (V) into the calcium salt of the corresponding aldobionic acid (VI), which was then subjected to the Ruff degradation and yielded $\beta$-D-glucopyranosyl $\alpha$-D-lyxopyranoside (VII).[12] Analogously, 2-$O$-?-D-mannopyranosyl-D-mannose gives the expected ?-D-mannopyranosyl $\beta$-D-arabinoside.[13]

## b) The Wohl degradation

The shortening of the carbon chain via the Wohl degradation consists of acetylating an aldose oxime with simultaneous dehydration to the per-*O*-acetyl derivative of the corresponding aldonic acid nitrile; deacetylation of this substance in alkaline solution, with simultaneous liberation of one hydrogen cyanide molecule, shortening the reducing part of the saccharide molecule by one carbon atom, and thereby forming a lower aldose. This shortening is widely used in the monosaccharide series;* in the oligosaccharide group it has been investigated mainly by Zemplén.[14-18]

In his first work,[14] Zemplén converted cellobiose (VIII) with a yield of 50% into the expected acetylated nitrile (IX), which then gave 3-*O*-β-D-glucopyranosyl-D-arabinose (X) in a yield of 80%. This substance was again converted into the acetylated nitrile (XI) and further shortening of the carbon chain gave 2-*O*-β-D-glucopyranosyl-D-erythrose (XII).

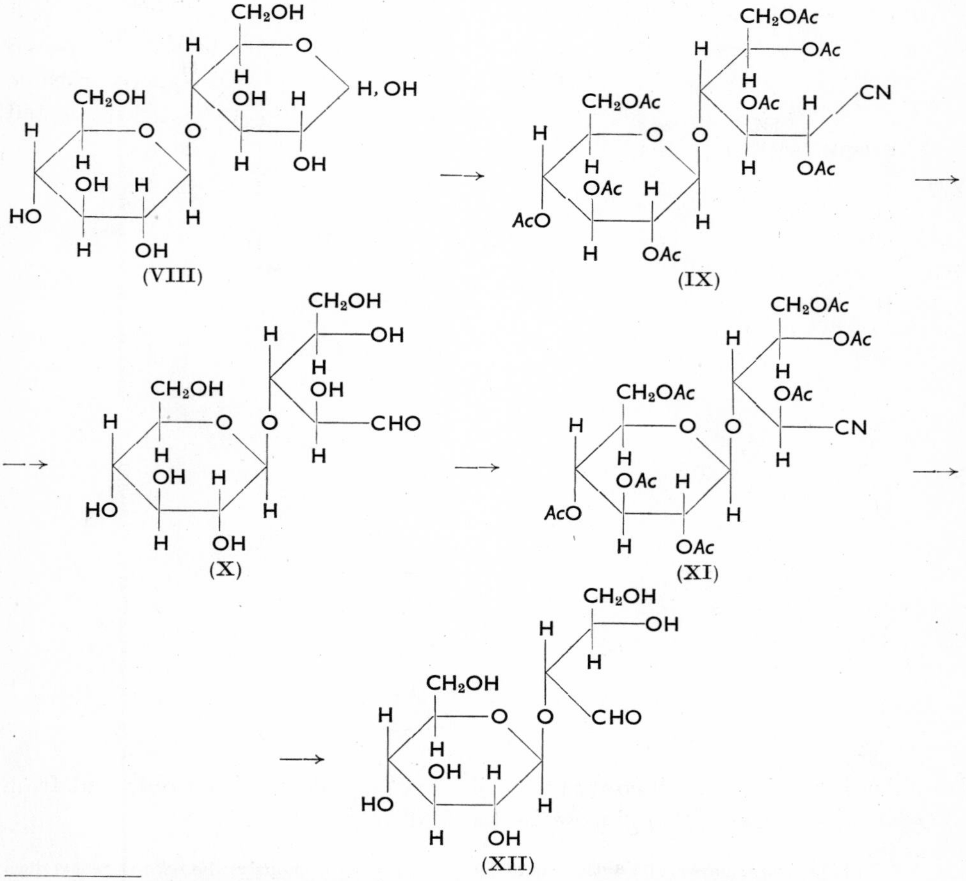

(VIII) → (IX) →

(X) → (XI) →

(XII) →

* For a review see V. Deulofeu, Advances in Carbohydrate Chem. *6*, 119 (1949).

*References see p. 100*

Zemplén carried out similar reactions with maltose[15] and lactose[16,17] (the reaction with lactose was recently also studied by Kuhn).[11] However, attempts to degrade melibiose were unsuccessful.[18] Zemplén did not succeed in converting this compound (1→6 disaccharide) into the expected 5-*O*-α-D-galacto-pyranosyl-D-arabinose, not even in the form of an osazone, and thus he concluded erroneously that D-galactose must be connected to the molecule of D-glucose in position -3-. In the case of another 1→6 disaccharide, gentiobiose, however, a similar degradation, carried out later, was successful[19] and gave rise to 5-*O*-β-D-glucopyranosyl-D-arabinose.

Gakhokidze prepared in this way again some non-reducing disaccharides.[20,21] He converted 2-*O*-β-D-glucopyranosyl-D-glucose (XIII) into the corresponding acetylated nitrile (XIV), from which β-D-glucopyranosyl α-D-arabinoside (XV) was isolated in the form of its hepta-*O*-acetyl derivative.[20]*

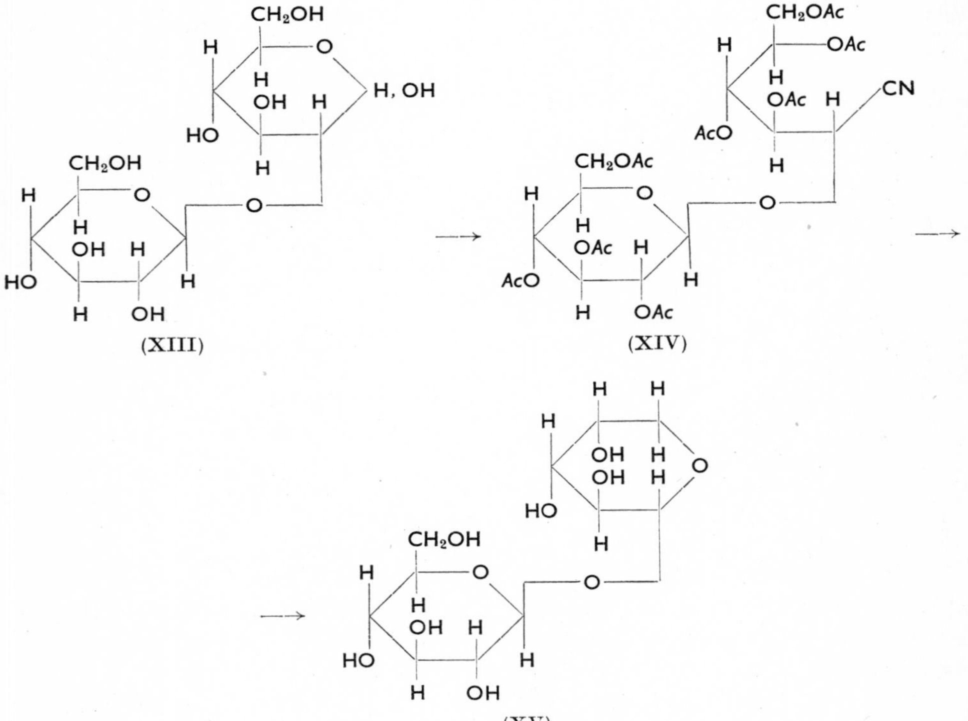

(XIII)

(XIV)

(XV)

Analogously, β-D-glucopyranosyl β-D-erythroside has been obtained from 3-*O*-β-D-glucopyranosyl-D-glucose by twofold degradation.[21]

---

* In his original paper, the author mentions, obviously erroneously, the octa-*O*-acetyl derivative, although analysis and structural formula correspond to the hepta-*O*-acetyl derivative.

## c) Degradation of glycals by oxidation

Gakhokidze was the only investigator concerned with the splitting of the glycal linkage in the oligosaccharide series.[22-29] For example, from hepta-*O*-acetyl-lactosyl bromide (XVI) he prepared hexa-*O*-acetyl-lactal (XVII), converted the latter in acetic acid into the corresponding ozonide and reduced this substance with zinc to the hexa-*O*-acetyl derivative of 3-*O*-β-D-galactopyranosyl-D-arabinose (XVIII). Free 3-*O*-β-D-galactopyranosyl-D-arabinose (XIX) was obtained by hydrolysis of the acetoxy groups in a total yield of 33%, related to the initial halogenose.[22]

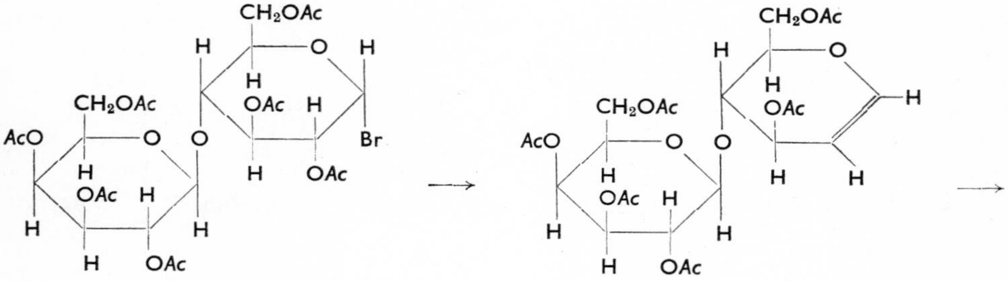

(XVI)  (XVII)

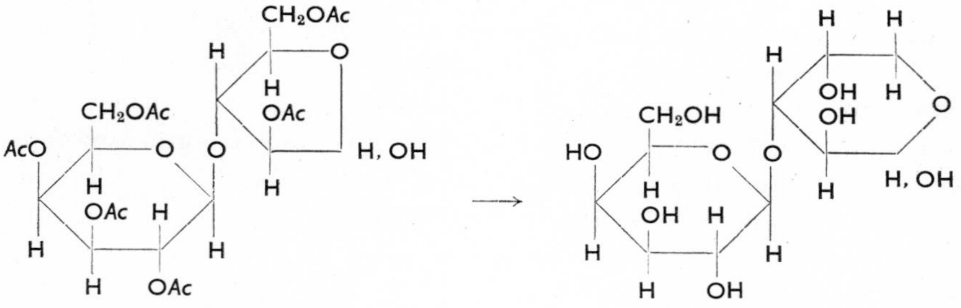

(XVIII)  (XIX)

By similar procedures, Gakhokidze converted cellobiose[23] into 3-*O*-β-D-glucopyranosyl-D-arabinose, maltose[24] into 3-*O*-α-D-glucopyranosyl-D-arabinose, and 3-*O*-α-D-glucopyranosyl-D-glucose[25] into 2-*O*-α-D-glucopyranosyl-D-arabinose.

As far as degradation of glycals is concerned, Gakhokidze introduced a further modification,[26,29] namely oxidation of the glycal with potassium permanganate to an aldonic acid shortened by one carbon atom and additional degradation of this acid according to Ruff. This procedure leads to an oligosaccharide shortened by two carbon atoms in the reducing part of the molecule; this reaction has been successfully employed for constitution studies. For example, maltal (XX) was converted in this way into 3-*O*-α-D-glucopyranosyl-

*References see p. 100*

7*

D-arabonic acid (XXI) whose calcium salt, on degradation according to Ruff, yielded 2-O-α-D-glucopyranosyl-D-erythrose (XXII).[27]

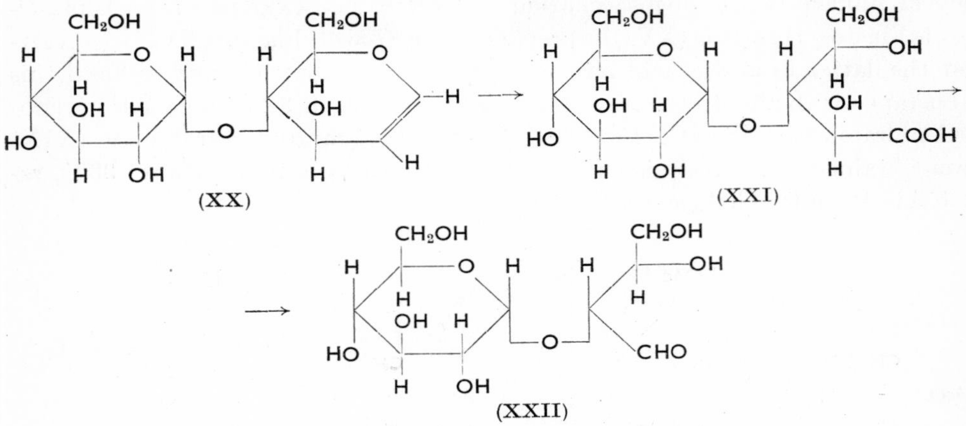

(XX)    (XXI)

(XXII)

Similar reactions were carried out with lactal[28] and cellobial.[29]

### d) Other degradation methods

Hardegger[30] described a new interesting method for degrading reducing disaccharides with oxygen in alkaline solution. On several 1→4 disaccharides (maltose, cellobiose, lactose), he demonstrated that these substances, when subjected to the action of oxygen in barium hydroxide solution, yield the corresponding lower carboxylic acid; for example, 3-O-α-D-glucopyranosyl-D-arabonic acid is thus obtained from maltose. The action of hypochlorous acid, too, shortens the molecule of a reducing disaccharide by C-1 so that maltose yields 3-O-α-D-glucopyranosyl-D-arabinose and lactose is converted into 3-O-β-D-galactopyranosyl-D-arabinose.[31]

A newer paper describes another possibility of shortening the molecule of a reducing disaccharide by one carbon atom.[32] Manganese dioxide degrades 1→3, 1→4 and 1→6 linked hexose disaccharides to 1→2, 1→3 and 1→5 linked hexopyranosylpentoses, respectively.

The action of lead tetra-acetate in reducing oligosaccharides offers another possibility of preparing new compounds with a shortened carbon chain in the reducing part of the molecule (see p. 44).

#### REFERENCES

1. E. Fischer, Ber. *23*, 932 (1890).
2. O. Reinbrecht, Ann. *272*, 197 (1892).
3. R. M. Hann and C. S. Hudson, J. Am. Chem. Soc. *56*, 1390 (1934).
4. M. Uenaka, Scientific Papers Osaka Univ. *1951*, No. 23; Chem. Abstr. *46*, 8883 (1952).

5.  M. Uenaka, Scientific Papers Osaka Univ. *1951*, No. 24; Chem. Abstr. *46*, 8883 (1952).
6.  H. L. Frush and H. S. Isbell, J. Research Natl. Bur. Standards *50*, 133 (1953).
7.  H. S. Isbell and R. Schaffer, J. Am. Chem. Soc. *78*, 1887 (1956).
8.  J. C. Sowden, Advances in Carbohydrate Chem. *6*, 291 (1951).
9.  O. Ruff and G. Ollendorf, Ber. *33*, 1798 (1900).
10. G. Zemplén, Ber. *60*, 1309 (1927).
11. R. Kuhn and W. Kirschenlohr, Ann. *600*, 135 (1956).
12. A. M. Gakhokidze and N. D. Kutidze, Zhur. Obshcheĭ Khim. *22*, 139 (1952); Chem. Abstr. *46*, 11116 (1952).
13. A. M. Gakhokidze and N. D. Kutidze, Zhur. Obshcheĭ Khim. *22*, 247 (1952); Chem. Abstr. *46*, 11117 (1952).
14. G. Zemplén, Ber. *59*, 1254 (1926).
15. G. Zemplén, Ber. *60*, 1555 (1927).
16. G. Zemplén, Ber. *59*, 2402 (1926).
17. G. Zemplén, Ber. *60*, 1309 (1927).
18. G. Zemplén, Ber. *60*, 923 (1927).
19. V. S. MacDonald and W. L. Evans, J. Am. Chem. Soc. *64*, 2731 (1942).
20. A. M. Gakhokidze, Zhur. Obshcheĭ Khim. *11*, 117 (1941); Chem. Abstr. *35*, 5467 (1941).
21. A. M. Gakhokidze, Zhur. Obshcheĭ Khim. *16*, 1923 (1946); Chem. Abstr. *41*, 6210 (1947).
22. A. M. Gakhokidze, Zhur. Obshcheĭ Khim. *16*, 1907 (1946); Chem. Abstr. *41*, 6208 (1947).
23. A. M. Gakhokidze, Zhur. Obshcheĭ Khim. *16*, 1914 (1946); Chem. Abstr. *41*, 6209 (1947).
24. A. M. Gakhokidze, Zhur. Obshcheĭ Khim. *18*, 60 (1948); Chem. Abstr. *42*, 4948 (1948).
25. A. M. Gakhokidze, Zhur. Obshcheĭ Khim. *19*, 2082 (1949); Chem. Abstr. *44*, 3914 (1950).
26. A. M. Gakhokidze, Zhur. Obshcheĭ Khim. *19*, 2100 (1949); Chem. Abstr. *44*, 5813 (1950).
27. A. M. Gakhokidze, Zhur. Obshcheĭ Khim. *20*, 116 (1950); Chem. Abstr. *44*, 5819 (1950).
28. A. M. Gakhokidze, Zhur. Obshcheĭ Khim. *20*, 120 (1950); Chem. Abstr. *44*, 5819 (1950).
29. A. M. Gakhokidze, Zhur. Obshcheĭ Khim. *20*, 289 (1950); Chem. Abstr. *44*, 6822 (1950).
30. E. Hardegger, K. Kreis, and H. El Khadem, Helv. Chim. Acta *35*, 618 (1952).
31. R. L. Whistler and K. Yagi, J. Org. Chem. *26*, 1050 (1961).
32. J. L. Bose, A. B. Foster, N. Selin, M. Stacey, and J. M. Webber, Tetrahedron *14*, 201 (1961).

## 3. SYNTHESIS BY STRUCTURAL CHANGE OF ONE MONO-SACCHARIDE UNIT IN THE OLIGOSACCHARIDE MOLECULE

### A. ANOMERIZATION OF THE GLYCOSIDIC LINKAGE IN THE DISACCHARIDE MOLECULE

This problem was investigated by Lindberg, who was the first to observe that the octa-*O*-acetyl derivative of gentiobiose (6-*O*-β-D-glucopyranosyl-D-glucose, I) is changed by the action of sulphuric acid in acetic acid solution into the corresponding anomer, namely the octa-*O*-acetyl derivative of isomaltose (6-*O*-α-D-glucopyranosyl-D-glucose, II). The reaction was first followed according to the changes of the values of specific rotations, but later, with the use of titanium tetrachloride, employed for preparation purposes with a yield of 46%.[1,2]

(I)                                                                                         (II)

In the latter case, the action of titanium tetrachloride gives rise to an acylated halogenose as intermediate product, which must be converted into the per-*O*-acetyl derivative of isomaltose by means of mercuric acetate. Lindberg[3] carried out a similar reaction with the per-*O*-acetyl derivative of 6-*O*-β-D-galactopyranosyl-D-glucopyranose, from which he obtained the per-*O*-acetyl derivative of melibiose. This reaction was unsuccessful in the series of per-*O*-acetyl derivatives of trisaccharides[4] but was recently employed with satisfactory results in syntheses of saccharinic acids of oligosaccharides[5] (see Chapter XXXIII).

6-*O*-α-D-Glucopyranosyl-D-galactose octa-*O*-acetate has been prepared from the corresponding 6-*O*-β-D-glucopyranosyl-D-galactose octa-*O*-acetate by the action of titanium tetrachloride, see I. J. Goldstein and W. J. Whelan, J. Chem. Soc. *1963*, 4264. On the other hand, 4-*O*-α-6-*O*-β-di-D-glucopyranosyl-D-glucose undeca-*O*-acetate has been recovered unchanged, see I. J. Goldstein and B. Lindberg, Acta Chem. Scand. *16*, 283 (1962).

## B. EPIMERIZATION IN ONE OF THE MONOSACCHARIDE UNITS

Only a very few papers have so far been published on this subject. The per-*O*-acetyl derivative of cellobiose (4-*O*-β-D-glucopyranosyl-D-glucose, III), on treatment with hydrogen fluoride, yields the per-*O*-acetyl derivative of *epi*-cellobiose (4-*O*-β-D-glucopyranosyl-D-mannose, IV).[6]

CH₂OAc ... (III) ... CH₂OAc ... (IV)

(The structures III and IV are depicted with the following labels:)

**(III):** CH₂OAc, H, H, OAc, H, OAc, H, OAc; CH₂OAc, H, O, O, H, OAc, H; AcO, H, OAc, H; H, OAc

**(IV):** CH₂OAc, H, H, OAc, OAc, H, OAc; CH₂OAc, H, O, O, H, OAc, H; AcO, H, H; H, OAc

6-*O*-α-D-Galactopyranosyl-D-glucose (melibiose), in this case by the action of ammonia, leads likewise to the corresponding epimer, i. e. 6-*O*-α-D-galacto-pyranosyl-D-mannose (*epi*-melibiose).[7]

## C. TWOFOLD INVERSION OF THE CONFIGURATION AT C-2 AND C-3 IN THE REDUCING PART OF THE DISACCHARIDE MOLECULE

An interesting reaction takes place when octa-*O*-acetyl-lactose (V) is treated with a mixture of aluminium chloride and phosphorus pentachloride;[8,9] the product obtained in this way and termed *neo*-lactose was originally assumed to be 4-*O*-β-D-galactopyranosyl-D-mannose,[8] however, the reaction is accompanied by inversions at C-2 and C-3, so that the octa-*O*-acetyl derivative thus produced is that of 4-*O*-β-D-galactopyranosyl-D-altrose (VI).[9]

**(V):** CH₂OAc, H, H, OAc, H, H, OAc; CH₂OAc, AcO, O, O, H, OAc; H, OAc, H, H; H, OAc

**(VI):** CH₂OAc, H, H, AcO, H, OAc; CH₂OAc, AcO, O, O, H, OAc, H; H, OAc, H, H; H, OAc

Similarly, the octa-*O*-acetyl derivative of cellobiose[10,11] yields the octa-*O*-acetyl derivative of celtrobiose, namely 4-*O*-β-D-glucopyranosyl-D-altrose.

## D. HYDROXYLATION OF GLYCALS

This reaction, rather common in the monosaccharide series (see for example the preparation of D-talose from D-galactal), has several times been applied to the disaccharide group also. Cellobiose is converted via the usual intermediate products, i. e. octa-$O$-acetyl derivative, acetylated halogenose and acetylated cellobial, into 4-$O$-$\beta$-D-glucopyranosyl-D-mannose,[12,13] and cellobiose is formed in a similar way from *epi*-cellobiose.[14] A number of papers[15–18] are concerned with the conversion of acetylated lactose (VII) into 4-$O$-$\beta$-D-galactopyranosyl-D-mannose (IX) through hexa-$O$-acetyl-lactal (VIII).

A similar procedure was employed for converting *epi*-lactose into lactose[19,20] and gentiobiose into 6-$O$-$\beta$-D-glucopyranosyl-D-mannose through gentiobial.[21] The yields of these reactions are quite satisfactory, between 34%[14] and 58%.[19,20]

## E. ISOMERIZATION OF THE REDUCING ALDOSE INTO A KETOSE IN THE DISACCHARIDE MOLECULE

The isomerization of aldoses to ketoses in alkaline solution can also be utilized for reducing disaccharides. For example, lactose (4-$O$-$\beta$-D-galactopyranosyl-D-glucose, X) gives lactulose (4-$O$-$\beta$-D-galactopyranosyl-D-fructose, XI).[22–26] Analogously, 4-$O$-$\beta$-D-galactopyranosyl-D-psicose is formed from *neo*-lactose.[25]

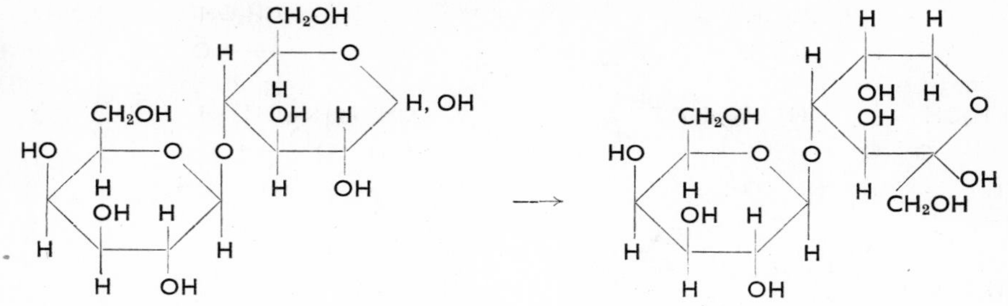

(X) ⟶ (XI)

Of interest in this connection is the discovery[27] that lactulose is also formed by the heating of milk (besides a small amount of D-tagatose).

The preparation of lactulose from lactose on ion exchangers has been described by Z. B. Shaposhnikova, I. V. Alekseeva, and I. R. Rominskiĭ, Ukr. Khim. Zh. *28*, 724 (1962); Chem. Abstr. *59*, 1735 (1963).

The other reducing disaccharides isomerize in a similar way, maltose is converted into maltulose[23] and cellobiose into cellobiulose.[28] The action of pyridine on 3-*O*-β-D-glucopyranosyl-D-glyceraldehyde (XII) gives rise to 3-*O*-β-D-glucopyranosyldihydroxyacetone (XIII).[29]

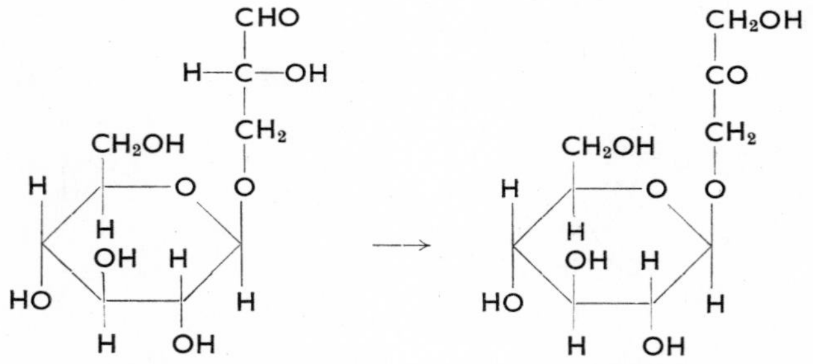

(XII) ⟶ (XIII)

Another possibility of obtaining lactulose from lactose was recently described by Kuhn.[30] He converted lactose (XIV) first into the corresponding *N*-arylglycosylamine (XV), which then was transformed by Amadori re-arrangement into the compound (XVI). This substance reacts in pyridine with benzenediazonium chloride to form the triazene derivative (XVII), and just this product can be exceptionally readily isolated from the reaction mixture. By the action of hydrochloric acid in the presence of iodide ions it is reconverted into the pure compound (XVI); catalytic reduction offers the possibility of removing the aryl remainder with the formation of 1-amino-1-deoxylactulose (XVIII), and this substance, on treatment with nitrous acid, yields lactulose (XIX) in an overall yield of 17%.

*References see p. 107*

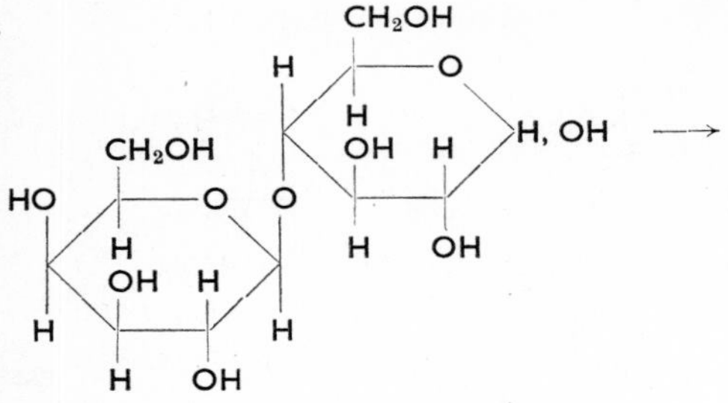

(XIV)

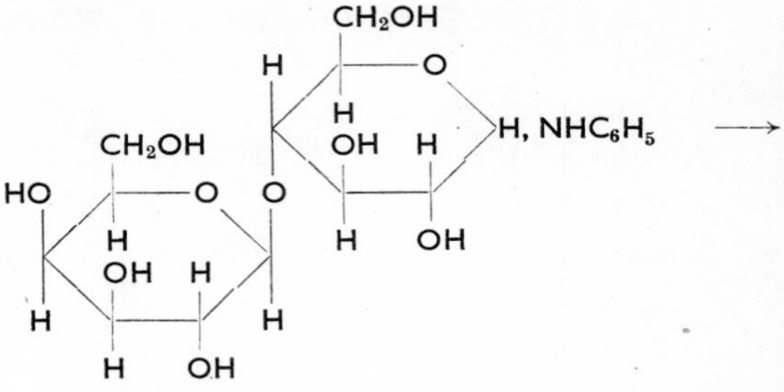

(XV)

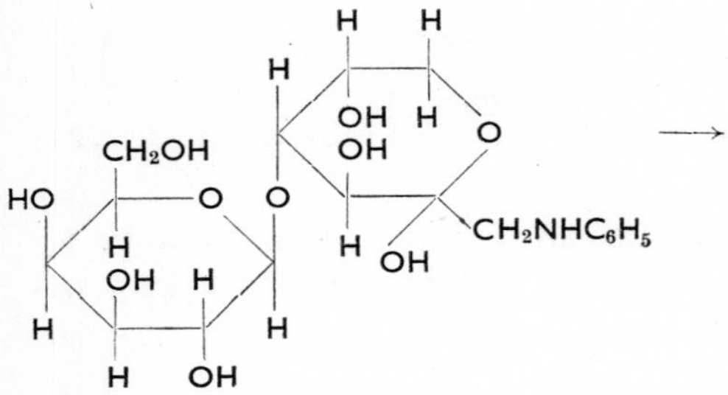

(XVI)

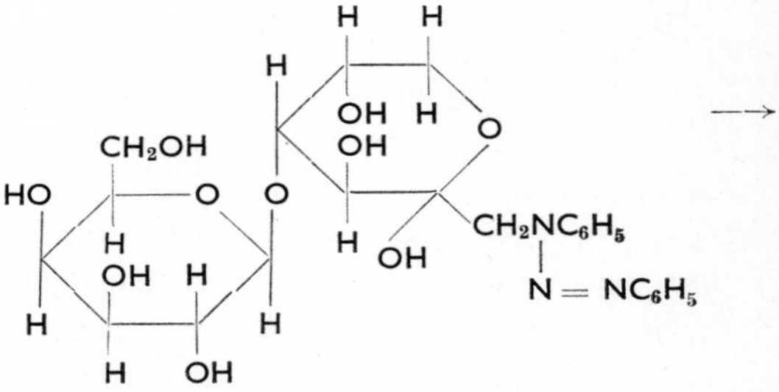

(XVII)

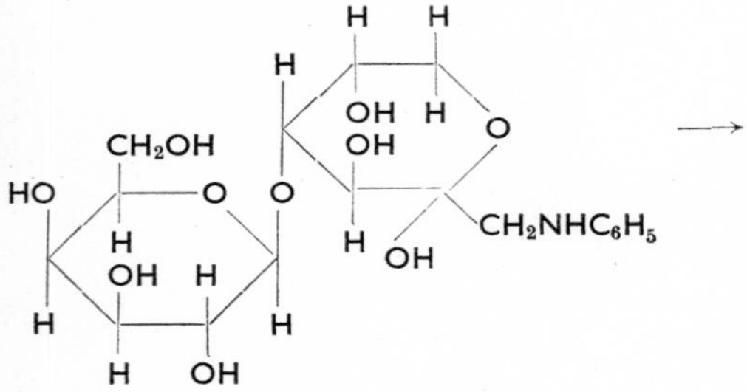

(XVI)

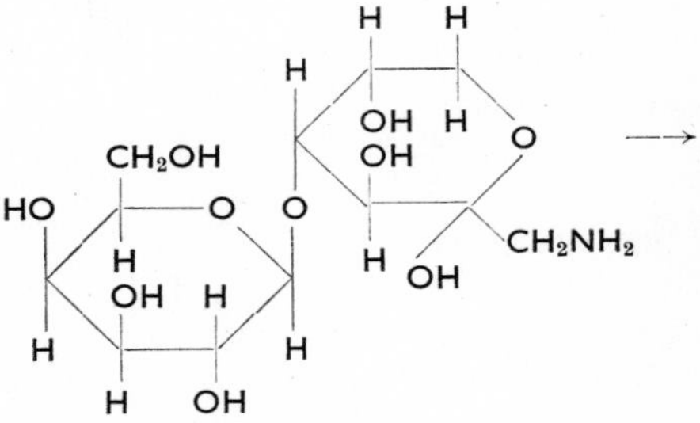

(XVIII)

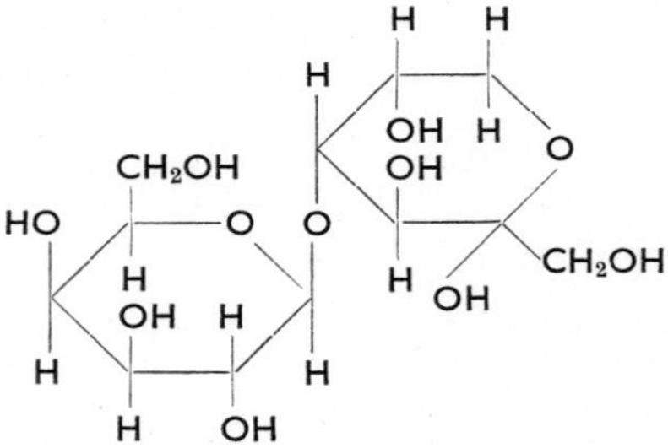

(XIX)

## F. REDUCTION OF URONIC ACIDS

The uronic acids of the series of reducing oligosaccharides can be converted into these latter compounds provided that the carboxyl group of the uronic acid is esterified and the aldehydic group is transformed into a glycosidic group. In practice, this is carried out in such a way that, for example, aldo-biouronic acid is converted by heating with ethyl orthoformate in the presence of hydrogen chloride into the corresponding glycoside, whereupon, on esterification of the carboxyl group (for example with diazomethane), the carbomethoxy group is reduced by the action of a hydride.[31-34]

## G. REDUCTION OF OLIGOSACCHARIDE KETO DERIVATIVES

From 3-ketolactose and 3-ketomaltose which were produced by the action of enzymes on lactose and maltose (see Chap. VI, 5) new reducing disaccharides 4-O-β-D-gulosyl-D-glucose and 4-O-β-D-allosyl-D-glucose have been prepared.[35] Conditions have been described in which the 3-keto function has been reduced much faster than the hemiacetal group by Raney nickel. The other isomeric sugars have been obtained in both cases, too, and have been removed by the oxidative action of micro-organisms, lactose by the action of *Aerobacter cloacae* and maltose by the action of *Paracolobactrum*. D-Allose is no more considered to belong to the group of inaccessible sugars.

Similarly, 3-ketosucrose has been reduced to α-D-allopyranosyl β-D-fructofuranoside.[35]

**REFERENCES**

1. B. Lindberg, Nature *164*, 706 (1946).
2. B. Lindberg, Acta Chem. Scand. *3*, 1355 (1949).
3. B. Lindberg, Acta Chem. Scand. *5*, 340 (1951).
4. L. Asp and B. Lindberg, Acta Chem. Scand. *5*, 665 (1951).
5. R. L. Whistler and J. N. BeMiller, J. Org. Chem. *26*, 2886 (1961).
6. D. H. Brauns, J. Am. Chem. Soc. *48*, 2776 (1926).
7. L. Hough, J. K. N. Jones, and E. L. Richards, J. Chem. Soc. *1954*, 295.
8. A. Kunz and C. S. Hudson, J. Am. Chem. Soc. *48*, 1978 (1926).
9. A. Kunz and C. S. Hudson, J. Am. Chem. Soc. *48*, 2435 (1926).
10. N. K. Richtmyer and C. S. Hudson, J. Am. Chem. Soc. *57*, 1716 (1935).
11. N. K. Richtmyer and C. S. Hudson, J. Am. Chem. Soc. *58*, 2534 (1936).
12. M. Bergmann and H. Schotte, Ber. *54*, 1564 (1921).
13. W. N. Haworth, E. L. Hirst, H. R. L. Streight, H. A. Thomas, and J. I. Webb, J. Chem. Soc. *1930*, 2636.
14. W. T. Haskins, R. M. Hann, and C. S. Hudson, J. Am. Chem. Soc. *64*, 1289 (1942).
15. M. Bergmann, M. Kobel, H. Schotte, E. Rennert, and S. Ludewig, Ann. *434*, 79 (1923).
16. A. J. Waters and C. S. Hudson, J. Am. Chem. Soc. *52*, 3472 (1930).

17. W. N. Haworth, E. L. Hirst, M. T. Plant, and R. J. W. Reynolds, J. Chem. Soc. *1930*, 2644.
18. W. N. Haworth, E. L. Hirst, and R. J. W. Reynolds, J. Chem. Soc. *1934*, 302.
19. W. T. Haskins, R. M. Hann, and C. S. Hudson, J. Am. Chem. Soc. *64*, 1490 (1942).
20. W. T. Haskins, R. M. Hann, and C. S. Hudson, J. Am. Chem. Soc. *64*, 1852 (1942).
21. H. J. Dauben and W. L. Evans, J. Am. Chem. Soc. *60*, 886 (1938).
22. E. M. Montgomery and C. S. Hudson, J. Am. Chem. Soc. *52*, 2101 (1930).
23. W. M. Corbett and J. Kenner, J. Chem. Soc. *1953*, 2245.
24. W. M. Corbett and J. Kenner, J. Chem. Soc. *1954*, 1789.
25. J. P. L. Bots, Rec. trav. chim. *76*, 515 (1957).
26. F. J. Bates, *Polarimetry, Saccharimetry and the Sugars*, National Bureau of Standards, Washington *1942*, p. 467.
27. S. Adachi, Nature *181*, 840 (1958).
28. W. M. Corbett and J. Kenner, J. Chem. Soc. *1955*, 1431.
29. H. W. Arnold and W. L. Evans, J. Am. Chem. Soc. *58*, 1890 (1936).
30. R. Kuhn and G. Krüger, Ann. *628*, 240 (1959).
31. J. K. N. Jones and W. W. Reid, J. Chem. Soc. *1955*, 1890.
32. S. A. Barker, A. Gómez-Sánchez, and M. Stacey, J. Chem. Soc. *1959*, 3264.
33. G. A. Adams, Can. J. Chem. *37*, 29 (1959).
34. W. D. S. Bowering and T. E. Timell, J. Am. Chem. Soc. *82*, 2827 (1960).
35. M. J. Bernaerts, J. Furnelle, and J. De Ley, Biochim. et Biophys.Acta *69*, 322 (1963).

## 4. SYNTHESIS OF OLIGOSACCHARIDES BY THE ACTION OF MINERAL ACIDS; REVERSION*

The fact, already known for a long time, that oligosaccharides are split in acid solution with the formation of monosaccharides gave rise as early as the end of the last century to attempts to synthesize oligosaccharides by the action of mineral acids on monosaccharides. The first experiments[1-6] resulted in undefined products throughout, probably of the type of higher oligosaccharides or even polysaccharides. The laboratory technique of that time did not permit the separation of the forming, usually rather complicated, oligosaccharide mixtures, and the substances so obtained and designated by various names (such as gallisin,[7-9] revertose,[10,11] δ-dextrose,[12] and dextrinose[13,14]) were undoubtedly not chemical individuals. The investigators reported in all cases that the products obtained are not fermentable and exhibit but a negligible reducing effect on Fehling solution. Some of these writers were convinced that they had in this way produced a disaccharide yielding phenylmaltosazone by reaction with phenylhydrazine.[5]

From the historical viewpoint it will be sufficient just to mention experiments undertaken by other investigators,[15-17] who believed that D-glucose reacts with acetic anhydride to form the octa-*O*-acetyl derivative of sucrose.

---

\* For reviews see W. R. Fetzer, E. K. Crosby, C. E. Engel, and L. C. Kirst, Ind. Eng. Chem. *45*, 1057 (1953); K. Müller and K. Täufel, Z. Lebensm. Untersuch. *100*, 437 (1955); Chem. Abstr. *49*, 13673 (1955); S. Suzuki, Tôhoku Yakka Daigaku Kiyô *5*, 1 (1958); Chem. Abstr. *53*, 10053 (1959).

The first actual synthesis of a disaccharide from a monosaccharide by the action of a mineral acid was carried out by Fischer in 1890;[18] he dissolved D-glucose in four times the quantity of concentrated hydrochloric acid, and from the reaction mixture he isolated, in the form of its phenylosazone, a new disaccharide which he named isomaltose.[18,19] Fischer's procedure was repeated several times,[20–25] but as late as 1926 a pure disaccharide could be isolated from the mixture of the reaction products.[26]

The reaction of D-glucose, D-mannose and D-xylose in hydrochloric acid had already been investigated earlier, with regard to changes of reducing power and molecular weight;[27] in this way, however, the problem was not elucidated, and the same applies to later experiments[28] based upon observation of the changes of optical rotation and reducing power.

The first substance isolated as a chemical individual after the reaction of D-glucose in hydrochloric acid[26] was termed gentiobiose (originally it was erroneously believed that Fischer's isomaltose and Berlin's gentiobiose are identical); the formation of gentiobiose was confirmed in the same year by another writer.[29] In the following 25 years, however, practically no advance was achieved in this respect. Some papers reported that obviously oligosaccharides with 1→6 linkages are preferentially formed under the given reaction conditions.[30,31] No detailed information was obtained, however, although the reaction was carried out at various temperatures[32,33] and various hydrochloric acid concentrations.[34,35] It was found that high concentrations of mineral acids are disadvantageous because polysaccharides are produced under such conditions.[34–37] Gentiobiose continued to be the only isolated and identified substance.[26,29,38,39]

A more profound insight into the course of the reaction of D-glucose in mineral acids and into the complicated mixture of the substances formed was not possible prior to the introduction of chromatographic methods, in particular chromatography on paper as practised after the year 1951.[40–43] The first finding was[40–42] that D-glucose treated in this way yields two disaccharides, namely gentiobiose and isomaltose;[42] in another paper[43] this number was supplemented by trehalose and a fourth disaccharide, named isogentiobiose at that time.[43]

Since 1953, the synthesis of oligosaccharides from monosaccharides in mineral acids has been systematically investigated by Wolfrom and associates; the old name given to this reaction by Wohl,[6] i. e. reversion,[43,44] was reintroduced in the same year.

Wolfrom subjected the mixture obtained by the reaction of D-glucose in hydrochloric acid to acetylation and subsequent chromatographic separation of the per-O-acetyl derivatives of disaccharides on carbon and silicagel. First he described the isolation of the per-O-acetyl derivatives of isomaltose and gentiobiose;[44] the per-O-acetyl derivative of isomaltose in the pure state was shortly afterwards prepared by other investigators,[45] and this reaction was later developed into a method for preparing isomaltose and gentiobiose from

*References see p. 113*

D-glucose by the action of hydrochloric acid.[46] Besides these per-*O*-acetyl derivatives of isomaltose and gentiobiose, Wolfrom and associates[47] isolated shortly afterwards the per-*O*-acetyl derivatives of maltose, cellobiose, sophorose and β,β-trehalose, in addition to a further per-*O*-acetyl derivative characterized at that time only by its melting point and [α]$_D$ value, which, however, are in good agreement with the constants of the per-*O*-acetyl derivative of nigerose. This substance was found besides maltose and isomaltose by other investigators, too.[48,49]

The number of isolated disaccharides was then increased by α,α-trehalose[50] and, finally, in a very thorough study,[51] Peat confirmed that among the reversion products isomaltose and gentiobiose are prevalent over maltose, cellobiose, sophorose, nigerose and trehalose; recently he described the isolation of kojibiose and laminaribiose, whose formation was also confirmed by Japanese writers.[52]

Noteworthy are the report[53] that gentiobiose is formed from D-glucose also on acid ion exchangers and the finding[54] that D-glucose in hydrochloric acid yields even a tetrasaccharide containing predominantly 1→6 linkages besides a small number of 1→2 or 1→3 linkages. The predominance of 1→6 linkages has also been confirmed in later communications.[55]

In the last, thorough study it was found by means of paper chromatography[56] that D-glucose yields preferentially disaccharides with 1→6 linkages, then disaccharides with 1→4 and 1→3 linkages, followed by trisaccharides and tetrasaccharides.

Laevoglucosan in concentrated hydrochloric acid obviously reacts in a similar way on the assumption that the anhydro ring undergoes hydrolysis; this assumption is strongly supported by the isolation of a considerable amount of D-glucose in such a reaction of laevoglucosan.[57] Secondary reaction products formed from D-glucose produced in this way are isomaltose and gentiobiose besides a smaller amount of cellobiose and a very noticeable, in this case predominating, quantity of trisaccharides and higher oligosaccharides.[57] It is very likely that the so-called γ-glucose, once prepared by the reaction of laevoglucosan with hydrochloric acid,[58,59] was a mixture of oligosaccharides of similar compositions.

A mixture of maltose and D-glucose in acid solution yields nigerose, see M. L. Wolfrom, A. Thompson, and R. H. Moore, Cereal Chem. *40*, 182 (1963); Chem. Abstr. *59*, 6493 (1963).

* * *

It is certain that the oligosaccharides contained in "hydrol" (i. e. the mother liquors left after the preparation of D-glucose by starch hydrolysis) are formed in a similar way; consequently, under the conditions of acid hydrolysis

i. e. inversion, the opposite process, i. e. reversion, takes place. Disacchari-des were found in hydrol besides monosaccharides in 1926,[60] when gentiobiose was detected in this material. The composition of hydrol was then studied by many investigators.[43,50,61-68] The substances safely identified were gentiobio-se,[50,62,63,66,67] isomaltose,[50,62,67] (in one paper the name brachiose is used[65]), maltose,[64-67] cellobiose,[50,66,67] kojibiose,[64,66,67] laminaribiose,[66,68] sophorose,[66,67] nigerose,[66,67] 5-$O$-$\beta$-D-glucopyranosyl-D-glucose,[50] $\alpha,\alpha$-trehalose,[65] and $\beta,\beta$-trehalose.[64,66,67] Gentiobiose is obtainable from hydrol in amounts sufficient for the preparation of this compound.[69]

Among the products isolated from hydrol, only isomaltose[44] and nigerose [70,71] correspond in the type of their glycosidic bonds to the original linkages of starch; in particular in the isolation of nigerose, careful measures were taken to ensure prevention of reversion. The formation of isomaltose in the hydro-lysis of amylopectin[44,72] proves that the amylopectin molecule must contain native $\alpha$, 1→6 linkages, since isomaltose is produced from amylopectin in an amount about two hundred times as high as in the hydrolysis of starch.[44,72]

The problem of reversion also complicates the question whether the lower oligosaccharide produced by acid hydrolysis of a higher oligosaccharide or a polysaccharide actually is a native oligosaccharide. In some cases,[73,74] the course of acid hydrolysis was controlled so as to reliably prevent simultaneous re-version.

\* \* \*

Reversion was also observed in the treatment of other monosaccharides. In the aldohexose series it was found by means of chromatography on paper[42] that D-galactose in acid solution yields four disaccharides, but only 6-$O$-$\alpha$-D-galactopyranosyl-D-galactose could later be isolated and identified.[75] Another paper even reports the formation of trisaccharides.[56] In the case of D-mannose, where the formation of polysaccharidic fractions had been observed previously,[34] four oligosaccharides were obtained later and three of them identified with certainty as 6-$O$-$\alpha$-D-mannopyranosyl-D-mannose, 6-$O$-$\beta$-D-mannopyranosyl-D-mannose and 3-$O$-$\alpha$-D-mannopyranosyl-D-mannose;[76] the fourth substance is most probably 4-$O$-$\beta$-D-mannopyranosyl-D-mannose. Later chromatographic investigation[56] revealed no new results.

The formation of 6-$O$-$\alpha$-D-mannopyranosyl-D-mannose and 6-$O$-$\beta$-D-mannopyrano-syl-D-mannose from D-mannose in acid solution has been followed again in a recent paper, see S. Peat, W. J. Whelan, and T. E. Edwards, J. Chem. Soc. *1961*, 29.

As far as aldopentoses are concerned, D-arabinose was converted into the non-reducing D-arabopyranosyl D-arabopyranoside[77] in the form of its hexa-$O$-acetyl derivative; because of its low value of specific rotation, this substance is regarded as the $\alpha,\alpha$-anomer. The course of the reversion of L-arabinose was

*References see p. 113*

investigated in more detail; the first communications on the formation of polysaccharidic fractions[34] and one reducing disaccharide[78] were considerably supplemented by the application of modern methods.[76,79] Thus, L-arabinose was converted into $\beta$-L-arabinopyranosyl $\beta$-L-arabinopyranoside,[76,79] 3-*O*-$\beta$-L-arabinopyranosyl-L-arabinose[76,79,92] and 4-*O*-$\beta$-L-arabinopyranosyl-L-arabi-nose.[79,92] According to a communication [92] the presence of 2-*O*-L-arabinopyra-nosyl-L-arabinose in the reversion mixture is very probable.

Reversion of L-arabinose has also been observed in its oxidation with hydrogen peroxide, where the evaporation of a moderately acid solution leads to oligosaccharides.[79]

The reaction of D-xylose, previously reported to yield di- and trisacchari-des,[78] was subjected to thorough investigation,[80] and the reaction products found were $\alpha$-D-xylopyranosyl $\alpha$-D-xylopyranoside, 2-*O*-$\alpha$-D-xylopyranosyl-D-xylose, 3-*O*-$\alpha$-D-xylopyranosyl-D-xylose, 4-*O*-$\alpha$-D-xylopyranosyl-D-xylose and 4-*O*-$\beta$-D-xylopyranosyl-D-xylose (i. e. xylobiose). The last one was reported in another paper[92] together with 5-*O*-$\alpha$-D-xylopyranosyl-D-xylose and another, unidentified disaccharide.

Ketoses are not likely to yield oligosaccharides under similar reaction conditions; it has been reported[81] that in the hydrolysis of inulin proceeding accompanying reversion gives rise to secondary oligosaccharides; later studies, [41,56] however, show that neither D-fructose nor L-sorbose can be converted into disaccharides by reversion. Insofar as substances with larger molecules are formed, they are anhydro derivatives of the type of di-D-fructose anhydrides or diheterolaevulosans.[82,83] It is not possible also to prepare oligosaccharides containing D-glucose and D-fructose by reversion involved in the action of mi-neral acids on a mixture of these two monosaccharides.[56]

Aldohexoses exhibit an interesting tendency to form reversion products;[56] D-glucose reacts most readily, followed by D-galactose and D-mannose. In the treatment of monosaccharides with acids a number of side-reactions may be expected, such as the formation of furan derivatives,[56,84] conversion of aldoses into the corresponding ketoses[85] (D-glucose gives in acid solution D-fructose but not D-mannose[85]), as well as the formation of anhydro derivatives. The formation of laevoglucosan from D-glucose in a mineral acid was reported,[47,51] however, this finding was not confirmed by a later investigation.[56]

Some investigators observed the formation of reversion products in the hydrolysis of oligosaccharides; for example, it was reported that, in the hydro-lysis of lactose, reversion in acid solution gives rise to three new oligosacchari-des,[86,87] and a similar behaviour was found in the case of maltose.[56] One of the newer papers deals with the formation of reversion products by the action of hydrochloric acid on maltose or lactose, in both cases in the presence of mono-saccharides.[88]

\* \* \*

Recently, a new advance was achieved in reversion studies, when it was found possible to obtain even trisaccharides from hydrol.[89,90] One paper[89] describes the isolation of isomaltotriose (dextrantriose) and panose besides gentiobiose, sophorose and cellobiose, another paper[90] is reporting the isolation of 3-$O$-α-isomaltosyl-D-glucose from hydrol.

The formation of oligosaccharides in the action of cationic resins on molten D-glucose, in particular with the use of Amberlite IR—120(H) is described, too. The substances isolated in this way are isomaltose, gentiobiose, cellobiose, laminaribiose, trehalose, and probably 5-$O$-D-glucopyranosyl-D-glucose.[91]

## REFERENCES

1. F. Musculus, Bull. soc. chim. France (2) *18*, 66 (1872).
2. A. Gautier, Bull. soc. chim. France (2) *22*, 145 (1874).
3. F. Musculus and A. Meyer, Compt. rend. *92*, 528 (1881).
4. H. Hönig and S. Schubert, Monatsh. Chem. *7*, 455 (1886).
5. E. Grimaux and L. Lefèvre, Compt. rend. *103*, 146 (1886).
6. A. Wohl, Ber. *23*, 2084 (1890).
7. C. Schmitt and A. Cobenzl, Ber. *17*, 1000 (1884).
8. C. Schmitt and J. Rosenhek, Ber. *17*, 2456 (1884).
9. C. Scheibler and H. Mittelmeier, Ber. *24*, 301 (1891).
10. A. C. Hill, J. Chem. Soc. *1898*, 634.
11. A. C. Hill, J. Chem. Soc. *1903*, 578.
12. A. Roessing, Chem. Ztg. *29*, 867 (1905).
13. W. Syniewski, Ann. *309*, 311 (1900).
14. W. Syniewski, Ann. *324*, 212 (1902).
15. F. Schützenberger and Naudin, Bull. soc. chim. France (2) *12*, 1940 (1869).
16. A. P. N. Franchimont, Ber. *12*, 1940 (1879).
17. E. Demole, Ber. *12*, 1935 (1879).
18. E. Fischer, Ber. *23*, 3687 (1890).
19. E. Fischer, Ber. *28*, 3024 (1895).
20. H. T. Brown and J. H. Millar, J. Chem. Soc. *75*, 305 (1899).
21. E. F. Armstrong, Proc. Royal Soc. London *76* B, 592 (1905); Chem. Zentr. *1905*, II, 1806.
22. O. Fridrichs, Arkiv Kemi, Mineral., Geol. *5*, No. 4, 1 (1913).
23. M. M. Harrison, J. Am. Chem. Soc. *36*, 586 (1914).
24. A. Pictet and A. Georg, Compt. rend. *181*, 1035 (1925).
25. A. Georg and A. Pictet, Helv. Chim. Acta *9*, 612 (1926).
26. H. Berlin, J. Am. Chem. Soc. *48*, 1107 (1926).
27. P. A. Levene and R. Ulpts, J. Biol. Chem. *64*, 475 (1925); Chem. Abstr. *19*, 2642 (1925).
28. H. Frahm, Ber. *74*, 622 (1941).
29. B. Isajev, Chem. listy *20*, 251 (1926); Chem. Abstr. *20*, 3159 (1926).
30. A. Georg, Compt. rend. soc. phys. hist. nat. Genève *47*, 94 (1930).
31. K. Myrbäck, Svensk Kem. Tidskr. *53*, 67 (1941); Chem. Abstr. *35*, 264 (1941).
32. E. A. Moelwyn-Hughes, Trans. Faraday Soc. *25*, 86 (1929).
33. P. M. Silin and E. A. Sapegina, Trudy Voronezh Khim. Tekhnol. Inst. *3—4*, 79 (1939); Chem. Abstr. *35*, 8338 (1941).

34.  E. Pacsu and P. T. Mora, J. Am. Chem. Soc. *72*, 1045 (1950).
35.  V. I. Sharkov and M. G. Smirnov, Zhur. Priklad. Khim. *27*, 975 (1954); Chem. Abstr. *49*, 10859 (1955).
36.  H. Schlubach and E. Lühre, Ann. *547*, 73 (1941).
37.  C. R. Ricketts and C. E. Rowe, J. Chem. Soc. *1955*, 3809.
38.  T. C. Taylor and D. Lifschitz, J. Am. Chem. Soc. *54*, 1054 (1932).
39.  G. H. Coleman, M. A. Buchanan, and P. T. Paul, J. Am. Chem. Soc. *57*, 1119 (1935).
40.  K. Täufel and R. Reiss, Z. anal. Chem. *134*, 232 (1951).
41.  K. Müller and K. Täufel, Lebensm. Unters. u. -Forsch. *95*, 401 (1952); Chem. Abstr. *47*, 3246 (1953).
42.  K. Müller and K. Täufel, Naturwissenschaften *40*, 140 (1953); Chem. Abstr. *48*, 9331 (1954).
43.  W. R. Fetzer, E. K. Crosby, C. E. Engel, and L. C. Krist, Ind. Eng. Chem. *45*, 1075 (1953).
44.  A. Thompson, M. L. Wolfrom, and E. J. Quinn, J. Am. Chem. Soc. *75*, 3003 (1953).
45.  E. E. Bacon and J. S. D. Bacon, Biochem. J. *58*, 396 (1954).
46.  M. L. Wolfrom, A. Thompson, and A. M. Brownstein, J. Am. Chem. Soc. *80*, 2015 (1958).
47.  A. Thompson, K. Anno, M. L. Wolfrom, and M. Inatome, J. Am. Chem. Soc. *76*, 1309 (1954).
48.  J. H. Pazur and T. Budovich, J. Am. Chem. Soc. *78*, 1885 (1956).
49.  S. Peat, W. J. Whelan, and K. A. Hinson, Chem. & Ind. (London) *1955*, 385.
50.  J. C. Sowden and A. S. Spriggs, J. Am. Chem. Soc. *78*, 2503 (1956).
51.  S. Peat, W. J. Whelan, T. E. Edwards, and O. Owen, J. Chem. Soc. *1958*, 586.
52.  K. Anno, N. Seno, E. Nakamura, H. Saito, and R. Hoshii, Bull. Agr. Chem. Soc. Japan *23*, 67 (1959); Chem. Abstr. *53*, 21677 (1959).
53.  G. Zemplén and L. Kisfaludi, Acta Chim. Acad. Sci. Hung. *4*, 79 (1954).
54.  K. Myrbäck, M. Hammarstrand, and H. Gelinder, Arkiv. Kemi *1*, 235 (1949); Chem. Abstr. *44*, 1913 (1950).
55.  G. Noto La Diega, Chemie ind. (Milan) *41*, 598 (1959); Chem. Abstr. *54*, 4396 (1960).
56.  H. C. Suberman, J. Org. Chem. *26*, 1967 (1961).
57.  L. Reichel and H. Schiweck, Naturwissenschaften *48*, 696 (1961)
58.  H. Pringsheim, S. Kolodny, and A. Beiser, Ber. *59*, 1135 (1926).
59.  H. Pringsheim and A. Beiser, Ber. *59*, 2241 (1926).
60.  H. Berlin, J. Am. Chem. Soc. *48*, 2627 (1926).
61.  C. D. Hurd and S. M. Cantor, J. Am. Chem. Soc. *60*, 2677 (1938).
62.  M. L. Wolfrom, A. T. Thompson, A. N. O'Neill, and T. T. Galkowski, J. Am. Chem. Soc. *74*, 1062 (1952).
63.  J. C. Sowden and A. S. Spriggs, J. Am. Chem. Soc. *76*, 3539 (1954).
64.  A. Sato and K. Aso, Nature *180*, 984 (1957).
65.  E. M. Montgomery and F. B. Weakley, J. Assoc. Offic. Agr. Chemists *36*, 1096 (1953); Chem. Abstr. *48*, 14261 (1954).
66.  K. Aso and K. Shibasaki, Tôhoku J. Agr. Res. *6*, 159 (1956).
67.  K. Aso and K. Shibasaki, J. Agr. Chem. Soc. Japan *29*, 856 (1955); Chem. Abstr. *50*, 17497 (1956).
68.  A. Sato, K. Watanabe, and K. Aso, Chem. & Ind. (London) *1958*, 887.
69.  F. J. Bates, *Polarimetry, Saccharimetry and the Sugars*, National Bureau of Standards, Washington *1942*, p. 463.
70.  M. L. Wolfrom and A. Thompson, J. Am. Chem. Soc. *77*, 6403 (1955).
71.  M. L. Wolfrom and A. Thompson, J. Am. Chem. Soc. *78*, 4116 (1956).

72. M. L. Wolfrom, J. T. Tyree, T. T. Galkowski, and A. N. O'Neill, J. Am. Chem. Soc. 73, 4927 (1951).
73. R. L. Whistler and H. E. Conrad, J. Am. Chem. Soc. 76, 1673 (1954).
74. M. L. Wolfrom and A. Thompson, J. Am. Chem. Soc. 78, 4182 (1956).
75. C. N. Turton, A. Bebbington, S. Dixon, and E. Pacsu, J. Am. Chem. Soc. 77, 2565 (1955).
76. J. K. N. Jones and W. N. Nicholson, J. Chem. Soc. 1958, 27.
77. F. A. H. Rice, J. Am. Chem. Soc. 78, 6167 (1956).
78. K. Müller and K. Täufel, Lebensm. Unters. u.-Forsch. 95, 429 (1952); Chem. Abstr. 47, 11134 (1953).
79. L. Hough and J. B. Pridham, Chem. & Ind. (London) 1957, 1178.
80. D. H. Ball and J. K. N. Jones, J. Chem. Soc. 1958, 33.
81. K. Müller and K. Täufel, Pharmazie 9, 498 (1954).
82. H. Schlubach and C. Behre, Ann. 508, 16 (1933).
83. K. Täufel and K. J. Steinbach, Nahrung 3, 832 (1959); Chem. Abstr. 54, 14132 (1960).
84. J. Staněk, M. Černý. J. Kocourek, and J. Pacák, The Monosaccharides, Acad. Press, New York 1963.
85. Y. Ohno and K. Ward, J. Org. Chem. 26, 3928 (1961).
86. M. Aronson, Arch. Biochem. Biophys. 39, 370 (1952); Chem. Abstr. 47, 2800 (1953).
87. G. Malyoth and H. W. Stein, Angew. Chem. 64, 399 (1952).
88. K. Täufel and H. Ruttloff, Nahrung 2, 631 (1958); Chem. Abstr. 53, 13633 (1959).
89. A. Sato, Y. Ito, and H. Ono, Chem. & Ind. (London) 1962, 301.
90. A. Sato and H. Ono, Chem. & Ind. (London) 1962, 1536.
91. P. S. O'Colla, E. E. Lee, and D. McGrath, J. Chem. Soc. 1962, 2730.
92. D. H. Ball, J. K. N. Jones, W. H. Nicholson, and T. J. Painter, Tappi 39, 438 (1956); Chem. Abstr. 50, 12469 (1956).

# 5. ENZYMIC SYNTHESIS AND RESYNTHESIS OF OLIGOSACCHARIDES

## A. SYNTHESIS OF OLIGOSACCHARIDES BY THE ACTION OF ENZYMES ON MONOSACCHARIDES

Since oligosaccharides can be split by enzymic action, it was assumed that they could also be synthesized by the action of enzymes on monosaccharides. Probably the oldest paper on this subject is a communication from the end of the past century,[1] reporting that the action of yeast on D-glucose gives rise to maltose; the reaction product of this synthesis was very incompletely defined.

A more exact procedure was described for the preparation of gentiobiose from D-glucose with the use of emulsin;[2] this method was later recommended as an advantageous preparation of gentiobiose in general.[3–5] * This reaction, however, does not proceed quite unambiguously; it was known previously[6] that also cellobiose is formed besides gentiobiose, and by application of modern

---

* For a comment on the priority in the preparation of gentiobiose from D-glucose by the action of emulsin see S. Peat and W. J. Whelan, Chem. Ber. 95, 2829 (1962).

References see p. 120

methods it was found later[7] that, in addition to these two disaccharides, are formed cellobiose, laminaribiose, sophorose, and $\beta,\beta$-trehalose.

The enzyme produced by the micro-organism *Acetobacter acetigenus* is likewise capable to synthesize oligosaccharides from D-glucose. The first communications on this subject,[8,9] reporting the formation of cellobiose in this enzymic synthesis, must be supplemented by further findings regarding the production of cellotriose[9,10] and cellotetraose.[10] If the reaction liquid is sufficiently aerated, even melibiose is formed.[11] Other micro-organisms of the same genus, such as *Acetobacter aceti*, *A. rancens*, *A. acidum-mucosum* and *A. acetosum* var. *nairobiense*, synthesize gentiobiose and sophorose from D-glucose.[12]

The enzymes produced by the micro-organism *Aspergillus oryzae* convert D-glucose into isomaltose;[13,14] the enzymes excreted by the micro-organism *Aspergillus niger* synthesize from D-glucose, besides isomaltose, also maltose, nigerose, kojibiose, and $\alpha,\alpha$-trehalose.[15] It is interesting to note that *Aspergillus niger* is able to synthesize maltose and $\alpha,\alpha$-trehalose even in its growth on an inorganic acetate solution, where these two oligosaccharides are produced besides mannitol, arabitol, erythritol, and glycerol.[16]

*Schizosaccharomyces pombe*, too, synthesize oligosaccharides from D-glucose.[17,18] Exactly identified reaction products were maltose, nigerose (termed sakébiose at that time), and kojibiose.

The synthesizing power of emulsin was also investigated with the use of D-galactose. The first investigation in this respect[19-21] led to the rather inexact conclusion that reducing disaccharides with $\beta,1{\rightarrow}6$ and $\beta,1{\rightarrow}4$ linkages are formed. Later it was found[22] that D-galactose is converted by the enzymic action of emulsin into 3-O-$\beta$-D-galactopyranosyl-D-galactose and 6-O-$\beta$-D-galactopyranosyl-D-galactose. The enzymes produced by the micro-organism *Saccharomyces carlsbergensis* (brewers' yeast) likewise exhibit a synthesizing effect; thus, from D-galactose have been obtained[23] 6-O-$\alpha$-D-galactopyranosyl-D-galactose, 3-O-$\alpha$-D-galactopyranosyl-D-galactose, 4-O-$\alpha$-D-galactopyranosyl-D-galactose, and 5-O-$\alpha$-D-galactopyranosyl-D-galactose.

Oligosaccharides may also be produced by the action of unspecified enzymes. For example, some plants are able to synthesize disaccharides containing 2-deoxy-D-glucose,[24] e. g. 6-O-$\beta$-D-fructofuranosyl-2-deoxy-D-glucose, and enzymic preparations from liver convert D-glucose into a mixture of oligosaccharides, from which maltose, nigerose, isomaltose, and isomaltotriose were separated chromatographically.[25]

The enzymes of some species of the genus *Propionibacterium* (*arabinosum*, *schermanii*, *pentosaceum*) synthesize from D-glucose a non-reducing disaccharide,[26,27] which was identified as trehalose.[28] The same disaccharide is produced in the form of its phosphoric ester from D-glucose 6-phosphate and D-glucose in the presence of uridine diphosphoglucose (UDPG).[29,30]

Special attention has been devoted to the formation of trehalose in the bodies of insects, especially locusts, where trehalose acts most probably as an energy source, since it rapidly diminishes during the flight of the insect.[31,32] Injection of radioactive D-glucose into the body of the insect leads to a very rapid production of radioactive trehalose,[33] whose formation is favourably, but not principally,[34] influenced by the presence of either adenosine triphosphate (ATP) or uridine diphosphoglucose (UDPG); in particular the simultaneous presence of both these factors greatly promotes the synthesis of trehalose.

In some cases it was possible[35,36] to synthesize a disaccharide from a monosaccharide and a monosaccharide glycoside. In this way, D-glucose and phenyl β-D-galactopyranoside are converted by the action of the enzyme from *Escherichia coli* into 6-O-β-D-galactopyranosyl-D-glucose (*allo*-lactose).[35] Another enzyme, α-galactosidase from coffee beans, transfers the D-galactose molecule from phenyl α-D-galactopyranoside to D-mannose to form 6-O-α-D-galactopyranosyl-D-mannose (*epi*-melibiose).[36]

Invertase synthesizes 6-O-β-D-fructofuranosyl-D-glucose from methyl β-D-fructofuranoside and D-glucose.[37] Monosaccharide glycosides have also been employed in several cases in more complicated enzymic oligosaccharide syntheses, termed transglycosylation (see p. 123).

Even a synthesis of a non-reducing trisaccharide has been described; trehalose and phenyl α-D-galactopyranoside can be used as starting materials for an enzymic synthesis of 6-O-α-D-galactopyranosyltrehalose, see E. Guilloux and F. Percheron, Compt. rend. *257*, 545 (1963).

Very suitable initial substances for oligosaccharide syntheses are obviously aldose 1-phosphates. The enzyme from *Neisseria meningitis* synthesizes 4-O-α-D-glucopyranosyl-D-xylose from D-glucose 1-phosphate and D-xylose.[38] Other investigators[39,40] have obtained 3-O-α-D-glucopyranosyl-L-arabinose from D-glucose 1-phosphate and L-arabinose by the action of enzymes of *Pseudomonas saccharophila*.

The enzyme excreted by the micro-organism *Pseudomonas saccharophila* is in general suited for the synthesis of sucrose analogues from D-glucose 1-phosphate and various ketoses. Such reactions were successfully carried out with L-sorbose,[41] D-xylulose[42] and L-ribulose[40] and yielded the expected non-reducing oligosaccharides α-D-glucopyranosyl α-L-sorboside, α-D-glucopyranosyl β-D-xyluloside and α-D-glucopyranosyl α-L-ribuloside (the formation of the latter substance seems more probable than that of α-D-glucopyranosyl β-L-ribuloside mentioned in the original paper).[40]

It has already been pointed out that the synthesis of oligosaccharides proceeds well in the presence of adenosine triphosphate or of substances of the type of uridine diphosphoglucose (UDPG, see p. 116). Here it may be added that the action of phenyl β-D-glucopyranoside on UDPG gives rise to phenyl β-gentiobioside and uridine diphosphate.[43] Later, an enzyme has been detected

*References see p. 120*

in a bean starch granules preparation which catalyses the reaction, in which uridine diphosphoglucose reacts with an acceptor to form uridine diphosphate and an oligosaccharide with $O$-$\alpha$,1→4 linkages.[44]

Similarly, lactose 1-phosphate is formed from uridine diphospho-D-galactose and D-glucose 1-phosphate.[45]

Sucrose has been enzymically synthesized from D-glucose 1-phosphate and D-fructose, and sucrose analogues have been obtained from 1-phosphates of other aldoses (see p. 119).

It is not known to date how the various oligosaccharides are formed in living matter; the exception is sucrose, as the problem of its biosynthesis is obviously most important and very interesting.

### Synthesis of sucrose*

The problem of the biosynthesis of sucrose has conceivably been investigated very thoroughly; the formation of sucrose is explained, in full agreement with the biosynthesis of saccharides in general, by means of the Calvin cycle.[46, 47] Attention has also been paid to the determination of the place where the final phase of sucrose biosynthesis proceeds in the beet,[48] as well as to the investigation of sucrose synthesis with the use of radioactive organic compounds [49,50]

Invertase, which readily splits sucrose into a molecule of D-glucose and a molecule of D-fructose, is not able to synthesize sucrose in the opposite way from these two monosaccharides; the energy conditions (and certainly also the energy contained in the hemiacetal bond itself) and, moreover, the presence of water in the reaction medium counteract a possible resynthesis of sucrose.

Although sucrose could be converted by the enzymic action of invertase in the presence of methanol into methyl $\beta$-D-fructofuranoside,[51] it has so far not been possible to obtain sucrose from this compound and D-glucose by enzymic synthesis. Application of takadiastase for this purpose was unsuccessful,[52] and invertase synthesizes 6-$O$-$\beta$-D-fructofuranosyl-D-glucose[37] from the initial components mentioned.

As late as 1943—1947, Doudoroff and Hassid succeeded in carrying out a biosynthesis of sucrose.[40,53,54] The enzyme excreted by the micro-organism *Pseudomonas saccharophila* (sucrose-phosphorylase) catalyses the reaction:

D-glucose 1-phosphate + D-fructose → sucrose + phosphoric acid.

The enzyme influencing the reaction in this way was also obtained from other sources, such as sugar beet leaves,[55,56] germinating peas,[57,58] or barley extracts.[59] Finally, this enzyme has been isolated in the pure state from sugar cane.[60,61]

---

* For reviews see W. Z. Hassid and M. Doudoroff, Advances in Carbohydrate Chem. *5*, 29 (1950); M. Calvin, Angew. Chem. *68*, 253 (1956); M. Calvin, Angew. Chem. *74*, 165 (1962).

R. B. Frydman and W. Z. Hassid, Nature *199*, 382 (1963), re-examined the in-vitro biosynthesis of sucrose with enzyme preparations from sugar cane leaves. They were unable to confirm the results of Ramakhrisnan[55,56] and Shukla and Prabhu[60,61] that sugar cane contains a sucrose-phosphorylase capable of synthesizing sucrose from D-glucose 1-phosphate and D-fructose. The only sucrose-synthesizing enzyme was a transglycosylation that transfers the D-glucose unit from UDPG to D-fructose.

In 1953 and shortly afterwards, a number of investigators arrived at the conclusion[59,62-66] that D-glucose 1-phosphate contains insufficient energy for this enzymic synthesis, and that the actual energy source is uridine triphosphate, which rapidly reacts with D-glucose to form uridine diphospho-D-glucose and phosphoric acid. According to this interpretation, uridine diphospho-D-glucose reacts with D-fructose, with the action of the enzyme mentioned, to form sucrose and uridine diphosphate. This hypothesis was followed chromatographically with the use of isotopes,[62,63] and the results obtained supported this interpretation. The synthesis of sucrose from uridine diphospho-D-glucose and D-fructose by the action of enzyme extractions of the root of the sugar beet was likewise successful.[67]

According to further findings,[68] it is possible to replace uridine triphosphate by other substances of this group, such as adenosine triphosphate (ATP) or diphosphopyridine nucleotide (DPN), and it seems very probable that D-glucose 1-phosphate is yet sufficiently rich in energy.[57,60,68]

Leloir[59] reported that a similar synthesis cannot be carried out with ketoses other than D-fructose; this finding was not quite exact and later supplemented by the statement[58] that D-fructose can be replaced by D-xylulose, D-rhamnulose or L-sorbose. Of the non-reducing disaccharides produced in this way, namely α-D-glucopyranosyl β-D-rhamnuloside, α-D-glucopyranosyl β-D-xyluloside and α-D-glucopyranosyl α-L-sorboside, the two latter compounds are identical with those obtained from D–glucose 1-phosphate and the corresponding ketoses by the action of enzymes from *Pseudomonas saccharophila*[41,42] (see p. 117).

It is interesting to note that in syntheses of sucrose analogues, D-glucose may also be replaced by some other aldoses,[69,70] such as D-xylose, D-galactose or L-arabinose, and in this way have been prepared α-D-xylopyranosyl β-D-fructofuranoside, α-D-galactopyranosyl β-D-fructofuranoside and α-L-arabinopyranosyl β-D-fructofuranoside.

From these findings, the rule has been derived that the enzymic synthesis is possible only with a certain arrangement of the hydroxyl groups in the aldose molecule. The hydroxyl group at the second carbon atom must be in D-position and the hydroxyl group at the third carbon atom must be in the *threo*-position to it, i. e. L-oriented.

Independent communications by other writers state that α-D-xylopyranosyl β-D-fructofuranoside is also synthesized by the enzymic action of *Aerobacter laevanicum*;[71] the same enzyme has also been employed for the preparation of

*References see p. 120*

α-D-galactopyranosyl β-D-fructofuranoside,[72] however, with the use of raffinose as source of D-fructose.

\* \* \*

The enzymic synthesis of lactose 1-phosphate from uridine diphospho-D-galactose and D-glucose 1-phosphate has also been described[45] (see p. 118). Much work has been expended on the elucidation of the biosynthesis in living organisms,[73–76] as summarized by Malpress.[77] However, the situation is far from being clear. Lactose is claimed to be formed preferentially from D-glucose[74] directly contained in the plasma, but an injection of radioactive D-glucose into the organism exerts no noticeable influence on the formation of lactose.[75] According to Wood,[76] the use of [1—14C]-acetic acid leads to D-galactose 1-phosphate labelled at C-4 (perhaps by the Krebs cycle), and the reaction of this compound is claimed to give rise to lactose. Another paper[78] reports that D-galactose 1-phosphate is produced in the livers of rats fed on D-galactose; it is assumed that there exists an enzyme able to convert D-galactose 1-phosphate into D-glucose 1-phosphate.

## REFERENCES

1. A. Croft-Hill, J. Chem. Soc. 73—74, 634 (1898).
2. E. Bourquelot, H. Hérissey and J. Coirre, Compt. rend. 157, 732 (1913).
3. Org. Syntheses 22, 53 (1942).
4. V. D. Stefanovič, J. Chromatog. 5, 453 (1961).
5. V. D. Stefanovič, Chem. Ber. 94, 2359 (1961).
6. E. Bourquelot and M. Bridel, Compt. rend. 168, 1016 (1919).
7. S. Peat, W. J. Whelan, and K. A. Hinson, Nature 170, 1056 (1952).
8. A. E. Creedy, P. Jowett, and T. K. Walker, Chem. & Ind. (London) 1954, 1297.
9. T. K. Walker and H. B. Wright, Arch. Biochem. Biophys. 69, 362 (1957).
10. R. Steel and T. K. Walker, Nature 180, 201 (1957).
11. H. B. Wright and T. K. Walker, Chem. & Ind. (London) 1955, 18.
12. T. K. Walker, D. N. Pellegrino, and A. W. Khan, Arch. Biochem. Biophys. 83, 161 (1959).
13. J. Pfanmüller and A. Noe, Science 115, 240 (1952).
14. K. Shibasaki and K. Aso, Tôhoku J. Agr. Research 5, 131 (1954); Chem. Abstr. 53, 5053 (1959).
15. S. Peat, W. J. Whelan, and K. A. Hinson, Chem. & Ind. (London) 1955, 385.
16. S. A. Barker, A. Gómez-Sánchez, and M. Stacey, J. Chem. Soc. 1958, 2583.
17. K. Shibasaki, J. Ferment. Technol. (Japan) 31, 354 (1953); Chem. Abstr. 48, 7109 (1954).
18. K. Shibasaki, Tôhoku J. Agr. Research 6, 171 (1954).
19. E. Bourquelot and A. Aubry, Compt. rend. 163, 60 (1916).
20. E. Bourquelot and A. Aubry, Compt. rend. 164, 443 (1917).
21. E. Bourquelot and A. Aubry, Compt. rend. 164, 521 (1917).

22. A. M. Stephen, S. Kirkwood, and F. Smith, Can. J. Chem. *40*, 151 (1962).
23. S. A. Barker, M. Stacey, and D. B. E. Stroud, Nature *189*, 138 (1961).
24. G. A. Barber, J. Am. Chem. Soc. *81*, 3722 (1959).
25. I. S. Lukomskaya, Doklady Akad. Nauk S. S. S. R. *142*, 1190 (1962); Chem. Abstr. *57*. 11522 (1962).
26. H. G. Wood and C. H. Werkman, J. Biol Chem. *105*, 63 (1934).
27. H. G. Wood and C. H. Werkman, Biochem. J. *34*, 129 (1940).
28. R. Stjernholm, Acta Chem. Scand. *12*, 646 (1958).
29. E. Cabib and L. F. Leloir, J. Biol. Chem. *231*, 259 (1958).
30. L. F. Leloir and E. Cabib, J. Am. Chem. Soc. *75*, 5445 (1953).
31. T. Bücher and M. Klingenberg, Angew. Chem. *70*, 552 (1958).
32. D. R. Evans and V. G. Dethier, J. Insect. Physiol. *1*, 3 (1957).
33. J. E. Treherne, J. Exptl. Biol. *35*, 297 (1958).
34. D. J. Candy and B. A. Kilby, Nature *183*, 1594 (1959).
35. R. Kuhn, H. H. Baer, and A. Gauhe, Chem. Ber. *88*, 1713 (1955).
36. J. E. Courtois and F. Petek, Bull. soc. chim. biol. *39*, 715 (1957).
37. W. J. Whelan and D. M. Jones, Biochem. J. *54*, XXXIV (1953).
38. E. W. Putman, C. F. Litt, and W. Z. Hassid, J. Am. Chem. Soc. *77*, 4351 (1955).
39. W. Z. Hassid, M. Doudoroff, A. L. Potter, and H. A. Barker, J. Am. Chem. Soc. *70*, 306 (1948).
40. M. Doudoroff, W. Z. Hassid, and H. A. Barker, J. Biol. Chem. *168*, 733 (1947).
41. W. Z. Hassid, M. Doudoroff, H. A. Barker, and W. H. Dore, J. Am. Chem. Soc. *67*, 1394 (1945).
42. W. Z. Hassid, M. Doudoroff, H. A. Barker, and W. H. Dore, J. Am. Chem. Soc. *68*, 1465 (1946).
43. T. Yamaka and C. E. Cardini, Arch. Biochem. Biophys. *86*, 133 (1960).
44. L. F. Leloir, M. A. Rongine de Fekete, and C. E. Cardini, J. Biol. Chem. *236*, 636 (1961).
45. J. E. Gander, W. E. Petersen, and P. D. Boyer, Arch. Biochem. Biophys. *69*, 85 (1957).
46. M. Calvin, Angew. Chem. *68*, 253 (1956).
47. M. Calvin, Angew. Chem. *74*, 165 (1962).
48. V. E. Sokolova, Biokhimiya *19*, 115 (1954).
49. E. W. Putman and W. Z. Hassid, J. Biol. Chem. *207*, 885 (1954).
50. J. Liebster, J. Kopoldová, J. Kozel, and M. Dobiášová, Collection Czechoslov. Chem. Communs *26*, 1582 (1961).
51. J. S. D. Bacon and D. J. Bell, J. Chem. Soc. *1957*, 3581.
52. H. J. Breuer and J. S. D. Bacon, Biochem. J. *66*, 462 (1957).
53. M. Doudoroff, N. Kaplin, and W. Z. Hassid, J. Biol. Chem. *148*, 67 (1943).
54. W. Hassid, M. Doudoroff, and H. Barker, J. Am. Chem. Soc. *66*, 1416 (1944).
55. C. V. Ramakhrisnan, Naturwissenschaften *43*, 352 (1956).
56. C. V. Ramakhrisnan, Experientia *14*, 91 (1959).
57. J. F. Turner, Nature *172*, 1149 (1953).
58. R. C. Bean and W. Z. Hassid, J. Am. Chem. Soc. *77*, 5337 (1955).
59. L. F. Leloir and C. E. Cardini, J. Am. Chem. Soc. *75*, 6084 (1953).
60. J. P. Shukla and K. A. Prabhu, Naturwissenschaften *46*, 325 (1959).
61. J. P. Shukla and K. A. Prabhu, Experientia *16*, 202 (1960).
62. J. G. Buchanan, Arch. Biochem. Biophys. *44*, 140 (1953).
63. E. W. Putman and W. Z. Hassid, J. Biol. Chem. *207*, 885 (1954).
64. C. E. Cardini, L. F. Leloir, and J. Chiriboga, J. Biol. Chem. *214*, 149 (1955).

65. L. F. Leloir and C. E. Cardini, J. Biol. Chem. *214*, 157 (1955).
66. D. P. Burma and D. C. Martimer, Arch. Biochem. Biophys. *62*, 16 (1956).
67. J. V. Dutton, A. Carruthers, and J. F. T. Oldfield, Biochem. J. *81*, 266 (1961).
68. J. F. Turner, Biochem. J. *67*, 451 (1957).
69. C. Péaud-Lenoel, Compt. rend. *241*, 1518 (1955).
70. C. Péaud-Lenoel, Bull. soc. chim. biol. *39*, 747 (1957).
71. G. Avigad, D. S. Feingold, and S. Hestrin, Biochim. et Biophys. Acta *20*, 129 (1956).
72. D. S. Feingold, G. Avigad, and S. Hestrin, J. Biol. Chem. *224*, 295 (1957).
73. R. Heyworth and J. S. D. Bacon, Biochem. J. *61*, 224 (1951).
74. M. Kleiber, A. L. Black, M. A. Brown, C. F. Baxter, J. R. Luick, and F. H. Stadtman, Biochim. et Biophys. Acta *17*, 252 (1955).
75. R. Venkataraman and F. J. Reithel, Arch. Biochem. Biophys. *70*, 205 (1957).
76. H. G. Wood, P. Siu, and P. Schambye, Arch. Biochem. Biophys. *69*, 390 (1957).
77. F. H. Malpress, Proc. Roy. Soc. *149 B*, 362 (1958).
78. H. W. Kosterlitz, Biochem. J. *37*, 322 (1943).

## B. TRANSGLYCOSYLATION

The name "transglycosylation" was given by Rabaté[1] to enzymic processes by which a certain glycoside is converted in the presence of a suitable acceptor into a new compound corresponding to the initial substance. The acceptor may be either a hydroxy compound or a substance with an unsubstituted amino group; a reaction of the latter type, however, was described only recently.[2]

Transglycosylation in the monosaccharide series has already been known for a longer time. In the group of oligosaccharides it was described in 1944 by Pigman,[3,4] who obtained unfermentable products from maltose by the action of enzymes produced by the micro-organisms *Aspergillus niger, A. oryzae* and *Bacillus mesentericus.* He did not succeed in preparing similar substances by the action of the same enzymes upon D-glucose and, consequently, this reaction involves the cleavage of maltose into other components, which were then re-synthesized into other oligosaccharides.

Many similar reactions are known today; the term "transglycosylation" in the oligosaccharide series denotes the formation of new substances from an oligosaccharide by the action of enzymes, as a rule of microbial origin.* The resulting oligosaccharide may be of the same, a lower or a higher order.

Some papers on this subject were published in about 1950. Unfermentable products were obtained from maltose by the action of micro-organisms,[5-9] such as *Aspergillus oryzae,*[5] *A. niger,*[8-9] and *Bacillus macerans.*[7] These products contain on the one hand a reducing disaccharide,[8] later identified as iso-

---

* For reviews see: R. L. Whistler and D. I. McGilvray, Ann. Reports Chem. Soc. *50*, 281 (1953); R. L. Whistler and D. I. McGilvray, Ann. Revs Biochem. *23*, 82 (1953); M. Stacey, Biokhimiya *22*, 241 (1957); K. Wallenfels, Bull. soc. chim. biol. *42*, 1715 (1960); D. J. Manners, Bull. soc. chim. biol. *42*, 1789 (1960).

maltose[10-12] and, on the other hand, a trisaccharide,[9] whose constitution was then established and which was named panose.[10-12]

Preliminary reports of similar resyntheses from lactose[5] and sucrose[13-15] were published at the same time.

* * *

From these and further findings it may be deduced that the disaccharide is split by enzymic action with the formation of a monosaccharide as one component and a complex of a monosaccharide with an enzyme as second component. And it is just this second component that can react with the acceptor which may be a split-off monosaccharide molecule or another substance. The reactions proceeding in this way can be represented by the following scheme (G = D-glucose, Gal = D-galactose, E = enzyme):

$$G—Gal + E = G + Gal—E$$
$$G—Gal + Gal—E = G—Gal—Gal + E$$
$$G—Gal—Gal + Gal—E = G—Gal—Gal—Gal + E, \text{ etc.}$$

Of great importance here is evidently the energy contained in the glycosidic linkage of the oligosaccharide and preserved in this way. It is not possible, therefore, to obtain disaccharides from a monosaccharide under similar conditions.[16]

In some cases, glycosides of monosaccharides were formed by enzymic splitting of oligosaccharides in the presence of an appropriate alcohol. Thus, α-galactosidase from coffee transfers the D-galactose molecule from melibiose to methanol to form methyl α-D-galactopyranoside,[17] and the same substance can also be obtained by the transfer of D-galactose from a molecule of raffinose or stachyose.[17] Similarly, the action of a yeast invertase preparation on sucrose in methanol gives rise to methyl β-D-fructofuranoside.[18] Finally, sucrose is converted by takadiastase in the presence of aniline into N-phenyl-D-fructosylamine.[2]

On the other hand, the energy of the glycosidic linkage can be utilized for enzymic syntheses of oligosaccharides from monosaccharide glycosides by the reaction of the latter with monosaccharides. Several cases of this type have been described; for example, methyl β-D-fructofuranoside reacts with D-glucose in the presence of invertase to form 6-O-β-D-fructofuranosyl-D-glucose.[19] Takadiastase synthesizes from the same two initial compounds a disaccharide which is not identical with sucrose.[20] Some α-D-glucopyranosides[21,22] were also employed for this purpose; they react with D-fructose to form isomaltulose (palatinose, 6-O-α-D-glucopyranosyl-D-fructose).[22] D-Galactose glycosides, too, were used for these reactions.[23,24] For example, α-galactosidase from coffee beans transfers the D-galactose molecule from phenyl α-D-galactopyranoside to D-mannose to form *epi*-melibiose (6-*O*-α-D-galactopyranosyl-D-mannose),[23] and the enzymes from the micro-organism *Escherichia coli* convert phenyl β-D-galactopyranoside and D-glucose into *allo*-lactose (6-*O*-β-D-galactopyranosyl-D-glucose),[24] and the same glycoside and *N*-acetyl-D-glucosamine into the corresponding 6-*O*-β-D-galactopyranosyl-*N*-acetyl-D-glucosamine.[24]

The enzyme from *Escherichia coli* are able to transfer the L-arabinose molecule from *o*-nitrophenyl α-L-arabinopyranoside to D-glucose;[25] in this way, three isomeric disaccharides are formed, namely 6-*O*-α-L-arabinopyranosyl-, 3-*O*-α-L-arabinopyranosyl- and 4-*O*-α-L-arabinopyranosyl-D-glucose.[25]

Even a trisaccharide was synthesized by this method: phenolic β-D-glucopyranosides and sucrose are converted by the action of β-glucosidase into gentianose.[26] *

### a) Enzymic transfers of a monosaccharide molecule from an oligosaccharide to a monosaccharide or its derivative

#### Transglucosylation

Some disaccharides have been synthesized by transfer of a D-glucose molecule from maltose to D-glucose. In the presence of enzymes from *Aspergillus oryzae*, nigerose (3-*O*-α-D-glucopyranosyl-D-glucose)[27] is produced besides three other oligosaccharides, one of them probably having the structure of *O*-α-D-glucopyranosyl-(1→6)-*O*-α-D-glucopyranosyl-(1→3)-D-glucopyranose.[27] According to Japanese investigators, kojibiose (2-*O*-α-D-glucopyranosyl-D-glucose) is formed under similar conditions.[12,28–31]

Interesting is the course of transglucosylation when a sucrose solution is subjected to the action of the micro-organism *Leuconostoc mesenteroides* (also named *Betacoccus arabinosaceus* — in this monograph the first of these terms is consistently used). As a rule, the polysaccharide dextran** is formed under these conditions, but the enzymic synthesis proceeds quite differently when more than 20% of D-glucose is present. In this case, no dextran is formed and the products of the enzymic action are isomaltose,[32,33] isomaltotriose (also named dextrantriose),[32,33] the trisaccharide panose (see p. 127),[32] and other, so far unidentified, oligosaccharides.[32] Here the D-glucose molecule of the sucrose is obviously transferred to the D-glucose present, and a further D-glucose molecule may be transferred to the synthesized isomaltose.

---

* See also E. Guilloux and F. Percheron, Compt. rend. *257*, 545 (1963).

** For reviews see: T. H. Evans and H. Hibbert, Advances in Carbohydrate Chem. *2*, 203 (1946); W. B. Neely, Advances in Carbohydrate Chem. *15*, 341 (1960).

The enzymes of the micro-organism *Leuconostoc mesenteroides* can transfer the D-glucose molecule from sucrose even to 3-*O*-methyl-D-glucose;[34] this gives rise to the reducing disaccharide 6-*O*-α-D-glucopyranosyl-3-*O*-methyl-D-glucose besides the trisaccharide *O*-α-D-glucopyranosyl-(1→6)-*O*-α-D-glucopyranosyl-(1→6)-3-*O*-methyl-D-glucose and the tetrasaccharide *O*-α-D-glucopyranosyl-(1→6)-*O*-α-D-glucopyranosyl-(1→6)-*O*-α-D-glucopyranosyl-(1→6)-3-*O*-methyl-D-glucose.

The same enzymes are also able to transfer the D-glucose molecule from sucrose to methyl α-D-glucopyranoside;[35,36] the products formed in this way are a series of similarly constituted glycosides, namely methyl α-isomaltoside, methyl α-isomaltotrioside, methyl α-isomaltotetraoside, and methyl α-isomaltopentaoside.[35,36] Transfers of this type have been observed in the enzymic action of *Bacillus macerans* on both anomeric methyl D-glucopyranosides as acceptors and cyclohexa-amylose as source;[37] this process leads to the formation of methyl glycosides derived from maltose, maltotriose and maltotetraose. Methyl α-glycosides of the same oligosaccharides may be obtained[38] by transfer of a D-glucose molecule from amylopectin to methyl α-D-glucopyranoside.

The D-glucose molecule may be transferred from sucrose even to D-galactose by the action of *Leuconostoc mesenteroides*;[39] from the disaccharide mixture obtained only one defined substance, having the character of a non-reducing disaccharide, could be isolated, namely α-D-glucopyranosyl D-galactofuranoside.[39]

D-Glucose transfer by means of *Leuconostoc mesenteroides* was also thoroughly investigated with other sugars as acceptors.[40] Unsuitable for this purpose are xylose, arabinose, ribose, rhamnose, mannose, sophorose, cellobiose, trehalose, lactose, melezitose, and raffinose; the reaction proceeds, however, not only with D-glucose and D-galactose, as already mentioned, but also with fructose, maltose, isomaltose, leucrose, and melibiose – most readily with isomaltose and maltose.

Interesting D-glucose transfers are also effected by micro-organisms other than *Leuconostoc mesenteroides*. The enzymes from *Bacillus macerans* convert cyclohexa-amylose and D-glucose into maltotriose, maltotetraose, maltopentaose and maltohexaose,[41,42] as has been proved by the application of radioactive D-glucose.

Sucrose, too, has been employed in several further cases as source of D-glucose; the action of enzymes of *Pseudomonas saccharophila* converts sucrose and D-rhamnulose (6-deoxy-D-fructose) into D-glucosyl D-rhamnuloside.[43] Transfer of the D-glucose molecule from sucrose to D-fructose by yeast α-glucosidase[44] leads to isomaltulose (palatinose, i. e. 6-*O*-α-D-glucopyranosyl-D-fructose) and 1-*O*-α-D-glucopyranosyl-D-fructose. By-products of this reaction are maltulose, isomaltose, isomaltotriose and isomaltotriulose.[44] Attention has also been paid to D-glucose transfer from sucrose to D-glucosamine by the action of microbial enzymes.[45]

D-Glucosyl derivatives of D-xylose have also been obtained in some cases by enzymic synthesis. The transfer of a D-glucose molecule from cellobiose to D-xylose gives rise to 3-O-β-D-glucopyranosyl-D-xylose;[46,47] this transfer can be effected by enzymes of either *Aspergillus niger*[46] or *Cladophora rupestris*.[47] In the first case, products of resynthesis have also been isolated, namely laminaribiose and two further disaccharides.[46]

*Penicillium lilacinum* synthesizes 3-O-α-D-glucopyranosyl-D-xylose from maltose and D-xylose.[48]

### Transfructosylation

In some cases it was possible to synthesize sucrose by transfer of a D-fructose molecule from a suitable source, for instance, from the polysaccharide laevan when subjected to the action of *Bacillus subtilis*,[49] or raffinose treated with either takadiastase[20] or with laevansucrase from *Aerobacter laevanicum*.[50]

Laevan-sucrase from *Aerobacter laevanicum* transfers D-fructose from sucrose to other suitable acceptors; thus, D-glucose treated in this way gives a mixture of 2-O-β-D-fructofuranosyl-D-glucose, 3-O-β-D-fructofuranosyl-D-glucose and 6-O-β-D-fructofuranosyl-D-glucose,[51] while D-fructose yields a mixture of two disaccharides composed of D-fructose i. e. inulobiose and laevanbiose.[51] An enzyme from artichokes, so far not specified, is able to transfer a D-fructose molecule from inulin to D-fructose but not to D-glucose.[52]

Transfructosylation has also been employed to synthesize some disaccharides of so far not exactly defined structure. Transfructosidase from *Aspergillus oryzae* transfers D-fructose from sucrose to D-fructose with the formation of a new reducing disaccharide consisting of two D-fructose molecules.[53] Some analogues of sucrose have been synthesized with the use of laevan-sucrase from *Aerobacter laevanicum*, which splits off a D-fructose molecule from raffinose and transfers it to monosaccharides.[54,55] Thus, α-D-galactopyranosyl β-D-fructofuranoside (galsucrose)[54] has been synthesized from D-galactose, and α-D-xylopyranosyl β-D-fructofuranoside (xylsucrose) from D-xylose.[55]

### Other transglycosylations

Other monosaccharides have also been transferred from oligosaccharides to monosaccharides. Thus, α-galactosidase from coffee transfers D-galactose from raffinose to D-glucose,[17] and melibiose is a source of D-galactose in syntheses of α-D-galactosyl derivatives of N-acetyl-D-glucosamine and N-acetyl-D-galactosamine effected by enzymes from *Trichomonas foetus*.[56] Attention has also been paid to enzymic transfers from lactose and from maltose to xylose and to fucose.[57]

### b) Enzymic changes of disaccharides

### Transglycosylation of maltose

The action of microbial enzymes on maltose has given rise to a number of interesting substances. Maltose treated with *Aspergillus niger* yields isomaltose, [8,10-12] the trisaccharides panose[9-12] and isomaltotriose (dextrantriose).[10] Similarly, the enzyme produced by the micro-organism *Aspergillus oryzae* converts maltose into isomaltose,[6,58,59] the trisaccharide panose,[59] isomaltotriose (dextrantriose),[58,59] maltotriose,[6] 6-*O*-α-D-glucopyranosylmaltose,[58] the tetrasaccharide 4-*O*-α-D-isomaltotriosyl-D-glucose,[58,59] and other products.[6]

Enzymic changes of maltose have been very carefully investigated by Japanese chemists.[60] In the action of enzymes from *Aspergillus niger*, *A. oryzae* or *Rhizopus japonicus* on maltose, they observed first[60] the formation of isomaltose, panose and (erroneously) cellobiose besides other not identified oligosaccharides. The statement regarding cellobiose was soon corrected;[61] the substance in question was identified as kojibiose, and, in addition to this, nigerose[61] was detected, at that time termed sakébiose according to the Japanese version.

The same substances were found at about the same time and under equal conditions by Shibasaki,[29,62,63] who detected further products, namely panose, isomaltotriose and a tetraose whose composition probably corresponds to 4-*O*-α-isomaltotriosyl-D-glucose.[63] The same substances are also formed[63] by the action of the enzymes from *Aspergillus usamii*, *A. awomori*, *Rhizopus japonicus*, *R. péka*, and others. The enzymes of the yeast *Schizosaccharomyces pombe* likewise convert[12,29,64] maltose into nigerose, kojibiose, isomaltose, panose and isomaltotriose.

Matsuda detected nigerose[65,66] as a by-product formed in the known synthesis of the polysaccharide nigeran[67] (enzymic synthesis in the presence of *Aspergillus niger*).

This procedure has evidently also given rise to oligosaccharides, isolated by Japanese investigators from saké prepared by fermentation of rice syrups by the micro-organisms *Aspergillus niger*, *A. oryzae* and *Schizosaccharomyces pombe*.[30,31,68-74] Isolated and identified were isomaltose,[30,31,68-71] kojibiose (originally reported erroneously as cellobiose),[30,31,68,69,71-73] nigerose (sakébiose),[30,31,69,70] α,α-trehalose,[71,74] α,β-trehalose,[71,74] panose,[30,31,68] isomaltotriose (dextrantriose),[30,31] and kojitriose.[30,31]

Similar substances as given above have also been found in a mixture of unfermentable sugars in fermented mash from barley by the amylo process.[75-80]

*References see p. 135*

Noteworthy is here the detection of laminaribiose,[77,79,80] and a trisaccharide composed of three D-glucose molecules,[78-80] whose structure, according to recent investigations, corresponds to the formula of $O$-$\beta$-D-glucopyranosyl-(1→4)-$O$-$\beta$-D-glucopyranosyl-(1→3)-D-glucose.[80] Moreover, there have been isolated a tetrasaccharide composed of four D-glucose molecules,[79] as well as more complicated oligosaccharides containing, besides D-glucose, also D-xylose and L-arabinose.[79]

Other micro-organisms, or enzymes, are likewise able to resynthesize oligosaccharides from maltose. For example, the enzyme of the micro-organism *Penicillium chrysogenum* converts maltose into isomaltose.[81] The action of maltase on maltose leads to isomaltose[82] and the corresponding series from isomaltotriose up to isomaltohexaose, as well as to panose.[82] Green gram seeds enzyme synthesizes maltotriose and maltotetraose from maltose,[83] and protein preparations of liver muscle tissues of rabbits form from maltose besides maltotriose also nigerose.[84]

Enzymes of *Alcaligenes faecalis* produce an oxidative effect on maltose with the formation of 4-$O$-(3-keto-$\alpha$-D-glucopyranosyl)-D-glucose, see M. J. Bernaerts and J. De Ley, Biochim. et Biophys. Acta *30*, 661 (1958); J. Gen. Microbiol. *22*, 129 (1960); J. Gen. Microbiol. *22*, 137 (1960); Ant. v. Leeuwenh. J. Microbiol. Serol. *27*, 247 (1961); M. J. Bernaerts, J. Furnelle, and J. De Ley, Biochim. et Biophys. Acta *69*, 322 (1963).

According to the last communication, as well as to those by M. J. Bernaerts and J. De Ley, Nature *197*, 406 (1963) and E. E. Grebner, R. Durbin, and D. S. Feingold, Nature *201*, 419 (1964) the micro-organism has been identified to be *Agrobacterium tumefaciens*.

### Transglycosylation of isomaltose

Fewer experiments than with maltose were undertaken with isomaltose which is a comparatively rarer substance. *Aspergillus oryzae* converts isomaltose into isomaltotriose,[85] while the action of *Bacillus macerans* leads to a higher oligosaccharide with a branched structure of the heptasaccharide order.[86]

### Transglycosylation of cellobiose

A number of papers[87-89] deal with the formation of undefined oligosaccharides by the action of microbial enzymes on cellobiose. These communications are concerned with the micro-organisms *Aspergillus niger*,[87,88] *A. aureus*,[88] *A. oryzae*,[89] and *Myrothecium verrucaria*.[88] An analysis of the action of *Aspergillus niger* enzymes has revealed[90] that cellobiose is converted into gentiobiose, laminaribiose, sophorose, cellotriose, $O$-$\beta$-D-glucopyranosyl-(1→6)-$O$-$\beta$-D-glucopyranosyl-(1→4) D-glucose and another trisaccharide. The formation of laminaribiose besides two further disaccharides was confirmed later.[46] Other organisms, too, resynthesize oligosaccharides from cellobiose; thus, the marine algae *Cladophora rupestris* and *Ulva lactuca* synthesize laminaribiose, gentiobiose and cellotriose;[47] the micro-organism *Aspergillus flavus* produces gentiobiose and further oligosaccharides,[91] while the action of *Chaetomium globosum* leads to cellotriose and cellotetraose.[92]

### Transglycosylation of nigerose

The problem of enzymic changes of nigerose by the action of potato T-enzyme is the subject of a recent paper;[93] as transglycosylation products, isomaltose and $O$-$\alpha$-D-glucopyranosyl-(1→6)-$O$-$\alpha$-D-glucopyranosyl-(1→3)-D-glucose have been isolated.

### Transglycosylation of lactose*

The first investigations of enzymic changes of lactose were carried out by Wallenfels.[5,6,94] In the action of the enzyme from *Aspergillus niger*[5] he observed the formation of a trisaccharide, and as products of the action of $\beta$-galactosidase from yeast[5,94] he found lactobiose, galactobiose and a triose having the composition of either G—Gal—Gal or Gal—Gal—G.

Great attention has been paid to enzymic changes of lactose effected by *Saccharomyces fragilis*. Aronson[95] obtained four oligosaccharides; one of them contained D-glucose and D-galactose in the ratio 1 : 1, the second one the same substances in the ratio 1 : 2, the third product was composed of D-galactose only, while the yield of the fourth substance was too small to permit determination. Other investigators[96,97] isolated under similar conditions ten oligosaccharides, seven of them in the pure state, namely three oligosaccharides containing D-galactose only and four substances composed of D-galactose and D-glucose. In a further paper,[98] eleven oligosaccharides are mentioned.

Exactly defined substances were isolated by Pazur,[99,100] namely 3-$O$-$\beta$-D-galactopyranosyl-D-glucose, 6-$O$-$\beta$-D-galactopyranosyl-D-glucose and 6-$O$-$\beta$-D-galactopyranosyl-D-galactose.

Pazur[16] investigated also the action of lactase from various species of *Saccharomyces*, *Torulopsis* and *Candida* upon lactose. He always obtained four oligosaccharides: 6-$O$-$\beta$-D-galactopyranosyl-D-glucose, 6-$O$-$\beta$-D-galactopyranosyl-D-galactose, $O$-$\beta$-D-galactopyranosyl-(1→6)-$O$-$\beta$-D-galactopyranosyl-(1→4)-

---

* For a review see K. Wallenfels, Bull. soc. chim. biol. *42*, 1715 (1960).

*References see p. 135*

D-glucose, and $O$-$\beta$-D-galactopyranosyl-(1→6)-$O$-$\beta$-D-galactopyranosyl-(1→6)-D-glucose.

Enzymes from *Penicillium chrysogenum* convert lactose[101–104] into $O$-$\beta$-D-galactopyranosyl-(1→6)-$O$-$\beta$-D-galactopyranosyl(1→4)-D-glucose. Data on the action of other enzymes are less exact. *Escherichia coli*[95] synthesizes three oligosaccharides from lactose; two of them contain D-glucose and D-galactose in the ratio 1 : 1, while the third one is composed of D-galactose only. These products are assumed to be lactobiose, galactobiose and lactotriose.[105]

Some microbial enzymes produce an oxidative effect on lactose; thus, *Alcaligenes faecalis* oxidazes lactose to 4-$O$-$\beta$-3-keto-D-galactopyranosyl-D-glucose, as proved by identification of the degradation products of this substance.[106]

This reaction was followed carefully in others papers, see M. J. Bernaerts, J. Furnelle, and J. De Ley, Biochim. et Biophys. Acta *69*, 322 (1963); M. J. Bernaerts and J. De Ley, Nature *197*, 406 (1963). The micro-organism in question has been identified as *Agrobacterium tumefaciens*.

### Transglycosylation of allo-lactose

The action of enzymes from *Saccharomyces fragilis* upon this disaccharide gives rise to the trisaccharide $O$-$\beta$-D-galactopyranosyl-(1→6)-$O$-$\beta$-D-galactopyranosyl-(1→6)-D-glucose.[107]

### Transglycosylation of sucrose

The action of microbial enzymes on sucrose is of great importance (see for instance dextran manufacture) and, for this reason, sucrose as a relatively easily accessible source became soon a subject of special attention in the study of enzymic processes. The first papers in this respect, from 1951,[5,13,14,108] did not contain many concrete results, except the finding that the action of invertase on sucrose leads to oligosaccharides containing D-glucose and D-fructose, among them a non-reducing trisaccharide[14] composed of two D-fructose molecules and one D-glucose molecule. Swiss investigators[15] separated this oligosaccharide mixture into three fractions containing defined non-reducing oligosaccharides.

Since that time great progress has been made in this field of enzymic syntheses, and several very significant compounds have been isolated. The importance of enzymic processes taking place in sucrose solutions is due to the fact that several industrial products, such as dextran,* are manufactured in this way. However, these reactions are complicated because either a D-glucose or a D-fructose molecule can be enzymically transferred from the sucrose molecule, cases of the second type being perhaps more numerous. Even resyntheses of a new disaccharide from D-glucose and D-fructose are known in the enzymic cleavage of sucrose.

### Resynthesis of disaccharides from sucrose

In the action of microbial enzymes on sucrose it was in some cases possible to isolate a new saccharide, usually likewise composed of D-glucose and D-fructose. For example, it was found[19] that the substance produced in the action of yeast on sucrose[13,109] is 6-*O*-β-D-fructofuranosyl-D-glucose.[19] Another microorganism, *Protaminobacter ruber*, converts sucrose into isomaltulose (palatinose, 6-*O*-α-D-glucopyranosyl-D-fructofuranose).[110]

Isomaltulose (palatinose) is also produced by the action of one species of *Enterobacterium* on sucrose,[111,112] also as well as leucrose (see later), in the synthesis of dextran from sucrose by some micro-organisms, such as *Leuconostoc mesenteroides* (*Betacoccus arabinosaceus*)[113] or *Streptococcus bovis*,[114] which in addition to this produces isomaltose.[114]

Another isomer, leucrose (5-*O*-α-D-glucopyranosyl-D-fructose), is formed as a by-product in the synthesis of dextran from sucrose by the action of enzymes from *Leuconostoc mesenteroides*,[115,116] and also by dextran producing *Streptococcus bovis*.[114,117,118]

The action of takadiastase, probably from *Aspergillus oryzae*, on sucrose yields, besides other substances, a disaccharide composed of two D-fructose molecules.[119]

### Resynthesis of oligosaccharides from sucrose by transfer of D-fructose

Whalley was the first investigator[120] to obtain a non-reducing trisaccharide by the action of yeast invertase on sucrose; he named the isolated product kestose without determining its structure. The same substance was isolated again by a group of other chemists,[121] who at the same time established the structure of kestose as *O*-α-D-glucopyranosyl-(1→2)-*O*-β-D-fructofuranosyl-(6→2) β-D-fructofuranoside. A further investigator[122] obtained kestose under similar conditions besides two other trisaccharides and three disaccharides, one of them in a very small yield. Gross[123] proved by electrophoresis that besides kestose two further trisaccharides are formed, which is in agreement with the foregoing result. With his collaborators, he then isolated [124] another trisaccharide, *neo*-kestose, having the composition of *O*-β-D-fructofuranosyl-(2→6)-*O*-α-D-glucopyranosyl-(1→2) β-D-fructofuranoside. *neo*-Kestose is likely to be

---

* For reviews see T. H. Evans and H. Hibbert, Advances in Carbohydrate Chem. *2*, 203 (1946); W. B. Neely, Advances in Carbohydrate Chem. *15*, 341 (1960).

*References see p. 135*

9*

synthesized from sucrose also by plant enzymes;[125] this assumption is supported by the enzymic synthesis of *neo*-kestose in bananas *Musa cavendishii*.[126]

The action of takadiastase, probably from the micro-organism *Aspergillus oryzae*, on sucrose gives rise to several substances.[53,119,127] Bacon and Bell[128] isolated a trisaccharide having the structure of $O$-$\alpha$-D-glucopyranosyl-(1→2)-$O$-$\beta$-D-fructofuranosyl-(1→2) $\beta$-D-fructofuranoside. Japanese investigators who had also obtained this compound,[129] termed it isokestose. It is produced from sucrose by various plant enzymes, too.[125]

Japanese investigators subjected the action of the enzymes of the micro-organism *Aspergillus oryzae* to a very thorough study.[130-133] They isolated three non-reducing and fermentable oligosaccharides. One of them consists only of D-fructose, the other two of D-fructose and D-glucose, and one of these two substances is an isomer of kestose, which was termed isokestose.[129] The formation of isokestose (defined as 1-$O$-inulobiosyl D-glucoside) by the enzymic action of *Aspergillus oryzae* has also been observed by another writer[53] who, as well as Japanese investigators,[134] also obtained a non-reducing tetrasaccharide, which was named, on the one hand, 1-$O$-inulotriosyl D-glucoside[53] and, on the other hand, fungitetraose,[134] and whose structure is given by the formula $O$-$\alpha$-D-glucopyranosyl-(1→2)-$O$-$\beta$-D-fructofuranosyl-(1→2)-$O$-$\beta$-D-fructofurano-syl-(1→2) $\beta$-D-fructofuranoside.[134]

The action of the enzymes of the micro-organism *Aspergillus niger* is not uniform, since they are able to transfer both D-fructose and D-glucose. One of the two trisaccharides formed besides the tetrasaccharide in this process is certainly identical with isokestose.[11,135]

Isokestose is also produced by enzymes of the micro-organism *Penicillium chrysogenum*,[136,137] along with several other substances.[137]

Another group of investigators described interesting transfers of D-fructose from the sucrose molecule by enzymic processes, in particular by the action of laevan-sucrase from *Aerobacter laevanicum*.[51,138-140] In this way, both iso-kestose[51,138] and kestose[51] are produced.

An original nomenclature is employed in the papers in question; for example, iso-kestose is named $1^F$-$\beta$-fructosylsucrose[51] or 1-kestose,[138] while the names $6^F$-$\beta$-fructosyl-sucrose[51] or 6-kestose[138] are used for kestose. The term erlose[139] is employed for $\alpha$-maltosyl $\beta$-D-fructofuranoside.

Moreover, a general rule has been formulated for the attachement of D-fructose to C-1 of the molecule of the aldose;[140] the latter must have a certain steric arrangement of the hydroxyl groups at C-2 and C-3. The hydroxyl group at C-2 must be in the D-position and the other hydroxyl groups (that at C-3) must be *trans* to the foregoing. Neither of them can be substituted or replaced, nor can the primary alcoholic group be replaced by a carboxyl group.

## Resynthesis of oligosaccharides from sucrose by transfer of D-glucose

The action of the enzymes from the micro-organism *Aspergillus niger*, as already pointed out, effects transfructosylation as well as transglucosylation; the latter reaction leads to panose,[9,141,142] which in its structure corresponds to *O*-α-D-glucopyranosyl-(1→6)-*O*-α-D-glucopyranosyl-(1→4)-D-glucopyranose and is sometimes also named 4-*O*-α-isomaltosyl-D-glucose. Honey invertase produces a different effect on sucrose from yeast invertase. Enzymic synthesis leads in this case to six oligosaccharides, five of which differ from those formed by the action of yeast invertase.[143] The structure of one of the isolated substances corresponds to α-maltosyl β-D-fructofuranoside (also termed glucosucrose or erlose).[144–146] This substance has also been isolated from honey[147,148] together with higher oligosaccharides[148] forming the series maltosucrose, maltotriosucrose and maltotetraosucrose.

Recent papers deal with interesting transfers of D-glucose from sucrose by the action of dextran-producing *Streptococcus bovis*.[114] Besides isomerization of sucrose itself, as proved by the formation of leucrose and isomaltulose (palatinose), this process yields isomaltose, further 5-*O*-α-isomaltosyl-D-fructose [*O*-α-D-glucopyranosyl-(1→6)-*O*-α-D-glucopyranosyl-(1→5)-D-fructose], isomaltotriulose and isomaltotriose.

The substances formed from sucrose by the enzymes of the micro-organism *Penicillium spinulosum*[119,127] have not been defined in detail.

* * *

Enzymes of some micro-organisms exhibit oxidative effects on sucrose with the formation of 3-ketosucrose, i. e. 3-keto-α-D-glucopyranosyl β-D-fructofuranoside or α-D-*ribo*-hexopyranosyl-3-ulose β-D-fructofuranoside. The formation of 3-ketosucrose by the action of *Agrobacterium tumefaciens* has been described by S. Fukui, R. M. Hochster, R. Durbin, E. E. Grebner, and D. S. Feingold, Bull. Res. Council Israel *11 A*, 262 (1963), later by S. Fukui and R. M. Hochster, J. Am. Chem. Soc. *85*, 1697 (1963), and E. E. Grebner, R. Durbin, and D. S. Feingold, Nature *201*, 419 (1964). The same reaction using enzymes of *Alcaligenes faecalis* has been described by M. J. Bernaerts, J. Furnelle, and J. De Ley, Biochim. et Biophys. Acta *69*, 322 (1963).

### c) Transglycosylation between two oligosaccharide molecules

#### Sucrose and lactose

Dextran-sucrase produced by the micro-organism *Leuconostoc mesenteroides* transfers the D-glucose molecule from sucrose to the lactose molecule with

*References see p. 135*

the formation of a branched trisaccharide* corresponding in its composition to O-β-D-galactopyranosyl-(1→4)-O-[α-D-glucopyranosyl-(1→2)]-D-glucopyranose.[149–153] The reaction was also carried out with labelled sucrose,[151] and the structure of the branched trisaccharide obtained is evident from the fact that it is split by lactase of *Saccharomyces fragilis* with the formation of kojibiose;[152] in the form of its per-O-acetyl derivative, kojibiose is also produced by acetolysis,[152] while acid hydrolysis leads to lactose,[149] or lactose and kojibiose.[151]

On the other hand, laevan-sucrase from *Aerobacter laevanicum* converts sucrose and lactose by transfer of a D-fructose molecule to lactose into the so-called lactsucrose, [139] i. e. α-lactosyl β-D-fructofuranoside. This substance has also been obtained as a by-product in the action of enzymes of *Leuconostoc mesenteroides* on a mixture of sucrose and lactose in addition to the above mentioned branched trisaccharide.

The structure of the oligosaccharide formed from sucrose and lactose by the action of the enzymes of *Penicillium chrysogenum* is not known.[154]

### Sucrose and cellobiose

Dextran-sucrase of the micro-organism *Leuconostoc mesenteroides* transfers the D-glucose molecule from sucrose to cellobiose with the formation of the branched trisaccharide O-α-D-glucopyranosyl-(1→4)-O-[α-D-glucopyranosyl-(1→2)]-D-glucopyranose.[150,155]

### Sucrose and maltose

The enzymes of *Leuconostoc mesenteroides* transfer the D-glucose molecule from sucrose also to maltose with the formation of panose;[33,36,156] besides this substance, D-fructose-containing disaccharides[36] as well as tetra- and pentasaccharides are produced.

The enzyme of *Aspergillus niger* synthesizes from sucrose and maltose[157] isokestose, panose and the trisaccharide Z,[157,158] which in its structure corresponds to O-α-D-glucopyranosyl-(1→6)-O-α-D-glucopyranosyl-(1→2) β-D-fructofuranoside.

### Sucrose and other disaccharides

The enzymes of *Leuconostoc mesenteroides* synthesize isomaltotriose and isomaltotetraose from sucrose and isomaltose.[33] Laevan-sucrase from *Aerobacter leavanicum* produces raffinose from sucrose and melibiose.[50]

---

* The same reaction was described by K. Shibasaki and K. Aso, J. Agr. Chem. Soc. Japan *33*, 359 (1959); Chem. Abstr. *57*, 17042 (1962).

### Sucrose and trisaccharides

The transfer of D-fructose or D-glucose from a sucrose molecule on a trisaccharide as well as other transglycosylations of this type have been observed in many cases. For example, transfructosidase from *Aspergillus oryzae* transfers the D-fructose molecule from sucrose to raffinose to form D-fructosyl derivatives of raffinose;[53] secondary substances in this transglycosylation, namely 1-*O*-inulobiosyl D-glucoside and 1-*O*-inulotriosyl D-glucoside,[53] obviously result from the transfer of a D-fructose molecule from sucrose to sucrose.

The D-glucose molecule, too, may be transferred in the presence of enzymes of *Leuconostoc mesenteroides*.[33] The use of panose as acceptor leads to 4-*O*-α-isomaltotriosyl-D-glucose, and a further transfer of a D-glucose molecule from sucrose to this compound gives rise to 4-*O*-α-isomaltotetraosyl-D-glucose.[33]

### Other disaccharides as a source of transglycosylation

D-Galactose can be transferred by the enzymes of *Saccharomyces fragilis* from lactose to planteose to form its D-galactosyl derivative.[159]

Melibiose, too, may be utilized as a D-galactose source; α-galactosidase from coffee is able to transfer D-galactose to raffinose or stachyose.

### Transglycosylation of trisaccharides, higher oligosaccharides and polysaccharides

Transglycosylations with the use of tri- and tetrasaccharides as source of monosaccharides have also been observed. Thus, α-galactosidase from coffee transfers a D-galactose molecule from raffinose to D-glucose, melibiose and stachyose, and also from stachyose to melibiose.[17] The enzyme of *Bacillus macerans* converts panose into a number of substances which have not been defined.[86]

It has already been mentioned (see p. 125) that a D-glucose molecule can be transferred from cyclohexa-amylose to D-glucose or to both anomeric methyl D-glucopyranosides.[37,41,42] Moreover, it has been pointed out (see p. 126) that the enzymes of *Bacillus subtilis* are able to transfer a D-fructose molecule from laevan to D-glucose with the formation of sucrose;[49] the enzyme of the artichoke, too, can transfer a D-fructose molecule, in this case from inulin, to D-fructose[52] (see p. 126) as well as to sucrose and raffinose, but not to D-glucose, maltose, lactose, and trehalose.

#### REFERENCES

1. J. Rabaté, Compt. rend. *204*, 153 (1937).
2. T. Miwa, M. Takeshita, and S. Nakamura, Biochim. et Biophys. Acta *37*, 541 (1960).

3. W. Pigman, J. Research Natl. Bur. Standards *33*, 105 (1944); Chem. Abstr. *38*, 6590 (1944).
4. M. G. Blair and W. Pigman, Arch. Biochem. Biophys. *48*, 17 (1954); Chem. Abstr. *48*, 4175 (1954).
5. K. Wallenfels, Naturwissenschaften *38*, 306 (1951).
6. K. Wallenfels and E. Bernt, Angew. Chem. *64*, 28 (1952).
7. E. Norberg and D. French, J. Am. Chem. Soc. *72*, 1202 (1950).
8. S. C. Pan, A. A. Andreasen, and P. Kolachov, Science *112*, 115 (1950); Chem. Abstr. *44*, 8968 (1950).
9. S. C. Pan, L. W. Nicholson, and P. Kolachov, J. Am. Chem. Soc. *73*, 2547 (1951).
10. S. A. Barker, E. J. Bourne, and M. Stacey, J. Chem. Soc. *1953*, 3084.
11. S. A. Barker and T. R. Carrington, J. Chem. Soc. *1953*, 3588.
12. K. Shibasaki and K. Aso, Tôhoku J. Agr. Research *5*, 131 (1954); Chem. Abstr. *50*, 5053 (1956).
13. J. S. D. Bacon and J. Edelman, Arch. Biochem. *28*, 467 (1950); Chem. Abstr. *45*, 3004 (1951).
14. P. H. Blanchard and N. Albon, Arch. Biochem. *29*, 220 (1950); Chem. Abstr. *45*, 2533 (1951).
15. E. H. Fischer, L. Kohtés, and J. Fellig, Helv. Chim. Acta *34*, 1132 (1951).
16. J. H. Pazur, J. Biol. Chem. *208*, 439 (1954).
17. C. Anagnostopoulos, J. E. Courtois, and F. Petek, Bull. soc. chim. biol. *36*, 1115 (1954).
18. J. S. D. Bacon and D. J. Bell, J. Chem. Soc. *1957*, 3581.
19. W. J. Whelan and D. M. Jones, Biochem. J. *54*, XXXIV (1953).
20. H. J. Breuer and J. S. D. Bacon, Biochem. J. *66*, 462 (1957).
21. S. Sugasawa, Y. Nakamura, and T. Shimomura, Bull. Agr. Chem. Soc. Japan *24*, 278 (1960); Chem. Abstr. *54*, 24929 (1960).
22. G. Avigad, Biochem. J. *73*, 587 (1959).
23. J. E. Courtois and F. Petek, Bull. soc. chim. biol. *39*, 715 (1957).
24. R. Kuhn, H. H. Baer, and A. Gauhe, Chem. Ber. *88*, 1713 (1955).
25. K. Wallenfels and D. Beck, Ann. *630*, 46 (1960).
26. J. E. Courtois and M. Leclerc, Bull. soc. chim. biol. *38*, 365 (1956).
27. J. H. Pazur, T. Budovich, and C. L. Tipton, J. Am. Chem. Soc. *79*, 625 (1957).
28. K. Aso and K. Shibasaki, Tôhoku J. Agr. Research *3*, 337 (1953); Chem. Abstr. *48*, 2980 (1954).
29. K. Shibasaki, Tôhoku J. Agr. Research *5*, 138 (1954); Chem. Abstr. *50*, 5053 (1956).
30. K. Shibasaki, Tôhoku J. Agr. Research *6*, 47 (1955); Chem. Abstr. *50*, 11693 (1956).
31. K. Shibasaki, Tôhoku J. Agr. Research *6*, 171 (1955); Chem. Abstr. *50*, 17494 (1956).
32. R. W. Bailey, S. A. Barker, E. J. Bourne, and M. Stacey, Nature *175*, 635 (1955).
33. K. Shibasaki, J. Agr. Chem. Soc. Japan (Nippon Nôgei-kagaku Kaishi) *32*, 133 (1958); Chem. Abstr. *53*, 498 (1959).
34. S. A. Barker, E. J. Bourne, P. M. Grant, and M. Stacey, J. Chem. Soc. *1958*, 601.
35. R. W. Jones, A. Jeanes, C. S. Stringer, and H. M. Tsuchiya, J. Am. Chem. Soc. *78*, 2499 (1956).
36. R. W. Bailey, S. A. Barker, E. J. Bourne, and M. Stacey, J. Chem. Soc. *1957*, 3536.
37. J. H. Pazur, J. M. Marsh, and T. Ando, J. Am. Chem. Soc. *81*, 2170 (1959).
38. S. Peat, W. J. Whelan, and G. Jones, J. Chem. Soc. *1957*, 2490.
39. E. J. Bourne, J. Hartigan, and H. Weigel, J. Chem. Soc. *1961*, 1088.
40. H. J. Koepsell, H. M. Tsuchiya, N. N. Hellman, A. Kazenko, C. A. Hoffman, E. S. Sharpe, and R. W. Jackson, J. Biol. Chem. *200*, 793 (1953).

41. J. H. Pazur, J. Am. Chem. Soc. 77, 1015 (1955).
42. J. H. Pazur and T. Budovich, J. Biol. Chem. 220, 25 (1956).
43. N. J. Palleroni and M. Doudoroff, J. Biol. Chem. 219, 957 (1956).
44. G. Avigad, Biochem. J. 73, 587 (1959).
45. S. Srinivasan and J. H. Quastel, Science 127, 143 (1958); Chem. Abstr. 52, 11139 (1958).
46. S. A. Barker, E. J. Bourne, G. C. Hewitt, and M. Stacey, J. Chem. Soc. 1957, 3541.
47. W. A. M. Duncan, D. J. Manners, and J. L. Thompson, Biochem. J. 73, 295 (1959).
48. S. A. Barker, M. Stacey, and D. B. E. Stroud, Nature 189, 138 (1961).
49. C. Péaud-Lenoel and R. Dedonder, Compt. rend. 241, 1418 (1955).
50. S. Hestrin, D. S. Feingold, and G. Avigad, J. Am. Chem. Soc. 77, 6710 (1955).
51. D. S. Feingold, G. Avigad, and S. Hestrin, Biochem. J. 64, 351 (1956).
52. J. Edelman and J. S. D. Bacon, Biochem. J. 49, 529 (1951).
53. J. H. Pazur, J. Biol. Chem. 199, 217 (1952).
54. D. S. Feingold, G. Avigad, and S. Hestrin, J. Biol. Chem. 224, 295 (1957).
55. G. Avigad, D. S. Feingold, and S. Hestrin, Biochim. et Biophys. Acta 20, 129 (1956).
56. W. N. Watkins, Nature 181, 117 (1958).
57. K. Täufel and H. Ruttloff, Nahrung 2, 631 (1958); Chem. Abstr. 53, 13633 (1959).
58. J. H. Pazur and D. French, J. Am. Chem. Soc. 73, 3536 (1951).
59. J. H. Pazur and D. French, J. Biol. Chem. 196, 265 (1952).
60. K. Aso, K. Shibasaki, and F. Yamanouchi, J. Ferm. Technol. (Japan) 30, 316 (1952); Chem. Abstr. 47, 2933 (1953).
61. K. Matsuda and K. Aso, J. Ferm. Technol. (Japan) 31, 211 (1953); Chem. Abstr. 47, 7731 (1953).
62. K. Shibasaki, J. Ferm. Technol. (Japan) 31, 354 (1953); Chem. Abstr. 48, 7109 (1954).
63. K. Shibasaki and K. Aso, J. Ferm. Technol. (Japan) 31, 311 (1953); Chem. Abstr. 48, 7109 (1954).
64. K. Shibasaki and K. Aso, J. Ferm. Technol. (Japan) 32, 395 (1954); Chem. Abstr. 49, 2619 (1955).
65. K. Matsuda, G. Hiroshima, K. Shibasaki, and K. Aso, J. Ferm. Technol. (Japan) 32, 498 (1954); Chem. Abstr. 49, 8554 (1955).
66. K. Matsuda, G. Hiroshima, K. Shibasaki, and K. Aso, Tôhoku J. Agr. Research 5, 239 (1954); Chem. Abstr. 50, 4043 (1956).
67. J. L. Yuill, Chem. & Ind. (London) 1952, 755; Chem. Abstr. 47, 3398 (1953).
68. K. Aso, K. Shibasaki, and F. Yamanouchi, J. Ferm. Technol. (Japan) 30, 311 (1952); Chem. Abstr. 47, 2933 (1953).
69. K. Matsuda and K. Aso, Tôhoku J. Agr. Research 5, 123 (1954); Chem. Abstr. 50, 5053 (1956).
70. K. Matsuda and K. Aso, J. Ferm. Technol. (Japan) 32, 399 (1954); Chem. Abstr. 49, 2670 (1955).
71. K. Matsuda, Tôhoku J. Agr. Research 6, 271 (1956); Chem. Abstr. 50, 13366 (1956).
72. K. Aso and K. Shibasaki, Tôhoku J. Agr. Research 3, 337 (1953).
73. K. Matsuda, J. Agr. Chem. Soc. Japan 22, 719 (1959).
74. K. Matsuda, J. Agr. Chem. Soc. Japan 30, 119 (1956).
75. E. Mariani and L. Franguelli, Ricerca sci. 28, 2296 (1958); Chem. Abstr. 53, 16463 (1959).
76. H. Ono and M. Dazai, J. Agr. Chem. Soc. Japan 33, 639 (1959).
77. H. Ono and M. Dazai, J. Agr. Chem. Soc. Japan 33, 644 (1959).
78. H. Ono and M. Dazai, J. Agr. Chem. Soc. Japan 33, 645 (1959).

79. H. Ono and M. Dazai, Kôgyô Gijutsuin Hakkô Kenkyûsho Kenkyû Hôkoku No. 14, 51 (1957); Chem. Abstr. *52*, 13294 (1958).
80. H. Ono and M. Dazai, Nature *183*, 1055 (1959).
81. K. V. Giri, K. Saroja, R. Venkataran an. and P. L. N. Rao, Arch. Biochem. Biophys. *51*, 62 (1954); Chem. Abstr. *48*, 10826 (1954).
82. S. Sugasawa, Y. Nakamura, and T. Shimomura, Bull. Agr. Chem. Soc. Japan *24*, 281 (1960); Chem. Abstr. *54*, 24929 (1960).
83. V. N. Nigam and K. V. Giri, J. Biol. Chem. *235*, 947 (1960).
84. I. S. Lukomskaya, Doklady Akad. Nauk S.S.S.R. *129*, 1172 (1959); Chem. Abstr. *54*, 14326 (1960).
85. J. H. Pazur, Biochim. et Biophys. Acta *13*, 158 (1954); Chem. Abstr. *48*, 5243 (1954).
86. R. Summer and D. French, J. Biol. Chem. *222*, 469 (1956).
87. E. M. Crook and B. A. Stone, Proc. Biochem. Soc. London, 17. 7. 1953.
88. E. M. Crook and B. A. Stone, Biochem. J. *55*, XXV (1953).
89. M. A. Jermyn and R. Thomas, Australian J. Biol. Sci. *6*, 70 (1953); Chem. Abstr. *47*, 6999 (1953).
90. S. A. Barker, E. J. Bourne, and M. Stacey, Chem. & Ind. (London) *1953*, 1287; Chem. Abstr. *48*, 5284 (1954).
91. K. V. Giri, V. N. Nigam, and K. S. Srinivasan, Nature *173*, 953 (1954).
92. H. W. Buston and A. Jabbar, Chem. & Ind. (London) *1954*, 48; Chem. Abstr. *49*, 5578 (1955).
93. M. Abdulah, I. J. Goldstein, and W. J. Whelan, J. Chem. Soc. *1962*, 176.
94. K. Wallenfels, E. Bernt, and G. Limberg, Ann. *579*, 113 (1953).
95. M. Aronson, Arch. Biochem. Biophys. *39*, 370 (1952); Chem. Abstr. *47*, 2800 (1953).
96. H. R. Roberts and E. F. McFarren, Arch. Biochem. Biophys. *43*, 233 (1953); Chem. Abstr. *47*, 8794 (1953).
97. H. R. Roberts and E. F. McFarren, J. Dairy Sci. *36*, 620 (1953); Chem. Abstr. *47*, 8112 (1953).
98. H. R. Roberts and J. D. Pettinati, Agr. and Food Chem. *5*, 130 (1957); Chem. Abstr. *51*, 15637 (1957).
99. J. H. Pazur, Science *117*, 355 (1953); Chem. Abstr. *47*, 6994 (1953).
100. J. H. Pazur, C. L. Tipton, T. Budovich, and J. M. Marsh, J. Am. Chem. Soc. *80*, 119 (1958).
101. A. Ballio, E. B. Chain, and F. B. DiAccadia, Gazz. chim. ital. *87*, 194 (1957); Chem. Abstr. *52*, 13818 (1958).
102. A. Ballio, E. B. Chain, and F. B. DiAccadia, Rend. Inst. Sup. Sanità (Rome) *18*, 1183 (1955).
103. A. Ballio and S. Russi, Boll. soc. ital. biol. sper. *33*, 1748 (1957).
104. A. Ballio and S. Russi, Tetrahedron *9*, 125 (1960).
105. K. Wallenfels, E. Bernt, and G. Limberg, Ann. *584*, 63 (1853).
106. M. J. Bernaerts and J. De Ley, Biochim. et Biophys. Acta *30*, 661 (1958).
107. J. H. Pazur, J. M. Marsh, and C. L. Tipton, J. Am. Chem. Soc. *80*, 1433 (1958).
108. J. W. White, Arch. Biochem. Biophys. *39*, 238 (1952); Chem. Abstr. *47*, 1203 (1953).
109. L. M. White and G. E. Secor, Arch. Biochem. Biophys. *36*, 490 (1952); Chem. Abstr. *47*, 645 (1953).
110. Ger. Patent 1,049,800; Chem. Abstr. *55*, 2030 (1961).
111. R. Weidenhagen and S. Lorenz, Angew. Chem. *69*, 641 (1957).
112. R. Weidenhagen and S. Lorenz, Z. Zuckerind. *82*, 533 (1957).
113. E. S. Sharpe, F. H. Stodola, and H. J. Koepsell, J. Org. Chem. *25*, 1062 (1960).
114. E. J. Bourne, D. H. Hutson, and H. Weigel, Biochem. J. *79*, 549 (1961).

115. F. H. Stodola, E. S. Sharpe, and H. J. Koepsell, J. Am. Chem. Soc. *74*, 3202 (1952).
116. F. H. Stodola, E. S. Sharpe, and H. J. Koepsell, J. Am. Chem. Soc. *78*, 2514 (1956).
117. R. W. Bailey and A. E. Oxford, Nature *182*, 185 (1958).
118. R. W. Bailey and E. J. Bourne, Nature *184*, Suppl. 12, 904 (1959).
119. J. Edelman, Biochem. J. *57*, 22 (1954).
120. H. C. S. De Whalley, Intern. Sugar J. *54*, 127 (1952); Chem. Abstr. *46*, 7801 (1952).
121. N. Albon, D. J. Bell, P. H. Blanchard, D. Gross, and J. T. Rundell, J. Chem. Soc. *1953*, 24.
122. J. S. D. Bacon, Biochem. J. *57*, 320 (1954).
123. D. Gross, Nature *173*, 487 (1954).
124. D. Gross, P. H. Blanchard, and D. J. Bell, J. Chem. Soc. *1954*, 1727.
125. P. J. Allen and J. S. D. Bacon, Biochem. J. *63*, 200 (1956).
126. R. W. Henderson, R. K. Morton, and W. A. Rawlinson, Biochem. J. *72*, 340 (1959).
127. F. J. Bealing and J. S. D. Bacon, Biochem. J. *53*, 277 (1953).
128. J. S. D. Bacon and D. J. Bell, J. Chem. Soc. *1953*, 2528.
129. F. Kurasawa, Y. Yamamoto, I. Igaue, and Y. Nakamura, J. Agr. Chem. Soc. Japan *30*, 524 (1956); Chem. Abstr. *52*, 20376 (1958).
130. F. Kurasawa, S. Saito, N. Honma, and Y. Yamamoto, Symposia on Enzyme Chem. (Japan) 8, 122 (1953); Chem. Abstr. *47*, 12509 (1953).
131. F. Kurasawa, S. Saito, N. Honma, and Y. Yamamoto, J. Agr. Chem. Soc. Japan *28*, 818 (1954); Chem. Abstr. *50*, 16965 (1956).
132. F. Kurasawa, S. Saito, N. Honma, and Y. Yamamoto, Symposia on Enzyme Chem. *9*, 38 (1954); Chem. Abstr. *48*, 7082 (1954).
133. F. Kurasawa, S. Saito, N. Honma, and Y. Yamamoto, J. Agr. Chem. Soc. Japan *29*, 332 (1955); Chem. Abstr. *50*, 16965 (1956).
134. F. Kurasawa, Y. Yamamoto, I. Igaue, and Y. Nakamura, J. Agr. Chem. Soc. Japan *30*, 696 (1956); Chem. Abstr. *52*, 20376 (1958).
135. S. A. Barker, E. J. Bourne, and T. R. Carrington, J. Chem. Soc. *1954*, 2125.
136. S. Russi and A. Ballio, Boll. soc. ital. biol. sper. *31*, 1362 (1955); Chem. Abstr. *50*, 10855 (1956).
137. A. Ballio and S. Russi, Gazz. chim. ital. *86*, 476 (1956); Chem. Abstr. *52*, 3922 (1958).
138. S. Hestrin, D. S. Feingold, and G. Avigad, Biochem. J. *64*, 340 (1956).
139. G. Avigad, J. Biol. Chem. *229*, 121 (1957).
140. G. Avigad and S. Hestrin, Bull. Research Council Israel *6 A*, 310 (1957).
141. D. French, Science *113*, 352 (1951).
142. M. L. Wolfrom, A. Thompson, and T. T. Galkowski, J. Am. Chem. Soc. *73*, 4093 (1951).
143. J. W. White and J. Maher, Arch. Biochem. Biophys. *42*, 360 (1953); Chem. Abstr. *47*, 8791 (1953).
144. J. W. White and J. Maher, J. Am. Chem. Soc. *75*, 1259 (1953)
145. H. E. Gray and G. Fraenkel, Physiol. Zool. *27*, 56 (1954); Chem. Abstr. *48*, 9474 (1954).
146. H. E. Gray and G. Fraenkel, Science *118*, 304 (1953); Chem. Abstr. *48*, 895 (1954).
147. J. P. Wolf and W. H. Ewart, Science *122*, 973 (1955); Chem. Abstr. *50*, 5929 (1956).
148. J. P. Wolf and W. H. Ewart, Arch. Biochem. Biophys. *58*, 365 (1955).
149. R. W. Bailey, S. A. Barker, E. J. Bourne and M. Stacey, Nature *176*, 1164 (1955).
150. R. W. Bailey, S. A. Barker, E. J. Bourne, P. M. Grant, and M. Stacey, J. Chem. Soc. *1958*, 1895.
151. E. J. Bourne, J. Hartigan, and H. Weigel, J. Chem. Soc. *1959*, 2332.
152. K. Aso, K. Shibasaki, and M. Nakamura, Nature *182*, 1303 (1958).

153. F. Yamauchi and K. Aso, Nature *189*, 753 (1961).

154. A. Ballio, Boll. soc. ital. biol. sper. *31*, 1338 (1955); Chem. Abstr. *50*, 11430 (1956).

155. S. A. Barker, E. J. Bourne, P. M. Grant, and M. Stacey, Nature *178*, 1221 (1956).

156. M. Killey, R. J. Dimler, and J. E. Cluskey, J. Am. Chem. Soc. *77*, 3315 (1955).

157. S. A. Barker, E. J. Bourne, and O. Theander, J. Chem. Soc. *1957*, 2064.

158. R. W. Bailey, S. A. Barker, E. J. Bourne, M. Stacey, and O. Theander, Nature *179*, 310 (1957).

159. J. H. Pazur, J. M. Marsh, and C. L. Tipton, J. Biol. Chem. *233*, 277 (1958).

# VII

# Reactions of Oligosaccharides in a Strongly Alkaline Medium

The glycosidic linkage is as a rule stable in alkaline solution;* this property has been further studied by Soviet investigators.[1] In some instances, the formation of monosaccharides has been observed in the treatment of oligosaccharides with solutions of strong bases, and this would suggest hydrolysis of the glycosidic linkage; however, the monosaccharides isolated are mostly secondary products accompanying the degradation of the oligosaccharide with the formation of saccharinic acids.[2,3]**

The alkaline hydrolysis proper of the glycosidic linkage in the oligosaccharide was described by Isbell in 1941;[4] according to him, turanose (3-$O$-α-D-glucopyranosyl-D-fructose) is split by the action of an aqueous solution of potassium or barium hydroxide into a molecule of D-glucose and a molecule of D-fructose before any other decomposition can set in. Kuhn and co-workers[5] have found that fucosyl-lactose [$O$-α-L-fucopyranosyl-(1→2)-$O$-β-D-galactopyranosyl-(1→4)-D-glucose (I)] is hydrolysed by an aqueous sodium carbonate solution to form D-glucose and 2-$O$-α-L-fucopyranosyl-D-galactose (II).

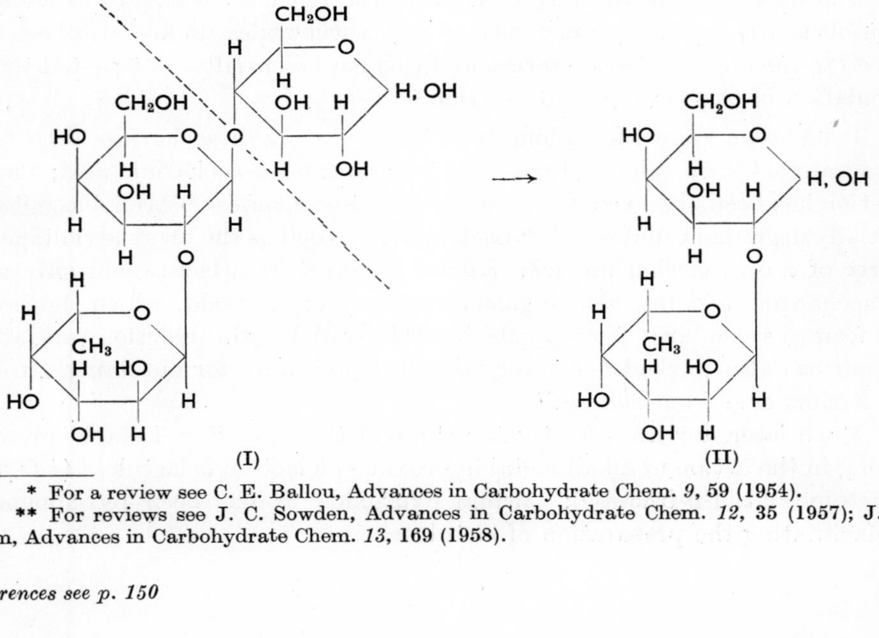

(I)        (II)

---

* For a review see C. E. Ballou, Advances in Carbohydrate Chem. *9*, 59 (1954).

** For reviews see J. C. Sowden, Advances in Carbohydrate Chem. *12*, 35 (1957); J. D. Crum, Advances in Carbohydrate Chem. *13*, 169 (1958).

*References see p. 150*

In a similar way proceeds the splitting of lactodifucotetraose and some other nitrogen-containing oligosaccharides (see Chapter XXIV).

French writes,[6] too, report the successful hydrolytic elimination of a D-glucose molecule from manninotriose [$O$-α-D-galactopyranosyl-(1→6)-$O$-α-D-galactopyranosyl-(1→6)-D-glucose (III)] in barium hydroxide solution with the formation of the reducing disaccharide swietenose (6-$O$-α-D-galactopyranosyl-D-galactose, IV):

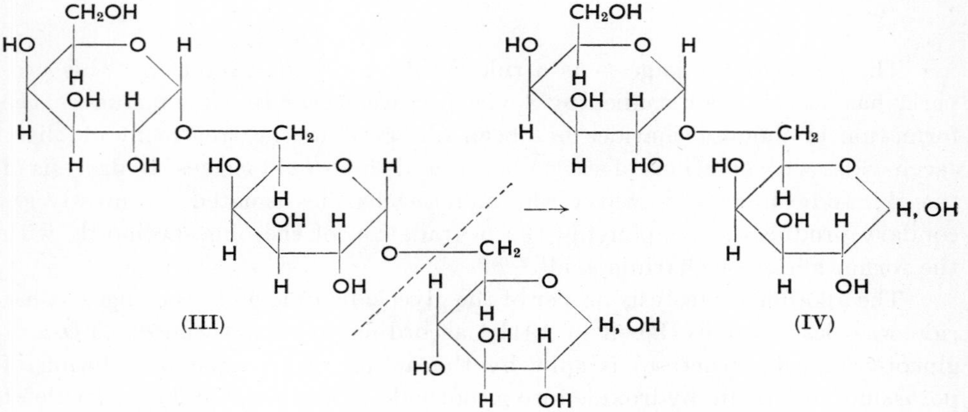

In another paper[7] it is stated that both maltose and lactose in alkaline solution are not only subject to isomerization with the formation of the respective "-uloses" and degradation but also to hydrolysis.

The formation of saccharinic acids in the reaction of sugars in alkaline solution is a characteristic not only of monosaccharides. It has also been observed in the oligosaccharide series, and this has essentially contributed to the elucidation of this complicated reaction.[2,3]

It has been known for a long time that reducing disaccharides with 1→4 linkages react with calcium hydroxide to form α-D-isosaccharinic acid; such a reaction has been observed in the cases of maltose,[8] lactose,[9,10] cellobiose,[11] and partially degraded celluloses.[12–15] Lactose is regarded as the most advantageous source of α-D-isosaccharinic acid. Kiliani obtained from lactose not only α-D-isosaccharinic acid but also D-galactometasaccharinic acid, which, however, was formed secondarily from D-galactose[16] liberated in this reaction (see later). Kiliani has also worked out a very detailed procedure for obtaining α-D-isosaccharinic acid from lactose.[17]

Much later, further investigators[18] found that the first isolable product arising in the action of alkali metal hydroxides on lactose is lactulose (4-$O$-β-D-galactopyranosyl-D-fructose); calcium hydroxide[19,20] has been recommended for facilitating the preparation of lactulose.

Thorough paper-chromatographic investigations of the changes of lactose in alkaline solution has revealed[21,22] that lactose (V) first isomerizes to form lactulose (VI), which is then converted through the expected intermediate products (VII—IX) into α-D-isosaccharinic acid (X).*

French writers[7] have not only confirmed the formation of lactulose from lactose and the degradation of the molecule in this direction, but they have also proved the simultaneous hydrolysis of lactose in alkaline solution. The course of the enolization of lactose in alkaline solution and the formation of an enediol has been studied by Soviet investigators.[23]

According to a communication by Z. B. Shaposhnikova, I. V. Alekseeva, and I. R. Rominskiĭ, Ukr. Khim. Zh. *28*, 724 (1962); Chem. Abstr. *59*, 1735 (1963), lactulose can be obtained on a preparative scale from lactose on ion exchangers.

The reaction mechanism involves the possibility of the formation of a double bond between C-2 and C-3, and hence all reducing disaccharides with 1→4 linkages should behave analogously; 4-O-methyl ethers of monosaccharides, too, should react in this way, and this has been confirmed.[24]

Degradation of lactose in a metal amide-liquid ammonia solution proceeds similarly o that in aqueous alkali. However, saccharinic acids have been obtained in lower yields, as fragmentation occurs to a greater degree, see R. L. Whistler and D. G. Medcalf, J. Org. Chem. *27*, 3560 (1962).

* According to R. L. Whistler and J. N. BeMiller, J. Org. Chem. *26*, 2886 (1961), α-D-isosaccharinic acid is here represented as 3-deoxy-2-C-hydroxymethyl-D-*threo*-pentonic acid, contrary to the last review,[2] where the problem of the configuration at C-2 has not been definitely established.

*References see p. 150*

Other reducing oligosaccharides with 1→4 linkages should obviously react similarly to lactose. According to this, maltose in alkaline solution yields maltulose,[7,22] and its degradation leads to a mixture of α- and β-isosaccharinic acids. However, there is a certain difference between lactose and maltose, since maltulose decomposes so fast in alkaline solution that its detection is practically impossible. Neither is it possible to prove the formation of maltose by the action of calcium hydroxide on maltulose, although lactulose is converted by a similar reaction into lactose.

According to more recent papers, maltose in alkaline solution is also subject to hydrolysis,[7] and the degradation products vary depending on the hydroxide employed.[25,26] The reaction with barium hydroxide gives rise to α-D-isosaccharinic acid (named in the paper in question[25] D-glucoisosaccharinic acid), while the action of sodium hydroxide leads to products of degradative decomposition, of acidic nature throughout, such as β,γ-dihydroxybutyric acid and glycolic acid. The key substance is here 4-deoxy-3-oxo-D-fructose (IX), which could be isolated[26] and may yield on the one hand α-D-isosaccharinic acid (X) and on the other hand, by oxidative splitting, glycolic acid (XI) and β,γ-dihydroxybutyric acid (XII).

$$
\begin{array}{c}
\text{COOH} \\
|\\
\text{HO—C—CH}_2\text{OH} \\
|\\
\text{CH}_2 \\
|\\
\text{H—C—OH} \\
|\\
\text{CH}_2\text{OH} \\
\text{(X)}
\end{array}
$$

$$
\begin{array}{c}
\text{CH}_2\text{OH} \\
|\\
\text{COOH} \\
\text{(XI)}
\end{array}
$$

$$
\begin{array}{c}
\text{CH}_2\text{OH} \\
|\\
\text{CO} \\
|\\
\text{CO} \\
|\\
\text{CH}_2 \\
|\\
\text{H—C—OH} \\
|\\
\text{CH}_2\text{OH} \\
\text{(IX)}
\end{array}
$$

$$
\begin{array}{c}
\text{COOH} \\
|\\
\text{CH}_2 \\
|\\
\text{H—C—OH} \\
|\\
\text{CH}_2\text{OH} \\
\text{(XII)}
\end{array}
$$

The stability of β-methyl maltoside in alkaline solution[27] is also an indirect proof of the validity of the scheme suggested for the formation of α-D-isosaccharinic acid from lactose and 1→4 disaccharides, since all changes depend on the presence of the unsubstituted aldehydic group.

Cellobiose reacts in an aqueous solution of calcium hydroxide[28] to form cellobiulose, D-glucose, D-fructose and α-D-isosaccharinic acid. The problem of the formation of organic acids in this reaction was studied in greater detail by Green,[29] who succeeded in separating them as their anilides. Besides α-D-isosaccharinic acid and α-D-glucosaccharinic acid, he identified α-D- and β-D-glucometasaccharinic, DL-lactic and DL-2,4-dihydroxybutyric acids; furthermore, he obtained unidentified acids containing five carbon atoms. Cellobiulose reacts in aqueous calcium hydroxide in the same way as lactu-lose, namely with the formation of cellobiose, D-fructose, D-glucose and α-D-isosaccharinic acid.[28] Cellotetraose yields cellobiose, cellobiulose, cellotriose and cellotriulose.[28]

Analogously to the reactions of these 1→4 disaccharides, *neo*-lactose in calcium hydroxide solution gives 4-*O*-β-D-galactopyranosyl-D-psicose.[20]

The degradation of xylobiose, i. e. 4-*O*-β-D-xylopyranosyl-D-xylose (XIII), proceeds analogously,[30,31] leading through xylobiulose (XIV) and intermediates of types similar to that described for lactose down to DL-2,4-dihydroxy-2-hydroxymethylbutyric acid (XV). The decomposition of xylotriose takes place similarly.[30-32]

Cellobiose and maltose, when treated with a 2% sodium hydroxide solution at 100°C, yielded catechol and methylcyclopentenol, see T. Enkvist, Finska Kemistsam-fundets Medd. *71*, 104 (1962); Chem. Abstr. *59*, 10213 (1963).

In the alkaline degradation of reducing disaccharides with 1→3 linkages, the formation of a 1,2-enediol might also be assumed; such an intermediate product could then only yield a metasaccharinic acid. In fact, laminaribiose,

*References see p. 150*

i. e. 3-*O*-β-D-glucopyranosyl-D-glucose, gives D-glucometasaccharinic acid besides D-glucose and D-fructose.[33]

Originally it was stated[4] that turanose, i.e. 3-*O*-α-D-glucopyranosyl-D-fructose (XVI), is degraded in alkaline solution to D-arabonic acid, D-glucose and D-fructose, but later it was found that D-glucometasaccharinic acid (XVII) is formed from turanose (XVI) via the usual intermediate products.[33]

According to this, linkages of other types in the molecules of reducing disaccharides should not exert any decisive influence upon the course of the reaction in alkaline solution. It has been reported[7] that the degradation of these compounds in alkaline solution proceeds more slowly than that of reducing 1→3 disaccharides, as observed in the investigation of the degradation rate of palatinose (6-*O*-α-D-glucopyranosyl-D-fructose) and turanose (3-*O*-α-D-glucopyranosyl-D-fructose).[7] Melibiose (6-*O*-α-D-galactopyranosyl-D-glucose) yields in alkaline solution a mixture of D-galactometasaccharinic and α-D-isosaccharinic acids.[34,35]

Small quantities of saccharinic acids are also produced by the action of ammonia on melibiose;[36] here, however, the reaction is more complicated because, besides *epi*-melibiose and melibiulose (6-*O*-α-D-galactopyranosyl-D-fructose, it also yields D-galactose and small amounts of other acidic products.

Similar conditions have also been observed in the alkaline decomposition of the polysaccharide guaran;[37] the part of the molecule containing D-galactose connected by 1→6 linkages to D-glucose gives rise to a mixture of α-D-iso-saccharinic and β-D-isosaccharinic acids besides the correctly determined 5-*O*-α-D-galactopyranosyl-β-D-isosaccharinic acid (XVIII), which is the first saccharinic acid in the oligosaccharide series whose isolation is confirmed. In addition to this substance, the less precisely characterized D-mannosyl-D-iso-saccharinic acid has also been described.

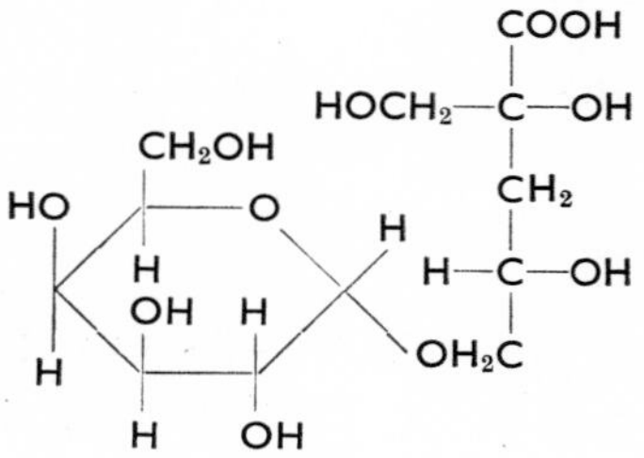

(XVIII)

A recent paper by A. Klemer and K. Homberg, Chem. Ber. *96*, 631 (1963), describes the isolation of 6-*O*-β-D-glucopyranosyl derivatives of both α-D-glucometasaccharinic and β-D-glucometasaccharinic acids by the action of 0,05N barium hydroxide solution on 3-*O*-β-6-*O*-β-di-D-glucopyranosyl-D-glucose.

The trisaccharide manninotriose [*O*-α-D-galactopyranosyl-(1→6)-*O*-α-D-galactopyranosyl-(1→6)-D-glucopyranose] reacts with barium hydroxide so-lution to form besides the disaccharide swietenose (6-*O*-α-D-galactopyranosyl-D-galactose), produced by hydrolytic elimination of a D-glucose molecule, also two trisaccharides arising from isomerization of the terminal reducing D-glucose unit,[6] namely *O*-α-D-galactopyranosyl-(1→6)-*O*-α-D-galactopyranosyl-(1→6)-D-mannose and *O*-α-D-galactopyranosyl-(1→6)-*O*-α-D-galactopyranosyl-(1→6)-D-fructose.[6]

Reducing disaccharides with 1→2 linkages should be stable in alkaline solution. Thus, 2-*O*-α-D-xylopyranosyl-L-arabinose is unchanged in this me-dium at 25°C[38] and undergoes decomposition only when the alkaline solutions are heated up to 100°C.

The interesting behaviour of one reducing 1→2 disaccharide was observed by Kuhn in the reaction of fucosyl-lactose (I) in alkaline solution (see also p. 141); besides 2-*O*-α-L-fucopyranosyl-D-galactose (II), produced in an amount of about 60%, the reaction also yields an appreciable quantity of the correspond-ing epimer (about 30%), i. e. 2-*O*-α-L-fucopyranosyl-D-talose (XIX). The for-mation of the latter substance cannot be explained otherwise than by a Lobry de Bruyn re-arrangement.

*References see p. 150*

10*

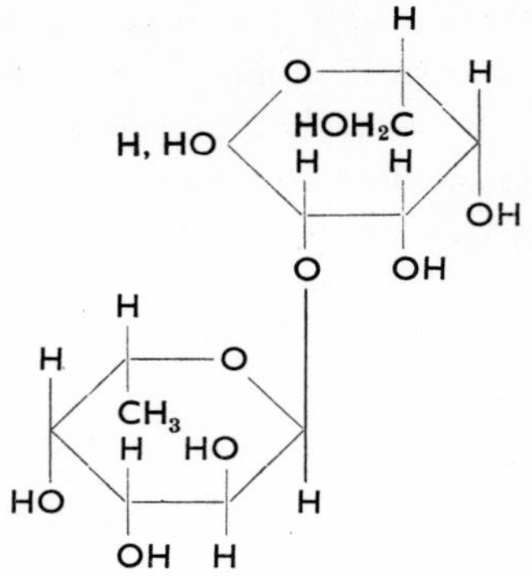

(XIX)

Non-reducing disaccharides, which are said to be far more stable in alkaline solution than reducing disaccharides,[7] are subject to severe decomposition only under drastic reaction conditions. Thus, sucrose is degraded to lactic acid.[39,40]*

Ammonolysis of oligosaccharides yields generally heterocyclic derivatives, mostly derivatives of pyrazine and imidazole. It is supposed that 2-amino-2-deoxy sugars are ntermediates of the reaction of oligosaccharides with ammonia, as it has been shown on the example of sucrose [see I. Ježo, Chem. Zvesti 17, 126 (1963)], lactose and cellobiose [see I. Ježo and I. Lužák, Chem. Zvesti 17, 255 (1963)].

Radioactive disaccharides can be converted into labelled saccharinic acids, for example [1—¹⁴C]-lactose into labelled α-D-isosaccharinic acid.[41] The observed distribution of labelled carbon atoms is in agreement with the proposed mechanism for this reaction.

Comparatively few data are available on saccharinic acids of the oligosaccharide series. An older statement[4] that lactulose yields 3-O-β-D-galactosyl-D-arabonic acid is probably not correct, so that the only known compound of this type remains the already mentioned 5-O-α-D-galactopyranosyl-β-D-isosaccharinic acid[37] obtained by alkaline degradation of guaran. This acid was also synthesized by a very elegant method;[37] β-D-isosaccharinic acid 1,4-lactone (XX) was converted by its reaction with acetone in the presence of concentrated sulphuric acid into the corresponding 2,2'-O-isopropylidene derivative (XXI). This substance, on condensation with 2,3,4,6-tetra-O-acetyl-α-D-galactopyranosyl bromide in chloroform in the presence of silver oxide, Drierite and iodine, yields the expected condensation product (XXII), from which the screening isopropylidene group is hydrolytically eliminated by 80% acetic acid with the formation of the compound (XXIII). This in turn is acetylated to the

---

* For a review on the decomposition of sucrose in alkaline solutions see M. Athenstedt, Z. Zuckerind. 11, 605 (1961); Chem. Abstr. 56, 10434 (1962); Z. Zuckerind. 13, 563 (1963); Chem. Abstr. 60, 1918 (1964).

corresponding per-*O*-acetyl derivative (**XXIV**). The final stage is the conversion of the glycosidic linkage of the hexa-*O*-acetyl derivative (**XXIV**) from -$\beta$- to -$\alpha$- by the action of titanium tetrachloride in chloroform; the resulting product (**XXV**) is then deacetylated to 5-*O*-$\alpha$-D-galactopyranosyl-$\beta$-D-isosaccharinic acid (**XVIII**).

*References see p. 150*

A similar procedure was employed for the synthesis of 5-$O$-α-D-galacto-pyranosyl-α-D-isosaccharinic acid.[37]

## REFERENCES

1.  Z. A. Rogovin and Yu. A. Rymashevskaya, Zhur. Priklad. Khim. *26*, 191 (1953); Chem. Abstr. *48*, 8740 (1954); English Translation see J. Appl. Chem. U.S.S.R. *26*, 163 (1953); Chem. Abstr. *49*, 4537 (1955).
2.  J. C. Sowden, Advances in Carbohydrate Chem. *12*, 35 (1957).
3.  J. D. Crum, Advances in Carbohydrate Chem. *13*, 169 (1958).
4.  H. S. Isbell, J. Research Natl. Bur. Standards *26*, 35 (1941); Chem. Abstr. *35*, 2862 (1941).
5.  R. Kuhn, H. H. Baer, and A. Gauhe, Ann. *611*, 242 (1958).
6.  A. de Grandchamp-Chaudun, E. J. Courtois, and P. Le Dizet, Bull. soc. chim. biol. *42*, 227 (1960); Chem. Abstr. *55*, 5356 (1961).
7.  J. E. Courtois, A. de Grandchamp-Chaudun, and P. Le Dizet, Ann. pharm. franç. *18*, 689 (1960); Chem. Abstr. *55*, 10327 (1961).
8.  A. O. Dubrunfaut, Monitor sci. Docteur Quesneville [3] *12*, 520 (1882).
9.  L. Cuisinier, Monitor sci. Docteur Quesneville [3] *12*, 521 (1882).
10. L. Cuisinier, Bull. soc. chim. France [2] *38*, 512 (1882).
11. S. V. Hintikka, Ann. Acad. Sci. Fennicae, Ser. A, II, No. 9 (1922); Chem. Abstr. *17*, 3486 (1923).
12. O. Faber and B. Tollens, Ber. *32*, 2589 (1899).
13. J. J. Murumow, J. Sack, and B. Tollens, Ber. *34*, 1427 (1901).
14. C. G. Schwalbe and E. Becker, J. prakt. Chem. [2] *100*, 19 (1920).
15. J. Palmén, Finska Kemistamfundets Medd. *38*, 106 (1929); Chem. Abstr. *24*, 1625 (1930).
16. H. Kiliani, Ber. *16*, 2625 (1883).
17. H. Kiliani, Ber. *42*, 3903 (1909).
18. E. M. Montgomery and C. S. Hudson, J. Am. Chem. Soc. *52*, 2101 (1930).
19. F. J. Bates, *Polarimetry, Saccharimetry and the Sugars*, National Bureau of Standards, Washington 1942, p. 467.
20. J. P. L. Bots, Rec. trav. chim. *76*, 515 (1957).
21. W. M. Corbett and J. Kenner, J. Chem. Soc. *1953*, 2245.
22. W. M. Corbett and J. Kenner, J. Chem. Soc. *1954*, 1789.
23. M. I. Nachmanovich and S. L. Berman, Trudy Vologodsk. Moloch.-Khoz. Inst. *1955*, No. 13, 193; Referat. Zhur. *1957*, No. 11814; Chem. Abstr. *53*, 16079 (1959).
24. J. Kenner and G. N. Richards, J. Chem. Soc. *1955*, 1810.
25. G. Machell and G. N. Richards, J. Chem. Soc. *1960*, 1924.
26. G. Machell and G. N. Richards, J. Chem. Soc. *1960*, 1932.
27. T. J. Schoch, E. J. Wilson, and C. S. Hudson, J. Chem. Soc. *64*, 2871 (1942).
28. W. M. Corbett and J. Kenner, J. Chem. Soc. *1955*, 1431.
29. J. W. Green, J. Am. Chem. Soc. *78*, 1894 (1956).
30. G. O. Aspinall, M. E. Carter, and M. Los, Chem. & Ind. (London) *1955*, 1553.
31. G. O. Aspinall, M. E. Carter, and M. Los, J. Chem. Soc. *1956*, 4807.
32. R. L. Whistler and W. M. Corbett, J. Am. Chem. Soc. *78*, 1003 (1956).
33. W. M. Corbett and J. Kenner, J. Chem. Soc. *1954*, 3274.
34. M. L. Evans and M. P. Benoy, J. Am. Chem. Soc. *52*, 294 (1930).

35. W. M. Corbett and J. Kenner, J. Chem. Soc. *1954*, 3281.
36. J. Hough, J. K. N. Jones, and E. L. Richards, J. Chem. Soc. *1954*, 295.
37. R. L. Whistler and J. N. BeMiller, J. Org. Chem. *26*, 2886 (1961).
38. R. L. Whistler and W. M. Corbett, J. Am. Chem. Soc. *77*, 3822 (1955).
39. C. Boelhouwer, E. F. Boon, J. A. Butter, H. I. Waterman, J. C. van Egmond, and J. Snelderwaard, J. Appl. Chem. *6*, 310 (1956); Chem. Abstr. *51*, 7045 (1957).
40. C. Boelhouwer, D. Korf, and H. I. Waterman, J. Appl. Chem. *10*, 113 (1960); Chem. Abstr. *54*, 16383 (1960).
41. J. C. Sowden, M. G. Blair, and D. J. Kuenne, J. Am. Chem. Soc. *79*, 6450 (1957).

# VIII

# Influence of Radiation on Oligosaccharides*

Earlier papers on this subject restrict themselves to the statement that sucrose in aqueous solution undergoes inversion when exposed to short-wave radiation. This applies to radiation emitted from radium salts,[1,2] as well as to the action of X-rays[3-5] and fast electrons (cathode rays);[6] the hydrolysis is accompanied mostly by the formation of acidic products.[3-5] Maltose and cellobiose are likewise subject to hydrolysis when exposed to fast electrons,[7] the glycosidic α-linkage of maltose being the more labile. The action of fast electrons on the surface of solid sucrose produces a pink coloration.[6]

In view to the progress in other scientific fields, special attention has been paid to the influence of γ-radiation on oligosaccharides,[8-17] generally with [60]Co as radiation source. Solid lactose and sucrose are not subject to principal changes under such conditions; pink coloration of the surface and change of the values of specific rotations have been observed. Non-reducing oligosaccharides showed reducing ability.[16]

In solution, sucrose undergoes hydrolysis,[10] accompanied by the formation of D-glucosone, D-gluconic acid, D-glucuronic acid and D-*arabino*-hexosonic acid,[10] as well as aldehydic fragments with two or three carbon atoms.[10] Formaldehyde has been found with certainty among the degradation products.[11,12] In the action of γ-radiation on maltose,[13] dihydroxyacetone has been found besides formaldehyde. Dihydroxyacetone has also been identified in the action of γ-radiation on dextran,[8] where it arises along with the hydrolytic products isomaltose and isomaltotriose. The formation of products with characteristic absorption in the region of 265 mμ,[8,11] as observed in the series of both reducing and non-reducing oligosaccharides, is obviously in agreement with the presence of dihydroxyacetone.

γ-Irradiation of maltose yields mainly D-glucose besides D-glucosone; among initial products, maltobionic acid has been identified, see G. O. Phillips and K. W. Davies, J. Chem. Soc. *1964*, 205.

Higher oligosaccharides, such as raffinose, are hydrolysed under these reaction conditions.[7,11] Solid raffinose is converted by γ-radiation into formaldehyde and D-fructose.[14]

---

* For a review see G. O. Phillips, Advances in Carbohydrate Chem. *16*, 13 (1961).

Oligosaccharides labelled with radioactive isotopes undergo self-decomposition in storage.[18,19] This problem has been extensively studied on [$^{14}$C]-sucrose,[19] and the possible decompositions and changes have been discussed in detail.[18,19]

Interesting decompositions are also effected by irradiation of oligosaccharides with ultra-violet light (wavelength 220—400 mµ) in the presence of air.[20,21] Besides the already mentioned lower fragments with a characteristic absorption at 260 mµ, the degradation in the homologous series of cellobiose leads not only to lower oligosaccharides but also to oligosaccharides shortened by one carbon atom in their reducing part. Thus, cellobiose yields 3-$O$-$\beta$-D-glucopyranosyl-D-arabinose,[20,21] and the same product is obtained from methyl $\beta$-cellobioside and cellobiitol.[20,21] Cellopentaose and cellopentaitol are converted under these conditions into cellobiose, cellotriose, cellotetraose and further into 3-$O$-$\beta$-cellobiosyl-D-arabinose and 3-$O$-$\beta$-cellotriosyl-D-arabinose.[20,21]

**REFERENCES**

1. A. Kailan, Monatsh. Chem. *33*, 1361 (1912).
2. A. Kailan, Monatsh. Chem. *34*, 1269 (1913).
3. M. C. Reinhard and K. L. Tucker, Radiology *12*, 151 (1929).
4. G. L. Clark and K. R. Fitch, J. Am. Chem. Soc. *52*, 465 (1930).
5. G. L. Clark, L. W. Pickett, and E. D. Johnson, Radiology *13*, 245 (1930).
6. M. L. Wolfrom, W. W. Binkley, and L. J. McCabe, J. Am. Chem. Soc. *81*, 1442 (1959).
7. M. L. Wolfrom, W. W. Binkley, L. J. McCabe, T. M. Shen Han, and A. M. Michelakis, Radiation Research *10*, 37 (1959).
8. G. O. Phillips and G. J. Moody, J. Chem. Soc. *1958*, 3534.
9. G. J. Moody and G. O. Phillips, Chem. & Ind. (London) *1959*, 1247.
10. G. O. Phillips and G. J. Moody, J. Chem. Soc. *1960*, 762.
11. M. A. Khenokh, Doklady Akad. Nauk S.S.S.R. *104*, 746 (1955); Chem. Abstr. *50*, 7603 (1956).
12. M. A. Khenokh, E. A. Kuzicheva, and V. F. Evdokimov, Doklady Akad. Nauk S.S.S.R. *131*, 684 (1960); Chem. Abstr. *54*, 16132 (1960).
13. S. V. Starodubtsev, M. P. Tikhomolova, E. L. Aizenshtat, and K. Tashmukhamedova, Zhur. Obshcheĭ Khim. *31*, 3115 (1961).
14. M. A. Khenokh, E. A. Kuzicheva, and V. F. Evdokinov, Doklady Akad. Nauk S.S.S.R. *135*, 471 (1960); Chem. Abstr. *55*, 11316 (1961).
15. S. Dilli and J. L. Garnell, Chem. & Ind. (London) *1963*, 409.
16. A. Nishimura and K. Takaoka, Hâkko Kogaku Zasshi *38*, 518 (1960); Chem. Abstr. *58*, 1522 (1963).
17. A. Ehrenberg, L. Ehrenberg, and G. Löfroth, Acta Chem. Scand. *17*, 53 (1963).
18. G. O. Phillips, Advances in Carbohydrate Chem. *16*, 13 (1961).
19. R. J. Bayly and H. Weigel, Nature *188*, 384 (1960).
20. A. Beélik and J. K. Hamilton, Das Papier *13*, 77 (1959).
21. A. Beélik and J. K. Hamilton, J. Org. Chem. *26*, 5074 (1961).

# IX

# Isolation of Oligosaccharides from Natural Material

A relatively large number of oligosaccharides has been obtained by isolation from natural sources, in particular plants, and in rare cases only from animal material, where as yet only trehalose, occuring in various insects obviously as a storage substance, is of any significance (see Table X). Otherwise, oligosaccharides are contained in milk and honey and, further, in some sources produced with the participation of micro-organisms, or characterized by many varied biological processes, e. g. yeast, some fungi (for instance ergot) and other products, such as mannas, beer, etc.

The isolation technique must be selected so as to exclude any chemical reactions and changes, such as hydrolytic splitting, or resyntheses. Of importance here are modern isolating methods, in particular chromatographic procedures of all kinds. Separation of oligosaccharides on ion-exchange resins has recently also found attention.[1]

Lactose is probably the earliest known reducing oligosaccharide. It was even described by Bartolettus, but the historical data in this respect are not uniform. According to one report,[2] lactose has been known since 1633, according to another one,[3] since 1583. Cow milk is poor in oligosaccharides and, according to an extensive modern study,[4] it contains only lactose.

A rich oligosaccharide source, however, is human milk, from which, besides lactose, *allo*-lactose (6-$O$-$\beta$-D-galactopyranosyl-D-glucose)[5-7] has been definitely isolated, while the so-called gynolactose[5,8-10] is a mixture of a larger number of substances (see Chapter XXII). Among the oligosaccharides of human milk must also be included a broad group of nitrogen-containing substances (see Chapters XXII and XXIV) and further deoxy compounds derived from L-fucose (see Chapter XXII).

Another abundant source of oligosaccharides is honey, whose composition, however, as well as that of other sources, may vary depending on external conditions. The usual constituents of honey are sucrose and maltose,[11] but when the bees do not have enough melliferous plants at their disposal, they collect their nutrition from other sources also. The honey then often contains melezitose.[12-15] Other constituents successively detected in honey are isomaltose,[11,15-17]maltulose,[11]turanose,[11]nigerose,[11,16,18]kojibiose,[16,19]raffinose,[15]isomaltotriose (dextrantriose),[15] kestose,[15] so-called glucosucrose ($\alpha$-maltosyl $\beta$-D-fructofuranoside),[20-24] which was termed erlose,[15] and finally 4-$O$-$\alpha$-D-glucopyranosylisomaltose.[15]

Other oligosaccharides contained in honey are said[24] to form a series of sucrose derivatives, namely maltosucrose, maltotriosucrose and maltotetraosucrose. A Japanese paper[14] states that, besides sucrose, maltose and melezitose, honey also contains eight disaccharides and trisaccharides and nine higher oligosaccharides.

Another rather frequently occuring substance is trehalose, which has been isolated from yeast[25-32] and ergot.[33-38] The usual source of trehalose, however, is trehala manna[39-46*] or the ressurection plant (*Selaginella lepidophylla*)[47] (see also Tab. X).

Mannas** in general are a source of oligosaccharides, whose production, however, varies depending on the origin of the manna. The manna from Briançon (on the European larch, *Larix decidua* ssp. *europaea*) contains melezitose, [48-53] and the same applies to Turkestan manna (an exudate on the Douglas fir tree, *Pseudotsuga taxifolia*). [54-60] In one of the latter cases, the isolation of sucrose has also been reported.[59] The manna on ash trees, such as *Fraxinus ornus* or *F. rotundifolia*, contains the reducing trisaccharide manninotriose.[61,62]

Other oligosaccharide sources have so far been of minor importance. Beer contains maltulose and nigerose;[63] the isolated maltulose is probably identical with a substance previously obtained by Czech investigators.[64] From malt extracts have been isolated sucrose, maltose, maltotriose and maltotetraose.[65] The last three compounds are also contained in the rat liver.[66]

The oligosaccharides obtained by direct isolation from plants and other natural material are given in Tables X-XVII.

---

* As the original papers on the isolation of trehalose from trehala manna are very old (1858 — 1859)[39,40] it is very difficult to specify the origin of the material used. According to the communications mentioned above and some other ones[41,43,44] trehala manna was considered to be a product of the action of insects. It has been stated[42,45] that trehala manna is the excretion of some scale insects (*Trabutina mannipara* and *Najacoccus serpentinus*) on the leaves of *Tamarix*. Even the last edition of *The Carbohydrates* by W. Pigman, Acad. Press, New York 1957, p. 507, gives the information that trehala manna is not a true manna but consists of an oval shell about the size of an olive formed by certain insects found in Syria. However, according to the latest communication,[46] trehala manna is an exudate of *Fraxinus ornus*, probably from insect-produced wounds. The exudate usually accumulates on the leaves until it falls to the ground.

** Mannas are generally classified as exudates only; however, as melezitose and manninotriose have never been reported as natural substances in the plant material given above (see also Table X), they should be considered to be secondary products, probably synthesized by some yet unknown parasitic action from insect-produced wounds.

*References see p. 170*

## Table X

Oligosaccharides from Natural Material

Non-reducing Disaccharides

| Non-reducing Disaccharide | Natural Material | References |
|---|---|---|
| Trehalose* | Trehala manna | 39 — 47 |
| | Micro-organisms** | |
| | *Mycobacterium phlei* | 67 — 69 |
| | *Mycobacterium leprae* | 70, 71 |
| | *Mycobacterium tuberculosis* | 72, 73 |
| | *Corynebacterium diphtheriae* | 74, 75 |
| | *Myxomycetes* | |
| | *Myxomycetes lycogola* | 76 |
| | *Algae* | |
| | *Bangia fuscopurpurea* | 77, 78 |
| | *Batrachospermum moniliforme* | 79 |
| | *Calothrix scopulorum* | 80 |
| | *Chondrus crispus* | 77, 78 |
| | *Cystochonium purpurescens* | 77, 78 |
| | *Fucus vesiculosus* | 81 |
| | *Furcillaria fastigiata* | 77, 78 |
| | *Lemanea nodosa* | 82 — 84 |
| | *Phormidium tenue* | 85 |
| | *Porphyra laciniata* | 77, 78 |
| | *Rhodymenia palmata* | 77, 78, 86, 87 |
| | *Rivularia bullata* | 88 |
| | *Tuomeya fluviabilis* | 89 |
| | Moulds | |
| | yeast (*Saccharomyces cerevisiae*) | 25 — 32, 90 — 109 |
| | *Neurospora tetrasperma* | 110 |
| | *Penicillium notatum* | 111 |
| | *Sclerotinia libertiana* | 112 |
| | *Sterigmatocystis nigra* | 113 |
| | *Phymatotrichum omnivorum* | 114 |
| | ergot (*Claviceps purpurea*) | 33 — 38 |
| | *Aspergillus niger* | 115, 116 |
| | Mushrooms | 117 — 140 |
| | *Boletus edulis* | 141 |
| | *Schizophyllum commune* | 142 |
| | *Fomes pinicola* | 143 |
| | *Polystictus versicolor* | 144, 145 |
| | *Polyporus pinicola* | 146 |
| | *Calocera viscosa* | 147 |
| | Lichens | 148 |
| | *Umbilicaria pustulata* | 149 |
| | *Dermatocarpon miniatum* | 150 |

* For reviews see K. Myrbäck, Ergeb. Enzymforsch. *10*, 168 (1949); Chem. Abstr. *45*, 9094 (1951); Chem. Abstr. *48*, 13740 (1954); M. Hayashibe and K. Aso, Hakkô Kyôkaishi *17*, 106 (1959); Chem. Abstr. *53*, 10321 (1959).

** Micro-organisms contain generally trehalose esterified with an aliphatic acid.

*Table X — continued*

| Non-reducing Disaccharide | Natural Material | References |
|---|---|---|
| | *Pteridophyta* | |
| | *Selaginella lepidophylla* | 151—154 |
| | Plants | |
| | *Carex brunescens* | 155 |
| | Insects | 156—171 |
| | *Agria affinis* | 169 |
| | *Antheraea polyphemus* | 158 |
| | *Australorbis glabratus* | 166 |
| | *Bombyx mori* | 158, 170 |
| | *Bulinus africanus* | 166 |
| | *Glossina brevipalpis* | 165 |
| | *Glossina morsitans* | 165 |
| | *Hyalophora cecropia* | 158 |
| | *Locusta migratoria* | 168 |
| | *Moniliformis dubius* | 166 |
| | *Periplaneta americana* | 168 |
| | *Pholiota spectabilis* | 160 |
| | *Phormia regina* | 159 |
| | *Porrocaecum decipiens* | 161 |
| | *Schistocerca gregaria* | 156, 162, 171 |
| | Other Animals | |
| | *Ascaris lumbricoides* | 172, 173 |
| | *Artemia salina* | 174, 175 |
| Sucrose* | *Beta vulgaris* | 176 |
| | *Saccharum officinarum* | |
| | Caprifoliaceae | 177 |
| | Cruciferae | 178 |
| | Myrtiflorae | 179 |
| | Ranunculaceae | 180 |
| | Sapindales | 181 |
| | Saxifragaceae | 182 |
| | Spermatophyta | 183 |
| | Umbelliferae | 184 |
| | *Abies concolor* | 185 |
| | *Abies grandis* | 185 |
| | *Abies magnifica* | 185 |
| | *Acacia arabica* | 186 |
| | *Achras sapota* | 187 |
| | *Aconitum septentrionale* | 188 |
| | *Aconitum* spp. | 189 |
| | *Agave vera-cruz* | 190 |
| | *Ajuga genevensis* | 191 |
| | *Ajuga reptans* | 191 |

* For reviews see E. O. Lippmann, *Die Geschichte des Zuckers*, Springer, Berlin, 1929; E. Ottenstad, R. Brochmann-Hansen, D. Oiseth, and A. Nordal, J. Pharm. and Pharmacol. *11*, 689 (1959).

For some older references on the sucrose-containing plants see *Beilstein's Handbuch der organischen Chemie*, Vol. 31, p. 426, Springer, Berlin 1938; C. Wehmer, *Pflanzenstoffe*, Fischer, Jena 1929—1931, Ergänzungsband 1935. For some more recent reviews see J. Parkin, Gardener's Chronicle (3) *103*, 12, 112, 167, 240 (1938); Chem. Abstr. *34*, 2032 (1940); J. Parkin, J. Indian Botan. Soc. *39*, 104 (1960); Chem. Abstr. *56*, 6368 (1962); L. F. Wiggins, Roy. Inst. Chem. (London), Lectures, Monographs, Repts. *1960*, No. 5, 1; Chem. Abstr. *55*, 11887 (1961).

*References see p. 170*

*Table X — continued*

| Non-reducing Disaccharide | Natural Material | References |
|---|---|---|
| | *Allium cepa* | 192 |
| | *Allium* spp. | 193—195 |
| | *Alnus glutinosa* | 196 |
| | *Anchusa sempervirens* | 197 |
| | *Angelica* spp. | 198 |
| | *Angelica archangelica* | 199 |
| | *Angelica silvestris* | 199 |
| | *Apera spica-venti* | 200 |
| | *Aponogeton distachyon* | 201 |
| | *Arbutus unedo* | 202 |
| | *Aristolochia longa* | 203 |
| | *Aristolochia serpentaria* | 203 |
| | *Arnica montana* | 204 |
| | *Artemisia annua* | 205 |
| | *Artemisia verlotorum* | 206 |
| | *Artemisia vulgaris* | 205 |
| | *Arum italicum* | 207 |
| | *Asarum europaeum* | 203 |
| | *Atropa belladonna* | 208, 209 |
| | *Avena flavescens* | 210 |
| | *Averrhoa carambola* | 211 |
| | *Ballota foetida* | 191 |
| | *Baccharis halimifolia* | 205 |
| | *Betula alba* | 212 |
| | *Betula papyrifera* | 213 |
| | *Betula pendula* | 214 |
| | *Borassus flabellifer* | 215, 216 |
| | *Brassica napus* | 217 |
| | *Brassica rapa* | 218 |
| | *Bryophyllum calycinum* | 219 |
| | *Bunias orientalis* | 220 |
| | *Butomus umbellatus* | 221 |
| | *Cajanus cajan* | 222 |
| | *Canavalia gladiata* | 223 |
| | *Carpinus betulus* | 224 |
| | *Caryota urens* | 216 |
| | *Catalpa bignonioides* | 225, 226 |
| | *Celastrus orbiculatus* | 227 |
| | *Celastrus rosthornianus* | 227 |
| | *Cephalotaxus drupacea* | 228 |
| | *Ceratonia siliqua* | 229 |
| | *Cetraria islandica* | 148 |
| | *Chamaecyparis obtusa* | 228, 230 |
| | *Chlorella* | 231 |
| | *Cicer arietinum* | 222 |
| | *Citrus* | 232 |
| | *Cladonia rangifera* | 148 |
| | *Coccus hesperidum* | 233 |
| | *Cocos nucifera* | 216, 234, 235 |
| | *Codium dichotomum* | 236 |
| | *Corylus* spp. | 237 |
| | *Crassula lactea* | 238 |
| | *Crassula portulacea* | 238 |
| | *Crataegus* spp. | 239 |
| | *Cryptomeria japonica* | 228, 230 |
| | *Cucubalus baccifer* | 240 |

*Table X — continued*

| Non-reducing Disaccharide | Natural Material | References |
|---|---|---|
| | *Cyperus esculentus* | 241, 242 |
| | *Dasycladus vermicularis* | 243 |
| | *Daucus carota* | 244 |
| | *Dermatocarpon miniatum* | 150 |
| | *Dianthus caryophyllus* | 240 |
| | *Diospyros kaki* | 245 |
| | *Dolichos biflorus* | 222 |
| | *Dolichos lablab* | 222, 230 |
| | *Echeveria glauca* | 238 |
| | *Ehretia thyrsiflora* | 246 |
| | *Elaeis guineensis* | 247 |
| | *Enteromorpha compressa* | 231 |
| | *Eremurus regelii* | 248 |
| | *Euonymus europaea* | 249 |
| | *Euonymus radicans* | 227 |
| | *Euonymus yedoensis* | 227 |
| | *Euphorbia resinifera* | 250 |
| | *Faba vulgaris* | 251 |
| | *Fagara coco* | 252 |
| | *Festuca arundinacea* | 253 |
| | *Festuca ovina* | 253 |
| | *Festuca pratensis* | 253 |
| | *Festuca tenuifolia* | 253 |
| | *Fontanesia* spp. | 254 |
| | *Fraxinus americana* | 255 |
| | *Fucus vesiculosus* | 81 |
| | *Gentiana asclepiadea* | 256, 257 |
| | *Gentiana cruciata* | 258 |
| | *Gentiana punctata* | 259, 260 |
| | *Gentiana purpurea* | 258 |
| | *Geranium palustre* | 620 |
| | *Ginkgo biloba* | 261 |
| | *Glycyrrhiza echinata* | 262 |
| | *Glycyrrhiza glabra* | 262 |
| | *Haematomma ventosum* | 148 |
| | *Helianthus tuberosus* | 263—265 |
| | *Heracleum mantegazzianum* | 266 |
| | *Hermidium alipes* | 267 |
| | *Hordeum,* see barley | |
| | *Juglans regia* | 268 |
| | *Lamium album* | 191 |
| | *Leucothoe grayana* | 269 |
| | *Libocedrus decurrens* | 185 |
| | *Lilium auratum* | 270 |
| | *Lithospermum purpureo-coeruleum* | 271 |
| | *Lolium multiflorum* | 253 |
| | *Lolium perenne* | 253, 272 |
| | *Lolium temulentum* | 253 |
| | *Lycopus lucidus* | 273 |
| | *Lycoris radiata* | 274 |
| | *Lysimachia vulgaris* | 275 |
| | *Macadamia integrifolia* | 276 |
| | *Madhuca latifolia* | 277 |
| | *Malus,* see apple | |
| | *Medicago sativa* (alfalfa) | 278—281 |
| | *Melampyrum arvense* | 282, 283 |

*References see p. 170*

*Table X — continued*

| Non-reducing Disaccharide | Natural Material | References |
|---|---|---|
| | *Metasequoia glyptostroboides* | 284 |
| | *Moringa oleifera* | 285 |
| | *Musa cavendishii* | 286 |
| | *Nicotiana rustica* | 287 |
| | *Nicotiana tabacum* | 288—296 |
| | *Nitella translucens* | 297 |
| | *Oryza*, see rice | |
| | *Panax ginseng* | 621 |
| | *Pancratium maritimum* | 298 |
| | *Papaver somniferum* | 299 |
| | *Paris polyphylla* | 300 |
| | *Passiflora edulis* | 301 |
| | *Pastinaca sativa* | 302 |
| | *Peucedanum alsaticum* | 303 |
| | *Phaseolus aureus* | 223 |
| | *Phaseolus chrysanthos* | 223 |
| | *Phaseolus radiatus* | 222 |
| | *Phaseolus vulgaris* | 223 |
| | *Phoenix paludosa* | 304 |
| | *Phoenix silvestris* | 216 |
| | *Phytolacca dioica* | 305 |
| | *Picea abies* | 266 |
| | *Pimpinella major* | 199 |
| | *Pimpinella saxifraga* | 199 |
| | *Pinus densiflora* | 230 |
| | *Pinus lambertiana* | 185 |
| | *Pinus sempervirens* | 185 |
| | *Pinus silvestris* | 306 |
| | *Pinus strobus* | 307 |
| | *Pinus thunbergii* | 230 |
| | *Pinus* spp. | 228 |
| | *Pisum sativum* | 230, 308 |
| | *Podocarpus* spp. | 228 |
| | *Polypodium vulgare* | 309 |
| | *Populus balsamifera* | 310 |
| | *Populus* spp. | 311, 312 |
| | *Prunus avium* | 313 |
| | *Pseudotsuga menziesii* | 185 |
| | *Pseudotsuga taxifolia* | 316 |
| | *Psidium guajava* | 314 |
| | *Psilotum* spp. | 315 |
| | *Quisqualis indica* | 317 |
| | *Raphanus sativus* | 318, 319 |
| | *Rauwolfia perakensis* | 320 |
| | *Rauwolfia serpentina* | 321 |
| | *Rhinanthus crista-galli* | 322, 323 |
| | *Robinia pseudacacia* | 224, 230 |
| | *Salvia pratensis* | 191 |
| | *Sandoricum koetjape* | 324 |
| | *Secale*, see rye | |
| | *Sedum acre* | 238 |
| | *Sedum rupestre* | 238 |
| | *Sedum spectabile* | 325 |
| | *Sedum spurium* | 238 |
| | *Sedum telephium* | 238 |

*Table X — continued*

| Non-reducing Disaccharide | Natural Material | References |
|---|---|---|
| | *Sempervivum verloti* | 238 |
| | *Senecio cinerca* | 205 |
| | *Senecio doria* | 205 |
| | *Senecio vulgaris* | 205 |
| | *Senega* spp. | 326 |
| | *Sequoia sempervirens* | 185 |
| | *Setaria italica* | 327 |
| | *Solanum*, see potato | |
| | *Sorgum saccharatum* | 328—335 |
| | *Soja hispida* | 336—339 |
| | *Sphagnum palustre* | 340 |
| | *Stachys tuberifera* | 341, 342 |
| | *Strychnos bakanko* | 343 |
| | *Strychnos ignatii* | 343 |
| | *Strychnos nux vomica* | 343 |
| | *Strychnos potatorum* | 343 |
| | *Strychnos spinosa* | 343 |
| | *Swartzia madagascariensis* | 344 |
| | *Symphytum officinale* | 345—347 |
| | *Taraxacum kok-saghyz* | 348, 349 |
| | *Taxus brevifolia* | 185 |
| | *Teucrium canadense* | 350 |
| | *Theobroma cacao* | 351—354 |
| | *Thuja occidentalis* | 355 |
| | *Tilia* spp. | 356 |
| | *Trifolium pratense* | 357 |
| | *Triticum*, see wheat | |
| | *Tsuga heterophylla* | 358 |
| | *Typha latifolia* | 359 |
| | *Umbilicaria pustulata* | 148, 360 |
| | *Umbilicaria rigida* | 148 |
| | *Vaccinium myrtillus* | 361 |
| | *Vicia faba* | 362, 363 |
| | *Vigna sesquipedalis* | 223, 230 |
| | *Vitis*, see grapes | |
| | *Withania somnifera* | 624 |
| | *Zea*, see maize | |
| | apples | 364—368 |
| | bamboo shoots | 369, 370 |
| | barley | 371—377 |
| | blackberries | 378 |
| | cabbage juice | 379, 380 |
| | cereals | 381 |
| | cherry-laurel leaves | 382 |
| | grains | 383 |
| | grapefruit | 384 |
| | grapes | 385—388 |
| | grasses | 389—391 |
| | halavé | 392 |
| | herbage | 393 |
| | hop cone | 394 |
| | kaki-fruit | 395 |
| | lettuce seeds | 396 |
| | maize | 397—403 |
| | mulberry tree | 404 |
| | nuts | 237, 405—407 |

*References see p. 170*

*Table X — continued*

| Non-reducing Disaccharide | Natural Material | References |
|---|---|---|
| | olives | 408 |
| | palm molasses | 409 |
| | potatoes | 410—412 |
| | rice | 413—415 |
| | Royal jelly | 416 |
| | rye | 417—419 |
| | sieve-tube exudates | 420 |
| | wheat | 413, 421—426 |
| | white iris | 427 |
| Alliuminoside | *Allium sewertzowi* | 428 |

A non-reducing disaccharide, produced by the micro-organism *Hemophilus influenzae* [see S. Zamenhof, G. Leidy, P. L. Fitzgerald, H. E. Alexander, and E. Chargaff, J. Biol. Chem. *203*, 695 (1953); S. Zamenhof and G. Leidy, Federation Proc. *13*, 327 (1954); E. Rosenberg and S. Zamenhof, Federation Proc. *19*, 315 (1960); E. Rosenberg and S. Zamenhof, J. Biol. Chem. *236*, 2845 (1960)], and supposed to be β-D-ribofuranosyl β-D-ribofuranoside, has been synthesized and the structure given above verified, see E. Rosenberg and S. Zamenhof, J. Biol. Chem. *237*, 1040 (1962).

**Table XI**

Oligosaccharides from Natural Material
Reducing Disaccharides

| Reducing Disaccharide | Natural Material | References |
|---|---|---|
| Kojibiose | *Typha latifolia* | 359 |
| Nigerose | *Typha latifolia* | 359 |
| Sophorose | *Sophora japonica* | 429, 430 |
| Maltose | *Aconitum napellus* | 189 |
| | *Bryophyllum calycinum* | 219 |
| | *Chlorella* | 231 |
| | *Chrysactinia mexicana* | 431 |
| | *Ceratonia siliqua* | 229 |
| | *Daucus carota* | 244 |
| | *Enteromorpha compressa* | 231 |
| | *Lathyrus silvestris* | 432 |
| | *Lathyrus tuberosus* | 433 |
| | *Lippia nodiflora* | 434 |
| | *Mercurialis perennis* | 435, 436 |
| | *Oryza*, see rice | |
| | *Panax ginseng* | 621 |
| | *Phaseolus radiatus* | 222 |
| | *Schizopepon fargesii* | 437 |
| | *Soja hispida* | 438—441 |
| | *Trifolium hybridum* | 442 |
| | *Trifolium pratense* | 625 |
| | *Tropaeolum majus* | 443, 444 |
| | *Typha latifolia* | 359 |
| | *Umbilicus pendulinus* | 445 |
| | bamboo wood | 370 |
| | barley grains | 377 |
| | mulberry tree | 404 |

*Table XI — continued*

| Reducing Disaccharide | Natural Material | References |
|---|---|---|
| | rice | 415, 446 |
| | rye seeds | 417 |
| | wheat | 447 |
| | wort | 448—451 |
| Cellobiose | *Pinus silvestris* | 306 |
| Isomaltose | *Typha latifolia* | 359 |
| | rice | 415 |
| Gentiobiose | *Betula papyrifera* | 213 |
| Leucrose | *Typha latifolia* | 359 |
| Turanose | *Typha latifolia* | 359 |
| Primeverose | *Ceratonia siliqua* | 229 |
| Lactose | *Ceratonia siliqua* | 229 |
| | *Forsythia* | 452 |
| | *Lippia nodiflora* | 434 |
| | *Mimusops roxburghiana* | 453 |
| | *Oldenlandia biflora* | 454 |
| | *Pinus silvestris* | 306 |
| | *Ponderia campechiana* | 453 |
| | *Achras sapota* | 453, 455 |
| | *Sarcina lutea* | 456 |
| Melibiose | *Aconitum napellus* | 457 |
| | *Betula papyrifera* | 213, 626 |
| | *Malva* spp. | 458 |
| | *Pinus silvestris* | 306 |
| | *Teucrium canadense* | 350 |
| | *Theobroma cacao* | 352 |
| | cotton seed extract | 459 |
| | herbage | 393 |
| | wheat bran | 459 |
| Planteobiose | *Fraxinus ornus* | 460 |
| | *Teucrium canadense* | 350, 460 |
| Ceratose | *Ceratonia siliqua* | 229 |
| Sogdianose | *Eremurus sogdianus* | 428, 461 |
| Swietenose | *Schrebera swietenoides* | 462, 463 |
| Fructosylfructose | *Helianthus tuberosus* | 464 |

## Table XII

Oligosaccharides from Natural Material
Non-reducing Trisaccharides

| Non-reducing Trisaccharide | Natural Material | References |
|---|---|---|
| Raffinose | *Ajuga genevensis* | 191 |
| | *Ajuga reptans* | 191 |
| | *Alnus glutinosa* | 196 |
| | *Ballota foetida* | 191 |
| | *Beta vulgaris* | 465—468 |
| | *Betula verrucosa* | 469 |
| | *Borassus flabellifer* | 216 |
| | *Butomus umbellatus* | 221 |

*References see p. 170*

11*

*Table XII — continued*

| Non-reducing Trisaccharide | Natural Material | References |
|---|---|---|
| | *Canavalia gladiata* | 223 |
| | *Cephalotaxus drupacea* | 228 |
| | *Chamaecyparis obtusa* | 228, 230 |
| | *Cocos nucifera* | 216 |
| | *Corchorus capsularis* | 470 |
| | *Corchorus olitorius* | 471, 472 |
| | *Corylus* spp. | 237 |
| | *Cryptomeria japonica* | 228, 230 |
| | *Cucubalus baccifer* | 473 |
| | *Cyperus esculentus* | 242 |
| | *Dianthus caryophyllus* | 240, 474 |
| | *Dolichos lablab* | 230 |
| | *Entada scandens* | 475 |
| | *Erodium cicutarium* | 476 |
| | *Faba vulgaris* | 251 |
| | *Festuca ovina* | 253 |
| | *Festuca tenuifolia* | 253 |
| | *Fraxinus americana* | 255 |
| | *Fraxinus ornus* | 460 |
| | *Gossipium herbaceum* | 477—482 |
| | *Lamium album* | 191 |
| | *Lycopus lucidus* | 273 |
| | *Medicago sativa* | 191, 279 |
| | *Nelumbo nucifera* | 483, 484 |
| | *Nicotiana tabacum* | 296 |
| | *Pastinaca sativa* | 302 |
| | *Phaseolus aureus* | 223 |
| | *Phaseolus chrysanthos* | 223 |
| | *Phaseolus radiatus* | 222 |
| | *Phaseolus vulgaris* | 223 |
| | *Phoenix silvestris* | 216 |
| | *Picea abies* | 485 |
| | *Picea pungens* | 485 |
| | *Pinus densiflora* | 230 |
| | *Pinus nigra* | 485 |
| | *Pinus palustris* | 485 |
| | *Pinus silvestris* | 306 |
| | *Pinus strobus* | 307, 485 |
| | *Pinus thunbergii* | 230, 486 |
| | *Pinus* spp. | 228 |
| | *Pisum sativum* | 230 |
| | *Podocarpus* spp. | 228 |
| | *Populus grandidentata* | 487 |
| | *Populus tremuloides* | 487 |
| | *Populus* spp. | 311, 312 |
| | *Prunus avium* | 313 |
| | *Pseudotsuga taxifolia* | 316 |
| | *Psilotum* spp. | 315 |
| | *Psoralea corylyfolia* | 488 |
| | *Raphanus sativus* | 318, 319 |
| | *Salvia pratensis* | 191 |
| | *Silene inflata* | 240 |
| | *Silene pendula* | 240 |
| | *Soja hispida* | 338, 339, 489 |
| | *Sorgum saccharatum* | 335 |
| | *Sphagnum palustre* | 340 |

*Table XII — continued*

| Non-reducing Trisaccharide | Natural Material | References |
|---|---|---|
| | *Stachys tuberifera* | 341, 342 |
| | *Taraxacum kok-saghyz* | 349 |
| | *Taxus baccata* | 490—492 |
| | *Teucrium canadense* | 350 |
| | *Theobroma cacao* | 351—353, 493 |
| | *Thuja plicata* | 485 |
| | *Tsuga canadensis* | 485 |
| | *Vicia faba* | 363 |
| | *Vicia sativa* | 191 |
| | *Vigna catjang* | 230 |
| | *Vigna sesquipedalis* | 223 |
| | barley | 373—375, 494, 495 |
| | broad beans | 496 |
| | cabbage juice | 397 |
| | cereals | 381 |
| | cotton seeds | 459, 477—482, 497—500 |
| | crucifer seeds | 178 |
| | fruit-plant shoots | 366 |
| | molasses | 477, 501—509 |
| | mulberry tree | 403, 404 |
| | nuts | 237, 405, 407 |
| | rye seeds | 417 |
| | sieve-tube exudates | 420 |
| | wheat | 459, 510—512 |
| | yeast | 107 |
| Umbelliferose | Daucaceae | 513 |
| | Umbelliferae | 184, 513 |
| | *Angelica archangelica* | 514 |
| | *Trifolium pratense* (?) | 357 |
| Gentianose | *Gentiana asclepiadea* | 515 |
| | *Gentiana cruciata* | 258, 516 |
| | *Gentiana lutea* | 517—520 |
| | *Gentiana punctata* | 521, 522 |
| | *Gentiana purpurea* | 258, 523, 524 |
| Melezitose | *Eucalyptus tiliae* | 525 |
| | *Populus nigra* | 526 |
| | *Tilia* spp. | 356 |
| | *Trifolium hybridum** | 527 |
| | mannas | 529-534 |
| Planteose | *Lavandula officinalis* | 535 |
| | *Majorana hortensis* | 535, 536 |
| | *Melissa officinalis* | 535 |
| | *Nicotiana tabacum* | 288, 537 |
| | *Ocimum basilicum* | 535 |
| | *Plantago major* | 538, 539 |
| | *Plantago ovata* | 538 |
| | *Plantago psyllium* | 540 |
| | *Salvia officinalis* | 535 |
| | *Sesamum indicum* | 541 |
| | *Teucrium canadense* | 350 |
| | *Theobroma cacao* | 352, 542, 543 |
| Impatiose | *Impatiens holstii* | 544 |

* This statement seems not to be verified.[528]

*References see p. 170*

*Table XII — continued*

| Non-reducing Trisaccharide | Natural Material | References |
|---|---|---|
| Kestose | *Arrhenatherum elatius* | 545 |
| | *Betula papyrifera* | 213 |
| | *Lolium multiflorum* | 545 |
| | *Lolium perenne* | 546 |
| | barley straw | 627 |
| | oats straw | 547 |
| | rye straw | 548 |
| Isokestose | *Allium cepa* | 545 |
| | *Allium porrum* | 545 |
| | *Arrhenatherum elatius* | 545 |
| | *Campanula rapanculus* | 549 |
| | *Helianthus tuberosus* | 550—553 |
| | *Lolium multiflorum* | 545 |
| | *Panax ginseng* | 622 |
| | *Populus grandidentata* | 487 |
| | *Populus tremuloides* | 487 |
| | barley straw | 627 |
| | rye straw | 548 |
| neo-Kestose | *Acer saccharum* | 554 |
| | *Allium cepa* | 545 |
| | *Allium porrum* | 545 |
| | *Arrhenatherum rapanculus* | 545 |
| | *Lolium multiflorum* | 545 |
| | *Musa cavendishii* | 555 |
| | oats straw | 547 |
| | wheat straw | 556 |
| Erlose | *Panax ginseng* | 623 |
| Labiose | *Eremostachys labiosa* | 557 |
| Glucosucrose | *Coccus hesperidum* | 233 |
| Glucodifructose | *Symphytum officinale* | 345 |
| | apricot fruit | 558 |
| | rye seeds | 417 |
| Trifructose | *Helianthus tuberosus* | 464 |

## Table XIII

Oligosaccharides from Natural Material
Reducing Trisaccharides

| Reducing Trisaccharide | Natural Material | References |
|---|---|---|
| Maltotriose | *Chlorella* | 231 |
| | *Enteromorpha compressa* | 231 |
| | *Sapota achras* | 455 |
| | *Typha latifolia* | 359 |
| | barley | 374 |
| | rice | 415 |
| | wort | 448, 450, 451 |
| Manninotriose | *Betula papyrifera* | 626 |
| | *Soja hispida* | 336 |
| | *Theobroma cacao* | 352, 353 |
| Panose | *Panax ginseng* | 622 |

## Table XIV

Oligosaccharides from Natural Material
Non-reducing Tetrasaccharides

| Non-reducing Tetrasaccharide | Natural Material | References |
|---|---|---|
| Stachyose | *Ajuga nipponensis* | 559 |
| | *Ajugoides humilis* | 560 |
| | *Ballota foetida* | 561 |
| | *Betula verrucosa* | 469 |
| | *Butomus umbellatus* | 221 |
| | *Canavalia gladiata* | 223 |
| | *Catalpa bignonioides* | 225, 226, 562 |
| | *Clinopodium chinense* | 560 |
| | *Clinopodium confine* | 560 |
| | *Clinopodium vulgare* | 561 |
| | *Corylus* spp. | 237 |
| | *Cryptomeria japonica* | 230, 563 |
| | *Cucubalus baccifer* | 473 |
| | *Dolichos lablab* | 230 |
| | *Dracocephalum argunense* | 560 |
| | *Eremostachys laciniata* | 564 |
| | *Ervum lens* | 565 |
| | *Fraxinus ornus* | 460 |
| | *Galega officinalis* | 565 |
| | *Jasminum officinale* | 566, 567 |
| | *Lamium album* | 560, 568, 569 |
| | *Larix leptolepis* | 230 |
| | *Lens esculenta* | 222, 570 |
| | *Leonurus sibiricus* | 560 |
| | *Leucaena glauca* | 571 |
| | *Lupinus angustifolius* | 572 |
| | *Lupinus lucidus* | 273 |
| | *Lupinus luteus* | 565, 573—577 |
| | *Lycopus maackianus* | 560 |
| | *Medicago sativa* | 570 |
| | *Mentha haplocalyx* | 560 |
| | *Mentha silvestris* | 561 |
| | *Nepeta glechoma* | 560 |
| | *Origanum vulgare* | 561 |
| | *Phaseolus aureus* | 223 |
| | *Phaseolus chrysanthos* | 223 |
| | *Phaseolus radiatus* | 222 |
| | *Phaseolus vulgaris* | 223, 565 |
| | *Picea abies* | 485 |
| | *Pices pungens* | 485 |
| | *Pinus densiflora* | 230 |
| | *Pinus nigra* | 485 |
| | *Pinus strobus* | 485 |
| | *Pinus thunbergii* | 230 |
| | *Pinus* spp. | 563 |
| | *Pisum sativum* | 565 |
| | *Plantago carnata* | 578 |
| | *Plantago maritima* | 578 |
| | *Podocarpus* spp. | 563 |
| | *Populus* spp. | 312 |
| | *Prunella asiatica* | 560 |
| | *Raphanus sativus* | 318, 319 |
| | *Salvia chinensis* | 560 |

*References see p. 170*

*Table XIV — continued*

| Non-reducing Tetrasaccharide | Natural Material | References |
|---|---|---|
| | *Salvia nipponica* | 560 |
| | *Salvia pratensis* | 561 |
| | *Salvia splendens* | 561 |
| | *Scrophularia kakudensis* | 579 |
| | *Scrophularia nodosa* | 580 |
| | *Scrophularia sambucifolia* | 580 |
| | *Silene inflata* | 240 |
| | *Silene pendula* | 240 |
| | *Soja hispida* | 336, 338, 339, 489, 565, 581—583 |
| | *Sorgum* spp. | 335 |
| | *Sphagnum palustre* | 340 |
| | *Stachys erecta* | 561 |
| | *Stachys lanata* | 561 |
| | *Stachys riederi* | 560 |
| | *Stachys silvatica* | 561 |
| | *Stachys tuberifera* | 342, 584—592 |
| | *Teucrium canadense* | 350 |
| | *Theobroma cacao* | 351—353, 493 |
| | *Thuja plicata* | 485 |
| | *Trifolium incarnatum* | 565 |
| | *Tsuga canadensis* | 485 |
| | *Verbascum thapsiforme* | 593, 594 |
| | *Verbascum thapsus* | 570 |
| | *Verbena bonariensis* | 595 |
| | *Verbena hispida* | 595 |
| | *Verbena officinalis* | 595—597 |
| | *Verbena venosa* | 595 |
| | *Vicia faba* | 363 |
| | *Vicia sativa* | 570 |
| | *Vigna catjang* | 230 |
| | *Vigna sesquipedalis* | 223 |
| | broad beans | 496 |
| | crucifer seeds | 178 |
| | fruit-plant shoots | 366 |
| | herbage | 393 |
| | mulberry tree | 404 |
| | nuts | 237, 351, 405, 407 |
| | sieve-tube exudates | 420 |
| | wheat flour | 598 |
| Bifurcose | oats straw | 547 |
| | barley straw | 627 |
| | rye straw | 548 |
| | wheat straw | 556 |
| *neo*-Bifurcose | oats straw | 547 |
| Sesamose | *Sesamum indicum* | 541 |
| Scodorose | *Allium* spp. | 599—601 |
| Lychnose | *Cucubalus baccifer* | 473 |
| | *Dianthus caryophyllus* | 474 |
| | *Lychnis dioica* | 602—605 |
| | *Sesamum indicum* | 541 |
| Isolychnose | *Cucubalus baccifer* | 473 |
| | *Dianthus caryophyllus* | 474 |
| | *Lychnis dioica* | 606 |
| Maltosucrose | *Coccus hesperidum* | 233 |
| Some other tetrasacchari-des | *Nicotiana tabacum* | 288, 537 |
| | *Helianthus tuberosus* | 550 |

### Table XV

Oligosaccharides from Natural Material
Reducing Tetrasaccharides

| Reducing Tetrasaccharide | Natural Material | References |
|---|---|---|
| Maltotetraose | *Achras sapota* | 455 |
| | rice | 415 |
| Verbascotetraose | *Betula papyrifera* | 213, 626 |
| | *Theobroma cacao* | 352, 353 |

### Table XVI

Oligosaccharides from Natural Material
Pentasaccharides

| Pentasaccharide | Natural Material | References |
|---|---|---|
| Verbascose | *Ajuga nipponensis* | 539 |
| | *Lens esculenta* | 191 |
| | *Medicago sativa* | 191 |
| | *Salvia pratensis* | 191, 607 |
| | *Theobroma cacao* | 352, 353 |
| | *Verbascum thapsiforme* | 590, 593, 594 |
| | *Verbascum thapsus* | 570, 608 |
| | *Vicia sativa* | 191 |
| | sieve-tube exudates | 420 |
| Type-bifurcose | rye straw | 548 |
| | barley straw | 627 |
| | wheat straw | 556 |
| Maltotriosucrose | *Coccus hesperidum* | 233 |

### Table XVII

Oligosaccharides from Natural Material
Hexasaccharides and Higher Oligosaccharides

| Oligosaccharide | Natural Material | References |
|---|---|---|
| Ajugose | *Ajuga nipponensis* | 559, 609 |
| Pentasaccharides-Octasaccharides* | *Cucubalus baccifer* | 473 |
| | *Dianthus caryophyllus* | 474 |
| | *Ajuga genevensis* | 191 |
| | *Ajuga reptans* | 191 |
| | *Lychnis dioica* | 593, 594, 602, 605—607, 610, 611 |
| | *Verbascum thapsiforme* | 593, 594 |
| | *Verbascum thapsus* | 570, 612 |
| | *Vicia sativa* | 570 |

\* For reviews see A. Wickström, Saertrykk av Meddelelser fra Norsk Farmaceutisk Selskap *18*, 129 (1956); J. E. Courtois, Bull. soc. chim. biol. *42*, 1451 (1960).

*References see p. 170*

*Table XVII — continued*

| Oligosaccharide | Natural Material | References |
|---|---|---|
| Hepta-D-galactosylsucrose | *Verbascum thapsus* | 613 |
| Octa-D-galactosyl- Dodeca-D-ga-lactosylsucrose | *Lychnis dioica* | 614 |
| Bifurcose-type hexasaccharide | wheat straw | 556 |
| Hexasaccharide (D-glucose only) | placenta | 615 |
| Sessilifolan (heptasaccharide 2 G : 5 Fru) | *Lobelia sessilifolia* | 616, 617 |
| Arctose (6 Fru) | *Arctium lappa* | 618 |
| Asparagose (7— 8 Fru) | *Asparagus officinalis* | 619 |

## REFERENCES

1. J. K. N. Jones, R. W. Wall, and A. O. Pittet, Can. J. Chem. *38*, 2285 (1960).
2. E. O. Whittier, Chem. Revs *2*, 85 (1926).
3. E. O. Lippmann, Die Geschichte des Zuckers, Springer, Berlin *1929*, 688.
4. R. E. Trucco, P. Verdier, and A. Rega, Biochim. et Biophys. Acta *15*, 582 (1954); Chem. Abstr. *49*, 5546 (1955).
5. M. Polonovski and A. Lespagnol, Compt. rend. *192*, 1319 (1931).
6. M. Polonovski and A. Lespagnol, Compt. rend. *195*, 465 (1932).
7. M. Polonovski and A. Lespagnol, Bull. soc. chim. biol. *15*, 320 (1933).
8. M. Polonovski and A. Lespagnol, Bull. soc. chim. biol. *12*, 1170 (1930).
9. M. Polonovski and J. Montreuil, Compt. rend. *238*, 2263 (1954).
10. J. Montreuil, Compt. rend. *239*, 510 (1954).
11. J. W. White, Arch. Biochem. Biophys. *80*, 386 (1959).
12. C. S. Hudson and S. F. Sherwood, J. Am. Chem. Soc. *42*, 116 (1926).
13. F. J. Bates, *Polarimetry, Saccharimetry and the Sugars*, National Bureau of Standards, Washington, USA *1942*, 472.
14. K. Aso, T. Watanabe, and K. Yamao, Hâkko-Kôgaku Zasshi *36*, 39 (1958); Chem. Abstr. *52*, 7566 (1958).
15. S. Goldschmidt and H. Burkert, Hoppe-Seyler's Z. physiol. Chem. *300*, 188 (1955).
16. T. Watanabe and K. Aso, J. Agr. Chem. Soc. Japan *33*, 1054 (1959).
17. T. Watanabe and K. Aso, Bull. Agr. Chem. Soc. Japan *23*, 342 (1959).
18. J. W. White, C. R. Eddy, J. Petty, and N. Hoban, Anal. Chem. *30*, 506 (1958).
19. T. Watanabe and K. Aso, Nature *183*, 1740 (1959).
20. J. W. White and J. Maher, J. Am. Chem. Soc. *75*, 1209 (1953).
21. H. E. Gray and G. Fraenkel, Science *118*, 304 (1953); Chem. Abstr. *48*, 895 (1954).
22. H. E. Gray and G. Fraenkel, Physiol. Zool. *27*, 56 (1954); Chem. Abstr. *48*, 9474 (1954).
23. J. P. Wolf and W. H. Ewart, Science *122*, 973 (1955); Chem. Abstr. *50*, 5929 (1956).
24. J. P. Wolf and W. H. Ewart, Arch. Biochem. Biophys. *58*, 365 (1955); Chem. Abstr. *50*, 2883 (1956).
25. E. M. Koch and F. C. Koch, Science *61*, 570 (1925); Chem. Abstr. *19*, 2361 (1925).
26. A. J. Kluyver and F. L. W. Roosmalen, Biochem. Z. *245*, 13 (1932).
27. A. Steiner and C. F. Cori, Science *82*, 422 (1935); Chem. Abstr. *30*, 506 (1936).
28. K. Myrbäck and B. Oertenblad, Biochem. Z. *288*, 329 (1936).

29. K. M. Brandt, Biochem. Z. *309*, 190 (1941); Chem. Abstr. *37*, 2770 (1943).
30. M. Elander and K. Myrbäck, Arch. Biochem. *21*, 249 (1949).
31. L. C. Stewart, N. K. Richtmyer, and C. S. Hudson, J. Am. Chem. Soc. *71*, 2277 (1949).
32. L. C. Stewart, N. K. Richtmyer, and C. S. Hudson, J. Am. Chem. Soc. *72*, 2059 (1950).
33. H. A. L. Wiggers, Ann. *1*, 174 (1832).
34. E. Mitscherlich, Ann. *106*, 15 (1888).
35. E. Mitscherlich, J. prakt. Chem. [1] *73*, 65 (1858).
36. E. O. Lippmann, Ber. *55*, 3038 (1922).
37. C. Tanret, Bull. soc. chim. France [4] *31*, 444 (1923).
38. G. Zemplén, Math. naturwiss. Anz. ungar. Akad. Wiss. *55*, 659 (1937); Chem. Abstr. *31*, 6203 (1937).
39. Guibourt, Compt. rend. *46*, 1213 (1858).
40. M. Berthelot, Ann. chim. et phys. [3] *55*, 272 (1859).
41. L. Maquenne, Compt. rend. *112*, 947 (1891).
42. F. S. Bodenheimer and O. Theodor, Ergebn. Sinai-Expedition *1927* der Hebräischen Universität Jerusalem, Lepzig, p. 45.
43. P. Harang, J. pharm. chim. [6] *23*, 471 (1906); Chem. Zentr. *1906*, II, 169.
44. A. Ebert, Ztschr. Allg. Oester. Apoth. Vereins *46*, 427 (1908); Chem. Zentr. *1908*, II, 1874.
45. J. Leibowitz, Biochem. J. *38*, 205 (1944); Chem. Abstr. *39*, 389 (1945).
46. Z. I. Sabry and N. A. Atallach, Nature *190*, 915 (1961).
47. T. S. Harding, Sugar *25*, 476 (1923); Chem. Abstr. *18*, 78 (1924).
48. Bonastre, J. Pharm. [2] *8*, 335 (1822).
49. Bonastre, J. Pharm. [2] *19*, 443 (1833).
50. Bonastre, J. Pharm. [2] *19*, 626 (1833).
51. M. Berthelot, Ann. chim. phys. [3] *46*, 86 (1856).
52. M. Berthelot, Ann. chim. phys. [3] *55*, 282 (1859).
53. C. Tanret, Bull. soc. chim. France [3] *35*, 817 (1906).
54. A. Villiers, Bull. soc. chim. France [2] *27*, 98 (1877).
55. A. Villiers, Ann. chim. phys. [5] *12*, 433 (1877).
56. A. Alekhin, Ann. chim. phys. [6] *18*, 532 (1889).
57. L. Maquenne, Bull. soc. chim. France [3] *9*, 725 (1893).
58. N. A. Orloff, Chem. Ztg. *21*, 954 (1897); Chem. Zentr. *1897*, II, 1068.
59. C. S. Hudson and S. F. Sherwood, J. Am. Chem. Soc. *40*, 1456 (1918).
60. C. S. Hudson and S. F. Sherwood, J. Am. Chem. Soc. *42*, 116 (1920).
61. C. Tanret, Compt. rend. *134*, 1588 (1902).
62. C. Tanret, Bull. soc. chim. France [3] *27*, 948 (1902).
63. I. C. MacWilliam and A. W. Phillips, Chem. & Ind. (London) *1959*, 364.
64. A. Kocková-Kratochvílová, A. Vlček, and R. Winkler, Pivovarství *11*, 2 (1958).
65. J. Büchi and R. Gräub, Pharm. Acta Helv. *33*, 547 (1958).
66. W. H. Fishmann and Hsien-Gieh Sie, J. Am. Chem. Soc. *80*, 121 (1958).
67. M. C. Pangborn and R. J. Anderson, J. Biol. Chem. *101*, 105 (1933); Chem. Abstr. *27*, 5095 (1933).
68. R. J. Anderson and M. S. Newman, J. Biol. Chem. *101*, 499 (1933); Chem. Abstr. *27*, 5364 (1933).
69. M. C. Pangborn and R. J. Anderson, J. Am. Chem. Soc. *58*, 10 (1936).
70. M. S. Newman and R. J. Anderson, Hoppe-Seyler's Z. physiol. Chem. *220*, 1 (1933).
71. R. J. Anderson, R. E. Reeves, and J. A. Crowder, J. Biol. Chem. *121*, 669 (1937).

72. J. A. Crowder, F. H. Stodola, M. C. Pangborn, and R. J. Anderson, J. Am. Chem. Soc. *58*, 636 (1936).

73. H. Bloch and H. Süllmann, Experientia *1*, 94 (1945); Chem. Abstr. *40*, 3795 (1946).

74. E. M. Gubarev, E. K. Lubenets, A. A. Kauchukh, and Yu. V. Galaev, Biokhimiya *16*, 139 (1951); Chem. Abstr. *45*, 7637 (1951).

75. E. M. Gubarev, E. K. Lubenets, and Yu. V. Galaev, Biokhimiya *18*, 37 (1953); Chem. Abstr. *47*, 7594 (1953).

76. N. N. Iwanoff, Biochem. Z. *162*, 455 (1925); Chem. Abstr. *20*, 2003 (1926).

77. H. Kylin, Hoppe-Seyler's Z. physiol. Chem. *94*, 360 (1915).

78. H. Kylin, Hoppe-Seyler's Z. physiol. Chem. *101*, 243 (1918).

79. J. Augier, Bull. soc. botan. France *82*, 652 (1935); Chem. Abstr. *32*, 6430 (1938).

80. H. Kylin, Kgl. Fysiograf. Sällskap. Lund, Förh. *13*, 64 (1943); Chem. Abstr. *42*, 4246 (1948).

81. B. Lindberg, Acta Chem. Scand. *7*, 1119 (1953).

82. H. Colin and J. Augier, Compt. rend. *196*, 1042 (1933).

83. H. Colin and J. Augier, Compt. rend. *197*, 423 (1933); Chem. Abstr. *28*, 3440 (1934).

84. J. Augier, Compt. rend. *222*, 929 (1946); Chem. Abstr. *40*, 4116 (1946).

85. J. Payen, Compt. rend. *236*, 1811 (1953); Chem. Abstr. *47*, 9433 (1953).

86. H. Colin and E. Guéguen, Compt. rend. *190*, 653 (1930); Chem. Abstr. *24*, 3033 (1930).

87. C. Sauvageu and G. Denigès, Compt. rend. *190*, 958 (1930); Chem. Abstr. *24*, 3534 (1930).

88. H. Colin and J. Payen, Compt. rend. *198*, 384 (1934); Chem. Abstr. *28*, 3762 (1934).

89. J. Augier, Compt. rend. *239*, 87 (1954); Chem. Abstr. *49*, 438 (1955).

90. G. Tanret, Compt. rend. *192*, 1056 (1931); Chem. Abstr. *25*, 4022 (1931).

91. G. Tanret, Bull. soc. chim. biol. *13*, 598 (1931); Chem. Abstr. *26*, 251 (1932).

92. S. Veibel, Biochem. Z. *252*, 305 (1932); Chem. Abstr. *26*, 5608 (1932).

93. K. Myrbäck, Svensk Kem. Tid. *48*, 55 (1936); Chem. Abstr. *30*, 4897 (1936).

94. K. Myrbäck, Svensk Kem. Tid. *51*, 36 (1939); Chem. Abstr. *33*, 3828 (1939).

95. R. Payen, Can. J. Res. *27B*, 749 (1949); Chem. Abstr. *44*, 3079 (1950).

96. R. Nilsson and F. Alm, Acta Chem. Scand. *3*, 213 (1949); Chem. Abstr. *43*, 7065 (1949).

97. G. E. Pollock and C. D. Holmstrom, Cereal Chem. *28*, 498 (1951); Chem. Abstr. *46*, 2197 (1952).

98. W. E. Trevelyan, J. H. Gammon, E. H. Wiggins, and J. S. Harrison, Biochem. J. *50*, 303 (1952); Chem. Abstr. *46*, 4053 (1952).

99. T. Sato and S. Tsumura, J. Agr. Chem. Soc. Japan *28*, 412 (1953); Chem. Abstr. *50*, 2885 (1956).

100. G. Milhaud and J. P. Aubert, Compt. rend. *241*, 525 (1955); Chem. Abstr. *50*, 3549 (1956).

101. B. Pazonyi and L. Márkus, Agrokémia és Talajtan *4*, 225 (1955); Chem. Abstr. *51*, 15702 (1957).

102. W. E. Trevelyan and J. S. Harrison, Biochem. J. *63*, 23 (1956); Chem. Abstr. *50*, 12168 (1956).

103. J. P. Aubert and G. Milhaud, Ann. Inst. Pasteur *90*, 320 (1956); Chem. Abstr. *50*, 12170 (1956).

104. H. L. Berke and A. Rothstein, Arch. Biochem. Biophys. *72*, 380 (1957); Chem. Abstr. *52*, 3920 (1958).

105. A. D. Panek, Compt. rend. *249*, 333 (1959); Chem. Abstr. *54*, 3600 (1960).

106. W. R. Eaton, Arch. Biochem. Biophys. *88*, 17 (1960); Chem. Abstr. *54*, 19864 (1960).

107. K. Täufel, K. J. Steinbach, and G. Meinert, Nahrung *4*, 295 (1960); Chem. Abstr. *54*, 25559 (1960).
108. E. R. Tully, R. F. Palmer, and T. G. Brady, Biochem. J. *80*, 17p (1961); Chem. Abstr. *55*, 26101 (1961).
109. H. Suomalainen and S. Pfäffli, J. Inst. Brewing *67*, 249 (1961); Chem. Abstr. *55*, 20323 (1961).
110. A. S. Sussman and B. T. Lingappa, Science *130*, 1343 (1959); Chem. Abstr. *54*, 6882 (1960).
111. Y. Abe, Proc. Faculty Eng. Keiogijulu Univ. *1*, No. 3, 42 (1948); Chem. Abstr. *44*, 4959 (1950).
112. M. Kitahara, Gifu Coll. Agr. (Japan) Research Bull. *68*, 64 (1950); Chem. Abstr. *46*, 5535 (1952).
113. F. Obaton, Compt. rend. *189*, 711 (1929); Chem. Abstr. *24*, 1136 (1930).
114. D. R. Ergle and L. M. Blank, Phytopathology *37*, 153 (1947); Chem. Abstr. *41*, 5174 (1947).
115. F. Obaton, Compt. rend. *189*, 711 (1929).
116. E. Bourquelot and H. Hérissey, Bull. soc. mycol. France *21*, 50 (1905).
117. A. Müntz, Compt. rend. *76*, 649 (1873).
118. A. Müntz, Ber. *6*, 451 (1873).
119. A. Müntz, Bull. soc. chim. France (2) *30*, 219 (1873).
120. A. Müntz, Compt. rend. *79*, 1183 (1874).
121. A. Müntz, Ann. chim. phys. (5) *8*, 60 (1876).
122. E. Bourquelot, Compt. rend. *108*, 568 (1889).
123. E. Bourquelot, Compt. rend. *111*, 534 (1890).
124. E. Bourquelot, Compt. rend. *111*, 579 (1890).
125. E. Bourquelot, Compt. rend. *113*, 750 (1891).
126. E. Bourquelot, Bull. soc. chim. France (3) *5*, 788 (1891).
127. E. Bourquelot, Bull. soc. chim. France (3) *11*, 353 (1899).
128. E. Bourquelot, Bull. soc. mycol. France *5*, 34 (1889).
129. E. Bourquelot, Bull. soc. mycol. France *6*, VII (1889).
130. E. Bourquelot, Bull. soc. mycol. France *6*, 150, 189 (1890).
131. E. Bourquelot, Bull. soc. mycol. France *7*, 5, 50, 121, 185, 208, 222 (1891).
132. E. Bourquelot, Bull. soc. mycol. France *8*, 13, 29, 196 (1892).
133. E. Bourquelot, Bull. soc. mycol. France *9*, 11, 51 (1893).
134. E. Winterstein, Ber. *26*, 3094 (1893).
135. N. Iwanoff, Biochem. Z. *162*, 455 (1925).
136. M. Braecke, J. pharm. Belg. *10*, 463, 479, 495 (1928); Chem. Abstr. *23*, 4486 (1929).
137. F. Obaton, Compt. rend. soc. biol. *93*, 304 (1929).
138. H. Euler and A. Euler, Arkiv Kemi *1*, 365 (1904); Chem. Zentr. *1906*, I, 1107.
139. S. Inagaki and M. Toki, J. pharm. Soc. Japan *64*, 132 (1944); Chem. Abstr. *45*, 721 (1951).
140. R. R. Paris, M. Durand, and J. L. Bonnet, Ann. pharm. franç. *16*, 186 (1958); Chem. Abstr. *52*, 20442 (1958).
141. A. Ratcliffe, Biochem, J. *31*, 240 (1937); Chem. Abstr. *31*, 4364 (1937).
142. H. Kojima, J. Chem. Soc. Japan, Pure Chem. Sect. *69*, 163 (1948); Chem. Abstr. *46*, 4558 (1952).
143. T. Shibamoto, K. Minami, and T. Tajima, J. Japan. Forest. Sci. *34*, 390 (1952); Chem. Abstr. *47*, 4436 (1953).
144. H. Kojima, J. Chem. Soc. Japan, Pure Chem. Sect. *73*, 377 (1952); Chem. Abstr. *47*, 4432 (1953).

145. T. Shimano, K. Taki, and K. Goto, Ann. Proc. Gifu Coll. Pharm. No, 3, 43 (1953); Chem. Abstr. *50*, 13183 (1956).
146. E. Hartmann and J. Zellner, Monatsh. Chem. *50*, 193 (1928).
147. N. Fröschl and J. Zellner, Monatsh. Chem. *50*, 201 (1928).
148. B. Lindberg, A. Misiorny, and C. A. Wachtmeister, Acta Chem. Scand. *7*, 591 (1953).
149. B. Lindberg and B. Wickberg, Acta Chem. Scand. *7*, 140 (1953).
150. B. Lindberg, Acta Chem. Scand. *9*, 917 (1955).
151. German Patent 271, 789; Chem. Zentr. *1914*, I, 1318.
152. T. Yamashita and F. Sato, J. Pharm. Soc. Japan *49*, 106 (1926); Chem. Zentr. *1929*, II, 1930.
153. O. Anselmino and E. Gilg, Ber. pharm. Ges. *23*, 326 (1913); Chem. Abstr. *7*, 3189 (1913).
154. T. Yamashita and F. Sato, J. Pharm. Soc. Japan *49*, 696 (1929); Chem. Abstr. *24*, 75 (1930).
155. E. O. Lippmann, Ber. *45*, 3431 (1913).
156. G. F. Howden and B. A. Kilby, Chem. & Ind. (London) *1956*, 1453.
157. G. R. Wyatt and G. F. Kalf, Federation Proc. *15*, 388 (1956).
158. G. R. Wyatt and G. F. Kalf, J. Gen. Physiol. *40*, 833 (1957); Chem. Abstr. *51*, 16985 (1957).
159. D. R. Evans and V. G. Dethier, J. Insect. Physiol. *1*, 3 (1957); Chem. Abstr. *51*, 13240 (1957).
160. G. Kurono, T. Sakai, K. Tochiori, T. Enami, and T. Ogawa, Kanazawa Daigaku Yakugakubu Kenkyu Nempô *8*, 42 (1958); Chem. Abstr. *53*, 3388 (1959).
161. D. Fairbairn, Nature *181*, 1593 (1958).
162. J. E. Treherne, J. Exptl. Biol. *35*, 611 (1958); Chem. Abstr. *53*, 2493 (1959).
163. G. F. Howden and B. A. Kilby, Chem. & Ind. (London) *1957*, 1453.
164. D. J. Candy and B. A. Kilby, Nature *183*, 1594 (1959).
165. R. Geigy, Acta Trop. *16*, 255 (1959); Chem. Abstr. *54*, 12398 (1960).
166. D. Fairbairn, Can. J. Zool. *36*, 787 (1958); Chem. Abstr. *53*, 5527 (1959).
167. H. Langer, Z. Naturforsch. *14b*, 480 (1959); Chem. Abstr. *54*, 4933 (1960).
168. V. Kubišta and Z. Bartoš, Physiol. Bohemoslov. *9*, 325 (1960); Chem. Abstr. *54*, 18813 (1960).
169. J. S. Barlow and H. L. House, J. Insect Physiol. *5*, 181 (1960); Chem. Abstr. *55*, 8674 (1961).
170. Y. Horie, Nature *188*, 583 (1960).
171. D. J. Candy and B. A. Kilby, Biochem. J. *78*, 531 (1961).
172. D. Fairbairn and R. F. Passey, Exptl. Parasitol. *6*, 566 (1957); Chem. Abstr. *52*, 5679 (1958).
173. D. J. Fairbairn, Can. J. Zool. *39*, 153 (1961); Chem. Abstr. *55*, 17931 (1961).
174. J. Dutrieu, Compt. rend. *248*, 1038 (1959); Chem. Abstr. *53*, 19186 (1959).
175. J. Dutrieu, Rend. ist. sci. univ. Camerino *1*, 196 (1960); Chem. Abstr. *55*, 17925 (1961).
176. E. Ottenstad, E. Brochmann-Hanssen, D. Oiseth, and A. Nordal, J. Pharm. and Pharmacol. *11*, 689 (1959).
177. A. Plouvier, Compt. rend. *232*, 1013 (1951); Chem. Abstr. *45*, 7646 (1951).
178. R. Dupéron, Compt. rend. *235*, 1331 (1952); Chem. Abstr. *47*, 4436 (1953).
179. V. Plouvier, Compt. rend. *232*, 1239 (1951); Chem. Abstr. *45*, 5769 (1951).
180. M. O. Remeaud, Compt. rend. soc. biol. *61*, 400 (1907); Chem. Abstr. *1*, 331 (1907).
181. V. Plouvier, Compt. rend. *227*, 85 (1948); Chem. Abstr. *42*, 8423 (1948).
182. A. Nordal and D. Öiseth, Acta Chem. Scand. *6*, 446 (1952); Chem. Abstr. *46*, 7182 (1952).

183. R. G. S. Bidwell, G. Krotkov, and G. B. Reed, Can. J. Botany *30*, 291 (1952); Chem. Abstr. *46*, 8699 (1952).

184. I. S. Kozhina, Trudy Botan. Inst. im. V. L. Komarova Akad. Nauk S.S.S.R., Ser. 5, *1961*, No. 8, 40; Chem. Abstr. *56*, 7724 (1962).

185. L. V. Smith and E. Zavarin, Tappi *43*, 218 (1960); Chem. Abstr. *54*, 17567 (1960).

186. J. B. Rao and K. N. N. Sastry, Bull. Central Leather Research Inst., Madras (India) *6*, 528 (1960); Chem. Abstr. *54*, 25084 (1960).

187. S. Pathak and J. V. Bhat, J. Univ. Bombay *21*, Pt. 5, Sect. A, 11 (1953); Chem. Abstr. *48*, 2187 (1954).

188. A. Jermstad and K. B. Jensen, Pharm. Acta Helv. *26*, 33 (1951); Chem. Abstr. *45*, 6803 (1951).

189. S. Lascombes and J. Carles, Compt. rend. *238*, 136 (1954); Chem. Abstr. *48*, 5944 (1954).

190. M. Srinivasan and I. S. Bhatia, Biochem. J. *56*, 256 (1954); Chem. Abstr. *48*, 5300 (1954).

191. J. E. Courtois, A. Archambault, and P. Le Dizet, Bull. soc. chim. biol. *38*, 351 (1956).

192. Z. N. Bryantseva, V. A. Valutina, and E. K. Fuzina, Uchenye Zapiski Gor'kovsk. Univ. *1959*, No. 1, 119; Chem. Abstr. *55*, 7562 (1961).

193. T. Mizuno and T. Kinpyo, J. Agr. Chem. Soc. Japan *29*, 665 (1955); Chem. Abstr. *50*, 3571 (1956).

194. N. S. Kapur, P. B. Mathur, and K. K. Singh, Indian J. Hort. *10*, 9 (1953); Chem. Abstr. *48*, 1601 (1954).

195. B. A. Rubin, Doklady Akad. Nauk S.S.S.R. *3*, 431 (1936); Chem. Abstr. *31*, 1463 (1937).

196. G. Pizelle, Compt. rend. *254*, 3028 (1962).

197. R. Bourdu and M. Quillet, Compt. rend. *237*, 1751 (1953).

198. A. B. Svendsen, Blyttia *11*, 96 (1953); Chem. Abstr. *50*, 7963 (1956).

199. A. B. Svendsen, Chemistry of Norvegian Umbelliferae, Johan Grundt Tanum Forlag, Oslo 1954, 144; Chem. Abstr. *52*, 2173 (1958).

200. A. de Cugnac and H. Belval, Bull. soc. botan. France *91*, 1 (1944); Chem. Abstr. *43*, 8014 (1949).

201. M. L. Rubat du Mérac, Rev. Gen. Botan. *65*, 215 (1958); Chem. Abstr. *56*, 2716 (1962).

202. A. Sosa, Bull. soc. chim. biol. *32*, 344 (1950).

203. M. Lesueur, J. pharm. chim. *3*, 399 (1911); Chem. Abstr. *5*, 3465 (1911).

204. H. Thies and F. Herrlinger, Pharmazie *5*, 347 (1950); Chem. Abstr. *44*, 11027 (1950).

205. H. Colin, Compt. rend. *201*, 1414 (1935); Chem. Abstr. *30*, 2604 (1936).

206. J. Susplugas, J. Pelinard, and P. Cazottes, Trav. soc. pharm. Montpellier *10*, No. 2, 11 (1950); Chem. Abstr. *48*, 7706 (1954).

207. R. Bourdu, Rev. gén. botan. *66*, 209 (1959); Chem. Abstr. *54*, 1673 (1960).

208. L. Rosenthaler, Arch. Pharm. *263*, 561 (1925); Chem. Abstr. *20*, 645 (1926).

209. E. D. Carkhuff and L. G. Grambling, J. Am. Pharm. Assoc. *41*, 660 (1952); Chem. Abstr. *47*, 1901 (1953).

210. H. H. Schlubach and H. O. A. Koehn, Ann. *606*, 130 (1957).

211. Y. S. Lewis, C. T. Dwarakanath, and D. S. Johar, Current Sci. (India), *23*, 54 (1954); Chem. Abstr. *48*, 7715 (1954).

212. A. Sosa, Ann. chim. *14*, 5 (1940); Chem. Abstr. *35*, 7947 (1941).

213. S. Haq and G. A. Adams, Can. J. Biochem. Physiol. *40*, 989 (1962); Chem. Abstr. *57*, 15211 (1962).

214. E. Löhr, Physiol. Plantarum *6*, 529 (1953); Chem. Abstr. *48*, 5303 (1954).

215. V. Subrahmanyan, G. S. Bains, C. P. Natarajan, and D. S. Bhatia, Arch. Biochem. Biophys. *60*, 27 (1956); Chem. Abstr. *50*, 6600 (1956).
216. N. Gopinathan, Intern. Sugar J. *64*, No. 757, 9 (1962); Chem. Abstr. *56*, 13256 (1962).
217. T. Mizuno, Nippon Nôgei-Kagaku Kaishi *32*, 340 (1958); Chem. Abstr. *54*, 19874 (1960).
218. P. du Vigneaud, Bull. soc. roy. botan. Belg. *74*, 20 (1941); Chem. Abstr. *42*, 7379 (1948).
219. F. P. Mehrlich, Bot. Gaz. *92*, 113 (1931); Chem. Abstr. *26*, 754 (1932).
220. A. Jermstad and K. Briseid, Bull. soc. chim. biol. *33*, 258 (1951); Chem. Abstr. *45*, 10505 (1951).
221. M. L. Rubat du Mérac, Bull. soc. botan. France *103*, 444 (1956); Chem. Abstr. *56*, 712 (1962).
222. V. N. Nigam and K. V. Giri, Can. J. Biochem. and Physiol. *39*, 1847 (1961); Chem. Abstr. *56*, 9130 (1962).
223. S. Kawamura, Sciencaj Studoj *1958*, 173; Chem. Abstr. *52*, 20430 (1958).
224. H. Wanner, Ber. schweiz. botan. Ges. *63*, 162 (1953); Chem. Abstr. *48*, 11574 (1954).
225. M. Cholet, Bull. soc. chim. biol. *28*, 672 (1946); Chem. Abstr. *41*, 3838 (1947).
226. M. Cholet, Compt. rend. *245*, 1820 (1957).
227. V. Plouvier, Compt. rend. *228*, 1886 (1949); Chem. Abstr. *44*, 190 (1950).
228. S. Ueno, Kagaku *24*, 90 (1954); Chem. Abstr. *48*, 12242 (1954).
229. K. Wallenfels and J. Lehmann, Chem. Ber. *90*, 1000 (1957).
230. M. Hasegawa, T. Takayama, and T. Shizoya, Kagaku *21*, 593 (1951); Chem. Abstr. *48*, 5297 (1954).
231. B. Lindberg, Acta Chem. Scand. *9*, 169 (1955).
232. A. R. C. Haas, Botan. Gaz. *98*, 65 (1936); Chem. Abstr. *31*, 434 (1937).
233. J. P. Wolf and W. H. Ewart, Arch. Biochem. Biophys. *58*, 365 (1955).
234. N. Gopinathan, Intern. Sugar. J. *64*, No. 757, 9 (1962); Chem. Abstr. *56*, 13256 (1962).
235. A. S. Bhown, Indian J. Appl. Chem. *25*, 97 (1962).
236. J. Augier and M. L. Rubat du Mérac, Bull. lab. maritime Dinard No. 40, 25 (1954); Chem. Abstr. *51*, 1395 (1957).
237. J. Cerbulis, J. Am. Chem. Soc. *77*, 6054 (1955).
238. A. Nordal and R. Klevstrand, Acta Chem. Scand. *5*, 85 (1951).
239. V. Plouvier, Ann. sci. nat. Botan *3*, 204 (1942); Chem. Abstr. *40*, 7311 (1946).
240. J. E. Courtois and U. Ariyoshi, Bull. soc. chim. biol. *44*, 31 (1962).
241. F. B. Power and V. K. Chestnut, J. Agr. Research *26*, 69 (1923); Chem. Abstr. *18*, 408 (1924).
242. A. M. Gad and F. Osman, Egypt. J. Chem. *2*, 123 (1959); Chem. Abstr. *54*, 7185 (1960).
243. M. L. Rubat du Mérac, Compt. rend. *241*, 88 (1955); Chem. Abstr. *49*, 14909 (1955).
244. A. G. Gawadi, Plant Physiol. *22*, 438 (1947); Chem. Abstr. *42*, 1632 (1948).
245. K. Hayashi and T. Mizuno, J. Agr. Chem. Soc. Japan *26*, 569 (1952); Chem. Abstr. *49*, 4803 (1955).
246. T. Koyama, J. Pharm. Soc. Japan *73*, 411 (1953); Chem. Abstr. *47*, 7162 (1953).
247. M. Chollet, D. Scheidecker, and M. Bouloux, Compt. rend. *244*, 2086 (1957).
248. A. Ya. Butkov and E. I. Milogradova, Uzbek. Biol. Zhur. *1959*, No. 6, 15; Chem. Abstr. *54*, 22866 (1960).
249. F. Obaton, Compt. rend. *195*, 823 (1932); Chem. Abstr. *27*, 752 (1933).

250. M. Yanagita, J. Pharm. Soc. Japan *64*, No. 7A, 9 (1944); Chem. Abstr. *45*, 3562 (1951).

251. J. B. Pridham, Nature *182*, 1687 (1958).

252. J. Comin, Anales asoc. quim. argentina *42*, 132 (1954); Chem. Abstr. *50*, 392 (1956).

253. A. M. McLeod and H. McCorquodate, Nature *182*, 815 (1958).

254. V. Plouvier, Compt. rend. *227*, 604 (1948); Chem. Abstr. *43*, 1840 (1949).

255. M. H. Zimmermann, Plant Physiol. *33*, 213 (1958); Chem. Abstr. *52*, 14773 (1958).

256. M. Bridel, J. pharm. chim. *4*, 445 (1912); Chem. Abstr. *6*, 1814 (1912).

257. M. Bridel, Compt. rend. *155*, 1164 (1913); Chem. Abstr. *7*, 812 (1913).

258. M. Bridel, J. pharm. chim. *21*, 306 (1920); Chem. Abstr. *14*, 2504 (1920).

259. M. Bridel, Compt. rend *156*, 627 (1913); Chem. Abstr. *7*, 1952 (1913).

260. M. Bridel, J. pharm. chim. *7*, 289 (1913); Chem. Abstr. *7*, 2662 (1913).

261. J. Augier, Bull. soc. botan. France *89*, 113 (1942); Chem. Abstr. *38*, 5878 (1944).

262. O. T. Baytop, Materiae Vegetabiles *1*, 369 (1954); Chem. Abstr. *52*, 10493 (1958).

263. H. Belval, Bull. soc. chim. biol. *29*, 444 (1947); Chem. Abstr. *42*, 253 (1948).

264. I. R. Rominskiĭ, A. S. Sushkova, and P. V. Golovin, Ukrain. Khim. Zhur. *21*, 394 (1955); Chem. Abstr. *50*, 3671 (1956).

265. I. N. Rashchenko, Trudy Kazakh. Sel'skokhoz. Inst. *6*, 40 (1959); Chem. Abstr. *56*, 7711 (1962).

266. H. Ziegler and T. E. Mittler, Z. Naturforsch. *14b*, 278 (1959); Chem. Abstr. *54*, 15538 (1960).

267. D. W. Buelow and O. Gisvold, J. Am. Pharm. Assoc. *33*, 270 (1944); Chem. Abstr. *38*, 5361 (1944).

268. L. Jurd, J. Org. Chem. *21*, 759 (1956).

269. M. Yamashita, Sci. Repts Tôhoku Imp. Univ., lst Series *24*, 197 (1935); Chem. Abstr. *29*, 7383 (1935).

270. M. Kotake and H. Arakawa, Naturwissenschaften *43*, 327 (1956).

271. A. Sosa, C. Sosa-Bourdonik, and C. Hardy, Compt. rend. *240*, 1570 (1955).

272. T. J. de Man and J. G. de Hens, Rec. trav. chim. *68*, 43 (1949).

273. K. Nakahara, Botan. Mag. (Tokyo) *68*, 81 (1955); Chem. Abstr. *49*, 16086 (1955).

274. T. Mizuno and K. Hayashi, J. Agr. Chem. Soc. Japan *28*, 349 (1954); Chem. Abstr. *49*, 4803 (1955).

275. J. Lys, Compt. rend. *241*, 1842 (1955).

276. W. W. Jones, Proc. Am. Soc. Hort. Sci. *25*, 239 (1938); Chem. Abstr. *32*, 7075 (1938).

277. C. R. Mitra and Y. C. Awasthi, J. Sci. & Ind. Research (India) *21D*, 102 (1962); Chem. Abstr. *56*, 15832 (1962).

278. J. M. Lagowski, H. M. Sell, C. F. Huffman, and C. W. Duncan, Arch. Biochem. Biophys. *76*, 306 (1958).

279. M. E. Henderson, L. Hough, and T. J. Painter, J. Chem. Soc. *1958*, 3519.

280. V. V. Rendig and E. A. McComb, Plant and Soil *14*, 176 (1961); Chem. Abstr. *55*, 27740 (1961).

281. M. Henrici, Onderstepoort J. Vet. Sci. Animal Ind. *22*, 373 (1949); Chem. Abstr. *44*, 3099 (1950).

282. M. Bridel and M. Braecke, Compt. rend. *173*, 1403 (1921).

283. M. Bridel and M. Braecke, Bull. soc. chim. biol. *4*, 96 (1922); Chem. Abstr. *16*, 1970 (1922).

284. T. Kariyone, M. Takahashi, K. Isoi, and M. Yoshihura, J. Pharm. Soc. Japan (Yaku-gaku Zasshi) *78*, 801 (1958); Chem. Abstr. *52*, 18390 (1958).

285. G. V. Joshi and I. M. Majumdar, J. Univ. Bombay Sect. B *28*, Pt 3, No. 46, 11 (1959); Chem. Abstr. *55*, 10592 (1961).

286. G. L. Poland, J. T. Manion, M. W. Brenner, and P. L. Harris, Ind. Eng. Chem. *30*, 340 (1938); Chem. Abstr. *32*, 4631 (1938).

287. F. D. H. MacDowall, Botan. Gaz. *123*, 180 (1962); Chem. Abstr. *56*, 15845 (1962).

288. D. French, J. Am. Chem. Soc. *77*, 1024 (1955).

289. P. G. Asmaev and I. G. Mokhnachev, Trudy Krasnodar. Inst. Pishchevoi Prom. *1958*, No. 19, 3; Chem. Abstr. *55*, 27786 (1961).

290. P. G. Asmaev and I. G. Mokhnachev, Bulgar Tyutyun *5*, 472 (1960); Chem. Abstr. *55*, 19145 (1961).

291. T. Mizuno, S. Kainuma, A. Nakagawa, and T. Kimpyo, Nippon Nôgei-Kagaku Kaishi *32*, 467 (1958); Chem. Abstr. *54*, 19875 (1960).

292. M. K. Mikhailov, Compt. rend. acad. bulgare sci. *10*, 201 (1957); Chem. Abstr. *52*, 4112 (1958).

293. H. Lumang, N. Fernandez, and C. Apon, Philippine J. Agr. *19*, 173 (1956); Chem. Abstr. *51*, 3094 (1957).

294. H. L. Pearse and L. Novellie, J. Sci. Food Agr. *4*, 108 (1953); Chem. Abstr. *47*, 5638 (1953).

295. M. Phillips and A. M. Bacot, J. Assoc. Offic. Agr. Chemists *36*, 504 (1953); Chem. Abstr. *47*, 12769 (1953).

296. M. E. Scarascia-Venezian and G. Giovannozzi Sermanni, Il Tabacco *58*, 264 (1954); Chem. Abstr. *49*, 2575 (1955).

297. D. M. W. Anderson and N. J. King, Biochim. et Biophys. Acta *52*, 441 (1961).

298. M. L. Rubat du Mérac, Compt. rend. *239*, 646 (1954).

299. E. Ottenstad, E. Brochmann-Hanssen, D. Oiseth, and A. Nordal, J. Pharm. and Pharmacol. *11*, 689 (1959); Chem. Abstr. *54*, 9203 (1960).

300. A. T. Dutt, N. R. Chatterjee, S. Ghosh, and R. N. Chopra, Arch. Pharm. *276*, 343 (1938).

301. S. Susheela, J. S. Puethi, and G. Lal, Ind. J. Appl. Chem. *23*, 169 (1960).

302. D. M. W. Anderson and C. T. Greenwood, J. Chem. Soc. *1956*, 220.

303. V. Dadák, Monatsh. Chem. *88*, 1116 (1957).

304. D. Hooper, Ann. Rep. Indian Mus. Indust. Sect. *1908—1909*, 5; Chem. Abstr. *4*, 89 (1910).

305. V. Arreguine, Anales soc. quim. argentina *8*, 229 (1920); Chem. Abstr. *15*, 2901 (1921).

306. A. Assarsson and O. Theander, Acta Chem. Scand. *12*, 1319 (1958).

307. J. Parker, Botan. Gazz. *121*, 46 (1959).

308. P. Boysen-Jansen, Jahrbuch. wiss. Botan. *61*, 431 (1915); Chem. Abstr. *10*, 69 (1916).

309. A. Jermstad, E. Brochmann- Hanssen and A. Baerheim, Medd. Norsk Farm. Selskap *11*, 63, 79, 97 (1949); Chem. Abstr. *44*, 2084 (1950).

310. A. Goris and H. Canal, Bull. soc. chim. France (5) *3*, 1982 (1936).

311. J. B. Pridham, Biochem. J. *75*, 13 (1960).

312. S. L. Larsson and L. Selleby, Svensk Papperstidn. *63*, 606 (1960); Chem. Abstr. *55*, 981 (1961).

313. Ch. Mentzer and L. Cronenberger, Bull. soc. chim. biol. *37*, 371 (1955); Chem. Abstr. *50*, 1133 (1956).

314. F. J. H. le Riche, J. S. African Chem. Inst. *1*, 35 (1948); Chem. Abstr. *43*, 3889 (1949).

315. A. Allsopp, J. Exptl. Botany (London) *2*, 121 (1951); Chem. Abstr. *48*, 3478 (1954).

316. G. W. Holmes and E. D. Kurth, Tappi *44*, 893 (1961); Chem. Abstr. *56*, 12015 (1962).

317. M. Yanagita, J. Pharm. Soc. Japan *64*, No. 7A, 8 (1944); Chem. Abstr. *45*, 3564 (1951).

318. R. Dupéron and A. Sosa, Bull. soc. chim. biol. *35*, 257 (1953); Chem. Abstr. *47*, 10248 (1953).

319. A. Sosa and R. Dupéron, Compt. rend. *235*, 82 (1952); Chem. Abstr. *47*, 2512 (1953).

320. A. A. King and A. S. C. Wan, J. Chem. Soc. *1960*, 1394.

321. H. Eder, Pharmazie *10*, 236 (1955).

322. M. Bridel and M. Braecke, Compt. rend. *175*, 532 (1922); Chem. Abstr. *17*, 299 (1923).

323. M. Bridel and M. Braecke, Bull. soc. chim. biol. *5*, 10 (1923); Chem. Abstr. *17*, 299 (1923).

324. T. S. Villegas, Univ. Philippines Nat. and Applied Sci. Bull. *5*, 449 (1936); Chem. Abstr. *32*, 972 (1938).

225. N. E. Tolbert and L. P. Zill, Plant Physiol. *29*, 288 (1954); Chem. Abstr. *48*, 11577 (1954).

326. R. Bienfang, J. Am. Pharm. Assoc. *23*, 396 (1934); Chem. Abstr. *28*, 6945 (1934).

327. Kim-Don Be, Vestnik Moskov. Univ. 12, Ser. Biol. Pochnoved., Geol., Geograph. No. 2, 111 (1957); Chem. Abstr. *52*, 633 (1958).

328. E. K. Ventre and S. Byall, J. Agr. Research *55*, 553 (1937); Chem. Abstr. *32*, 3185 (1938).

329. S. I. Kokina and A. Ya. Kokin, J. Bot. (S.S.S.R.) *21*, No. 6, 637 (1936); Chem. Abstr. *33*, 9034 (1939).

330. E. K. Ventre, S. Byall, and C. F. Walton, J. Agr. Research *59*, 139 (1939); Chem. Abstr. *33*, 9035 (1939).

331. E. K. Ventre, S. Byall, and J. L. Catlett, J. Agr. Research *76*, 145 (1948); Chem. Abstr. *44*, 5128 (1950).

332. F. Lanza, Agr. Nuova *2*, 229 (1950); Chem. Abstr. *45*, 8789 (1951).

333. Gh. Herman, A. Gheorghiu, and E. Ionescu-Matiu, Lucrarile prezentate conf. natl. farm. Bucharest *1958*, 406; Chem. Abstr. *53*, 9372 (1959).

334. H. Takebana and N. Ogura, Nippon Nôgei-Kagaku Kaishi *30*, 644 (1956); Chem. Abstr. *52*, 12436 (1958).

335. P. Nordin, Trans. Kansas Acad. Sci. *62*, 212 (1959); Chem. Abstr. *55*, 8548 (1961).

336. H. Yoshino, Nippon Jôzô Kyôkai Zasshi *46*, K7−13 (1951); Chem. Abstr. *46*, 7282 (1952).

337. H. R. Kraybill, R. L. Smith, and E. D. Walter, J. Am. Chem. Soc. *59*, 2470 (1937).

338. S. Kawamura, J. Agr. Chem. Soc. Japan *28*, 851 (1954); Chem. Abstr. *49*, 13375 (1955).

339. S. Kawamura, Tech. Bull. Kagawa Agr. Coll. *4*, 65 (1952); Chem. Abstr. *46*, 9743 1952).

340. M. M. Chollet and R. Dufon, Compt. rend. *241*, 1819 (1955); Chem. Abstr. *50*, 6604 (1956).

341. D. French, G. M. Wild, and W. J. James, J. Am. Chem. Soc. *75*, 3664 (1953).

342. D. Bourdon, L. Berthois, and M. L. Gielfrich, Bull. soc. sci. Bretagne *29*, 7 (1954); Chem. Abstr. *50*, 5856 (1956).

343. M. J. Laurent, J. pharm. chim. (6) *25*, 225 (1907); Chem. Abstr. *1*, 1166 (1907).

344. L. Beauquesne, Ann. pharm. franç. *5*, 470 (1947); Chem. Abstr. *42*, 4244 (1948).

345. R. Bourdu, Compt. rend. *246*, 973 (1957); Chem. Abstr. *52*, 11196 (1958).

346. R. Bourdu, Compt. rend. *239*, 1524 (1954); Chem. Abstr. *49*, 6387 (1955).

347. R. Bourdu, Rev. gén. botan. *64*, 153, 197 (1957); Chem. Abstr. *51*, 16751 (1957).

348. R. R. Gorham, Can. J. Res. *24C* 47 (1946); Chem. Abstr. *40*, 5104 (1946).

349. W. de Ráfols, Materiae Vegetabiles *1*, 278 (1953); Chem. Abstr. *48*, 3485 (1954).

350. G. M. Wild and D. French, Proc. Iowa Acad. Sci. *59*, 226 (1952); Chem. Abstr. *47*, 2834 (1953).

351. S. Thaler, Fette, Seifen, Anstrichmittel *62*, 701 (1960); Chem. Abstr. *55*, 1962 (1961).

352. J. Cerbulis, Arch. Biochem. Biophys. *58*, 406 (1955); Chem. Abstr. *50*, 2759 (1956).

353. J. Cerbulis, Arch. Biochem. Biophys. *49*, 442 (1954); Chem. Abstr. *48*, 8340 (1954).

354. H. C. Humpreis, Ann. Botany *11*, 219 (1947); Chem. Abstr. *41*, 7449 (1947).

355. V. Plouvier, Compt. rend. *236*, 317 (1953); Chem. Abstr. *47*, 12528 (1953).

356. J. Susplugas, M. Lalaurie, G. Privat, and J. Tarbouriech, Trav. soc. pharm. Montpellier *20*, 104 (1961); Chem. Abstr. *55*, 15833 (1961).

357. R. W. Bailey, J. Sci. Food Agr. *9*, 743 (1958); Chem. Abstr. *53*, 6479 (1959).

358. O. Goldschmid and H. L. Hergert, Tappi *44*, 858 (1961); Chem. Abstr. *56*, 13131 (1962).

359. T. Watanabe, Y. Motomura, and K. Aso, Tôhoku J. Agr. Research *12*, 173 (1961); Chem. Abstr. *56*, 5228 (1962).

360. B. Lindberg and B. Wickberg, Acta Chem. Scand. *7*, 140 (1953).

361. E. Ramstad, J. Am. Pharm. Assoc. *43*, 236 (1954); Chem. Abstr. *48*, 7260 (1954).

362. S. Kawamura, H. Nakamura, and K. Horike, Tech. Bull. Kagawa Agr. Coll. (Japan) *6*, 8 (1954); Chem. Abstr. *48*, 12922 (1954).

363. J. B. Pridham, Nature *182*, 1687 (1958).

364. A. T. Markh and Yu. G. Skorikova, Izvest. Vysshikh. Ucheb. Zavedenii, Pishchewaya Tekhnol. *1959*, No. 1, 37; Chem. Abstr. *53*, 18326 (1959).

365. G. Warcollier, Compt. rend. *144*, 987 (1907); Chem. Abstr. *1*, 2007 (1907).

366. A. E. Bradfield and A. E. Flood, Ann. Rept., East Malling Research Sta., Kent *1949*, 100; Chem. Abstr. *46*, 9667 (1952).

367. G. Vitte, E. Boussemart, and G. Guichard, Bull. soc. pharm. Marseille, Bull. trimest. *1952*, No. 3, 50; Chem. Abstr. *49*, 7651 (1955).

368. R. B. Dustman and V. B. Tish, Plant Physiol. *19*, 603 (1944); Chem. Abstr. *39*, 2540 (1945).

369. Y. Nakamura and T. Shimomura, J. Agr. Chem. Soc. Japan *19*, 317 (1943); Chem. Abstr. *45*, 8087 (1951).

370. H. Iwamoto, K. Kurihara, and M. Shiga, Hakkô Kyôkaishi *15*, 340 (1957); Chem. Abstr. *52*, 9594 (1958).

371. E. C. Humpreis, Ann. Botany *20*, 411 (1956); Chem. Abstr. *50*, 17000 (1956).

372. R. I. Lerman, Doklady Akad. Nauk S. S. S. R. *108*, 1191 (1956); Chem. Abstr. *51*, 1390 (1957).

373. L. Massart, Intern. Tijdschr. Brouw. en Mont. *15*, 6 (1955); Chem. Abstr. *50*, 442 (1956).

374. A. M. MacLeod, D. C. Travis, and D. G. Wreay, J. Inst. Brewing *59*, 154 (1953); Chem. Abstr. *49*, 9219 (1955).

375. A. M. MacLeod, J. Inst. Brewing *58*, 363 (1952); Chem. Abstr. *48*, 5290 (1954).

376. G. Bode, Fortschr. Landw. *4*, 545 (1929); Chem. Abstr. *24*, 2774 (1930).

377. A. M. MacLeod, J. Inst. Brewing *57*, 163 (1951); Chem. Abstr. *45*, 10482 (1951).

378. A. M. Lasheen and H. T. Blackhurst, Proc. Am. Soc. Hort. Sci. *67*, 331 (1956); Chem. Abstr. *51*, 4508 (1957).

379. M. Danilovič and E. Peci-Popovič, Acta Pharm. Jugoslav. *9*, 33 (1959); Chem. Abstr. *53*, 14413 (1959).

380. A. Krauja, Augsne Un Raža, Latv. S. S. R. Zemkopibas, Inst. Rakstu Krajums *1957*, No. 6, 175; Chem. Abstr. *53*, 15443 (1959).

381. H. Colin and H. Belval, Compt. rend. *196*, 1825 (1933); Chem. Abstr. *27*, 4556 (1933).

382. M. Bridel, J. pharm. chim. *12*, 249 (1915); Chem. Abstr. *10*, 802 (1916).

383. M. Rohrlich and W. Essner, Getreide u. Mehl *10*, 121 (1960); Chem. Abstr. *55*, 6622 (1961).

384. E. J. Deszyck and S. V. Ting, J. Sci. Food Agr. *7*, 259 (1956); Chem. Abstr. *53*, 19283 (1959).

385. W. B. Alwood, Ind. Eng. Chem. *2*, 481 (1911); Chem. Abstr. *5*, 325 (1911).

386. A. Astegiano and M. T. Graziano, Accad. ital. vite. e vino, Siena, Atti *10*, 614 (1959); Chem. Abstr. *54*, 18865 (1960).

387. N. M. Sisakyan and S. A. Marutyan, Doklady Akad. Nauk S. S. S. R. *61*, 491 (1948) Chem. Abstr. *43*, 280 (1949).

388. G. Barbera, Ann. chim. applicata *23*, 99 (1933); Chem. Abstr. *27*, 4557 (1933).

389. R. Waite and J. Boyd, J. Sci. Food Agr. *4*, 197 (1953); Chem. Abstr. *47*, 6001 (1953).

390. R. Waite, J. Sci. Food Agr. *9*, 39 (1958); Chem. Abstr. *52*, 5718 (1958).

391. R. Waite, J. Sci. Food Agr. *8*, 422 (1957); Chem. Abstr. *51*, 15711 (1957).

392. P. Lys and J. Adès, Lebanese Pharm. J. *3*, 89 (1955); Chem. Abstr. *50*, 12399 (1956).

393. E. G. V. Percival, Brit. J. Nutrition *6*, 104 (1952); Chem. Abstr. *46*, 6707 (1952).

394. H. O. Askew, R. J. Monk, and J. Hodgson, New Zealand J. Sci. Technol. *36*, 277 (1954); Chem. Abstr. *49*, 9109 (1955).

395. S. Komatsu and M. Ishimasa, Mem. Coll. Sci. Kyoto Imp. Univ. *7*, 165 (1924); Chem. Abstr. *18*, 1846 (1924).

396. A. Poljakoff-Mayber, Bull. Research Council Israel *3*, 248 (1953); Chem. Abstr. *49*, 9754 (1955).

397. O. Munerati and G. Mezzandroli, Boll. dell assoc. ital. dell'industria dello zucchero dell'alcool *8*, 25 (1915); Chem. Abstr. *10*, 984 (1916).

398. R. Van Reen and W. R. Singleton, Agron. J. *44*, 610 (1952); Chem. Abstr. *47*, 5996 (1953).

399. W. Nathan-Levy, Bull. assoc. chim. sucr. dist. *41*, 240 (1924); Chem. Abstr. *18*, 3119 (1924).

400. A. May Hurd-Karrer and H. Hasselbring, J. Agr. Research *34*, 191 (1927); Chem. Abstr. *21*, 2148 (1927).

401. J. Carles, L. Soubiès, R. Gadet, and P. Maury, Compt. rend. *234*, 1899 (1952); Chem. Abstr. *46*, 10311 (1952).

402. L. Boyer, Sucr. ind. coloniale *49*, 226, 252, 299, 343, 394 (1914); Chem. Abstr. *9*, 1406 (1915).

403. D. K. Roy and B. C. Guha, Science & Culture (India) *17*, 138 (1951); Chem. Abstr. *46*, 5147 (1952).

404. Y. Kashiwada, J. Sericult. Sci. Japan *24*, 76 (1915); Chem. Abstr. *50*, 5096 (1956).

405. F. Aylward and B. W. Nichols, J. Sci. Food Agr. *12*, 645 (1961); Chem. Abstr. *56*, 3818 (1962).

406. G. Weiss, Studia Univ. Babes-Bolyai Ser. 1, No. 2, 205 (1959); Chem. Abstr. *55*, 6613 (1961).

407. H. Thaler, Z. Lebensm. Unters. *105*, 198 (1957); Chem. Abstr. *51*, 9968 (1957).

408. M. J. Fernandéz Diéz, F. Gonzáles Pellisso, and J. M. R. de la Borbolla y Alcala, Anales real. soc. espan. fís. y quím. (Madrid) *48*, 437 (1952); Chem. Abstr. *48*, 4640 (1954).

409. P. G. Kamat and K. Solonie, J. Sci. & Ind. Research (India) *19C*, 257 (1960); Chem. Abstr. *55*, 8904 (1961).

410. H. I. Waterman, Chem. Weekbl. *13*, 122 (1916); Chem. Abstr. *10*, 1235 (1916).

411. S. Suzuki, T. Tamura, T. Hirohata, Y. Namoto, and K. Arai, Nippon Nôgei-Kagaku Kaishi *31*, 768 (1957); Chem. Abstr. *53*, 20300 (1959).

412. C. J. de Wolff, Biochem. Z. *176*, 225 (1926); Chem. Abstr. *21*, 968 (1927).

413. B. S. Ramachandra, R. G. Krishnamurthy, and Y. K. Raghunatha Rao, Food Sci. (Mysore) *8*, 83 (1959); Chem. Abstr. *53*, 20596 (1959).

414. H. Kurasawa, I. Igaue, T. Hayakawa, and H. Ogami, Nippon Nôgei-Kagaku Kaishi *33*, 388 (1959); Chem. Abstr. *54*, 9005 (1960).

415. D. B. Parihar, Nature *175*, 42 (1955).

416. G. M. Christensen, Nature *195*, 74 (1962).

417. S. Grzesiuk and K. Kulka, Acta Soc. Botan. Polon. *31*, 83 (1962); Chem. Abstr. *51*, 7619 (1962).

418. M. Rohrlich and W. Essner, Ber. Getreidechemiker-Tagung, Detmold *1960*, 27; Chem. Abstr. *55*, 10602 (1961).

419. D. J. Mackenzie and C. B. Wylan, J. Sci. Food Agr. *8*, 38 (1957); Chem. Abstr. *51*, 6787 (1957).

420. M. H. Zimmermann, Plant Physiol. *32*, 288 (1957); Chem. Abstr. *52*, 511 (1958).

421. W. E. Lyles, M. C. Futrell, and I. M. Atkins, Phytopathology *49*, 254 (1959); Chem. Abstr. *53*, 14244 (1959).

422. M. T. Yastrebov, Vestnik Moskov. Univ., Ser. Biol. Pochvoved., Geol., Geograph. *13*, No. 3, 63 (1958); Chem. Abstr. *53*, 8508 (1959).

423. H. L. Wood, Australian J. Agr. Res. *11*, 673 (1960); Chem. Abstr. *54*, 25349 (1960).

424. N. E. Krog, D. Le Tourneau, and H. Hart, Phytopathology *51*, 75 (1961); Chem. Abstr. *55*, 13558 (1961).

425. M. Dubois, W. F. Geddes, and F. Smith, Cereal Chem. *37*, 557 (1960); Chem. Abstr. *55*, 8684 (1961).

426. L. E. Lopatecki, E. L. Longair, and C. W. Farstad, Can. J. Bot. *35*, 9 (1957); Chem. Abstr. *51*, 5925 (1957).

427. J. Carles, Compt. rend. *229*, 552 (1949); Chem. Abstr. *44*, 2089 (1950).

428. S. M. Strepkov, Zhur. Obshcheĭ Khim. *28*, 3143 (1958); Chem. Abstr. *53*, 10053 (1959).

429. M. J. Clancy, J. Chem. Soc. *1960*, 4213.

430. K. Takiura and K. Koizumi, Chem. and Pharm. Bull (Tokyo) *10*, 134 (1962).

431. L. Lappas and C. B. Gustafson, J. Am. Pharm. Assoc. *39*, 591 (1950); Chem. Abstr. *44*, 11027 (1950).

432. A. Meunier, J. pharm. chim. *24*, 9 (1936); Chem. Abstr. *30*, 8310 (1936).

433. A. Meunier, Compt. rend. *197*, 98 (1933); Chem. Abstr. *27*, 4829 (1933).

434. B. C. Joshi and D. S. Bhakuni, J. Sci. & Ind. Research (India) *18B*, 525 (1959); Chem. Abstr. *54*, 17575 (1960).

435. P. Gillot, J. pharm. chim. *28*, 148 (1923).

436. P. Gillot, J. pharm. chim. (8) *1*, 205 (1925); Chem. Abstr. *19*, 2064 (1925).

437. H. Colin and R. Franquet, Compt. rend. *186*, 890 (1928); Chem. Abstr. *22*, 1993 (1928).

438. A. Levallois, Compt. rend. *90*, 1293 (1880).

439. A. Levallois, Compt. rend. *93*, 281 (1881).

440. T. Morawski and J. Stingl, Monatsh. Chem. *8*, 82 (1882).

441. M. Quiller and D. Bourdon, Compt. rend. *242*, 1054 (1956); Chem. Abstr. *50*, 11442 (1956).

442. F. Smith and H. C. Srivastava, J. Org. Chem. *22*, 987 (1957).

443. H. T. Brown and G. H. Morris, J. Chem. Soc. *53*, 604 (1893); Chem. Zentr. *1893*, I, 1070.

444. H. T. Brown and G. H. Morris, Chem. Ztg. *17*, 154 (1893).

445. M. Bridel, Compt. rend. *179*, 1190 (1924); Chem. Abstr. *19*, 843 (1925).

446. Shimoyama, Chem. Ztg. *19*, 1805, 1889 (1895).

447. J. Carles, Compt. rend. *241*, 1329 (1955); Chem. Abstr. *50*, 5105 (1956).
448. C. G. Greig, J. Inst. Brewing *68*, 48 (1962); Chem. Abstr. *56*, 12085 (1962).
449. P. Kolbach and K. Schwabe, Brauerei *1*, 1 (1948); Chem. Abstr. *45*, 7747 (1951).
450. E. C. Barton-Wright and G. Harris, Nature *167*, 560 (1951).
451. G. Harris, E. C. Barton-Wright, and N. S. Curtis, J. Inst. Brewing *57*, 264 (1951); Chem. Abstr. *46*, 9775 (1952).
452. R. Kuhn and I. Löw, Chem. Ber. *82*, 479 (1949).
453. F. J. Reithel and R. Venkataraman, Science *123*, 1083 (1956); Chem. Abstr. *50*, 13180 (1956).
454. B. C. Joshi and J. D. Tewari, Vijnana Parishad Anusandhan Patrika *2*, No. 2, 169 (1959); Chem. Abstr. *55*, 905 (1961).
455. R. Venkataraman and F. J. Reithel, Arch. Biochem. Biophys. *75*, 443 (1958); Chem. Abstr. *52*, 16502 (1958).
456. V. S. Mitina and V. I. Rubin, Trudy Saratov. Med. Inst. *26*, 260 (1959); Chem. Abstr. *55*, 16684 (1961).
457. S. Lascombes and J. Carles, Compt. rend. *242*, 664 (1956); Chem. Abstr. *50*, 7228 (1956).
458. W. Pigman, *The Carbohydrates*, Acad. Press, New York 1957, p. 500.
459. B. S. Ramachandra, R. G. Krishnamurthy, and Y. K. Raghunatha Rao, Food Sci. (Mysore) *8*, 83 (1959); Chem. Abstr. *53*, 20596 (1959).
460. D. French, G. M. Wild, B. Young, and W. J. James, J. Am. Chem. Soc. *75*, 709 (1953).
461. S. M. Strepkov, Zhur. Obshcheĭ Khim. *9*, 1990 (1939); Chem. Abstr. *34*, 4382 (1940).
462. T. R. Ingle and B. V. Bhide, J. Indian Chem. Soc. *31*, 943 (1954).
463. T. R. Ingle and B. V. Bhide, J. Indian Chem. Soc. *35*, 516 (1958).
464. S. M. Strepkov, Doklady Akad. Nauk S. S. S. R. *124*, 1344 (1956); Chem. Abstr. *53*, 21686 (1959).
465. E. O. Lippmann, Ber. *18*, 2088 (1885).
466. E. O. Lippmann, Ber. *18*, 3087 (1885).
467. W. E. Stone and W. H. Baird, J. Am. Chem. Soc. *19*, 116 (1897).
468. A. Herzfeld, Z. Ver. Rübenzuck. Ind. *1906*, 751; Chem. Zentr. *1906*, II, 894.
469. B. Lindberg and L. Selleby, Acta Chem. Scand. *12*, 1512 (1958).
470. E. Annett, Biochem. J. *11*, 1 (1917); Chem. Abstr. *11*, 2919 (1917).
471. G. Soliman and W. Saleh, J. Chem. Soc. *1950*, 2198; Chem. Abstr. *45*, 1153 (1951).
472. J. K. Chakravarti and N. K. Sen, J. Am. Chem. Soc. *76*, 2390 (1954).
473. J. E. Courtois and U. Ariyoshi, Bull. soc. chim. biol. *42*, 737 (1960).
474. J. E. Courtois and U. Ariyoshi, Bull. soc. chim. biol. *44*, 23 (1962).
475. E. Bourquelot and M. Bridel, Compt. rend. *149*, 361 (1909).
476. J. Leendert van Eijk, Pharm. Lab. Rijks. Univ., Utrecht *1951*; Chem. Abstr. *46*, 9262 (1952).
477. B. Tollens, Ber. *18*, 26 (1885).
478. H. Ritthausen, J. prakt. Chem. (2) *29*, 351 (1884).
479. H. Ritthausen and F. Weger, J. prakt. Chem. *30*, 32 (1884).
480. P. Rischbieth and B. Tollens, Ber. *18*, 2611 (1885).
481. D. T. Englis, R. T. Decker, and E. B. Adams, J. Am. Chem. Soc. *47*, 2724 (1925).
482. C. S. Hudson and T. S. Harding, J. Am. Chem. Soc. *36*, 2110 (1914).
483. H. Hummi, J. Coll. Agr. Hokkaido Imp. Univ. *9*, 249 (1921); Chem. Abstr. *15*, 2298 (1921).
484. M. Kitahara, Y. Takeuchi, K. Ishida, and M. Takemoto, Gifu Daigaku, Nôgukubu Kenkyû Hôkoku *11*, 133 (1959); Chem. Abstr. *54*, 25070 (1960).

485. J. Parker, Forest Sci. *5*, 56 (1959); Chem. Abstr. *53*, 11543 (1959).

486. S. Hattori and T. Siroya, Botan. Mag. (Tokyo) *64*, 137 (1951); Chem. Abstr. *46*, 1626 (1952).

487. J. B. Pridham, Biochem. J. *76*, 13 (1960).

488. S. Bhattacharji, J. Sci. & Ind. Research (India) *20 B*, 135 (1961); Chem. Abstr. *55*, 18886 (1961).

489. K. Y. Lee, C. Y. Lee, T. Y. Lee, and T. W. Kwon, Seoul Univ. J. *9*, 12 (1959); Chem. Abstr. *54*, 13295 (1960).

490. H. Hérissey and C. Lefebvre, Arch. Pharm. *245*, 481 (1908).

491. H. Hérissey and C. Lefebvre, J. pharm. chim. (6) *26*, 56 (1907); Chem. Abstr. *1*, 2811 (1907).

492. H. Hérissey and C. Lefebvre, Compt. rend. soc. biol. *62*, 788 (1907); Chem. Abstr. *1*, 2139 (1907).

493. M. Thaler and F. Bigi, Z. Lebensm. Unters. *105*, 73 (1957); Chem. Abstr. *51*, 7610 (1957).

494. A. M. MacLeod, J. Inst. Brewing *57*, 163 (1951); Chem. Abstr. *45*, 10482 (1951).

495. J. Montreuil and R. Scriban, Bull. soc. chim. biol. *45*, 674 (1952); Chem. Abstr. *47*, 3515 (1953).

496. S. Kawamura, Y. Tsuboi, and H. Nakamura, Tech. Bull. Kagawa Agr. Coll. (Japan) *6*, 27 (1954); Chem. Abstr. *48*, 12922 (1954).

497. E. P. Clark, J. Am. Chem. Soc. *44*, 210 (1922).

498. M. Bridel and H. Desmarest, Bull. soc. chim. biol. *10*, 510 (1928); Chem. Abstr. *22*, 2674 (1928).

499. M. Bridel and H. Desmarest, J. pharm. chim. *7*, 433 (1928); Chem. Abstr. *22*, 2674 (1928).

500. D. T. Englis, R. T. Decker, and A. B. Adams, J. Am. Chem. Soc. *47*, 2724 (1925).

501. D. Loiseau, Compt. rend. *82*, 1058 (1876).

502. D. Loiseau, Bull. soc. chim. France (2) *26*, 365 (1876).

503. B. Tollens, Ann. *232*, 172 (1886).

504. C. Scheibler, Ber. *18*, 1409 (1885).

505. C. Scheibler, Ber. *19*, 2868 (1886).

506. M. L. Lindet, Bull. soc. chim. France (3) *3*, 683 (1890).

507. T. S. Harding, Sugar *25*, 408 (1923).

508. E. H. Hungerford and A. R. Ness, Ind. Eng. Chem. *26*, 462 (1934).

509. F. J. Bates, *Polarimetry, Saccharimetry and the Sugars*, National Bureau of Standards, Washington 1942, p. 475.

510. E. Schulze, Ber. *27*, 64 (1894).

511. E. Schulze, Hoppe-Seyler's Z. physiol. Chem. *20*, 511 (1895).

512. F. B. Power and A. H. Salway, Pharm. J. (4) *37*, 157 (1913); Chem. Zentr. *1913*, II, 1232.

513. A. B. Svendsen, Acta Chem. Scand. *10*, 1500 (1956).

514. A. Wickström and A. B. Svendsen, Acta Chem. Scand. *10*, 1199 (1956).

515. M. Bridel, Compt. rend. *155*, 1164 (1913); Chem. Abstr. *7*, 812 (1913).

516. M. Bridel, J. pharm. chim. (7) *7*, 392 (1913); Chem. Abstr. *7*, 2622 (1913).

517. A. Meyer, Hoppe-Seyler's Z. physiol. Chem. *6*, 135 (1882).

518. E. Bourquelot and L. Nardin, Compt. rend. *126*, 280 (1898).

519. E. Bourquelot and H. Hérissey, Ann. chim. phys. (7) *27*, 403 (1902).

520. E. Bourquelot and H. Hérissey, Compt. rend. *132*, 571 (1901).

521. M. Bridel, J. pharm. chim. *7*, 289 (1913); Chem. Abstr. *7*, 2662 (1913).

522. M. Bridel, Compt. rend. *156*, 627 (1913); Chem. Abstr. *7*, 1852 (1913).

523. M. Bridel, J. pharm. chim. (7) *10*, 62 (1914); Chem. Abstr. *8*, 3218 (1914).

524. M. Bridel and M. Desmarest, J. pharm. chim. *9*, 465 (1929); Chem. Zentr. *1929*, II, 767.

525. J. S. D. Bacon and B. Dickinson, Biochem. J. *66*, 289 (1957).

526. G. Tanret, Compt. rend. *169*, 873 (1959); Chem. Abstr. *14*, 3445 (1920).

527. C. S. Hudson and S. F. Sherwood, J. Am. Chem. Soc. *42*, 116 (1920).

528. F. Smith and H. C. Srivastava, J. Org. Chem. *22*, 987 (1957).

529. C. S. Hudson and S. F. Sherwood, J. Am. Chem. Soc. *40*, 1456 (1918).

530. F. Dickie, Am. Forestry *26*, 84 (1920); Chem. Abstr. *15*, 3661 (1921).

531. J. Davidson, Canadian Field Naturalist *33*, 6 (1919); Chem. Abstr. *15*, 4057 (1921).

532. J. Henry, Pharm. J. *112*, 387 (1924); Chem. Abstr. *18*, 2724 (1924).

533. E. O. Lippmann, Ber. *60*, 161 (1927); Chem. Abstr. *21*, 1291 (1927).

534. H. Colin and H. Belval, Bull. assoc. chim. *54*, 12 (1937); Chem. Abstr. *31*, 2461 (1937).

535. D. French, R. W. Youngquist, and A. Lee, Arch. Biochem. Biophys. *85*, 471 (1959).

536. M. Hasegawa, T. Takayama, and T. Shiroya, Kagaku (Tokyo) *21*, 593 (1951); Chem. Abstr. *48*, 5297 (1954).

537. E. Wada and K. Yamazaki, J. Agr. Chem. Soc. Japan *24*, 398 (1951); Chem. Abstr. *45*, 10308 (1951).

538. N. Wattiez and M. Hans, Bull. acad. roy méd. Belg. *8*, 386 (1943); Chem. Abstr. *39*, 4849 (1945).

539. D. French, G. M. Wild, B. Young, and W. J. James, J. Am. Chem. Soc. *75*, 709 (1953).

540. H. Hérissey, Bull. soc. chim. biol. *39*, 1553 (1957); Chem. Abstr. *52*, 18688 (1958).

541. S. Hatanaka, Arch. Biochem. Biophys. *82*, 188 (1959); Chem. Abstr. *53*, 15230 (1959).

542. J. Cerbulis, Arch. Biochem. Biophys. *49*, 442 (1954).

543. J. Cerbulis, Arch. Biochem. Biophys. *58*, 406 (1955).

544. M. Zimmermann, Experientia *8*, 424 (1952); Chem. Abstr. *47*, 3411 (1953).

545. J. S. D. Bacon, Biochem. J. *73*, 507 (1959).

546. H. H. Schlubach, H. Lübbers, and H. Borowski, Ann. *595*, 229 (1955).

547. H. H. Schlubach and J. Berndt, Ann. *647*, 41 (1961).

548. H. H. Schlubach and H. O. A. Koehn, Ann. *614*, 126 (1958).

549. J. S. D. Bacon, Nature *184*, 1957 (1959).

550. I. R. Rominskiĭ, A. S. Sushkova, and A. V. Iĭina, Ukrain. Khim. Zhur. *24*, 236 (1958); Chem. Abstr. *52*, 15663 (1958).

551. J. S. D. Bacon and J. Edelman, Biochem. J. *48*, 114 (1951).

552. R. A. Dedonder, Bull. soc. chim. biol. *34*, 144 (1952).

553. P. J. Allen and J. S. D. Bacon, Biochem. J. *63*, 200 (1956).

554. S. Haq and G. A. Adams, Can. J. Chem. *39*, 1165 (1961).

555. R. W. Henderson, R. K. Morton, and W. A. Rawlinson, Biochem. J. *72*, 349 (1959).

556. H. H. Schlubach and F. Lederer, Ann. *635*, 154 (1960).

557. S. M. Strepkov, Zhur. Obshcheĭ Khim. *9*, 1489 (1939); Chem. Abstr. *34*, 2798 (1940).

558. A. S. F. Ash and T. M. Reynolds, Nature *174*, 602 (1954).

559. J. E. Courtois, G. Dillemann, and P. Le Dizet, Ann. pharm. franç. *18*, 17 (1960).

560. S. Murakami, Acta Phytochim. *13*, 161 (1943); Chem. Abstr. *45*, 8599 (1951).

561. L. Piault, J. pharm. chim. (7) *1*, 248 (1911); Chem. Abstr. *5*, 349 (1911).

562. M. Chollet, Compt. rend. *222*, 242 (1946); Chem. Abstr. *40*, 3501 (1946).

563. S. Ueno, Kagaku (Japan) *24*, 90 (1954); Chem. Abstr. *48*, 12242 (1954).

564. Y. Khouri, J. pharm. chim. (7) *2*, 211 (1909); Chem. Zentr. *1910*, II, 1484.

565. G. Tanret, Compt. rend. *155*, 1526 (1913); Chem. Abstr. *7*, 1739 (1913).

566. J. Vintilesco, Arch. Pharm. *247*, 81 (1909).

567. J. Vintilesco, J. pharm. chim. (6) *29*, 336 (1909); Chem. Abstr. *3*, 1442 (1909).

558. L. Piault, J. pharm. chim. (6) *29*, 236 (1909); Chem. Abstr. *3*, 1995 (1909).

569. L. Piault, J. pharm. chim. (7) *1*, 248 (1910); Chem. Zentr. *1910*, I, 1533.

570. H. Hérissey, P. Fleury, A. Wickström, J. E. Courtois, and P. Le Dizet, Bull. soc. chim. biol. *36*, 1507 (1954).

571. H. Hérissey and M. Mascré, J. pharm. chim. (9) *1*, 521 (1941); Chem. Abstr. *39*, 1735 (1945).

572. Merlis, Landwirtschaftliche Versuchs-Stationen *48*, 423.

573. E. Steiger, Ber. *19*, 827 (1886).

574. E. Schulze, Ber. *25*, 2213 (1892).

575. E. Schulze, Ber. *43*, 2230 (1910).

576. C. Tanret, Bull. soc. chim. France (4) *13*, 177 (1913).

577. E. Steiger, Hoppe-Seyler's Z. physiol. Chem. *11*, 372 (1887).

578. H. Hérissey and M. Gravot, J. pharm. chim. *22*, 537 (1935); Chem. Abstr. *30*, 4541 (1936).

579. S. Murakami, Proc. Imp. Acad. (Tokyo) *20*, 318 (1944); Chem. Abstr. *48*, 2838 (1954).

580. M. M. Chollet, Compt. rend. *220*, 334 (1945); Chem. Abstr. *41*, 5585 (1947).

581. R. A. Laidlaw and C. B. Wylam, J. Chem. Soc. *1953*, 567.

582. A. K. Mitra and A. S. Perlin, Can J. Chem. *35*, 1079 (1957).

583. K. Okano, J. Ohara, and J. Kato, J. Agr. Chem. Soc. Japan *12*, 714 (1936); Chem. Abstr. *31*, 1238 (1937).

584. A. Planta and E. Schulze, Ber. *23*, 1692 (1890).

585. A. Planta and E. Schulze, Ber. *24*, 2705 (1891).

586. C. Tanret, Comp. rend. *136*, 1570 (1903).

587. C. Tanret, Bull. soc. chim. France (3) *29*, 888 (1903).

588. C. Neuberg and S. Lachmann, Biochem. Z. *24*, 173 (1910).

589. M. Onuki, Sci. Papers Inst. Phys. Chem. Res. *20*, 213 (1932); Chem. Zentr. *1932*, II, 1007.

590. M. Onuki, J. Agr. Chem. Soc. Japan *8*, 445 (1932); Proc. Imp. Acad. Tokyo *8*, 496 (1932); Chem. Zentr. *1933*, II, 367.

591. M. L. Wolfrom, R. C. Burrell, A. Thompson, and S. S. Frush, J. Am. Chem. Soc. *74*, 6299 (1952).

592. R. S. Schallenberger, Chem. & Ind. (London) *1961*, 475.

593. H. Hérissey, P. Fleury, A. Wickström, J. E. Courtois, and P. Le Dizet, Compt. rend. *239*, 824 (1954); Chem. Abstr. *49*, 11565 (1955).

594. J. E. Courtois, A. Wickström, P. Fleury, and P. Le Dizet, Bull. soc. chim. biol. *37*, 2009 (1957).

595. J. Cheymol, Bull. soc. chim. biol. *19*, 1647 (1937).

596. J. Cheymol, Bull. soc. chim. biol. *19*, 1609 (1937).

597. J. Cheymol, J. Pharm. chim. *25*, 110 (1937); Chem. Abstr. *31*, 7473 (1937).

598. L. M. White and G. E. Secor, Arch. Biophys. *44*, 244 (1953); Chem. Abstr. *47*, 9432 (1953).

599. Y. Kihara, J. Agr. Chem. Soc. Japan *15*, 348 (1939); Chem. Abstr. *34*, 385 (1940).

600. Y. Kihara, J. Agr. Chem. Soc. Japan *13*, 363 (1937); Chem. Abstr. *31*, 8605 (1937).

601. Y. Kihara, J. Agr. Chem. Soc. Japan *12*, 1044 (1936); Chem. Abstr. *31*, 3013 (1937).

602. A. Archambault, J. E. Courtois, A. Wickström, and P. Le Dizet, Bull. soc. chim. biol. *38*, 1121 (1956).

603. A. Archambault, J. E. Courtois, A. Wickström, and P. Le Dizet, Bull. soc. chim. biol. *38*, 1133 (1956).

604. A. Archambault, J. E. Courtois, A. Wickström, and P. Le Dizet, Compt. rend. *242*, 2875 (1956).

605. A. Archambault, J. E. Courtois, A. Wickström, and P. Le Dizet, Can. Pharm. J., Sci. Sect. *91*, 419 (1958); Chem. Abstr. *53*, 3603 (1959).

606. A. Wickström, J. E. Courtois, P. Le Dizet, and A. Archambault, Bull. soc. chim. France *1959*, 871.

607. J. E. Courtois, A. Archambault, and P. Le Dizet, Bull. soc. chim. biol. *38*, 1117 (1956).

608. E. Bourquelot and M. Bridel, Compt. rend. *151*, 760 (1910).

609. S. Murakami, Acta Phytochim. *12*, 97 (1941).

610. A. Wickström, J. E. Courtois, P. Le Dizet, and A. Archambault, Compt. rend. *147*, 1911 (1958); Chem. Abstr. *53*, 11527 (1959).

611. J. E. Courtois, P. Le Dizet, and A. Wickström, Bull. soc. chim. biol. *40*, 1059 (1958).

612. J. E. Courtois, A. Archambault, and P. Le Dizet, Bull. soc. chim. biol. *38*, 359 (1958).

613. S. Hattori and S. Hatanaka, The Botanical Magazine (Tokyo) *71*, 417 (1958).

614. J. E. Courtois, P. Le Dizet, and J. Davy, Bull. soc. chim. biol. *42*, 351 (1960).

615. S. Akiya and M. Tomoda, J. Pharm. Soc. Japan *76*, 1092 (1956); Chem. Abstr. *51*, 1406 (1957); Chem. Abstr. *53*, 12416 (1959).

616. T. Sasaki, M. Mikami, and H. Euda, J. Pharm. Soc. Japan (Yakugaku Zasshi) *81*, 1626 (1961); Chem. Abstr. *56*, 7712 (1962).

617. T. Sasaki and M. Mikami, J. Pharm. Soc. Japan (Yakugaku Zasshi) *82*, 1520 (1962).

618. S. Murakami, Acta Phytochim. *15*, 135 (1949); Chem. Abstr. *43*, 8451 (1949).

619. S. Murakami, Acta Phytochim. *10*, 43 (1937); Chem. Abstr. *31*, 8570 (1937).

620. F. Gstirner and W. Hoch, Arch. Pharm. *296*, 97 (1963).

621. K. Takiura and J. Nakagawa, J. Pharm. Soc. Japan (Yakugaku Zasshi) *83*, 298 (1963); Chem. Abstr. *59*, 8849 (1963).

622. K. Takiura and J. Nakagawa, J. Pharm. Soc. Japan (Yakugaku Zasshi) *83*, 301 (1963); Chem. Abstr. *59*, 8849 (1963).

623. K. Takiura and J. Nakagawa, J. Pharm. Soc. Japan (Yakugaku Zasshi) *83*, 305 (1963); Chem. Abstr. *59*, 8849 (1963).

624. N. S. Narasimhan, J. Sci. & Ind. Research (India) *21 B*, 506 (1962); Chem. Abstr. *58*, 2652 (1963).

625. R. W. Bailey, Nature *199*, 1291 (1963).

626. S. M. Martin and G. A. Adams, Can. J. Botany *41*, 1605 (1963).

627. H. H. Schlubach, J. Berndt, and T. Chiemprasert, Ann. *665*, 191 (1963).

# X

# Preparation of Oligosaccharides by Hydrolysis of Higher Oligosaccharides or Polysaccharides

The largest number of oligosaccharides have so far been obtained by partial hydrolysis of higher oligosaccharides or polysaccharides. This procedure has not only increased the number of known oligosaccharides in general but also often contributed to the elucidation of the structure of higher oligosaccharides by identification of their cleavage products and sometimes even to the determination of the arrangement of the monosaccharide molecules in polysaccharides.*

The usual procedure is careful hydrolysis in acid solution, conducted so as to prevent, or at least impair, the formation of monosaccharides. The reagents currently used for this purpose are dilute mineral acids, however, attention must be paid to the risk of reversion, i. e. resynthesis of an oligosaccharide from monosaccharides in acid solution (see Chapter VI, 4), as otherwise artefacts would be produced by the hydrolysis; successful attempts in this respect have been reported.[1,2] Moreover, various types of glycosidic linkage differ in their stability in acid solution, which permits hydrolytic elimination of a certain monosaccharide from the oligosaccharide molecule and thus also permits structural studies, particularly in the group of branched oligosaccharides.[3,4]

The mineral acids may also be replaced by organic acids, mainly acetic acid[5,6] and formic acid.[7-10]

Another modification, likewise often employed, is the splitting of the oligosaccharide by sulphuric acid in acetic anhydride, termed acetolysis This method leads to per-$O$-acetyl derivatives of oligosaccharides and is mainly employed for the preparation of octa-$O$-acetylcellobiose from cellulose.[11-27]

Contrary to the readily proceeding hydrolysis of oligosaccharides in acid solution, these substances are highly resistant to alkaline hydrolysis. In a few cases only it was possible to hydrolyse an oligosaccharide in alkaline solution with the formation of monosaccharides (see Chapter VII), and two cases have so far been reported[28,29] where a lower oligosaccharide was obtained from a higher one under these conditions.

---

* For reviews see D. J. Manners, Quart. Revs 9, 73 (1955); A. Roudier, Bull. soc. chim. biol. 42, 1493 (1960).

A very frequently employed procedure is the enzymic hydrolysis of oligo-saccharides,* and in recent time it has been strongly recommended,[30] since acid hydrolysis yields as a rule not more than 35% of the di- or trisaccharide. The biochemical method utilizes the high stereoselectivity of enzymes, and appropriate combinations of them lead to miscellaneous substances, as recently demonstrated on the enzymolysis of poly-$\beta$-D-glucans.[31] The activity of the enzymes may also be further limited; for example, $\beta$-amylase hydrolyses $\alpha,1\rightarrow4$ glycosidic linkages if at least three of them are present;[32-35] for this reason, maltotriose is not hydrolysed by the action of $\beta$-amylase,[33,34] and malto-tetraose may be obtained as main product in good yield from corn syrup.[35]

There are also other, less usual, methods for splitting oligosaccharides and polysaccharides, the most important of them being treatment with zinc chloride in acetic anhydride,[36,37] autohydrolysis,[13,38,39] methanolysis,[40-43] and mer-captolysis.[44-46] Finally, $\gamma$-radiation may also split polysaccharides, for example dextran.[47]

---

* For a review see D. J. Manners, Quart. Revs 9, 73 (1955).

*References see p. 207*

**Table XVIII**

Oligosaccharides Obtained by Degradation of Higher Oligosaccharides or Polysaccharides

Non-reducing Disaccharides

| Disaccharide | Natural Substance | Degradation | References |
|---|---|---|---|
| Trehalose | trisaccharide 6-$O$-α-D-galactopyranosyltrehalose | acid | 252 |
| Sucrose* | trisaccharide gentianose | enzym. | 48—50 |
| | lactsucrose | acid | 51 |
| | melezitose | enzym. | 52 |
| | planteose | enzym. | 53 |
| | raffinose | enzym. | 54 |
| | umbelliferose | acid | 55 |
| | tetrasaccharide lychnose | enzym. | 56 |
| | stachyose | enzym. | 57—59 |
| | polysaccharide inulin | acid | 60, 61 |
| | *Agave vera-cruz* fructosan | acid | 62 |

* Sucrose has been reported again as a cleavage-product of higher oligosaccharides, such as trisaccharide C (erlose), see K. Takiura and J. Nakagawa, J. Pharm. Soc. Japan *83*, 305 (1963), and the unbranched oligosaccharide sessilifolan from *Lobellia sessilifolia*, see T. Sasaki and M. Mikami, J. Pharm. Soc. Japan (Yakugaku Zasshi) *82*, 1520 (1962).

**Table XIX**

Oligosaccharides Obtained by Degradation of Higher Oligosaccharides or Polysaccharides

Reducing Disaccharides with a Hemiacetal Group → Primary Alcoholic Group Bond

| Disaccharide | Natural Substance | Degradation | References |
|---|---|---|---|
| Inulobiose* | polysaccharide inulin | acid | 60, 61, 63, 64 |
| 1-$O$-α-D-Galactopyranosyl-D-fructose | tetrasaccharide lychnose | acid | 65, 66 |
| 5-$O$-β-D-Galactopyranosyl-L-arabinofuranose | corn hull hemicellulose | acid | 67 |
| 5-$O$-α-L-Arabinofuranosyl-L-arabinofuranose | sugar beet araban | acid | 68 |
| | *Virgilia oroboides* gum | acid | 69 |
| 5-$O$-α-L-Arabinopyranosyl-L-arabinofuranose | *Virgilia oroboides* gum | acid | 69, 70 |
| 5-$O$-β-D-Xylopyranosyl-L-arabinofuranose | peach gum | acid | 71, 72 |
| | *Virgilia oroboides* gum | acid | 69 |

* Inulobiose may be contaminated with traces of sucrose.[61] Inulobiose may be identical with fructobiose, isolated as one of the hydrolysis products of lycorisin (from *Lycoris radiata*); all constants, however, are slightly different from those of inulobiose, see T. Mizuno, Kagaku (Tokyo) *31*, 146 (1961); Chem. Abstr. *55*, 27099 (1961). The preparation of laevanbiose from laevan by the action of a laevan hydrolyzing enzyme has been reported by G. Avigad and R. Zelikson, Bull. Res. Council Israel *11 A*, 253 (1963).

*Table XIX — continued*

| Disaccharide | Natural Substance | Degradation | References |
|---|---|---|---|
| Isomaltose* | trisaccharide isomaltotriose | enzym. | 73 |
| | *Dilsea edulis* polysaccharide | acid | 74, 75 |
| | amylopectin | acid | 2, 76, 77 |
| | | enzym. | 78, 79 |
| | glycogen | acid | 80 |
| | dextran | acid | 81—84 |
| | | enzym. | 81—83, 85 |
| | | acetolysis | 86 |
| | | γ-irrad. | 47 |
| | laminarin | acid | 87 |
| | yeast mannans | acid | 88 |
| Gentiobiose** | trisaccharide gentianose | acid or enzym. | 89—94 |
| | odorotriose | ZnCl$_2$/Ac$_2$O | 36 |
| | strophanthotriose | ZnCl$_2$/Ac$_2$O | 37 |
| | O-β-D-glucopyranosyl-(1→6)-O-β-D-pyranosyl-(1→4)-D-glucose | acid | 95 |
| | Y from laminaran | acid | 96 |
| | *Rhizobium japonicum* polysaccharide | acid | 97, 98 |
| | yeast glucan | acid | 87, 99 |
| | yeast mannan | acid | 88 |
| | *Eisenia bicyclis* laminarin | acetolysis | 100 |
| | *Sclerotinia libertiana* polysaccharide | acid | 101 |
| 6-O-β-D-Glucopyranosyl-D-galactose | *Xanthomonas stewartii* polysaccharide | acid | 102 |
| Melibiose*** | trisaccharide raffinose | acid | 103—105 |
| | | enzym. | 106—112 |
| | tetrasaccharide lychnose | acid | 65, 66 |
| | fructosylraffinose | acid or enzym. | 113 |
| | *Lychnis dioica* pentasaccharide | acid | 111 |
| | hexasaccharide | acid | 111 |
| epi-Melibiose | guaran | acid | 114 |
| | | enzym. | 115 |
| | *Picea abies* glucomannan | acid | 114, 116 |
| | galactomannans | acid | 117, 118 |
| Swietenose | trisaccharide manninotriose | Ba(OH)$_2$ | 29 |
| | polysaccharide galactogen | acid | 119 |

* Isomaltose has been found recently among the hydrolysis products of *Pullularia pullulans* glucan, see H. O. Bouveng, H. Kiessling, B. Lindberg, and J. McKay, Acta Chem. Scand. *17*, 797 (1963); W. Sowa, A. C. Blackwood, and G. A. Adams, Can. J. Chem. *41*, 2314 (1963). Acid hydrolysis of *Polyporus giganteus* polysaccharide yielded also isomaltose, see V. P. Bhavanandan, H. O. Bouveng, and B. Lindberg, Acta Chem. Scand. *18*, 504 (1964).

** Gentiobiose has been obtained from *Claviceps purpurea* glucan using enzymic degradation, see A. S. Perlin and W. A. Taber, Can. J. Chem. *41*, 2278 (1963). Teichoic acid from *Staphylococcus aureus* yielded gentiobiose by acid hydrolysis, too, see U. L. Rajbhandary and J. Baddiley, Biochem. J. *87*, 429 (1963).

*** The enzymic hydrolysis of raffinose to melibiose has been described again, see P. Witonsky and F. Smith, J. Org. Chem. *24*, 124 (1959).

*References see p. 207*

*Table XIX — continued*

| Disaccharide | Natural Substance | Degradation | References |
|---|---|---|---|
| 6-*O*-β-D-Galactopyra-<br>nosyl-D-galactose* | trisaccharide O-β-D-galactopyranosyl-<br>(1→6)-*O*-β-D-galactopyranosyl-(1→4)-<br>D-glucose | acid | 120, 121 |
| | plant gums | acid | 122 |
| | gum ghatti | acid | 123 |
| | *Virgilia oroboides* gum | acid | 69 |
| | *Anogeissus schimperi* gum | acid | 124 |
| | *Albizza zygia* gum | acid | 125 |
| | *Pinus radiata* arabinogalactan | acid | 126 |
| | *Larix laricina* (tamarack) arabinogalactan | acid | 127, 128 |
| Planteobiose | trisaccharide planteose | acid | 53 ,65 |
| 6-*O*-α-D-Mannopyra-<br>nosyl-D-mannose | yeast mannans | acid | 88, 129 |
| 6-*O*-D-Mannosyl-D-<br>glucose (?) | konjackmannan | acetolysis | 130 |
| 6-*O*-α-D-Xylopyrano-<br>syl-D-glucose | *Pinus banksiana* (jack pine) glucomannan | enzym. | 131 |

\* 6-*O*-β-D-Galactopyranosyl-D-galactose has been reported again as one of the hydrolysis products of the periodate-oxidized polysaccharide from *Pinus silvestris*, see G. O. Aspinall and T. M. Wood, J. Chem. Soc. *1963*, 1686. According to a communication by P. Plackett a S. H. Buttery, Biochem. J. *90*, 201 (1964), 6-*O*-β-D-galactofuranosyl-D-galactose has been identified after acid hydrolysis of the *Mycoplasma mycoides* galactan.

## Table XX

Oligosaccharides Obtained by Degradation of Higher Oligosaccharides or Polysaccharides
Reducing Disaccharides with a 1→2 Bond

| Disaccharide | Natural Substance | Degradation | References |
|---|---|---|---|
| Kojibiose* | O-β-D-galactopyranosyl-(1→4)-O[α-D-glu-copyranosyl-(1→2)]-D-glucose, trisaccha-ride produced by *Leuconostoc mesenteroi-des* growing on a sucrose/lactose medium | acid acetolysis enzym. acetolysis | 132—134 135 133, 136 137, 138 139 |
| Sophorose 2-O-α-D-Galactopyra-nosyl-D-glucose 2-O-α-D-Mannopyrano-syl-D-mannose | dextran *Agrobacterium radiobacter* polysaccharide trisaccharide umbelliferose *Saccharomyces rouxii* mannan yeast mannan | acid acetolysis acetolysis | 140 141, 142 129 |
| 2-O-β-D-Galactopyra-nosyl-D-xylose 2-O-β-D-Xylopyrano-syl-L-arabinose*** | tragacanthic acid hemicelluloses | acid | ** 143–148† |

\* The preparation of kojibiose from the branched trisaccharide given above has been reported by K. Shibasaki and K. Aso, J. Agr. Chem. Soc. Japan (Nippon Nogeikagaku Kaishi) *33*, 359 (1959); Chem. Abstr. *57*, 17042 (1962), too.

\** This is a new compound reported by G. O. Aspinall and J. Baillie, J. Chem. Soc. *1963*, 1702; it has been found after stepwise degradation of tragacanthic acid.

\*** The compound previously believed to be 2-O-α-D-xylopyranosyl-L-arabinose[143] has been identified as 2-O-β-D-xylopyranosyl-L-arabinose.[146]

† 2-O-β-D-Xylopyranosyl-L-arabinose has been reported as one of the hydrolysis products of a xylan from the roots of *Lolium perenne*, see G. O. Aspinall, I. M. Cairncross, and K. M. Ross, J. Chem. Soc. *1963*, 1721.

*References see p. 207*

**Table XXI**

Oligosaccharides Obtained by Degradation of Higher Oligosaccharides or Polysaccharides Reducing Disaccharides with a 1→3 Bond

| Disaccharide | Natural Substance | Degradation | References |
|---|---|---|---|
| Nigerose, sakébiose* | trisaccharide from nigeran $O$-$\alpha$-$D$-glucopyranosyl-(1→4)-$O$-$\alpha$-$D$-glucopyranosyl-(1→3)-$D$-glucose | acid | 120 |
| | amylopectin | enzym. | 149 |
| | | acid | 2, 77 |
| | *Dilsea edulis* polysaccharide | acid | 75 |
| | dextran | acetolysis | 86, 138, 150 |
| | isolichenin | acid | 151 |
| | nigeran | acid | 120, 152–154 |
| Laminaribiose | trisaccharide Y from laminarin | acid | 96 |
| | 4-$O$-$\beta$-laminaribiosyl-$D$-glucose | acid | 155 |
| | *Rhizobium japonicum* polysaccharide | acid | 97 |
| | yeast glucan | acid | 99 |
| | unfermentable barley liquors | acid | 156 |
| | laminarin | acid | 87, 157, 158 |
| | laminaran | acetolysis | 100, 159, 160 |
| | pachymanan | acetolysis | 159, 160 |
| | *Sclerotinia libertiana* polysaccharide | acid | 101 |
| Turanose | trisaccharide melezitose | acid | 161—165 |
| Solabiose 3-$O$-$\beta$-$D$-glucopyranosyl-$D$-galactose | *Xanthomonas stewartii* polysaccharide | acid | 102 |
| | *Pneumococcus* Type XIV polysaccharide | acid | 166 |
| 3-$O$-$\alpha$-$D$-Galactopyranosyl-$D$-galactose | $\lambda$-carrageenin | acetolysis | 167 |
| | human blood group B | | 168 |
| 3-$O$-$\beta$-$D$-Galactopyranosyl-$D$-galactose** | plant gums | acid | 122 |
| | *Virgilia oroboides* gum | acid | 69 |
| | *Acacia pycnantha* gum | acid | 169—171 |
| | *Anogeissus schimperi* gum | acid | 124 |
| | *Albizzia zygia* gum | acid | 125 |
| | gum ghatti | acid | 123 |
| | galactans | acid | 122 |
| | *Pinus radiata* arabinogalactan | acid | 126 |
| | *Larix laricina* (tamarack) arabinogalactan | acid | 128 |
| | *Xanthomonas stewartii* polysaccharide | acid | 102 |
| | *Pneumococcus* Type XIV polysaccharide | acid | 166 |

* For the isolation of nigerose from *Pullularia pullulans* glucan (acid hydrolysis), see W. Sowa, A. C. Blackwood, and G. A. Adams, Can. J. Chem. *41*, 2314 (1963).

** The isolation of 3-$O$-$\beta$-$D$-galactopyranosyl-$D$-galactose from a water-soluble *Pinus silvestris* galactoglucomannan has been reported by G. O. Aspinall and T. M. Wood, J. Chem. Soc. *1963*, 1686.

*Table XXI — continued*

| Disaccharide | Natural Substance | Degradation | References |
|---|---|---|---|
| 3-*O*-α-D-Galactopyranosyl-L-arabinose* | *Acacia cyanophylla* gum | acid | 71, 172, 173 |
| 3-*O*-β-D-Galactopyranosyl-L-arabinose | *Albizzia zygia* gum<br>gum ghatti<br>*Anogeissus schimperi* gum | acid<br>acid<br>acid | 125<br>123<br>124 |
| 3-*O*-β-D-Galactopyranosyl-D-xylose | hemicelluloses | acid | 15 |
| 3-*O*-α-D-Mannopyranosyl-D-mannose | phosphomannan X-2448 | formic acid | 174 |
| 3-*O*-β-L-Arabinofuranosyl-L-arabinose | *Acacia pycnantha* gum<br>*Acacia karroo* gum<br>*Anogeissus schimperi* gum<br>*Virgilia oroboides* gum<br>sugar beet araban | acid<br>acid<br>acid<br>acid<br>acid | 171<br>175<br>124<br>69<br>68 |
| 3-*O*-β-L-Arabinopyranosyl-L-arabinose | plant gums<br>gum ghatti<br>*Larix decidua* ε-galactan<br>*Larix laricina* (tamarack) arabinogalactan<br>*Larix occidentalis* arabinogalactan<br>*Pinus taeda* polysaccharides<br>*Spondias cytheria* polysaccharide<br>*Anogeissus schimperi* gum | acid<br>acid<br>acid<br><br>acid<br>acid<br>acid<br>autohydrol.<br>acid | 12, 72<br>123<br>71<br><br>128<br>127<br>176<br>13<br>124 |
| 3-*O*-α-D-Xylopyranosyl-L-arabinose | corn hull hemicelluloses<br>*Spondias cytheria* polysaccharides | acid<br><br>autohydrol. | 14, 15, 67<br><br>13 |
| Rhodymenabiose | *Rhodymenia palmata* xylan | acid | 177, 253 |

* 3-*O*-α-D-Galactopyranosyl-L-arabinose has been obtained from carboxyl-reduced arabic gum (*Acacia senegal*), see G. O. Aspinall, A. J. Charlson, E. L. Hirst, and R. Young, J. Chem. Soc. *1963*, 1696.

### Table XXII

Oligosaccharides Obtained by Degradation of Higher Oligosaccharides or Polysaccharides
Reducing Disaccharides with a 1→4 Bond

| Disaccharide | Natural Substance | Degradation | References |
|---|---|---|---|
| Maltose | trisaccharide maltotriose<br>pentasaccharide maltopentaose<br>amylopectin<br>amylose<br>starch<br>waxy corn starch | enzym.<br>enzym.<br>acid<br>acid<br>enzym.<br>enzym. | 16<br>178<br>77<br>179<br>17—19, 21, 180<br>181 |

*References see p. 207*

13*

*Table XXII — continued*

| Disaccharide | Natural Substance | Degradation | References |
|---|---|---|---|
| | *Dilsea edulis* Floridean starch | acid | 74, 75 |
| | isolichenin | acid | 151 |
| | *Polyporus giganteus* | acid | 255 |
| | *Pullularia pullulans* glucan | | 182, 254 |
| Maltulose | waxy corn starch | enzym. | 181 |
| Cellobiose* | trisaccharide *O*-β-D-glucopyranosyl- (1→6)-*O*-β-D-glucopyranosyl- (1→4)-D-glucose | enzym. | 95 |
| | cellulose | acetolysis enzym. | 11—26, 183, 184 185, 186 |
| | *Thuja plicata* glucomannan | acid | 187 |
| | *Tsuga heterophylla* glucomannan | acid | 188 |
| | *Rhizobium japonicum* polysaccharide | acid | 97, 98 |
| | *Picea abies* polysaccharide | acid enzym | 116 256 |
| | *Picea glauca* glucomannan | acid | 257 |
| | *Scylla nonscripta* glucomannan | acetolysis | 258 |
| | *Acer rubrum* polysaccharide | formic acid | 9 |
| | β-cellulose | acetolysis | 189 |
| | *Pinus strobus* polysaccharide | acid | 190 |
| | *Larix decidua* polysaccharide | acid | 191 |
| *epi*-Cellobiose** | *Thuja plicata* glucomannan | acid | 187 |
| | *Tsuga heterophylla* glucomannan | acid | 188 |
| | β-cellulose | acetolysis | 189, 192 |
| | *Picea abies* glucomannan | acid | 116, 256 |
| | *Picea glauca* polysaccharide | acid | 203, 257 |
| | *Pinus strobus* polysaccharide | acid | 190 |
| | *Pinus baksiana* polysaccharide | acid | 131 |
| | *Pinus taeda* hemicellulose | acid | 193 |
| | *Acer rubrum* polysaccharide | formic acid | 9 |
| | *Scylla nonscripta* glucomannan | acetolysis | 258 |
| | *Xanthomonas hyacinthi* polysaccharide | acetolysis | 259 |
| | *Orchis latifolia* glucomannan | acid | 260 |
| | *Orchis longicruris* glucomannan | acid | 260 |
| | *Orchis maculata* glucomannan | acid | 260 |
| | *Orchis mascula* glucomannan | acid | 260 |
| | *Orchis morio* glucomannan | acid | 260 |
| | polysaccharide eremuran | | 194 |
| 4-*O*-α-D-Galactopyra- nosyl-D-galactose | *Hibiscus esculentus* polysaccharide | acid | 1 |
| Galactobiose | *Betula papyrifera* α-cellullose | acid | 195 |
| | *Picea abies* galactan | acid | 196 |
| | *Picea abies* glucomannan | acid | 116 |
| | *Larix decidua* glucomannan | acid | 191 |

* An improved method of preparing α-cellobiose octa-*O*-acetate from cellulose with a yield of 22—37% has been reported by P. E. Robbins and D. M. Hall, Ind. Eng. Chem., Prod. Res. Develop. *1*, 285 (1962); Chem. Abstr. *58*, 1626 (1963). The over-all reaction time of the acetolysis described is between 30 and 60 minutes.

** *epi*-Cellobiose has been prepared from polysaccharides from *Abies amabilis* [see T. E. Timell, Svensk Papperstid. *65*, 843 (1962); Chem. Abstr. *59*, 729 (1963)] and *Pinus silvestris* (see G. O. Aspinall and T. M. Wood, J. Chem. Soc. *1963*, 1686).

*Table XXII — continued*

| Disaccharide | Natural Substance | Degradation | References |
|---|---|---|---|
| 4-*O*-α-D-Galactopyra-<br>nosyl-D-mannose | *Picea abies* glucomannan | acid | 116 |
| Lactose* | *O*-β-D-galactopyranosyl-(1→6)-<br>  *O*-β-D-galactopyranosyl-(1→4)-<br>  D-glucose | acid | 121 |
| | *O*-β-D-galactopyranosyl-(1→4)-*O*-<br>  [α-D-glucopyranosyl-(1→2)]-D-<br>  glucose | acid | 132, 134 |
| | lactsucrose | enzym. | 51 |
| | fucosyl-lactose | acid | 197 |
| | *O*-β-D-galactopyranosyl-(1→4)-*O*-β-<br>  D-glucopyranosyl-(1→4)-*N*-ace-<br>  tyl-D-glucosamine | acid | 166 |
| | lactaminyl-lactose | acid | 198 |
| | lacto-*N*-tetraose | acid | 199, 200 |
| | lactodifucotetraose | acid | 201 |
| | *Pneumococcus* Type XIV polysac-<br>  charide | acid | 166 |
| 4-*O*-β-D-Galactopyra-<br>nosyl-D-xylose | corn hull hemicelluloses | acid | 15, 67 |
| Mannobiose** | mannotriose | acid | 115 |
| | *O*-α-D-mannopyranosyl-(1→4)-*O*-β-<br>  D-mannopyranosyl-(1→4)-D-<br>  mannose | acid | 202 |
| | *O*-β-D-mannopyranosyl-(1→4)-*O*-β-<br>  D-mannopyranosyl-(1→4)-D-<br>  glucose | acid | 202, 205 |
| | *Thuja plicata* glucomannan | acid | 187 |
| | *Tsuga heterophylla* glucomannan | acid | 188 |
| | *Larix decidua* polysaccharide | acid | 191 |
| | *Pinus taeda* holocellulose | acid | 193 |
| | *Pinus banksiana* polysaccharide | acid | 131 |
| | *Pinus strobus* polysaccharide | acid | 190 |
| | *Picea glauca* glucomannan | acid | 194, 203 |
| | *Acer rubrum* glucomannan | formic acid | 9 |
| | *Picea abies* glucomannan | acid<br>enzym. | 116<br>256 |
| | *Scylla nonscripta* glucomannan | acetolysis | 258 |
| | *Orchis latifolia* glucomannan | acid | 260 |
| | *Orchis longicruris* glucomannan | acid | 260 |
| | *Orchis maculata* glucomannan | acid | 260 |
| | *Orchis mascula* glucomannan | acid | 260 |
| | *Orchis morio* glucomannan | acid | 260 |
| | *Laminaria digitata* reduced<br>  polysaccharide | acid | 261 |
| | konjackmannan | acid | 130 |

* Lactose as one of the hydrolysis products of ganglio-*N*-tetraose has been reported by R. Kuhn and H. Wiegandt, Chem. Ber. *96*, 866 (1963).

** Mannobiose has been obtained several times: from *Tsuga canadensis* by T. E. Timell, Tappi *45*, 799 (1962); Chem. Abstr. *59*, 2922 (1963); from *Abies amabilis* by T. E. Timell, Svensk Papperstid. *65*, 843 (1962); Chem. Abstr. *59*, 729 (1963); from *Pinus silvestris* by G. O. Aspinall and T. M. Wood, J. Chem. Soc. *1963*, 1686.

*References see p. 207*

*Table XXII — continued*

| Disaccharide | Natural Substance | Degradation | References |
|---|---|---|---|
| 4-*O*-β-D-Mannopyra- nosyl-D-glucose* | lucerne galactomannan | acid | 117 |
| | glucomannan from unbleached Mit- scherlich pulp | acetolysis | 204 |
| | slash pine α-cellulose | acetolysis | 206 |
| | *O*-β-D-mannopyranosyl-(1→4)-*O*-β- D-mannopyranosyl-(1→4)-D-glu- cose | acid | 202 |
| | *Thuja plicata* glucomannan | acid | 187 |
| | *Larix decidua* polysaccharide | acid | 191 |
| | *Tsuga heterophylla* polysaccharide | acid | 188 |
| | *Pinus banksiana* polysaccharide | acid | 191 |
| | *Pinus taeda* holocellulose | acid | 193 |
| | *Pinus strobus* polysaccharide | acid | 190 |
| | *Picea glauca* polysaccharide | acid | 203 |
| | *Acer rubrum* polysaccharide | formic acid | 9 |
| | *Picea abies* glucomannan | enzym. | 256 |
| | *Scylla nonscripta* glucomannan | acetolysis | 258 |
| | glucomannan from unbleached Mit- scherlich pulp | acetolysis | 204 |
| | *Amorphophallus* plants glucomannan | acetolysis | 207 |
| | galactomannan | acid | 208 |
| | glucomannan | acid | 116 |
| 4-*O*-β-D-Mannopyra- nosyl-L-gulose | *Laminaria digitata* reduced polysaccharide | acid | 261 |
| Xylobiose** | *Pinus taeda* polysaccharide | acid | 176 |
| | corn hull xylans | acid | 39, 209, 210 |
| | | autohydrol. | 39 |
| | wheat flour arabinoxylan | acid | 211 |
| | corn hull hemicelluloses | acid | 67, 212 |
| | *Conium maculatum* xylan | acid | 67 |
| | esparto hemicelluloses | acid | 213 |
| | *Populus tremuloides* polysaccharide | acid | 214 |
| | *Betula papyrifera* glucuronoxylan | enzym. | 262 |
| | linseed mucilage | acid | 215 |
| 4-*O*-β-L-Arabinopyra- nosyl-L-arabinose | *Pinus taeda* polysaccharides | acid | 176 |

* 4-*O*-β-D-Mannopyranosyl-D-glucose has been prepared from polysaccharides of *Abies amabilis* by T. E. Timell, Svensk Papperstid. *65*, 843 (1962); Chem. Abstr. *59*, 729 (1963), and from *Pinus silvestris* by G. O. Aspinall and T. M. Wood, J. Chem. Soc. *1963*, 1686.

** Xylobiose has been reported as one of the hydrolysis products of *Lolium perenne* xylans, see G. O. Aspinall, I. M. Cairncross, and K. M. Ross, J. Chem. Soc. *1963*, 1721.

## Table XXIII
Oligosaccharides Obtained by Degradation of Higher Oligosaccharides or Polysaccharides
Reducing Disaccharides with a 1→5 Bond

| Disaccharide | Natural Substance | Degradation | References |
|---|---|---|---|
| 5-*O*-β-D-Galactofuranosyl-D- galactose | galactocarolose (synthesized by *Penicillium charlesii*) | acid | 216 |

## Table XXIV

Oligosaccharides Obtained by Degradation of Higher Oligosaccharides
Disaccharides of Unknown Constitution

| Disaccharide | Natural Substance | Degradation | References |
|---|---|---|---|
| D-Glucosyl-D-glucose | glucomannan from unbleached Mitscherlich pulp | acetolysis | 204 |
| D-Galactosyl-D-galactose (two substances) | *Hibiscus esculentus* mucilage | acid | 1 |
| D-Galactosyl-L-arabinose | linseed mucilage | acid | 215 |
| L-Arabinosyl-L-arabinose (three substances) | golden apple gum | autohydrolysis | 13 |
| L-Arabinosyl-D-galactose | linseed mucilage | acid | 215 |
| D-Xylosyl-L-arabinose | wheat straw xylan | enzym. | 217 |
|  | linseed mucilage | acid | 215 |
| D-Xylosyl-D-xylose | linseed mucilage | acid | 215 |

Galactoglucomannan from *Tsuga canadensis* yielded after hydrolysis with formic acid besides mannobiose, mannotriose and mannotetraose also D-mannosyl-D-glucose and D-glucosyl-D-mannose, as it has been reported by T. E. Timell, Tappi *45*, 799 (1962); Chem. Abstr. *59*, 2922 (1963). A reduced polysaccharide obtained from *Laminaria digitata* alginic acids could be hydrolysed to D-mannosyl-L-gulose, see E. L. Hirst, E. Percival and J. K. Wold, Chem. & Ind. (London) *1963*, 257; see Table XXII, p. 197.

## Table XXV

Oligosaccharides Obtained by Degradation of Higher Oligosaccharides or Polysaccharides
Non-reducing Trisaccharides

| Trisaccharide | Natural Substance | Degradation | References |
|---|---|---|---|
| Kestose | inulin | acid | 60 |
| Isokestose | inulin | acid | 60 |
| Planteose | tetrasaccharide lychnose | enzym. | 56 |
| Raffinose | tetrasaccharide lychnose | enzym. | 56 |
|  | stachyose | enzym. | 56 |
| $O$-$\alpha$-D-Glucopyranosyl(-1→2)-$O$-$\beta$-D-fructofuranosyl-(3→1) $\alpha$-D-galactopyranoside | *Lychnis dioica* pentasaccharides and hexasaccharides | enzym. | 218 |

*References see p. 207*

## Table XXVI

Oligosaccharides Obtained by Degradation of Higher Oligosaccharides or Polysaccharides
Reducing Trisaccharides

| Trisaccharide | Natural Substance | Degradation | References |
|---|---|---|---|
| Sophorotriose | *Agrobacterium radiobacter* polysaccharide | acid | 139 |
| Nigerotriose | isolichenin | acid | 151 |
| Laminaritriose | yeast glucan | acid | 87, 99, 157 |
| | *Eisenia bicyclis* laminaran | acetolysis | 100, 160 |
| | pachymanan | acetolysis | 160 |
| Maltotriose, amylotriose | starch | enzym. | 17, 21, 219—221 263 |
| | amylose | acid | 179, 222 |
| | *Dilsea edulis* Floridean starch | acid | 74, 75 |
| | waxy corn starch | enzym. | 181 |
| | isolichenin | acid | 151 |
| Cellotriose* | cellulose | acetolysis | 183, 223—226 |
| | | enzym. | 186 |
| Isomaltotriose, dextrantriose | dextran | enzym. | 83, 85 |
| | | γ-irradiation | 47 |
| | glycogen | acid | 230 |
| Gentiotriose | yeast glucan | acid | 99 |
| | *Rhizobium japonicum* poly-saccharide | acid | 98 |
| | *Eisenia bicyclis* laminaran | acid | 100 |
| Panose** 4-O-α-isomaltosyl-D-glucose | *Dilsea edulis* Floridean starch | acid | 74, 75 |
| 3-O-α-Isomaltosyl-D-glucose | dextran RNNL 1355-S | acetolysis | 86 |
| 3-O-α-Maltosyl-D-glucose | nigeran | acid | 154 |
| | isolichenin | acid | 151 |
| 6-O-α-Maltosyl-D-glucose, isopanose** | *Dilsea edulis* Floridean starch | acid | 74, 75 |
| 3-O-β-Gentiobiosyl-D-glucose | yeast glucan | acid | 87, 99 |
| | *Eisenia bicyclis* laminaran | acid | 100 |
| 6-O-β-Gentiobiosyl-D-glucose | *Rhizobium japonicum* poly-saccharide | acid | 98 |
| 4-O-β-Laminaribiosyl-D-glucose | *Cetraria islandica* lichenin | enzym. | 231 |
| | poly-β-D-glucan | enzym. | 31 |
| 6-O-β-Laminaribiosyl-D-glucose | *Eisenia bicyclis* laminaran | acid | 100 |
| 4-O-α-Nigerosyl-D-glucose | nigeran | acid | 154 |
| | laminarin | acid | 120 |
| | isolichenin | acid | 151 |
| 3-O-β-Cellobiosyl-D-glucose | *Cetraria islandica* laminarin | enzym. | 231 |
| | poly-β-D-glucan | enzym. | 31 |
| 4-O-β-Cellobiosyl-D-mannose | *Picea abies* glucomannan | acid | 116 |
| 4-O-β-D-Glucopyranosyl-mannobiose | *Picea abies* glucomannan | acid | 116, 196 |
| | *Pinus banksiana* glucoman-nan | enzym. | 256 |
| | | enzym. | 131 |

* The compound described as procellose is probably identical with cellotriose.[227-229]
** Panose and isopanose have been reported as hydrolysis products of *Pullularia pullulans* glucan, see H. O. Bouveng, H. Kiessling, B. Lindberg, and J. McKay, Acta Chem. Scand. *17*, 797 (1963); see also Ref. 256.

*Table XXVI — continued*

| Trisaccharide | Natural Substances | Degradation | References |
|---|---|---|---|
| Mannotriose* | *Acer rubrum* glucomannan | formic acid | 9 |
| | *Pinus banksiana* glucoman-nan | enzym. | 131 |
| | *Larix decidua* glucomannan | acetolysis | 191 |
| | *Pinus strobus* glucomannan | acid | 190 |
| | *Tsuga heterophylla* glucoman-nan | acid | 188 |
| | *Thuja plicata* glucomannan | acid | 187 |
| | *Picea abies* glucomannan | acid | 116 |
| | | enzym. | 256 |
| | *Picea glauca* glucomannan | acid | 203 |
| | *Borassus flabelifer* galacto-mannan | acid | 118 |
| | lucerne galactomannan | acid | 208 |
| | *Pinus taeda* hemicelluloses | acid | 193 |
| | guaran | enzym. | 115 |
| O-α-D-Mannopyranosyl-(1→2)-O-α-D-mannopyra-nosyl-(1→2)-D-mannose | *Saccharomyces rouxii* mannan | acetolysis | 141 |
| O-α-D-Mannopyranosyl-(1→6)-O-α-D-mannopyra-nosyl-(1→6)-D-mannose | yeast mannan | acid | 88 |
| O-α-D-Mannopyranosyl-(1→3)-O-α-D-mannopyra-nosyl-(1→3)-D-mannose | phosphomannan X-2448 | formic acid | 174 |
| 4-O-β-Mannobiosyl-D-glucose | *Pinus banksiana* glucoman-nan | enzym. | 131 |
| | *Picea abies* glucomannan | acid | 116 |
| | | enzym. | 256 |
| O-β-D-Mannopyranosyl-(1→4)-O-β-D-glucopyrano-syl-(1→4)-D-mannose | *Picea abies* glucomannan | acid | 116 |
| | | enzym. | 256 |
| 4-O-β-D-Mannopyranosyl-cellobiose | *Pinus banksiana* glucoman-nan | enzym. | 131 |
| Manninotriose | tetrasaccharide stachyose | acid or enzym. | 112, 232—239 |
| O-β-D-Galactopyranosyl-(1→6)-O-β-D-galactopyra-nosyl-(1→6)-D-galactose | *Virgilia oroboides* gum | acid | 69 |
| | *Anogeissus schimperi* gum | acid | 124 |
| | gum ghatti | acid | 123 |
| | *Larix laricina* arabinogalactan | acid | 128 |
| | *Fagus silvatica* galactan | acid | 240 |
| Galactotriose | *Picea abies* glucomannan | acid | 116 |
| O-α-D-Galactopyranosyl-(1→3)-O-α-D-galactopyra-nosyl-(1→3)-D-galactose | λ-carrageenin | acetolysis | 167 |
| | *Larix laricina* arabinogalac-tan | acid | 128 |

\* Mannotriose has been obtained after hydrolysis of *Abies amabilis* galactoglucomannan, see T. E. Timell, Svensk Papperstid. *65*, 843 (1962); Chem. Abstr. *59*, 729 (1963), and of *Tsuga canadensis* galactoglucomannan, see T. E. Timell, Tappi *45*, 799 (1962); Chem. Abstr. *59*, 2922 (1963).

*References see p. 207*

*Table XXVI — continued*

| Trisaccharide | Natural Substance | Degradation | References |
|---|---|---|---|
| O-β-D-Galactopyranosyl-(1→6)-O-β-D-galactopyranosyl-(1→4)-D-galactose | *Fagus silvatica* galactan | acid | 240 |
| O-β-D-Galactopyranosyl-(1→6)-O-β-D-galactopyranosyl-(1→3)-D-galactose | *Larix laricina* arabinogalactan | acid | 128 |
| 3,6-Di-O-β-D-galactopyranosyl-D-galactose | *Larix laricina* arabinogalactan | acid | 128 |
| O-α-D-Galactopyranosyl-(1→6)-O-α-D-galactopyranosyl-(1→1)-D-fructose | *Lychnis dioica* pentasaccharide | acid | 111 |
| O-α-D-Galactopyranosyl-(1→6)-O-α-D-mannopyranosyl-(1→6)-D-mannose | *Picea abies* glucomannan | acid | 116 |
| O-β-D-Galactopyranosyl-(1→6)-O-β-D-galactopyranosyl-(1→3)-L-arabinose | *Anogeissus schimperi* gum<br>gum ghatti | acid<br>acid | 124<br>123 |
| O-?-L-Galactopyranosyl-(1→4)-D-xylopyranosyl-(1→2)-L-arabinose | corn hull hemicelluloses | acid | 14 |
| Xylotriose* | xylans | acid | 210, 212, 241—243 |
|  |  | autohydrol. | 39 |
|  | flour arabinoxylan | acid | 211 |
|  | esparto hemicellulose | acid | 213 |
|  | *Betula papyrifera* glucuronoxylan | enzym. | 262 |
| Rhodymenatriose | *Rhodymenia palmata* xylan | acid | 177 |
| O-?-L-Arabinofuranosyl-(1→3)-O-β-D-xylopyranosyl-(1→4)-D-xylose | corn hull xylan<br>rye flour arabinoxylan | enzym. | 244<br>245 |
| O-α-D-Xylopyranosyl-(1→6)-O-β-D-glucopyranosyl-(1→4)-D-glucose | *Pinus banksiana* glucomannan | enzym. | 131 |
| Inulotriose** | inulin | acid | 60, 63 |
| G-G-G[β-(1→3),β-(1→6)] | *Sclerotinia libertiana* polysaccharide | acid | 101, 246 |
| G-Man-Man | konjackmannan | acetolysis | 130 |
| G-Man-G | glucomannan from unbleached Mitscherlich pulp | acetolysis | 204 |
| Man-Man-Man | glucomannan from unbleached Mitscherlich pulp | acetolysis | 204 |

\* Xylotriose has been obtained from a xylan of *Lolium perenne*, see G. O. Aspinall, I. M. Cairncross, and K. M. Ross, J. Chem. Soc. *1963*, 1721.

\*\* The oligosacchari delycorisin from *Lycoris radiata* yielded after hydrolysis a fructotriose, see T. Mizuno, Kagaku (Tokyo) *31*, 146 (1961); Chem. Abstr. *55*, 27099 (1961); there is no evidence about the identity of inulotriose and this fructotriose.

*Table XXVI — continued*

| Trisaccharide | Natural Substance | Degradation | References |
|---|---|---|---|
| Man-Man-Man | glucomannan from unbleach-ed Mitscherlich pulp | acetolysis<br>acid | <br>204 |
| Gal-Gal-Gal | *Picea abies* galactan<br>galactogen<br>galactocarolose | acid<br>acid | 196<br>247<br>216 |
| L-Ara-G-Man | *Pinus banksiana* glucoman-nan | enzym. | <br>131 |
| L-Ara-L-Ara-Gal | *Pinus banksiana* glucoman-nan | enzym. | 131 |
| L-Ara-L-Ara-Xyl | golden apple gum | autohydrol. | 13 |
| Xyl-Xyl-L-Ara | wheat straw xylan*<br>*Borassus flabellifer* galacto-mannan | enzym.<br><br>acid | 217<br><br>118 |

*O*-D-Galactopyranosyl-(1→4)-*O*-D-xylopyranosyl-(1→2)-L-arabinose has been reported as a hydrolysis product of the *Lolium perenne* xylan, see G. O. Aspinall, I. M. Cairncross, and K. M. Ross, J. Chem. Soc. *1963*, 1721.

\* This substance is probably identical with the *O*-?-L-arabinofuranosyl-(1→3)-*O*-β-D-xylo-pyranosyl-(1→4)-D-xylose, described later.[244]

## Table XXVII

Oligosaccharides Obtained by Degradation of Higher Oligosaccharides or Polysaccharides
Tetrasaccharides

| Tetrasaccharide | Natural Substance | Degradation | References |
|---|---|---|---|
| Sophorotetraose | *Agrobacterium radiobacter* polysaccharide | acid | 139 |
| Laminaritetraose | laminarin<br>*Eisenia bicyclis* laminaran<br>laminaran, pachymanan | acid<br>acetolysis<br>acetolysis | 87, 157<br>100<br>160 |
| Maltotetraose | starch<br>amylose | enzym.<br>acid | 21, 35, 263<br>179, 222 |
| Cellotetraose | cellulose | acid<br>acetolysis | 1—6, 183<br>183 |
| Gentiotetraose | yeast glucan<br>*Eisenia bicyclis* laminaran | acid<br>acetolysis | 99<br>100 |
| 4′-*O*-β-Laminaribiosylcello-biose | poly-β-D-glucan<br>*Cetraria islandica* poly-β-D-glucan | enzym.<br>enzym. | 31<br>231 |
| 3′-*O*-β-Cellobiosylcellobiose | poly-β-D-glucan<br>*Cetraria islandica* poly-β-D-glucan | enzym.<br>enzym. | 31<br>231 |
| 3-*O*-β-Cellotriosyl-D-glucose | poly-β-D-glucan | enzym. | 31 |

*References see p. 207*

*Table XXVII — continued*

| Tetrasaccharide | Natural Substance | Degradation | References |
|---|---|---|---|
| Mannotetraose* | *Picea abies* glucomannan | enzym. | 256 |
| | | acid | 116 |
| | *Picea glauca* | acid | 203 |
| | *Pinus strobus* glucomannan | acid | 190 |
| | yeast mannan | acid | 88 |
| Galactotetraose | *Picea abies* galactan | acid | 196 |
| Xylotetraose | corn hull hemicelluloses | autohydrol. | 39 |
| | xylans | acid | 210, 212 |
| | | | 241—243 |
| | *Betula papyrifera* glucuronoxylan | enzym. | 262 |
| Rhodymenatetraose | *Rhodymenia palmata* xylan | acid | 177 |
| Inulotetraose** | inulin | acid | 63 |
| Verbascotetraose | pentasaccharide verbascose | acetic acid | 5, 6 |
| O-β-D-Galactopyranosyl-(1→6)-O-β-D-galactopyranosyl-(1→6)-O-β-D-galactopyranosyl-(1→6)-D-galactose | gum ghatti | acid | 123 |
| | *Fagus silvatica* galactan | acid | 240 |
| | *Virgilia oroboides* gum | acid | 69 |
| O-β-D-Galactopyranosyl-(1→6)-O-β-D-galactopyranosyl-(1→6)-O-β-D-galactopyranosyl-(1→3)-D-galactose | *Larix laricina* arabinogalactan | acid | 128 |
| O-β-D-Galactopyranosyl-(1→6)-O-β-D-galactopyranosyl-(1→3)-O-β-D-galactopyranosyl-(1→3)-D-galactose | *Larix laricina* arabinogalactan | acid | 128 |
| O-β-D-Galactopyranosyl-(1→6)-O-β-D-galactopyranosyl-(1→6)-O-β-D-galactopyranosyl-(1→3)-L-arabinose | gum ghatti | acid | 123 |
| | *Anogeissus schimperi* gum | acid | 124 |
| O-α-D-Galactopyranosyl-(1→6)-O-α-D-galactopyranosyl-(1→6)-O-α-D-galactopyranosyl-(1→1)-D-fructose | *Lychnis dioica* hexasaccharide | acid | 111 |
| Gal-Gal-Gal-Gal | galactocarolose | acid | 216 |
| G-G-G-G (two substances) | *Eisenia bicyclis* laminaran | acetolysis | 100 |
| G-G-Man-Man | *Acer rubrum* glucomannan | formic acid | 9 |
| Xyl-Xyl-Xyl-L-Ara | wheat straw xylan | enzym. | 217 |

\* Mannotetraose has been reported among the hydrolysis products from *Tsuga canadensis* galactoglucomannan by T. E. Timell, Tappi *45*, 799 (1962); Chem. Abstr. *59*, 2922 (1963).

\*\* Fructotetraose obtained from lycorisin, see T. Mizuno, Kagaku (Tokyo) *31*, 146 (1961); Chem. Abstr. *55*, 27099 (1961), is probably not identical with inulotetraose.

An interesting branched tetrasaccharide has been obtained from arabinoxylan of wheat by enzymic degradation, see H. R. Goldschmid and A. S. Perlin, Can. J. Chem. *41*, 2272 (1963). The constitution of this tetrasaccharide corresponds to O-α-L-arabinofuranosyl-(1→3)-O-[β-D-xylopyranosyl-(1→4)]-O-β-D-xylopyranosyl-(1→4)-D-xylose.

### Table XXVIII
Oligosaccharides Obtained by Degradation of Higher Oligosaccharides or Polysaccharides
Pentasaccharides

| Pentasaccharide | Natural Substance | Degradation | References |
|---|---|---|---|
| Sophoropentaose | *Agrobacterium radiobacter* polysaccharide | acid | 139 |
| Laminaripentaose | pachymanan, laminaran | acetolysis | 160 |
| | laminarin | acid | 87, 157 |
| Maltopentaose | starch | enzym. | 21 |
| | amylose | acid | 179, 222 |
| Cellopentaose | cellulose | phosph. acid | 184, 248 |
| Mannopentaose | *Picea abies* glucomannan | enzym. | 256 |
| Galactopentaose | *Picea abies* galactan | acid | 196 |
| Xylopentaose | corn hull hemicelluloses | autohydrol. | 39 |
| | | acid | 210, 212 |
| | | | 241—243 |
| | *Betula papyrifera* glucurono-xylan | enzym. | 262 |
| O-β-D-Galactopyranosyl-(1→6)-O-β-D-galactopyra-nosyl-(1→6)-O-β-D-galac-topyranosyl-(1→6)-O-β-D-galactopyranosyl-(1→3)-L-arabinose | gum ghatti | acid | 123 |
| | *Anogeissus schimperi* gum | acid | 124 |
| Gal-Gal-Gal-Gal-Gal | galactocarolose | acid | 216 |
| | galactogen | acid | 247 |
| Xyl-Xyl-Xyl-L-Ara-L-Ara | wheat straw xylan | enzym. | 217 |

A pentasaccharide named fructopentaose has been obtained recently from lycorisin, see T. Mizuno, Kagaku (Tokyo) *31*, 146 (1961); Chem. Abstr. 55, 27099 (1961).

### Table XXIX
Oligosaccharides Obtained by Degradation of Higher Oligosaccharides or Polysaccharides
Hexasaccharides

| Hexasaccharide | Natural Substance | Degrada-tion | References |
|---|---|---|---|
| Sophorohexaose | *Agrobacterium radiobacter* poly-saccharide | acid | 139 |
| Laminarihexaose | pachymanan, laminaran | acetolysis | 160 |
| Maltohexaose | starch | enzym. | 21, 179, 249 |
| Cellohexaose | cellulose | acid | 183 |
| | | acetolysis | 250, 251 |
| Xylohexaose | xylans | acid | 39, 210, 212 241—243 |
| | *Betula papyrifera* glucurono-xylan | enzym. | 262 |
| Xyl-Xyl-Xyl-Xyl-Xyl-L-Ara | wheat straw xylan | enzym. | 217 |
| Gal-Gal-Gal-Gal-Gal-Gal | *Picea excelsa* galactan | acid | 196 |

*References see p. 207*

## Table XXX

Oligosaccharides Obtained by Degradation of Higher Oligosaccharides or Polysaccharides
Hepta- and Octasaccharides

| Oligosaccharide | Natural Substance | Degradation | References |
|---|---|---|---|
| Maltoheptaose | starch | enzym. | 21 |
| | amylose | acid | 179 |
| Celloheptaose | cellulose | acetolysis | 248 |
| Xyloheptaose | xylans | acid | 39, 212, 241–243 |
| Gal-Gal-Gal-Gal-Gal-Gal-Gal | *Picea excelsa* galactan | acid | 196 |
| Xyl-Xyl-Xyl-Xyl-Xyl-Xyl-L-Ara | wheat straw xylan | enzym. | 217 |
| Xylooctaose | xylan | acid | 39 |
| Gal-Gal-Gal-Gal-Gal-Gal-Gal-Gal | *Picea excelsa* galactan | acid | 196 |

## REFERENCES

1. R. L. Whistler and H. E. Conrad, J. Am. Chem. Soc. *76*, 1673 (1954).
2. M. L. Wolfrom and A. Thompson, J. Am. Chem. Soc. *78*, 4116 (1956).
3. A. Klemer, Chem. Ber. *92*, 218 (1959).
4. A. Klemer, Tetrahedron Letters *1960*, No. 22, 5.
5. S. Murakami, Acta Phytochim. *11*, 213 (1940); Chem. Abstr. *34*, 3694 (1940).
6. S. Murakami, Acta Phytochim. *13*, 161 (1943).
7. J. K. N. Jones and T. J. Painter, J. Chem. Soc. *1957*, 669.
8. J. K. N. Jones and T. J. Painter, J. Chem. Soc. *1959*, 573.
9. A. J. Mian and T. E. Timell, Can. J. Chem. *38*, 1511 (1960).
10. M. O. Gyaw and T. E. Timell, Can. J. Chem. *38*, 1957 (1960).
11. Org. Synth., Coll. Vol. *2*, 124 (1946).
12. P. Andrews and J. K. N. Jones, J. Chem. Soc. *1955*, 583.
13. P. Andrews and J. K. N. Jones, J. Chem. Soc. *1954*, 4134.
14. R. L. Whistler and W. M. Corbett, J. Am. Chem Soc. *77*, 6328 (1955).
15. R. Montgomery, F. Smith, and H. C. Srivastava, J. Am. Chem. Soc. *79*, 698 (1957).
16. J. H. Pazur and T. Budovich, Science *121*, 702 (1955); Chem. Abstr. *49*, 11736 (1955).
17. A. Herzfeld, Ann. *220*, 209 (1883).
18. T. S. Harding, Sugar *25*, 350 (1923).
19. U. S. Patent 1,657,079.
20. F. J. Bates, *Polarimetry, Saccharimetry and the Sugars,* National Bureau of Standards, Washington 1942, p. 459.
21. R. L. Whistler and J. H. Duffy, J. Am. Chem. Soc. *77*, 1017 (1955).
22. A. P. N. Franchimont, Ber. *12*, 1941 (1879).
23. Z. H. Skraup, Ber. *32*, 2413 (1899).
24. F. Klein, Z. angew. Chem. *25*, 1409 (1912).
25. G. Zemplén, Ber. *59*, 1258 (1926).
26. C. C. Spencer, Cellulosechemie *10*, 61 (1929).
27. G. Jayme and W. Demmig, Chem. Ber. *88*, 434 (1955).
28. R. Kuhn, H. H. Baer, and A. Gauhe, Ann. *611*, 242 (1958).
29. A. de Grandchamp-Chaudun, E. J. Courtois, and P. Le Dizet, Bull. soc. chim. biol. *42*, 227 (1960); Chem. Abstr. *55*, 5356 (1961).
30. T. J. Painter, Can. J. Chem. *37*, 497 (1959).
31. F. W. Parrish, A. S. Perlin, and E. T. Reese, Can. J. Chem. *38*, 2094 (1960).
32. R. H. Hopkins, Advances in Enzymol. *6*, 389 (1946).
33. K. Myrbäck and G. Nylander, Biochem. Z. *311*, 234 (1942).
34. D. French, M. L. Levine, J. H. Pazur, and E. Norberg, J. Am. Chem. Soc. *72*, 1746 (1950).
35. R. L. Whistler and J. L. Hickson, J. Am. Chem. Soc. *76*, 1671 (1954).
36. W. Rittel and T. Reichstein, Helv. Chim. Acta *35*, 2202 (1952).
37. J. C. Hess, A. Hunger, and T. Reichstein, Helv. Chim. Acta *35*, 2202 (1952).
38. P. Andrews and J. K. N. Jones, J. Chem. Soc. *1954*, 4134.
39. C. T. Bishop, Can. J. Chem. *33*, 1073 (1955).
40. C. Araki and S. Hirase, Bull. Chem. Soc. Japan *27*, 109 (1954); Chem. Abstr. *49*, 9518 (1955).
41. A. L. Clingman and J. R. Nunn, J. Chem. Soc. *1959*, 493.
42. S. Hirase, C. Araki, and T. Ito, Bull. Chem. Soc. Japan *31*, 428 (1958).
43. T. A. Scott and F. R. Scuti, J. Am. Chem. Soc. *77*, 3816 (1955).

44. C. Araki and S. Hirase, Bull. Chem. Soc. Japan *27*, 105 (1954); Chem. Abstr. *49*, 9517 (1955).
45. N. A. O'Neill, J. Am. Chem. Soc. *77*, 6324 (1955).
46. T. J. Painter, Can. J. Chem. *38*, 112 (1960).
47. G. O. Phillips and G. J. Moody, J. Chem. Soc. *1958*, 3534.
48. E. Bourquelot, Ann. chim. et phys. (7) *27*, 397 (1902).
49. E. Bourquelot and H. Hérissey, Compt. rend. *135*, 399 (1902).
50. E. Bourquelot and M. Bridel, Compt. rend. *171*, 13 (1920).
51. G. Avigad, J. Biol. Chem. *229*, 121 (1957).
52. E. J. Hehre and A. S. Carlson, Arch. Biochem. Biophys. *36*, 158 (1952).
53. D. French, G. M. Wild, B. Young, and W. J. James, J. Am. Chem. Soc. *75*, 709 (1953).
54. C. Neuberg, Biochem. Z. *3*, 528 (1907).
55. A. Wickström and A. B. Swendsen, Acta Chem. Scand. *10*, 1199 (1956).
56. A. Archambault, J. E. Courtois, A. Wickström, and P. Le Dizet, Bull. soc. chim. biol. *38*, 1133 (1955).
57. D. French, G. M. Wild, and W. J. James, J. Am. Chem. Soc. *75*, 3664 (1953).
58. J. E. Courtois, C. Anagnostopoulos, and F. Petek, Enzymologia *17*, 69 (1954).
59. J. E. Courtois, C. Anagnostopoulos, and F. Petek, Compt. rend. *238*, 2020 (1954).
60. D. S. Feingold and G. Avigad, Biochim. et Biophys. Acta *22*, 196 (1956).
61. K. Holzer, H. Wittmann-Zinke, and A. Zinke, Monatsh. Chem. *88*, 268 (1961).
62. G. O. Aspinall and P. C. Das Gupta, J. Chem. Soc. *1959*, 718.
63. J. H. Pazur and A. L. Gordon, J. Am. Chem. Soc. *75*, 3458 (1953).
64. H. H. Schlubach and A. Scheffler, Ann. *588*, 192 (1954).
65. A. Wickström, J. E. Courtois, P. Le Dizet, and A. Archambault, Compt. rend. *246*, 1624 (1958); Chem. Abstr. *52*, 18230 (1958).
66. A. Wickström, J. E. Courtois, P. Le Dizet, and A. Archambault, Bull. soc. chim. France *1958*, 1410.
67. H. C. Srivastava and F. Smith, J. Am. Chem. Soc. *79*, 982 (1957).
68. P. Andrews, L. Hough, and D B. Powell, Chem. & Ind. (London) *1956*, 658.
69. F. Smith and A. M. Stephen, J. Chem. Soc. *1961*, 4892.
70. A. M. Stephen, J. Chem. Soc. *1957*, 1919.
71. J. K. N. Jones, J. Chem. Soc. *1953*, 1672.
72. P. Andrews, D. H. Ball, and J. K. N. Jones, J. Chem. Soc. *1953*, 4090.
73. J. Larner, J. Am. Chem. Soc. *77*, 6385 (1955).
74. S. Peat, J. R. Turvey, and J. M. Evans, Nature *179*, 261 (1957).
75. S. Peat, J. R. Turvey, and J. M. Evans, J. Chem. Soc. *1959*, 3223.
76. A. Thompson, M. L. Wolfrom, and E. J. Quinn, J. Am. Chem. Soc. *75*, 3003 (1953).
77. M. L. Wolfrom and A. Thompson, J. Am. Chem. Soc. *77*, 6403 (1955).
78. E. M. Montgomery, F. B. Weakley, and G. E. Hilbert, J. Am. Chem. Soc. *69*, 2249 (1947).
79. E. M. Montgomery, F. B. Weakley and G. E. Hilbert, J. Am. Chem. Soc. *71*, 1682 (1949).
80. M. L. Wolfrom, E. N. Lassettre, and A. N. O'Neill, J. Am. Chem. Soc. *73*, 595 (1951).
81. M. L. Wolfrom, L. W. Georges, and I. L. Miller, J. Am. Chem. Soc. *69*, 473 (1947).
82. M. L. Wolfrom, L. W. Georges, and I. L. Miller, J. Am. Chem. Soc. *71*, 125 (1949).
83. R. W. Jones, D. J. Dimler, and C. E. Rist, J. Am. Chem. Soc. *77*, 1659 (1955).
84. E. E. Bacon and J. S. D. Bacon, Biochem. J. *58*, 396 (1954).
85. A. Jeanes, C. A. Wilham, R. W. Jones, H. M. Tsuchiya, and C. E. Rist, J. Am. Chem. Soc. *75*, 5911 (1953).

86. I. J. Goldstein and W. J. Whelan, J. Chem. Soc. *1962*, 170.

87. S. Peat, W. J. Whelan, and H. G. Lawley, J. Chem. Soc. *1958*, 729.

88. S. Peat, W. J. Whelan, and T. E. Edwards, J. Chem. Soc. *1961*, 29.

89. E. Bourquelot and H. Hérissey, Compt. rend. *126*, 280 (1898).

90. E. Bourquelot and H. Hérissey, Compt. rend. *132*, 571 (1901).

91. E. Bourquelot and H. Hérissey, Compt. rend. *135*, 290 (1902).

92. G. Zemplén, Ber. *48*, 233 (1915).

93. G. Zemplén, Hoppe-Seyler's Z. physiol. Chem. *85*, 399 (1913).

94. C. S. Hudson and J. Johnson, J. Am. Chem. Soc. *39*, 1272 (1917).

95. S. A. Barker, E. J. Bourne, and M. Stacey, Chem. & Ind. (London) *1953*, 1287.

96. J. R. Turvey and J. M. Evans, J. Chem. Soc. *1960*, 2366.

97. M. de Leizaola-Tripier, Compt. rend. *246*, 1761 (1958).

98. M. de Leizaola-Tripier, Compt. rend. *250*, 407 (1960).

99. S. Peat, W. J. Whelan, and T. E. Edwards, J. Chem. Soc. *1958*, 3862.

100. N. Handa a K. Nisizawa, Nature *192*, 1078 (1961).

101. M. Kitahara and Y. Takeuchi, Gifu Daigaku Nôgakubu Kenkyû Hôkoku *11*, 127 (1959); Chem. Abstr. *54*, 16529 (1960).

102. P. A. J. Gorin and J. F. T. Spencer, Can. J. Chem. *39*, 2282 (1961).

103. C. Scheibler and H. Mittelmeier, Ber. *22*, 1680 (1889).

104. C. Scheibler and H. Mittelmeier, Ber. *22*, 3120 (1889).

105. J. Pieraerts, Bull. de l'Assoc. des Chim. de Sucr. *23*, 1143 (1906); Chem. Zentr. *1906*, II, 23.

106. S. Hestrin, D. S. Feingold, and D. Avigad, J. Am. Chem. Soc. *77*, 6710 (1955).

107. A. Bau, Z. Verein deutsch. Zucker-Ind. *49*, 850 (1899).

108. M. Berthelot, Bull. soc. chim. France (3) *2*, 655 (1889).

109. C. S. Hudson and T. S. Harding, J. Am. Chem. Soc. *37*, 2734 (1915).

110. T. S. Harding, Sugar *25*, 514 (1923).

111. A. Wickström, J. E. Courtois, P. Le Dizet, and A. Archambault, Bull. soc. chim. France *1959*, 871.

112. R. A. Cooper and R. N. Greenshields, Nature *191*, 601 (1961).

113. L. M. White and G. E. Secor, Arch. Biochem. Biophys, *24*, 244 (1953); Chem. Abstr. *47*, 9432 (1953).

114. R. L. Whistler and D. F. Durso, J. Am. Chem. Soc. *73*, 4189 (1951).

115. R. L. Whistler and Ch. G. Smith, J. Am. Chem. Soc. *74*, 3795 (1952).

116. H. Meier, Acta Chem. Scand. *14*, 749 (1960).

117. M. E. Henderson, L. Hough, and T. J. Painter, J. Chem. Soc. *1958*, 3519.

118. A. K. Mukherjee, D. Choudhury, and P. Bagchi, Can. J. Chem. *39*, 1408 (1961).

119. H. Weinland, Hoppe-Seyler's Z. physiol. Chem. *305*, 87 (1856).

120. S. A. Barker, E. J. Bourne, and M. Stacey, J. Chem. Soc. *1953*, 3084.

121. A. Ballio and S. Russi, Tetrahedron *9*, 125 (1960).

122. B. O. Lindberg, Acta Chem. Scand. *11*, 1365 (1957).

123. G. O. Aspinall, B. J. Auret, and E. L. Hirst, J. Chem. Soc. *1958*, 4408.

124. G. O. Aspinall and T. B. Christensen, J. Chem. Soc. *1961*, 3461.

125. D. W. Drummond and E. Percival, J. Chem. Soc. *1961*, 3908.

126. D. J. Brasch and J. K. N. Jones, Can. J. Chem. *37*, 1538 (1959).

127. H. Bouveng and B. Lindberg, Acta Chem. Scand. *10*, 1515 (1956).

128. S. Haq and G. A. Adams, Can. J. Chem. *39*, 1563 (1961).

129. S. Peat, J. R. Turvey, and D. Doyle, J. Chem. Soc. *1961*, 3918.

130. K. Nishida and H. Hashima, J. Dept. Agr. Kyushu Imp. Univ. *2*, 277 (1930); Chem. Abstr. *25*, 498 (1931).

131. O. Perila and C. T. Bishop, Can. J. Chem. *39*, 815 (1961).

132. R. W. Bailey, S. A. Barker, E. J. Bourne, and M. Stacey, Nature *176*, 1164 (1955).

133. R. W. Bailey, S. A. Barker, E. J. Bourne, P. M. Grant, and M. Stacey, J. Chem. Soc. *1958*, 1895.

134. E. J. Bourne, J. Hartigan, and H. Weigel, J. Chem. Soc. *1959*, 2332.

135. K. Aso, K. Shibasaki, and M. Nakamura, Nature *182*, 1303 (1958).

136. F. Yamauchi and K. Aso, Nature *189*, 753 (1961).

137. K. Matsuda, K. Fujimoto, and K. Aso, J. Agr. Chem. Soc. Japan *25*, 1232 (1961).

138. K. Matsuda, H. Watanabe, K. Fujimoto, and K. Aso, Nature *191*, 278 (1961).

139. P. A. J. Gorin, J. F. T. Spencer, and D. W. S. Westlake, Can. J. Chem. *39*, 1067 (1961).

140. A. Wickström, Acta Chem. Scand. *11*, 1473 (1957).

141. P. A. J. Gorin and A. S. Perlin, Can. J. Chem. *35*, 262 (1957).

142. P. A. J. Gorin and A. S. Perlin, Can. J. Chem. *34*, 1796 (1956).

143. R. L. Whistler and D. I. McGilvray, J. Am. Chem. Soc. *77*, 1884 (1955).

144. R. L. Whistler and D. I. McGilvray, J. Am. Chem. Soc. *77*, 2212 (1955).

145. R. L. Whistler and W. M. Corbett, J. Am. Chem. Soc. *77*, 3822 (1955).

146. G. O. Aspinall and R. J. Ferrier, Chem. & Ind. (London) *1957*, 819.

147. G. O. Aspinall and R. J. Ferrier, J. Chem. Soc. *1957*, 4188.

148. G. O. Aspinall and R. J. Ferrier, J. Chem. Soc. *1958*, 1501.

149. S. A. Barker, E. J. Bourne, and J. G. Fleetwood, J. Chem. Soc. *1957*, 4865.

150. K. Matsuda, K. Fujimoto, and K. Aso, J. Agr. Chem. Soc. Japan *35*, 1228 (1961).

151. S. Peat, W. J. Whelan, J. R. Turvey, and K. Morgan, J. Chem. Soc. *1961*, 623.

152. K. Matsuda, G. Hiroshima, K. Shibasaki, and K. Aso, Tôhoku J. Agr. Research *5*, 239 (1954); Chem. Abstr. *50*, 4043 (1956).

153. K. Matsuda, G. Hiroshima, K. Shibasaki, and K. Aso, J. Ferment. Technol. (Japan) *32*, 498 (1954); Chem. Abstr. *49*, 8554 (1955).

154. S. A. Barker, E. J. Bourne, D. M. O'Mant, and M. Stacey, J. Chem. Soc. *1957*, 2448.

155. F. W. Parrish, A. S. Perlin, and E. T. Reese, Can. J. Chem. *38*, 2094 (1960).

156. H. Ono and M. Dazai, J. Agr. Chem. Soc. Japan *33*, 644 (1959).

157. S. Peat, W. J. Whelan, and T. E. Edwards, J. Chem. Soc. *1958*, 724.

158. V. C. Barry, Sci. Proc. Roy. Dublin Soc. *22*, 423 (1941).

159. K. Fujimoto, K. Matsuda, and K. Aso, J. Agr. Chem. Soc. Japan *36*, 346 (1962).

160. K. Fujimoto, K. Matsuda, and K. Aso, Tôhoku J. Agr. Res. *13*, 55 (1962); Chem. Abstr. *57*, 15211 (1962).

161. G. Tanret, Bull. soc. chim. France (3) *35*, 816 (1906).

162. G. Tanret, Compt. rend. *142*, 1424 (1906).

163. M. Bridel and T. Aagaard, Bull. soc. chim. biol. *9*, 884 (1927).

164. R. Kuhn and G. E. Grundherr, Ber. *59*, 1655 (1926).

165. C. S. Hudson and E. Pascu, J. Am. Chem. Soc. *52*, 2522 (1930).

166. S. A. Barker, M. C. Keith, and M. Stacey, Nature *189*, 746 (1961).

167. K. Morgan and A. N. O'Neill, Can. J. Chem. *37*, 1201 (1959).

168. T. J. Painter, W. M. Watkins, and W. T. J. Morgan, Nature *193*, 1042 (1962).

169. E. L. Hirst and A. S. Perlin, J. Chem. Soc. *1954*, 2622.

170. E. L. Hirst and A. S. Perlin, Anal. Chem. *27*, 396 (1955).

171. G. O. Aspinall, E. L. Hirst, and A. Nicholson, J. Chem. Soc. *1959*, 1697.

172. F. Smith, J. Chem. Soc. *1939*, 744.

173. A. J. Charlson, J. R. Nunn, and A. M. Stephen, J. Chem. Soc. *1955*, 269.

174. A. Jeanes, J. E. Pittsley, P. R. Watson, and J. H. Sloneker, Can. J. Chem. *40*, 2256 (1962).

175. A. J. Charlson, J. R. Nunn, and A. M. Stephen, J. Chem. Soc. *1955*, 1428.

176. D. H. Ball, J. K. N. Jones, W. H. Nicholson, and T. J. Painter, Tappi *39*, 438 (1956), Chem. Abstr. *50*, 13469 (1956).
177. B. H. Howard, Biochem. J. *67*, 643 (1957).
178. R. L. Whistler and J. H. Duffy, J. Am. Chem. Soc. *77*, 1017 (1955).
179. W. J. Whelan, J. M. Bailey, and P. J. P. Roberts, J. Chem. Soc. *1953*, 1293.
180. F. J. Bates, *Polarimetry, Saccharimetry and the Sugars*, National Bureau of Standards, Washington 1942, p. 470.
181. M. W. Radomski and M. Doreen, Cereal Chem. *39*, 30 (1962); Chem. Abstr. *56*, 2479 (1962).
182. H. O. Bouveng, H. Kiessling, B. Lindberg, and J. McKay, Acta Chem. Scand. *16*, 615 (1962).
183. G. L. Miller, J. Dean, and R. Blum, Arch. Biochem. Biophys. *91*, 21 (1960).
184. A. Beélik and J. K. Hamilton, J. Org. Chem. *26*, 5074 (1961).
185. R. L. Whistler and C. L. Smart, J. Am. Chem. Soc. *75*, 1916 (1953).
186. E. T. Reese, E. Smakula, and A. S. Perlin, Arch. Biochem. Biophys. *85*, 171 (1959).
187. J. K. Hamilton and E. V. Partlow, J. Am. Chem. Soc. *80*, 4880 (1958).
188. J. K. Hamilton and H. W. Kircher, J. Am. Chem. Soc. *80*, 4703 (1958).
189. T. Koshijima, K. Kitao, and T. Tachi, Mokuzai Kenkyu *1958*, No. 19, 19; Chem. Abstr. *52*, 21085 (1958).
190. M. O. Gyaw and T. E. Timell, Can. J. Chem. *38*, 1957 (1960).
191. G. O. Aspinall, R. Begbie, and J. E. McKay, J. Chem. Soc. *1962*, 214.
192. T. Koshijima and I. Tachi, Bull. Agr. Chem. Soc. Japan *22*, 11 (1958).
193. J. K. N. Jones and T. J. Painter, J. Chem. Soc. *1957*, 669.
194. B. N. Stepanenko and L. V. Slozhenikina, Doklady Akad. Nauk S.S.S.R. *138*, 1460 (1961); Chem. Abstr. *55*, 27099 (1961).
195. J. K. Gillham, A. S. Perlin, and T. E. Timell, Can. J. Chem. *36*, 1741 (1958).
196. H. O. Bouveng and H. Meier, Acta Chem. Scand. *13*, 1884 (1959).
197. R. Kuhn, H. H. Baer, and A. Gauhe, Chem. Ber. *88*, 1135 (1955).
198. R. Kuhn, Bull. soc. chim. biol. *40*, 297 (1958).
199. R. Kuhn, A. Gauhe, and H. H. Baer, Chem. Ber. *87*, 289 (1954).
200. R. Kuhn, A. Gauhe, and H. H. Baer, Chem. Ber. *89*, 1027 (1956).
201. R. Kuhn and A. Gauhe, Ann. *611*, 249 (1958).
202. G. O. Aspinall, R. B. Rashbrook, and G. Kessler, J Soc. Chem. *1958*, 215.
203. A. Tymynski and T. E. Timell, J. Am. Chem. Soc. *82*, 2823 (1960).
204. E. Merler and L. E. Wise, Tappi *41*, 80 (1958); Chem. Abstr. *52*, 11416 (1958).
205. R. L. Whistler and J. Z. Stein, J. Am. Chem. Soc. *73*, 4187 (1951).
206. A. Anthis, Tappi *39*, 401 (1956); Chem. Abstr. *50*, 12467 (1956).
207. F. Smith and H. C. Srivastava, J. Am. Chem. Soc. *78*, 1404 (1956).
208. M. E. Henderson, L. Hough, and T. J. Painter, J. Chem. Soc. *1958*, 3519.
209. R. L. Whistler, J. Bachrach, and C. C. Tu, J. Am. Chem. Soc. *74*, 3059 (1952).
210. R. L. Whistler, and C. C. Tu, J. Am. Chem. Soc. *74*, 3609 (1952).
211. M. Ewald and A. S. Perlin, Can, J. Chem. *37*, 1254 (1959).
212. J. K. Hamilton and N. S. Thompson, J. Am. Chem. Soc. *79*, 6464 (1957).
213. G. O. Aspinall, M. E. Carter, and M. Los, J. Chem. Soc. *1956*, 4807.
214. J. K. N. Jones and L. E. Wise, J. Chem. Soc. *1952*, 2750.
215. K. Hunt and J. K. N. Jones, Can. J. Chem. *40*, 1266 (1962).
216. P. A. J. Gorin and J. F. T. Spencer, Can. J. Chem. *37*, 499 (1959).
217. C. T. Bishop and D. R. Whitaker, Chem. & Ind. London *1955*, 119.
218. J. E. Courtois, P. Le Dizet, and F. Petek, Bull. soc. chim. biol. *41*, 1261 (1959); Chem. Abstr. *54*, 13003 (1960).

219. M. L. Wolfrom, L. W. Georges, A. Thompson, and I. L. Miller, J. Am. Chem. Soc. *71*, 2873 (1949).

220. L. W. Georges, I. L. Miller, and M. L. Wolfrom, J. Am. Chem. Soc. *69*, 473 (1947).

221. R. Venkataraman and F. J. Reithel, Arch. Biochem. Biophys. *75*, 443 (1958); Chem. Abstr. *52*, 16502 (1958).

222. K. Takiura and K. Koizumi, Chem. & Pharm. Bull. (Tokyo) *10*, 140 (1962).

223. R. Willstätter and L. Zechmeister, Ber. *62*, 722 (1929).

224. L. Zechmeister and G. Tóth, Ber. *64*, 854 (1931).

225. E. E. Dickey and M. L. Wolfrom, J. Am. Chem. Soc. *71*, 825 (1949).

226. M. L. Wolfrom and J. C. Dacons, J. Am. Chem. Soc. *74*, 5331 (1952).

227. G. Bertrand and S. Benoist, Bull. soc. chim. France (4) *33*, 1451 (1923).

228. G. Bertrand and S. Benoist, Compt. rend. *176*, 1583 (1923).

229. G. Bertrand and S. Benoist, Compt. rend. *177*, 85 (1923).

230. M. L. Wolfrom and A. Thompson, J. Am. Chem. Soc. *78*, 4182 (1956).

231. A. S. Perlin and S. Suzuki, Can. J. Chem. *40*, 52 (1962).

232. C. Tanret, Compt. rend. *134,* 1586 (1902).

233. C. Tanret, Bull. soc. chim. France (3) *27*, 947 (1902).

234. C. Tanret, Bull. soc. chim. France (3) *29*, 888 (1903).

235. C. Neuberg and S. Lachmann, Biochem. Z. *24*, 174 (1910).

236. H. Bierry, Biochem. Z. *44*, 446 (1912).

237. R. Adams, N. K. Richtmyer, and C. S. Hudson, J. Am. Chem. Soc. *65*, 1365 (1943).

238. J. E. Courtois, A. Wickström and P. Le Dizet, Bull. soc. chim. biol. *35*, 1117 (1953).

239. L. Piault, Bull. pharm. et chim. (7) *1*, 248 (1910).

240. H. Meier, Acta Chem. Scand. *16*, 2275 (1962).

241. R. L. Whistler and C. C. Tu, J. Am. Chem. Soc. *73*, 1389 (1951).

242. R. L. Whistler and C. C. Tu, J. Am. Chem. Soc. *74*, 4334 (1952).

243. R. L. Whistler and C. C. Tu, J. Am. Chem. Soc. *75*, 645 (1953).

244. C. T. Bishop, J. Am. Chem. Soc. *78*, 2840 (1956).

245. G. O. Aspinall, I. M. Cairncross, R. J. Sturgeon, and K. C. B. Wilkie, J. Chem. Soc. *1960*, 3881.

246. M. Kitahara and Y. Takeuchi, J. Agr. Chem. Soc. Japan *35*, 468 (1961).

247. F. May and H. Weinland, Hoppe Seyler's Z. physiol. Chem. *305*, 207 (1956).

248. M. L. Wolfrom and J. C. Dacons, J. Am. Chem. Soc. *74*, 5331 (1952).

249. R. L. Whistler and F. B. Moy, J. Am. Chem. Soc. *77*, 5761 (1955).

250. L. Zechmeister and G. Tóth, Ber. *64*, 854 (1931).

251. H. Staudinger and E. O. Leupold, Ber. *67*, 479 (1934).

252. E. Guilloux and F. Percheron, Compt. rend. *257*, 545 (1963).

253. D. J. Manners and J. P. Mitchell, Biochem. J. *89*, 92p (1963).

254. W. Sowa, A. C. Blackwood, and G. A. Adams, Can. J. Chem. *41*, 2314 (1963).

255. V. P. Bhavanandan, H. O. Bouveng, and B. Lindberg, Acta Chem. Scand. *18*, 504 (1964).

256. H. O. Bouveng, T. Iwasaki, B. Lindberg, and H. Meier, Acta Chem. Scand. *17*, 1796 (1963).

257. J. M. Vaughan and E. E. Dickey, J. Org. Chem. *29*, 715 (1964).

258. J. L. Thompson and J. K. N. Jones, Can. J. Chem. *42*, 1088 (1964).

259. P. A. J. Gorin and J. F. T. Spencer, Can. J. Chem. *41*, 2357 (1963).

260. F. Petek, J. E. Courtois, and M. Dahoul, Bull. soc. chim. biol. *45*, 1261 (1963).

261. E. L. Hirst, E. Percival, and J. K. Wold, J. Chem. Soc. *1964*, 1493.

262. R. H. Marchessault and T. E. Timell, J. Polymer. Sci. Pt. C. No 2, 49 (1963).

263. A. G. Clark and K. R. L. Mansford, Nature *200*, 30 (1963).

264. H. R. Goldschmid and A. S. Perlin, Can. J. Chem. *41*, 2272 (1963).

# XI

# Isolation of Oligosaccharides from Heterosides

Oligosaccharides are common components of heterosides and glycoalkaloids; their constitution is known in many cases, usually as a result of structural investigation of the natural substances mentioned. However, the number of free oligosaccharides, either of unchanged constitution or partially degraded, prepared from these sources, is relatively small.

The cleavage of heterosides or alkaloids has been most frequently carried out in acid solution by about 0.1N sulphuric acid or acetic acid, or by the action of enzymes. Other procedures employed for this purpose are cleavage with zinc chloride in acetic anhydride, obviously leading to per-O-acetyl derivatives of oligosaccharides, and exceptionally also reducing cleavage with zinc in acetic acid.[1] A quite remarkable case is the hydrogenation cleavage of amygdalin which, as an O-benzyl derivative, is hydrogenolysed in this way. The original method, namely hydrogenation of hepta-O-acetylamygdalin with hydrogen on palladium with the formation of hepta-O-acetylgentiobiose,[2,3] has been modified so as to yield gentiobiose by direct hydrogenation of amygdalin on palladium.[4]

A survey of the oligosaccharides obtained by cleavege of heterosides and glycoalkaloids, with indications of the sources and procedures, is presented in Table XXXI. Deoxy sugars containing oligosaccharides prepared from natural sources of the above mentioned type, such as condurangobiose, 2-deoxycellobiose, digilanidobiose, eryperobiose, D-glucodigilanidobiose, odorotriose, robinobiose, rutinose, scillabiose, scillatriose, solatriose, strophanthobiose (= periplobiose) and strophanthotriose are given in Chapter XXII and Tables LXIX—LXXI.

*References see p. 215*

## Table **XXXI**

Oligosaccharides Obtained from Heterosides

| Oligosaccharide | Natural Substance | Method of Preparation | References |
|---|---|---|---|
| Cellobiose | gitostin | ZnCl$_2$/acetic anhydride | 5 |
| Gentiobiose | octa-$O$-acetylacovenoside | ZnCl$_2$/acetic anhydride | 29 |
| | odorotrioside | ZnCl$_2$/acetic anhydride | 6 |
| | odorotrioside K | ZnCl$_2$/acetic anhydride | 7 |
| | *neo*-gitostine | ZnCl$_2$/acetic anhydride | 5 |
| | bryodulcoside | acid | 8 |
| | amygdalin | H$_2$/Pd | 4 |
| hepta-$O$-acetate | hepta-$O$-acetate | H$_2$/Pd | 2, 3 |
| Lycotriose $I$ | tomatine | acid | 9, 10 |
| Lycotriose $II$ | demissine | acid | 9 |
| Lycotetraose | tomatine | acid | 9 |
| Primeverose | gentiacauline | enzymic | 11 |
| | macrozamin | Zn/acid | 1 |
| | monotropidin | enzymic | 12, 13 |
| | morindin | enzymic | 30 |
| | primeverin | enzymic | 14—16 |
| | primeveroside | enzymic | 31 |
| | primulaverin | enzymic | 14—16 |
| | primulaveroside | enzymic | 31 |
| | rhamnicoside | enzymic | 17 |
| | caesioside | enzymic | 18 |
| | ruberythric acid | enzymic | 19 |
| | galiosin | acid | 20 |
| Sophorose | sophoraflavonoloside | acid | 21 |
| | caempferolsophoroside | acid | 22 |
| Solabiose | demissine | acid | 9 |
| | solanine | acid | 23 |
| | solasonine | acid | 32 |
| Vicianose | gein | enzymic | 24 |
| | vicianin | enzymic | 25 |
| | violutoside | enzymic | 26 |
| D-Glucoxylose | glycoside from *Daviesia latifolia* | | 27, 28 |

## REFERENCES

1. B. Lythgoe and N. V. Riggs, J. Chem. Soc. *1949*, 2716.
2. M. Bergmann and W. Freudenberg, Ber. *62*, 2783 (1929).
3. B. Lindberg, Acta Chem. Scand. *3*, 1355 (1949).
4. R. Kuhn and A. Kolb, Chem. Ber. *91*, 2408 (1958).
5. A. Okano, Chem. Pharm. Bull. (Tokyo) *6*, 178 (1958).
6. A. Rheiner, A. Hunger, and T. Reichstein, Helv. Chim. Acta *35*, 687 (1952).
7. W. Rittel and T. Reichstein, Helv. Chim. Acta *37*, 1361 (1954).
8. P. Tunmann and F. H. Schehrer, Arch. Pharm. *292*, 745 (1959).
9. R. Kuhn, I. Löw, and H. Trischmann, Chem. Ber. *90*, 203 (1957).
10. R. Kuhn and I. Löw, Chem. Ber. *86*, 1027 (1953).
11. M. Bridel, Compt. rend. *179*, 780 (1924); Chem. Abstr. *19*, 817 (1925).
12. M. Bridel and S. Grillon, Compt. rend. *187*, 609 (1928).
13. M. Bridel, Compt. rend. *179*, 991 (1924); Chem. Abstr. *19*, 842 (1925).
14. A. Goris, M. Mascré, and Ch. Vischniac, Bull. sci. pharmacol. *19*, 577 (1912).
15. A. Goris and Ch. Vischniac, Compt. rend. *169*, 975 (1919); Chem. Abstr. *14*, 539 (1920).
16. M. Bridel, Compt. rend. *180*, 1421 (1926); Chem. Abstr. *19*, 2514 (1925).
17. M. Bridel and C. Charaux, Compt. rend. *180*, 1219 (1925); Chem. Abstr. *19*, 2108 (1925).
18. J. Rabaté, J. pharm. chim. *29*, 584 (1939); Chem. Abstr. *33*, 9309 (1939).
19. D. Richter, J. Chem. Soc. *1936*, 1701.
20. R. Hill and D. Richter, J. Chem. Soc. *1936*, 1713.
21. J. Rabaté and J. Dussy, Bull. soc. chim. biol. *20*, 467 (1938).
22. K. Freudenberg, H. Knauer, and F. Cramer, Chem. Ber. *84*, 144 (1951).
23. R. Kuhn, I. Löw, and H. Trischmann, Chem. Ber. *88*, 1492 (1955).
24. H. Hérissey and J. Cheymol, Compt. rend. *183*, 1307 (1926).
25. G. Bertrand and G. Weissweiler, Compt. rend. *150*, 180 (1910).
26. D. Picard, Compt. rend. *182*, 1167 (1926).
27. F. B. Power and A. H. Salway, J. Chem. Soc. *105*, 767 (1914).
28. F. B. Power and A. H. Salway, J. Chem. Soc. *105*, 1062 (1914).
29. P. Hauschild-Rogat, J. von Euw, O. Schindler, F. Weiss, and T. Reichstein, Helv. Chim. Acta *45*, 2116 (1962).
30. R. A. Paris and Nguyen Ba Tuoc, Ann. pharm. franç. *12*, 794 (1954); Chem. Abstr. *49*, 8897 (1955).
31. A. Goris, Ind. parfum. *5*, 121, 177 (1950); Chem. Abstr. *44*, 8062 (1950).
32. L. H. Briggs, R. C. Cambie, and J. L. Hoare, J. Chem. Soc. *1963*, 2848.

# XII

# Description and Properties of Oligosaccharides

Today a great many oligosaccharides are known whose structures have been established with certainty. They have been obtained from natural material, in many cases by direct isolation (see Chapter IX), further by partial hydrolysis of higher oligosaccharides or polysaccharides (see Chapter X), and also by hydrolysis of heterosides (see Chapter XI). Numerous oligosaccharides have been prepared by reversion (see Chapter VI, 4), as well as by synthetic methods, either chemical (see Chapter VI,1-3) or enzymic (see Chapter VI,5).

The structures have been derived from the cleavage products identified by routine methods, from the course of the cleavage of oligosaccharide per-*O*-methyl ethers, or, also, from the course of the oxidation of the oligosaccharides with periodic acid or lead tetra-acetate.

In general it may be stated that oligosaccharides, with few exceptions (see Chapters VII and X), are not subject to hydrolysis in alkaline solution.[1] In a strongly alkaline medium they are degraded with the formation of saccharinic acids (see Chapter VII) derived from monosaccharides throughout; the formation of the saccharinic acids usually involves the splitting of the glycosidic linkage in the oligosaccharide, and one case only has so far been reported[2] where a glycosyl derivative of a saccharinic acid could be obtained (see Chapter VII).

In acid solution,* the oligosaccharides undergo hydrolysis; higher oligosaccharides yield lower oligosaccharides in moderately acid solution (see Chapter X), while at higher acidity they are completely hydrolysed. The hydrolysis of lower oligosaccharides, as a rule disaccharides, in acid solution has been investigated in many cases from the kinetic viewpoint.[3-10] There are great differences in the behaviour of individual disaccharides; for example, sucrose is hydrolysed in acid solution much faster than are the other disaccharides.[11,12]

Very interesting observations in this respect have been published by Japanese authors. The stability of glycosidic linkages is dependent not only on the type of the linkage, but also on the kind of cleavage. According to K. Matsuda, H. Watanabe, K. Fujimoto,

---

* Synthetic polysaccharides can be prepared from several reducing disaccharides — like maltose, cellobiose and lactose — by an acid-catalysed condensation in dimethyl sulphoxide, see F. Micheel and R. Puchta, Makromol. Chem. *48*, 17 (1961); Chem. Abstr. *59*, 15365 (1963).

and K. Aso, Nature *191*, 278 (1961), the 1→6 linkage is more stable under the conditions of acid hydrolysis than the other ones, however, the least stable under the conditions of acetolysis; this permits the isolation of kojibiose from dextran.

K. Fujimoto, K. Matsuda, and K. Aso, J. Agr. Chem. Soc. Japan *36*, 770 (1962); Tôhoku J. Agr. Research *13*, 61 (1952); Chem. Abstr. *57*, 15211 (1962), have reported that from possible isomers of D-glucosyl derivatives of D-glucose gentiobiose is the most stable compound being followed by the slightly less stable isomaltose. Kojibiose, nigerose and maltose are hydrolysed more quickly.

The influence of metal ions on the hydrolysis of oligosaccharides has been followed by H. Trapmann and S. Sethi, Arch. Pharm. *295*, 925 (1962); especially thorium and zirconium salts exhibit a catalytic effect.

Glycosidic linkages in branched oligosaccharides are hydrolysed more slowly than the corresponding linkages of simple oligosaccharides, see A. Klemer, Tetrahedron Letters *1960*, No. 22, 5.

Acid hydrolysis is complicated by the possibility of the formation of secondary oligosaccharides in consequence of reversion (see Chapter VI, 4). The cleavage of lactose by acids proceeds, as was found in 1952,[13] with the simultaneous formation of new oligosaccharides, whereas this is not the case in enzymic cleavage (however, there are known a number of cases — see Chapter VI, 5 — where the initial oligosaccharide is converted into the new ones by enzymic transfer). Nevertheless, enzymic cleavage is recommended,[14] in particular for higher oligosaccharides or polysaccharides. The enzymic cleavage, of course, is strictly stereoselective, as observed, for example, on maltose[15] and cellobiose.[16]

Recent papers deal with the possibility of cleavage of some oligosaccharides, mainly sucrose, on ion exchangers.[17-20] Maltose and lactose are said to be stable under similar conditions.[17]

In a strongly acid medium, oligosaccharides are profoundly degraded; this has been investigated in particular on sucrose, which is converted into 5-hydroxymethylfurfural;[21] this substance is formed by the action of a 0.25% aquaeous solution of oxalic acid from the fructose unit of the sucrose molecule.[22]

In a special way proceeds the degradation of lactose by the action of an ethanolic solution of piperidine acetate in the presence of trimethylamine or triethylamine.[23,24] Thus, lactose (I) yields a substance termed O-β-D-galactopyranosylisomaltol (II), the structure being based on the assumption[23*] that isomaltol is 2-acetyl-3-hydroxyfuran. The formation of this substance is in agreement with the scheme proposed for the mechanism of formation of furan derivatives from sugar.[25]

Complexes of oligosaccharides with different metals have been followed recently by S. Mahdihassan et al., see Pakistan J. Sci. Ind. Res. *6*, 103, 105, 107, 109, 111, 114 (1963).

---

** This assumption has been verified recently, see B. E. Fischer and J. E. Hodge, J. Org. Chem. *29*, 776 (1964).

*References see p. 218*

(I)                                                        (II)

The following paragraphs deal in greater detail with the more significant oligosaccharides, while their physico-chemical constants together with those of less important substances are summarized in the attached tables. The origin of the oligosaccharide is here not usually given, and the same applies to its synthesis; data in this respect are contained in the respective chapters. If no details are given regarding the structure of an individual oligosaccharide, it is understood that its constitution has been established by some routine method.

### REFERENCES

1. Z. A. Rogovin and I. A. Rymashevskaya, Zhur. Priklad. Khim. *26*, 191 (1953).
2. R. L. Whistler and J. N. BeMiller, J. Org. Chem. *26*, 2886 (1961).
3. K. Freudenberg, W. Kuhn, W. Dürr, F. Bolz, and G. Steinbrunn, Ber. *63*, 1510 (1930).
4. K. Freudenberg and G. Blomquist, Ber. *68*, 2070 (1935).
5. W. R. Fetzer, E. K. Crosby, C. E. Engel, and L. C. Kirst, Ind. Eng. Chem. *45*, 1075 (1953).
6. R. W. Jones, D. J. Dimler, and C. E. Rist, J. Am. Chem. Soc. *77*, 1659 (1955).
7. K. Täufel and H. Ruttloff, Ernährungsforschung *4*, 44 (1959); Chem. Abstr. *53*, 16830 (1959).
8. G. N. La Diega, Chim. e Ind. (Milan) *41*, 408 (1959); Chem. Abstr. *54*, 2733 (1960).
9. J. F. Bunnett, J. Am. Chem. Soc. *83*, 4956 (1961).
10. C. Armour, C. A. Bunton, S. Patai, L. H. Selman, and C. A. Vernon, J. Chem. Soc. *1961*, 412.
11. H. C. Silberman, J. Org. Chem. *26*, 1967 (1961).
12. J. Staněk and J. Černá, Tetrahedron Letters *1963*, 35.
13. G. Malyoth and H. W. Stein, Angew. Chem. *64*, 399 (1952).
14. T. J. Painter, Can. J. Chem. *37*, 497 (1959).
15. E. Ben-Gersham and J. Leibowitz, Enzymologia *20*, 148 (1958).
16. N. K. Richtmyer and C. S. Hudson, J. Am. Chem. Soc. *61*, 1834 (1939).
17. M. Abdel-Akher, Alexandria J. Agr. Research *6*, No. 2, 13 (1958); Chem. Abstr. *56*, 11681 (1962).
18. K. Täufel and K. S. Grunert, Arch. Pharm. *294*, 439 (1961).
19. K. J. Steinbach, K. S. Grunert, and K. Täufel, Nahrung *5*, 617 (1961); Chem. Abstr. *58*, 1522 (1963).

20. K. Täufel and K. S. Grunert, Nahrung *6*, 93 (1962); Chem. Abstr. *57*, 11438 (1962).
21. L. F. Wiggins, Advances in Carbohydrate Chem. *4*, 293 (1949).
22. W. N. Haworth and W. G. M. Jones, J. Chem. Soc. *1944*, 667.
23. J. E. Hodge and E. C. Nelson, Cereal Chem. *38*, 207 (1961); Chem. Abstr. *56*, 6063 (1962).
24. U. S. Patent 3,015,654; Chem. Abstr. *56*, 13000 (1962).
25. E. F. L. J. Anet, Chem. & Ind. (London) *1962*, 262.

# 1. DISACCHARIDES

## A. NON-REDUCING DISACCHARIDES

Trehalose, α-D-glucopyranosyl α-D-glucopyranoside (I), is most easily obtained from trehala manna (see Chapter IX).[1] The material is extracted with 75% ethanol, the extract is concentrated, clarified with basic lead acetate and, on removal of the lead ions with hydrogen sulphide, the solution is concentrated until crystallization sets in. Another trehalose source may be yeast.[2,3]

The structure of trehalose follows from the finding that its hydrolysis yields D-glucose only, whereas the hydrolysis of the permethylated trehalose derivative leads to two molecules of 2,3,4,6-tetra-*O*-methyl-D-glucopyranose.[4] On the basis of his Isorotation Rules, Hudson correctly concluded that both glucose units are mutually bound by α-glycosidic linkages.[5,6] This structure is in full agreement with the course of the periodic acid oxidation.[7,8]

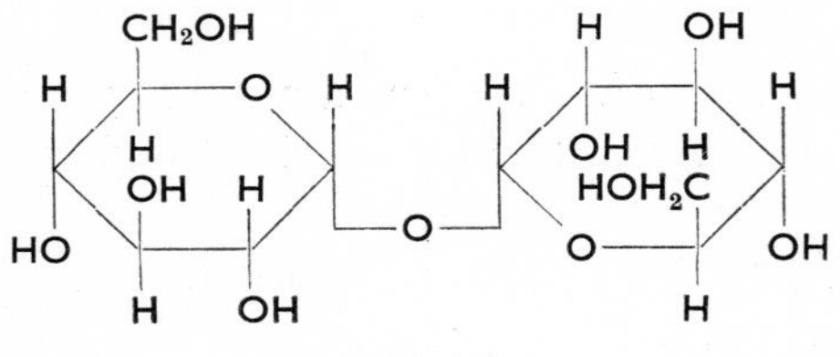

(I)

*neo*-Trehalose, α-D-glucopyranosyl β-D-glucopyranoside (II), has so far been obtained only by syntheses (see Chapter VI). The structure of this substance is indisputable, supported by the course of the periodic acid oxidation;[8] however, the values of melting points and specific rotations given by one group of writers[8,9] differ considerably from the values reported by other investigators[10,11] (see Table XXXII).

*References see p. 226*

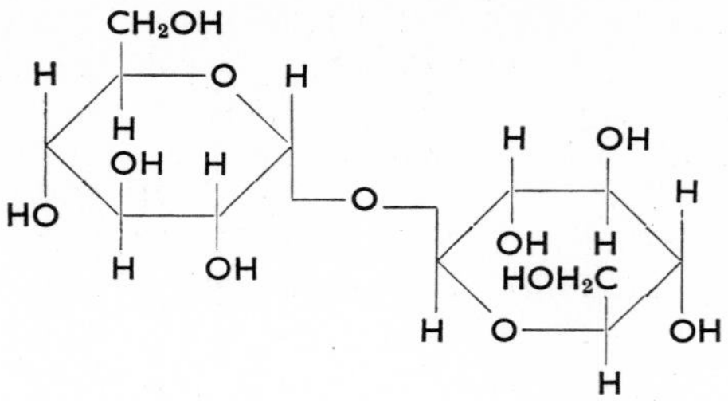

(II)

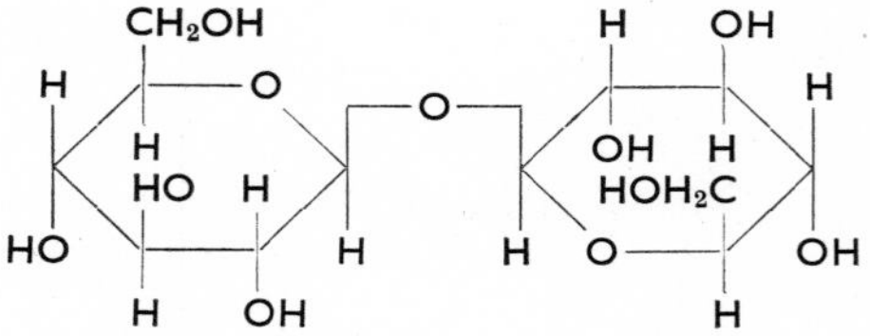

(III)

Isotrehalose, $\beta$-D-glucopyranosyl $\beta$-D-glucopyranoside (III), is likewise a product of chemical syntheses[12-15] (see Chapter VI).

All three analogous D-galactopyranosyl D-galactopyranosides have been prepared by syntheses,[10,11,16] as well as some D-mannopyranosyl D-mannopyranosides[17] and D-galactopyranosyl D-glucopyranosides.[15,18] The properties of these synthetic compounds (see Chapter VI) are summarized in Table XXXII.

Sucrose, $\alpha$-D-glucopyranosyl $\beta$-D-fructofuranoside (IV), has been known for a very long time; according to Lippmann,[19] it was manufactured in India as early as about 300 A. D. Cane sugar was brought to America in the time of Columbus' voyages, and in the year 1747, A. S. Marggraf detected sucrose in the sugar beet.*

Sucrose has frequently been found as a natural product (see Chapter IX) and obtained in the hydrolysis of most various higher oligosaccharides (see Chapter X).

Is has been known for a very long time that the hydrolysis of sucrose leads to a molecule of D-glucose and to a molecule of D-fructose.[20] This process is termed inversion since the resultant solution is laevorotatory, contrary to the initial dextrorotatory sucrose solution. Inversion is effected by acids[21] as well as by enzymes; more recent papers describe the course of the hydrolysis of sucrose on cation exchange resins [22-25] and by the action of $\beta$-radiation.[26] The hydrolysis has also been investigated in a medium of $D_2O$;[27] it has been found that acid hydrolysis of sucrose in $D_2O$ proceeds faster than in water, while the contrary applies to the action of enzymes.

---

* For a review see L. F. Wiggins, Advances in Carbohydrate Chem. 4, 293 (1949).

Sucrose can be split by the action of phenylhydrazine, too; phenyl-D-glucosazone is the product of this reaction, see L. Jurd, J. Org. Chem. *21*, 759 (1956).

The structure of sucrose[28]* follows from the course of the splitting of its permethylated derivative, which is now easily obtainable.[29]

The determination of the structure of sucrose is the result of the classical investigations carried out by Haworth's school.[30,31] The hydrolysis of the per-*O*-methylated sucrose derivative (V) yields 2,3,4,6-tetra-*O*-methyl-D-glucopyranose (VI) and 1,3,4,6-tetra-*O*-methyl-D-fructofuranose (VII). The structure of the latter compound is evident from the fact that by nitric acid oxidation it is converted into 3,4,6-tri-*O*-methyl-2-keto-D-gluconic acid (VIII), which in turn is further oxidized by potassium permanganate to 2,3,5-tri-*O*-methyl-D-arabonic acid γ-lactone (IX). This compound, on further oxidation, yields 2,3-di-*O*-methyl-D-threaric acid (i. e. di-*O*-methyl-D-tartaric acid, X), whereby the relative positions of the methoxy groups are exactly defined.

* For a review see I. Levi and C. B. Purves, Advances in Carbohydrate Chem. *4*, 1 (1949).

*References see p. 226*

```
                                                            (VII)
                                                              |
                                                              ↓

                                                           COOH
                                                            |
                          CO───┐                            CO
       COOH              |     |                            |
        |         CH₃O──C──H   |                 CH₃O──C──H
 CH₃O──C──H   ←──   |         O              ──→      |
        |          H──C──OCH₃ |                  H──C──OCH₃
  H──C──OCH₃        |         |                       |
        |          H──C───────┘                  H──C──OH
      COOH              |                             |
                    CH₂OCH₃                        CH₂OCH₃
       (X)             (IX)                         (VIII)
```

The configurations at the anomeric carbon atoms in the sucrose molecule have been ascertained from the course of its enzymic hydrolysis. Sucrose is split by α-glucosidase from yeast, but not by emulsin,[32–35] and from this it follows that the glucose part has the α-configuration. Sucrose is also split by yeast invertase,[35,36] which attacks the β-D-fructofuranose linkages. The structure is thereby established with certainty, but some time ago it was considered questionable[37] whether the fructose part has the β-configuration. Further proof of the known configuration, given in 1957,[38] was a report that enzymic cleavage of sucrose in methanol yielded methyl β-D-fructofuranoside.

The confirmation of the structure of sucrose obtained by oxidation with periodic acid [39–42] (see Chapter III, 2) and lead tetra-acetate[41,42] (see Chapter III, 3) is in full agreement with the structure (IV) given above, and the same applies to some other additional proofs.[43]

Besides its importance in the food industry, sucrose is of high significance as a chemical raw material[44,45] (see for example the preparation of other oligosaccharides by enzymic action - Chapter VI, 5 - or the use of esters of higher fatty acids).[46] Sucrose may also be utilized to replace D-glucose in injection solutions.[47,48] This necessitated, however, investigating the behaviour of sucrose solutions during sterilization,[49] since aqueous solutions, on heating, become discoloured to yellow and even brown with simultaneous caramelization. By paper chromatography it was found that the decomposition products formed contain D-glucose, D-fructose, D-glyceraldehyde, dihydroxyacetone, pyruvic acid and also hydroxymethylfurfural,[50] which was found already earlier in such decompositions.[51] According to a recent finding, hydroxymethylfurfural is formed only from the fructofuranose part of the sucrose molecule[52] and the decomposition proceeds particularly well in dimethylformamide in the presence of iodine.

The decomposition of sucrose in alkaline solution[53] yields lactic acid.

Ammonolysis of sucrose is a subject of a thorough recent paper by I. Ježo, Chem. Zvesti *17*, 126 (1963). Mostly pyrazine derivatives were obtained.

Attention has recently been paid also to the influence of $\gamma$-radiation on sucrose and its aqueous solutions[26,54-58] (see Chapter VIII).

Sucrose crystallizes, depending upon the crystallization conditions and the solvent employed, in two forms differing in their melting points. The question of solubility is the subject of an extensive study,[59] as well as the problem of crystallization from solutions,[60] in particular when supersaturated.[61] It is recommended that the crystallization be carried out in the presence of salts of divalent manganese or divalent cobalt.[62,63]

Interesting studies of recent years are concerned with the course of the hydrogenation of sucrose.[64,65] Besides low splitting products, such as glycerol, propane-1,2-diol and similar compounds,[64] the hydrogenolysis of sucrose in dioxane yields 2,6-anhydro-$\beta$-D-fructofuranose (2,5-anhydro-$\alpha$-D-fructopyranose, XI), while the hydrogenolysis in ethanol under similar conditions gives rise to a mixture of both anomeric ethyl D-fructofuranosides.[65]

(XI)

\* \* \*

An interesting property of sucrose is the formation of compounds with inorganic hydroxides, and even with ammonia.[66] Substances of this type can as a rule be obtained without difficulty by mixing aqueous solutions of sucrose and the inorganic base and addition of ethanol to this mixture. A number of studies have been concerned with the problem of the composition of these substances, termed saccharates, which are of variable composition, since the reaction of sucrose with the inorganic base may take place in various ratios. Attention has been paid to saccharates of sodium,[67-72] potassium,[67-69,73,74] calcium,[75-80] strontium,[78,81-86] barium,[78,81,82] and iron.[87,88]

Of special interest among these substances are compounds of sucrose with hydroxides of alkali metals, in patricular sodium saccharates.[71,72] It seems that in principle two types of substances of this group can be differentiated, on the one hand, adducts of sucrose and alkali metal hydroxides,[73] formed in aqueous

*References see p. 226*

solution, and, on the other, true alkoxides, produced by the action of sodium in liquid ammonia on sucrose[70,72] for which the term sucrates has been proposed[71] to distinguish them from the foregoing saccharates. Although substances with a higher sodium content are obtainable, special attention has been paid to mono-sodium sucrate;[71,72] this substance, however, is evidently no chemical individual because it reacts with methyl iodide[72] to form three different sucrose mono-$O$-methyl ethers. In this respect, sodium sucrates may be suitable initial substances for preparing various other derivatives by reactions with alkyl chlorides and acyl chlorides.[89,90]

* * *

Isosucrose, $\beta$-D-glucopyranosyl $\alpha$-D-fructofuranoside (XII), has been prepared exclusively by syntheses[91–93] (see Chapter VI). The values of specific rotations as calculated by Wolfrom[94] are in agreement with the experimental values.

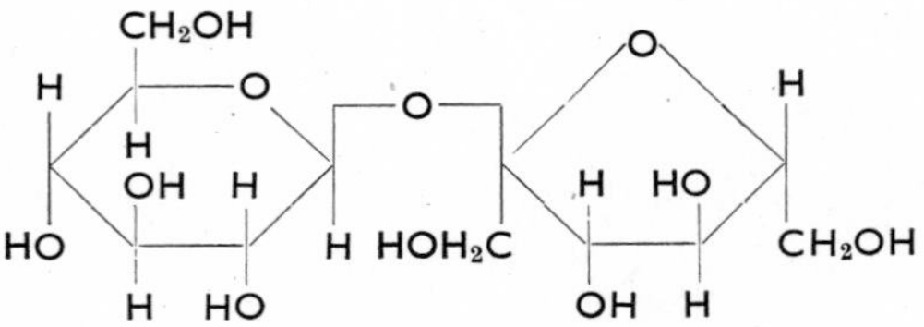

(XII)

The so-called sucrose D, prepared by Pictet,[95] is evidently a mixture containing predominantly isosucrose.[96] This is also supported by the value of the specific rotation, which is in absolute disagreement with Wolfrom's calculation[94] for the sucrose isomer having both anomeric C-linkages with $\alpha$-configuration. The sucrose C, likewise prepared by Pictet,[97] might correspond to the $\beta,\beta$-isomer of sucrose because the optical rotation given approximates to the specific rotation calculated for this anomer.[94].

Other non-reducing disaccharides are substances of miscellaneous origin, either directly isolated from plant material (see Chapter IX) or obtained by reversion processes (see Chapter VI, 4), or various enzymic syntheses (see Chapter VI, 5). Many of these substances have not as yet been completely characterized, and some of them have been obtained in syrupy form only. Their enumeration together with their physical constants is included in Table XXXII.

## Table XXXII

Physical Properties of Non-reducing Disaccharides

| Disaccharide | Melting Point °C | $[\alpha]_D(H_2O)$ | References |
|---|---|---|---|
| Trehalose | | | |
| α-D-glucopyranosyl α-D-glucopyranoside | | | |
|   anhydrous | 203 | +197·1° | 98, 99 |
|   dihydrate | 97 | +178·3° | 3, 98, 100, 101 |
| neo-Trehalose | | | |
| α-D-glucopyranosyl β-D-glucopyranoside | 145 | + 95° | 8, 9 |
| | 85—88 | + 67·1° | 10 |
| | 80 | + 64° | 11 |
| Isotrehalose | | | |
| β-D-glucopyranosyl β-D-glucopyranoside | 130—135 | − 41·5° | 12—14 |
| | 135—140 | − 40·2° | 15 |
| | | − 38·2° | 102 |
| α-D-Galactopyranosyl α-D-galactopyranoside | amorphous | +194·3° | 16 |
| α-D-Galactopyranosyl β-D-galactopyranoside | 110 | + 56° | 11 |
| | 122 | + 67·8° | 10 |
| β-D-Galactopyranosyl β-D-galactopyranoside | 108 | + 20° | 16 |
| α-D-Mannopyranosyl α-D-mannopyranoside | 240—243 | +124° | 17 |
| α-D-Mannopyranosyl β-D-mannopyranoside | 115—120 | + 44° | 17 |
| | | + 53° | 103 |
| α-D-Glucopyranosyl β-D-galactopyranoside | syrup | + 79° | 15 |
| α-D-Glucopyranosyl β-D-galactofuranoside | not given | not given | 104 |
| β-D-Glucopyranosyl β-D-galactopyranoside | | + 9° | 18 |
| Sucrose, saccharose | | | |
| α-D-glucopyranosyl β-D-fructofuranoside | | | |
|   modification A | 184—185 | + 66·5° | 105, 106 |
|   modification B | 169—170 | + 66·5° | 107—111 |
| | | + 67·1° | 112 |
| Isosucrose | | | |
| β-D-glucopyranosyl α-D-fructofuranoside | 194 (dec.) | + 34·2° | 91—93 |
| "Sucrose C?" | 104 | − 24·6° | 97 |
| "Sucrose D?" | 127 | + 19° | 95, 96 |
| α-D-Glucopyranosyl α-L-sorboside | 178—180 | + 33° | 113, 114 |
| α-D-Galactopyranosyl β-D-fructofuranoside | 179 | + 81·5° | 115—117 |
| α-D-Arabinopyranosyl α-D-arabinopyranoside | 112 | − 22° | 118 |
| α-L-Arabinopyranosyl α-L-arabinopyranoside | | + 18·9° | 119 |
| β-L-Arabinopyranosyl β-L-arabinopyranoside | | +264° | 5 |
| | not given | not given | 120, 121 |
| α-D-Xylopyranosyl α-D-xylopyranoside | 269—270 | +210° | 122 |
| | 262—268 | +215° | 123 |
| α-D-Xylopyranosyl β-D-xylopyranoside | 208·5—210·5 | + 84·5° | 123 |
| β-D-Xylopyranosyl β-D-xylopyranoside | 211—213 | − 74·1° | 123 |
| α-D-Glucopyranosyl β-D-xyluloside | 156—157 | + 43° | 123, 124 |
| α-D-Glucopyranosyl α-L-ribuloside | not given | not given | 125 |
| α-D-Xylopyranosyl β-D-fructofuranoside | amorphous | +62° | 115, 116, 126 |
| β-L-Arabinopyranosyl β-D-fructofuranoside | not given | not given | 115, 116 |
| ?-D-Glucopyranosyl ?-D-xylofuranoside | amorphous | −36·5° | 127, 128 |
| β-D-Ribofuranosyl β-D-ribofuranoside | amorphous | −88° ± 5° | 129 |
| | 158—160 | −102 | 130 |
| Non-reducing difructoside | not given | not given | 131 |

3-Ketosucrose, i. e. α-D-*ribo*-hexopyranosyl-3-ulose β-D-fructofuranoside has been described with m. p. 82—83°C and $[\alpha]_D$ + 40,04° ($H_2O$), see S. Fukui, R. M. Hochster, R. Durbin, E. E. Grebner, and D. S. Feingold, Bull. Res. Council Israel *11 A*, 262 (1963). α-D-Allopyranosyl β-D-fructofuranoside has been prepared in syrupy form only, see M. J. Bernaerts, J. Furnelle, and J. De Ley, Biochim. et Biophys. Acta *69*, 322 (1963).

*References see p. 226*

## REFERENCES

1. T. S. Harding, Sugar *25*, 476 (1923).
2. L. C. Stewart, N. K. Richtmyer, and C. S. Hudson, J. Am. Chem. Soc. *71*, 2277 (1949).
3. L. C. Stewart, N. K. Richtmyer, and C. S. Hudson, J. Am. Chem. Soc. *72*, 2059 (1950).
4. H. Schlubach and K. Maurer, Ber. *58*, 1179 (1925).
5. C. S. Hudson, J. Am. Chem. Soc. *38*, 1566 (1916).
6. C. S. Hudson, J. Am. Chem. Soc. *52*, 1710 (1930).
7. E. L. Johnson and C. S. Hudson, J. Am. Chem. Soc. *61*, 1530 (1939).
8. R. U. Lemieux and H. F. Bauer, Can. J. Chem. *32*, 340 (1954).
9. W. N. Haworth and W. J. Hickinbottom, J. Chem. Soc. *1931*, 2847.
10. H. Vogel and H. Debowska-Kurnicka, Helv. Chim. Acta *11*, 910 (1928).
11. V. E. Sharp and M. Stacey, J. Chem. Soc. *1951*, 285.
12. E. Fischer and K. Delbrück, Ber. *42*, 2776 (1909).
13. H. H. Schlubach and W. Schetelig, Hoppe-Seyler's Z. physiol. Chem. *213*, 83 (1932).
14. C. M. McClosky, R. E. Pyle, and G. H. Coleman, J. Am. Chem. Soc. *66*, 349 (1940).
15. B. Helferich and K. Weis, Chem. Ber. *89*, 314 (1956).
16. H. Bredereck, G. Höschele, and K. Ruck, Chem. Ber. *86*, 1277 (1953).
17. F. Micheel and D. Borrmann, Chem. Ber. *93*, 1143 (1960).
18. K. Wallenfels and J. Lehmann, Ann. *635*, 166 (1960).
19. E. O. Lippmann, *Geschichte des Zuckers*, Springer, Berlin 1929.
20. Dubrunfaut, Compt. rend. *42*, 901 (1856).
21. H. C. Silberman, J. Org. Chem. *26*, 1967 (1961).
22. M. Abdel-Akher, Alexandria J. Agr. Research *6*, No. 2, 13 (1958); Chem. Abstr. *56*, 11681 (1962).
23. K. J. Steinbach, K. S. Grunert, and K. Täufel, Nahrung *5*, 617 (1961); Chem. Abstr. *58*, 1522 (1963).
24. K. Täufel and K. S. Grunert, Arch. Pharm. *294*, 439 (1961).
25. K. Täufel and K. S. Grunert, Nahrung *6*, 93 (1962); Chem. Abstr. *57*, 11438 (1962).
26. M. L. Wolfrom, W. W. Binkley, and L. J. McCale, J. Am. Chem. Soc. *81*, 1442 (1959).
27. J. Nicolle and F. Weisbuch, Compt. rend. *246*, 3164 (1958); Chem. Abstr. *52*, 18228 (1958).
28. I. Levi and C. B. Purves, Advances in Carbohydrate Chem. *4*, 1 (1949).
29. H. Bredereck, G. Hagellock, and E. Hambsch, Chem. Ber. *87*, 35 (1954).
30. J. Avery, W. N. Haworth, and E. L. Hirst, J. Chem. Soc. *1927*, 2308.
31. W. N. Haworth, E. L. Hirst, and A. Learner, J. Chem. Soc. *1927*, 2432.
32. E. F. Armstrong, J. Chem. Soc. *83*, 1305 (1903).
33. C. S. Hudson, J. Am. Chem. Soc. *30*, 1160 (1908).
34. C. S. Hudson, J. Am. Chem. Soc. *31*, 655 (1909).
35. H. H. Schlubach and G. Rauchalles, Ber. *58*, 1842 (1925).
36. C. B. Purves and C. S. Hudson, Ber. *59*, 49 (1937).
37. E. Berner, Ber. *66*, 1077 (1933).
38. J. S. D. Bacon and D. J. Bell, J. Chem. Soc. *1957*, 3581.
39. P. Fleury and J. Courtois, Compt. rend. *216*, 65 (1943).
40. P. Fleury and J. Courtois, Bull. soc. chim. France (5) *10*, 245 (1943).
41. A. K. Mitra and A. S. Perlin, Can. J. Chem. *37*, 2047 (1950).
42. R. C. Hockett and M. Zief, J. Am. Chem. Soc. *72*, 2130 (1950).
43. F. Micheel and L. Tork, Chem. Ber. *93*, 1013 (1960).

44. L. F. Wiggins, Advances in Carbohydrate Chem. *4*, 293 (1949).
45. H. Lange, Gaz. Cukrownicza *61*, 34 (1959); Chem. Abstr. *53*, 15999 (1959).
46. G. R. Ames, Chem. Revs *60*, 541 (1960).
47. G. W. Burksser, Pharm. Zentralhalle *89*, 22 (1950); Chem. Zentr. *1948*, II, 1323.
48. J. C. De Jong and W. A. Noyes, J. Pharm. Pharmacol. *5*, 647 (1953).
49. W. T. Wing, J. Pharm. Pharmacol. *12*, Suppl. 191 T (1960).
50. H. Lukesch, Naturwissenschaften *43*, 108 (1956).
51. R. Montgomery and L. F. Wiggins, J. Soc. Chem. Ind. *66*, 31 (1947).
52. T. G. Bonner, E. J. Bourne, and M. Ruszkiewicz, J. Chem. Soc. *1960*, 787.
53. C. Boelhouwer, E. F. Boon, J. A. Butter, H. I. Waterman, J. C. van Egmond, and J. Sneldervaard, J. Appl. Chem. *6*, 310 (1956).
54. G. J. Moody and G. O. Phillips, Chem. & Ind. (London) *1959*, 1247.
55. G. O. Phillips and G. J. Moody, J. Chem. Soc. *1960*, 762.
56. M. A. Khenokh, Doklady Akad. Nauk S.S.S.R. *104*, 746 (1955); Chem. Abstr. *50*, 7603 (1956).
57. R. J. Bayly and H. Weigel, Nature *188*, 384 (1960).
58. M. A. Khenokh, E. A. Kuzicheva, and V. F. Evdokimov, Doklady Akad. Nauk S.S.S.R. *131*, 684 (1960); Chem. Abstr. *54*, 16132 (1960).
59. L. A. Reber, J. Am. Pharm. Assoc., Sci. Ed. *42*, 192 (1953).
60. H. E. C. Powers, Nature *188*, 289 (1960).
61. J. Yamaguchi, K. Imazaki, and K. Kaneguchi, Ann. Rep. Takamine Lab. *11*, 75 (1959).
62. K. Suzuki, J. Chem. Soc. Japan *57*, 763 (1954).
63. K. Suzuki, Kogyo Kagaku Zasshi *64*, 910 (1961); Chem. Abstr. *56*, 6193 (1962).
64. C. Boelhouwer, D. Korf, and H. I. Waterman, J. Appl. Chem. (London) *10*, 292 (1960); Chem. Abstr. *55*, 396 (1961).
65. H. R. Goldschmid and A. S. Perlin, Can. J. Chem. *38*, 2178 (1960).
66. W. A. P. Black and E. T. Dewar, J. Appl. Chem. (London) *10*, 134 (1960); Chem. Abstr. *54,* 19503 (1960).
67. E. Soubeyran, Ann. *43*, 223 (1842).
68. F. Brendecke, Arch. Pharm. (2) *29*, 72 (1842).
69. T. Pfeiffer and B. Tollens, Ann. *210*, 296 (1881).
70. P. C. Arni, W. A. P. Black, E. T. Dewar, J. C. Patterson, and D. Rutherford, J. Appl. Chem. (London) *9*, 186 (1959).
71. V. Prey and F. Grundschober, Monatsh. Chem. *91*, 1185 (1960).
72. F. Grundschober and V. Prey, Monatsh. Chem. *92*, 1290 (1961).
73. E. G. V. Percival, J. Chem. Soc. *1935*, 648.
74. M. Amagasa and N. Onikura, J. Chem. Soc. Japan, Ind. Chem. Sect. *52*, 2 (1949); Chem. Abstr. *45*, 2414 (1951).
75. R. Benedict, Ber. *6*, 413 (1873).
76. E. O. Lippmann, Ber. *16*, 413 (1883).
77. E. O. Lippmann, Ber. *16*, 2764 (1883).
78. J. E. Mackenzie and J. P. Quin, J. Chem. Soc. *1929*, 951.
79. W. Reinders and D. W. van Gelden, Rec. trav. chim. *51*, 253 (1932).
80. P. V. Golovin, A. A. Gerasimenko and G. S. Tret'yakova, Ukrain. Khim. Zhur. *25*, 781 (1959); Chem. Abstr. *54*, 12623 (1960).
81. Y. Hachihama and K. Hishizawa, J. Soc. Chem. Ind. (Japan) *31*, 294B (1928).
82. Y. Hachihama and K. Nishizawa, Z. Elektrochem. *35*, 385 (1929).
83. W. Reinders and A. Klingenberg, Rec. trav. chim. *48*, 1227 (1929).
84. W. Reinders and A. Klingenberg, Rec. trav. chim. *48*, 1246 (1929).

85. C. Scheibler, Ber. *16*, 984 (1883).
86. C. Scheibler, Ber. *18*, 1411 (1885).
87. T. Bersin, Pharm. Acta Helv. *26*, 407 (1951).
88. Czechoslov. Patent 97,467; Chem. Abstr. *55*, 27795 (1961).
89. W. A. P. Black, E. T. Dewar, J. C. Paterson, and D. Rutherford, J. Appl. Chem. (London) *9*, 256 (1959); Chem. Abstr. *53*, 19893 (1959).
90. E. T. Dewar, Manufact. Chemist *29*, 458 (1958); Chem. Abstr. *53*, 4784 (1959).
91. J. C. Irvine, J. W. H. Oldham, and A. F. Skinner, J. Am. Chem. Soc. *51*, 1279 (1929).
92. J. C. Irvine, J. W. H. Oldham, and A. F. Skinner, J. Soc. Chem. Ind. *47*, 494 (1928).
93. J. C. Irvine and J. W. H. Oldham, J. Am. Chem. Soc. *51*, 3609 (1929).
94. M. L. Wolfrom and F. Shafizadeh, J. Org. Chem. *21*, 88 (1956).
95. A. Pictet and H. Vogel, Helv. Chim. Acta *11*, 436 (1928).
96. A. Georg, Helv. Chim. Acta *17*, 1566 (1934).
97. A. Pictet and H. Vogel, Helv. Chim. Acta *11*, 905 (1928).
98. I. Schukow, Z. Ver. deutsch. Zuckerind. *50*, 818 (1900); Chem. Zentr. *1900*, II, 948.
99. E. O. Lippmann, Ber. *45*, 3431 (1912).
100. J. C. Sowden and A. S. Spriggs, J. Am. Chem. Soc. *78*, 2503 (1956).
101. R. Stjernholm, Acta Chem. Scand. *12*, 646 (1958).
102. S. Peat, W. J. Whelan, and K. A. Hinson, Nature *170*, 1056 (1952).
103. K. Freudenberg, A. Wolf, E. Knopf, and S. H. Zaheer, Ber. *61*, 1743 (1928).
104. E. J. Bourne, J. Hartigan, and H. Weigel, J. Chem. Soc. *1961*, 1088.
105. F. J. Bates and R. F. Jackson, Bull. Natl. Bur. Standards *13*, 125 (1916).
106. R. U. Lemieux and G. Huber, J. Am. Chem. Soc. *75*, 4118 (1953).
107. A. Pictet and H. Vogel, Helv. Chim. Acta *11*, 436 (1928).
108. A. Pictet and H. Vogel, Helv. Chim. Acta *11*, 901 (1928).
109. A. Pictet and H. Vogel, Helv. Chim. Acta *13*, 698 (1930).
110. E. O. Lippmann, Chem. Ztg. *51*, 873 (1927).
111. W. D. Heldermann, Z. physik. Chem. *130*, 396 (1927).
112. R. Kuhn and H. Grassner, Ann. *610*, 122 (1957).
113. R. C. Bean and W. Z. Hassid, J. Am. Chem. Soc. *77*, 5737 (1955).
114. W. Z. Hassid, M. Doudoroff, A. Barker, and W. H. Dore, J. Am. Chem. Soc. *67*, 1394 (1945).
115. C. Péaud-Lenoel, Compt. rend. *241*, 1518 (1955).
116. C. Péaud-Lenoel, Bull. soc. chim. biol. *39*, 747 (1957).
117. D. S. Feingold, G. Avigad, and S. Hestrin, J. Biol. Chem. *224*, 295 (1957).
118. F. A. H. Rice, J. Am. Chem. Soc. *78*, 6167 (1956).
119. H. Vogel, Helv. Chim. Acta *11*, 1210 (1928).
120. J. K. N. Jones and W. H. Nicholson, J. Chem. Soc. *1958*, 27.
121. L. Hough and J. B. Pridham, Chem. & Ind. (London) *1957*, 1178.
122. D. H. Ball and J. K. N. Jones, J. Chem. Soc. *1958*, 33.
123. B. Helferich and W. Ost, Chem. Ber. *95*, 2616 (1962).
124. W. Z. Hassid, M. Doudoroff, A. Barker, and W. H. Dore, J. Am. Chem. Soc. *68*, 1465 (1946).
125. M. Doudoroff, W. Z. Hassid, and A. Barker, J. Biol. Chem. *168*, 733 (1947).
126. G. Avigad, D. S. Feingold, and S. Hestrin, Biochim. et Biophys. Acta *20*, 129 (1956).
127. F. B. Power and A. H. Salway, J. Chem. Soc. *105*, 767 (1914).
128. F. B. Power and A. H. Salway, J. Chem. Soc. *105*, 1062 (1914).
129. E. Rosenberg and S. Zamenhof, J. Biol. Chem. *237*, 1040 (1962).
130. J. A. Zderic, Experientia *20*, 48 (1964).
131. J. Edelman, Biochem. J. *57*, 22 (1954).

## B. REDUCING DISACCHARIDES WITH A LINKAGE 1→PRIMARY ALCOHOLIC GROUP

Isomaltose (brachiose), 6-$O$-α-D-glucopyranosyl-D-glucopyranose (I), is obtainable by reversion (see Chapter VI, 4). Of more importance, however, is the fact that this substance presents the basis for the structure of the polysaccharide dextran, from which isomaltose can be prepared by hydrolysis either by conventional procedures (see Chapter X) or by γ-irradiation.[1]

The structure of isomaltose has been elucidated from the course of its methylation splitting,[2,3] and the question whether it actually is a glycoside with an α-linkage was solved definitely by the investigation of Wolfrom,[4] who worked out a synthesis of this compound.[5]

The hydrolysis of isomaltose has also been investigated from the kinetic viewpoint.[6]

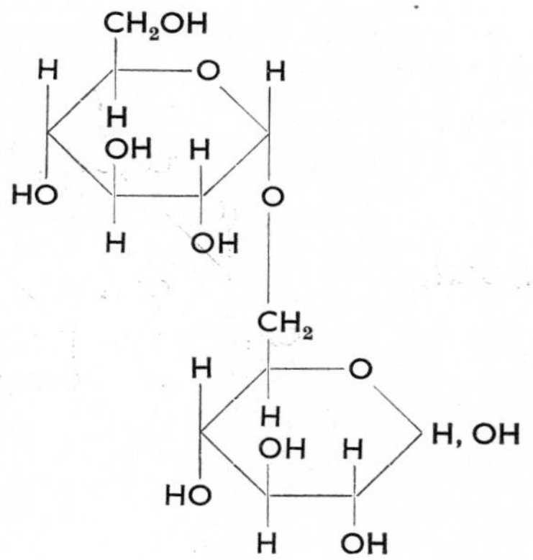

CH₂OH

H — O H

H

OH H

HO

H OH

O

CH₂

H — O

H

OH H — H, OH

HO

H OH

(I)

Gentiobiose, 6-$O$-β-D-glucopyranosyl-D-glucose (II), is a more common substance. It has been obtained in a number of very varied cases (see the respective chapters) and can also be found in some commercial D-glucose preparations.[7] The structure of gentiobiose (II) has been established by the usual methods.[8,9] The per-$O$-methyl derivative of gentiobiose (III) yields, on splitting in acid solution, 2,3,4,6-tetra-$O$-methyl-D-glucopyranose (IV) and 2,3,4-tri-$O$-methyl-D-glucopyranose (V). Its structure has been established by its conversion into the corresponding methyl glycoside (VI). This compound is identical with the product obtained from methyl D-glucoside (VII) by tritylation, methylation and removal of the trityl group. Since gentiobiose is split by emulsin, it must be a β-glycoside.

Isomaltulose (palatinose), 6-$O$-α-D-glucopyranosyl-D-fructose,[10-12] is a comparatively rare oligosaccharide.

*References see p. 235*

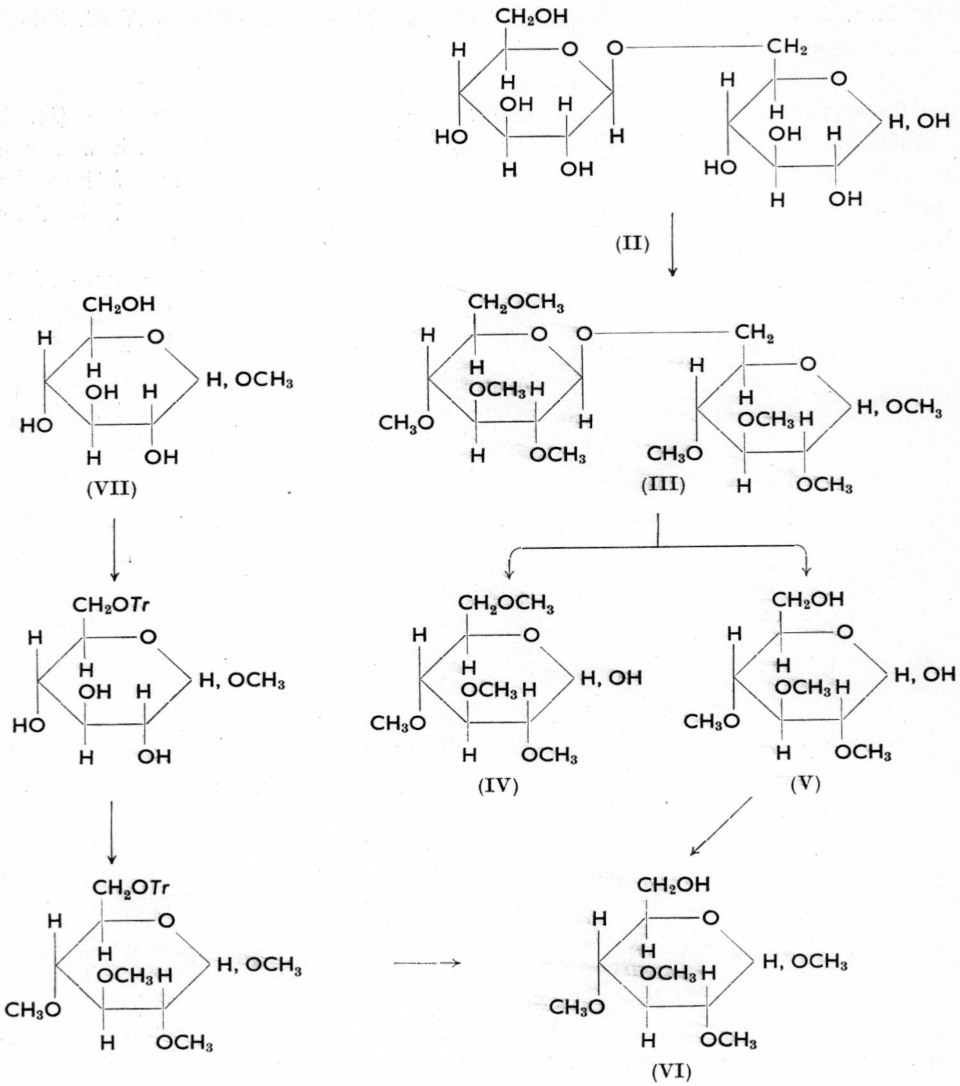

CH₂OH

(II)

CH₂OH                        CH₂OCH₃

(VII)                         (III)

CH₂OTr                  CH₂OCH₃              CH₂OH

(IV)                  (V)

CH₂OTr                                        CH₂OH

⟶

(VI)

Melibiose, 6-$O$-α-D-galactopyranosyl-D-glucose (VIII),[13-15] yields on oxidation the corresponding aldobionic acid, namely melibionic acid (IX), which in turn is converted by permethylation into the corresponding octa-$O$-methyl derivative (X).[13] Splitting of this substance in acid solution yields, on the one hand, 2,3,4,6 tetra-$O$-methyl-D-galactose (XI), whose structure has been established with certainty, and, on the other, 2,3,4,5-tetra-$O$-methyl-D-gluconic acid (XII). The structure of the latter compound follows from the finding[13] that it does not form a lactone and is converted by oxidation with nitric acid into 2,3,4,5-tetra-$O$-methyl-D-glucaric acid (XIII). From these facts it is evident that melibiose is a reducing disaccharide with a 1→6 linkage, and the presence of an α-linkage has been proved by its splitting with yeast melibiase, which belongs to the α-galactosidases.

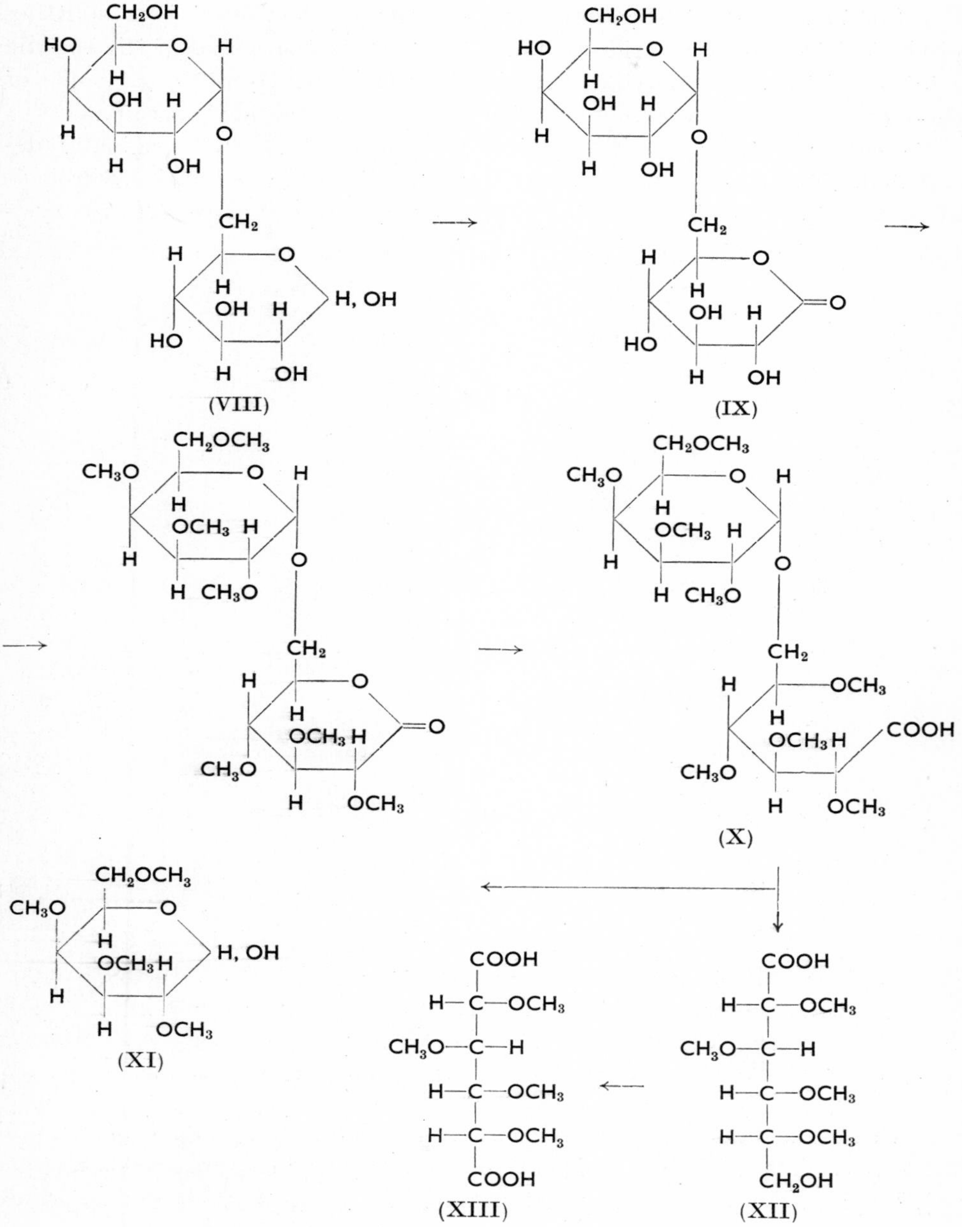

(VIII) ⟶ (IX) ⟶

(X)

(XI)

COOH
H—C—OCH₃
CH₃O—C—H
H—C—OCH₃
H—C—OCH₃
COOH
(XIII)

⟵

COOH
H—C—OCH₃
CH₃O—C—H
H—C—OCH₃
H—C—OCH₃
CH₂OH
(XII)

*References see p. 235*

The disaccharides structurally related to melibiose, namely *allo*-lactose, i. e. 6-*O*-β-galactopyranosyl-D-glucose,[16-22] and melibiulose (planteobiose), i. e. 6-*O*-α-D-galactopyranosyl-D-fructose,[23-25] are not frequently encountered. The same applies to swietenose, 6-*O*-α-D-galactopyranosyl-D-galactose.[26-30]

Other noteworthy oligosaccharides of this group are inulobiose and vicianose.

Inulobiose, 1-*O*-β-D-fructofuranosyl-D-fructose (XIV),[31-34] is a splitting product of the polysaccharide inulin. Differences in the values of the specific rotation of this substance are explained by the assumption[34] that some of the samples prepared were not sufficiently pure and contained sucrose.

Vicianose, 6-*O*-α-L-arabinopyranosyl-D-glucose (XV),[35-37] originally designated as 6-*O*-β-L-arabinopyranosyl-D-glucose,[36] is a product of the hydrolysis of some heterosides (see Chapter XI), as well as primeverose, 6-*O*-β-D-xylopyranosyl-D-glucose (XVI).[38-44]

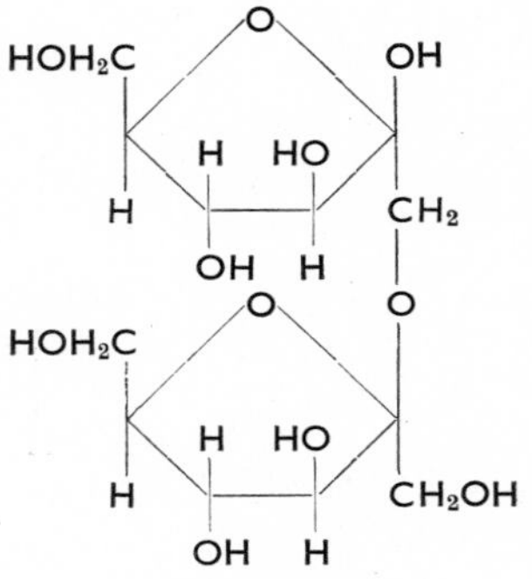

(XIV)

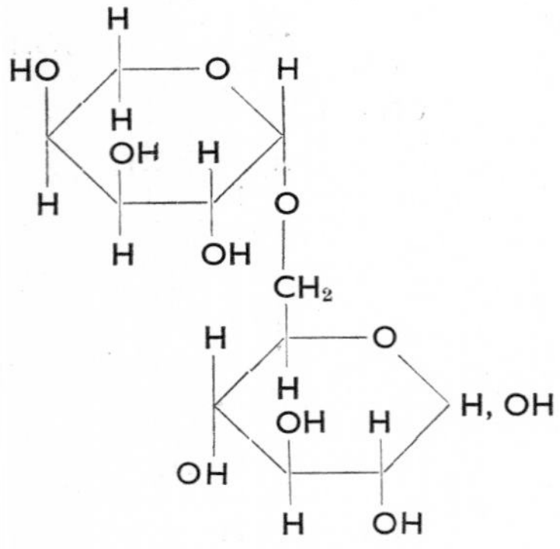

(XV)

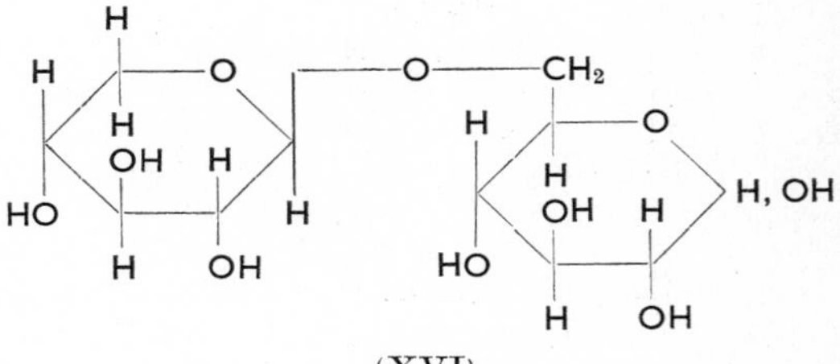

(XVI)

Other substances of this group with trivial names are products of chemical syntheses. This applies to *epi*-gentiobiose (6-*O*-β-D-glucopyranosyl-D-mannose),[45] *epi*-melibiose (6-*O*-α-D-galactopyranosyl-D-mannose)[46-49] and isoprimeverose (6-*O*-α-D-glucopyranosyl-D-xylose).[44] Somewhat more complicated is the establishment of the structures of substances obtained by syntheses with the use of 2,3,4,6-tetra-*O*-acetyl-α-D-mannopyranosyl bromide.[50] Since the Koenigs-Knorr reaction usually proceeds with Walden inversion (see Chapter VI), the products obtained in this way were designated without exception as 6-*O*-β-D-mannopyranosyl derivatives;[50] a similar classification was applied to robinobiose and rutinose (see Chapter XXII), which are 6-*O*-L-rhamnopyranosyl derivatives. More recently it was indisputably established[51] that these reactions take place without Walden inversion, so that the products thus obtained must be regarded as 6-*O*-α-D-mannopyranosyl derivatives.[51]

This finding gave rise to a systematic investigation of the Koenigs-Knorr synthesis with the use of various substituted derivatives of α-D-mannopyranosyl bromide;[52] the reactions proceed without Walden inversion throughout and, of all the substances employed, it is only 4,6-di-*O*-acetyl-2,3-di-*O*-carbonyl-α-D-mannopyranosyl bromide that yields substituted 6-*O*-β-D-mannopyranosyl derivatives.

The Koenigs-Knorr reaction was also investigated in its application to substituted derivatives of α-L-arabinopyranosyl bromide and β-D-ribofuranosyl bromide.[53]

The physical properties of all substances mentioned and of a number of others are presented in Table XXXIII.

## Table **XXXIII**

Physical Properties of Reducing Disaccharides
Disaccharides with a 1 → Primary Hydroxyl Group Bond

| Disaccharide | Melting Point °C | $[\alpha]_D(H_2O)$ | References |
|---|---|---|---|
| Isomaltose 6-*O*-α-D-glucopyranosyl-D-glucose | amorphous | $+103\cdot2°$ | 2, 3 |
| | | $+103\cdot5°$ | 54 |
| | | $+120°$ | 55, 56 |
| | | $+121°$ | 51, 57—59 |
| | | $+122°$ | 60 |
| | | $+122\cdot9°$ | 61 |
| | | $+125°$ | 62 |
| Gentiobiose 6-*O*-β-D-glucopyranosyl-D-glucose α-anomer, hydrate | | $+ 30\cdot7°$ | 63 |
| | 85—86 | $+21\cdot4° → + 8\cdot7°$ | 64 |
| | | $+31\cdot0° → + 9\cdot6°$ | 65 |
| β-anomer | 190—195 | $-11\cdot0° → + 9\cdot6°$ | 65 |
| | 190 | $-0\cdot85° → +10\cdot3°$ | 66 |
| | | $- 3\cdot0° → +10\cdot5°$ | 67 |
| | | $+ 8°$ | 57, 58 |
| | 191—192 | $+10°$ | 68 |
| | | $+11\cdot5°$ | 69, 70 |

*References see p. 235*

*Table XXXIII — continued*

| Disaccharide | Melting Point °C | $[\alpha]_D (H_2O)$ | References |
|---|---|---|---|
| *epi*-Gentiobiose | | | |
| 6-*O*-β-D-glucopyranosyl-D-mannose | 168 | $-5 \cdot 1° \rightarrow -11 \cdot 1°$ | 45 |
|   hydrate | 137—138 | | 45 |
| 6-*O*-β-D-Glucopyranosyl-D-galactose | | $+1 \cdot 6° \rightarrow +13 \cdot 6°$ | 71 |
| | | $+10°$ | 72 |
|   hydrate | | $-8 \cdot 2° \rightarrow +20 \cdot 6°$ | 73 |
| 1-*O*-α-D-Glucopyranosyl-D-fructose | | $+49°$ | 55 |
| 1-*O*-β-D-Glucopyranosyl-D-fructose | 132—135 | $-59 \cdot 2°$ | 74—76 |
| | 134—138 | $-1 \cdot 2° \rightarrow -59 \cdot 4°$ | 77 |
| Isomaltulose, palatinose | | | |
| 6-*O*-α-D-glucopyranosyl-D-fructose | | $+ 97 \cdot 2°$ | 11, 12 |
| | | $+103°$ | 10 |
| | | $+ 94°$ | 55 |
| 6-*O*-α-D-Mannopyranosyl-D-mannose | 196 | $+ 52°$ | 78 |
| | | $+ 50°$ | 57 |
| | | $+ 57°$ | 51 |
| | | $+ 58°$ | 79 |
| 6-*O*-β-D-Mannopyranosyl-D-mannose | | $- 16°$ | 80 |
| | | $- 8°$ | 81 |
| 6-*O*-β(?)-D-Mannopyranosyl-D-mannose* | 70—95 (dec.) | $+ 61 \cdot 5°$ | 50 |
| 6-*O*-α-D-Mannopyranosyl-D-glucose | | $+ 75°$ | 51 |
| 6-*O*-β-D-Mannopyranosyl-D-glucose | 209—210 | $0° \rightarrow -5°$ | 80 |
| 6-*O*-?-D-Mannopyranosyl-D-glucose | 150—160 | $+ 10 \cdot 5°$ | 82 |
| 6-*O*-β-D-Mannopyranosyl-D-galactose | | $+142° \rightarrow +134°$ | 71 |
| Melibiose | | | |
| 6-*O*-α-D-galactopyranosyl-D-glucose | | | |
|   monohydrate | 179—181 | $+157° \rightarrow +137°$ | 14 |
|   dihydrate | 82—85 | $+111 \cdot 7° \rightarrow +129 \cdot 5°$ | 15 |
| | | $+129°$ | 57 |
| | 75—76 | | 107 |
| *allo*-Lactose | | | |
| 6-*O*-β-D-galactopyranosyl-D-glucose | 165 | $+ 25°$ | 16—19 |
| | 167 | $+ 37 \cdot 5°$ | 20 |
| | 174—176 | $+54 \cdot 2° \rightarrow +30 \cdot 7°$ | 21 |
| | | $+ 9 \cdot 6°$ | 63 |
| *epi*-Melibiose | | | |
| 6-*O*-α-D-galactopyranosyl-D-mannose | 201 | $+120° \rightarrow +124 \cdot 6°$ | 46—48 |
| | 198—202 | | 49 |
| | | $+124°$ | 81 |
| Swietenose | | | |
| 6-*O*-α-D-galactopyranosyl-D-galactose | | $+106 \cdot 3°$ | 26 |
| | | $+142 \cdot 5°$ | 27 |
| | | $+149°$ | 28 |
| | | $+154°$ | 30 |
| 6-*O*-β-D-Galactopyranosyl-D-galactose | 97—100 | $+ 26°$ | 83 |
| | 110, 148 | $+ 29°$ | 84 |
| | 106, 136 | $+24° \rightarrow +32°$ | 85 |
| | syrup | $+ 26°$ | 86 |
| | | $+ 29 \cdot 3°$ | 87 |

  * This compound is very probably the corresponding 6-*O*-α-D-mannopyranosyl derivative.[51]
5-*O*-β-D-Glucopyranosyl-D-xylose has been prepared in syrupy form with $[\alpha]_D$-2,6° ($H_2O$), see
J. K. N. Jones and P. E. Reid, Can. J. Chem. *41*, 2382 (1963).

*Table XXXIII — continued*

| Disaccharide | Melting Point °C | $[\alpha]_D(H_2O)$ | References |
|---|---|---|---|
|  |  | $+\ 30°$ | 88, 89 |
|  |  | $+\ 34°$ | 90—92 |
|  |  | $+25\cdot1° \rightarrow +34\cdot1°$ | 71 |
|  |  | $+32\cdot1° \rightarrow +35\cdot8°$ | 29 |
| 1-*O*-α-D-Galactopyranosyl-D-fructose |  | $+\ 58\cdot9°$ | 93 |
| Planteobiose (melibiulose) |  |  |  |
| 6-*O*-α-D-galactopyranosyl-D-fructose |  | $+125°$ | 23—25 |
| 5-*O*-β-D-Galactopyranosyl-L-arabinose |  | $-\ 13°$ | 94 |
|  |  | $-\ 18°$ | 95 |
| Inulobiose |  |  |  |
| 1-*O*-β-D-fructofuranosyl-D-fructose*,** |  | $-\ 32\cdot5°$ | 31, 96 |
|  |  | $-\ 71°$ | 32 |
| 6-*O*-β-D-Fructofuranosyl-D-glucose |  | $+\ 5\cdot5°$ | 96—98 |
| 6-*O*-β-D-Fructofuranosyl-D-fructose(?)*** |  |  | 96 |
| 5-*O*-α-L-Arabinofuranosyl-L-arabinose |  | $-\ 87°$ | 84 |
|  |  | $-\ 72°$ | 99 |
|  |  | $-\ 94°$ | 100 |
| 5-*O*-α-L-Arabinopyranosyl-L-arabinose | 143 | $-\ 14°$ | 101 |
|  |  | $-\ 18°$ | 84 |
| Vicianose |  |  |  |
| 6-*O*-α-L-arabinopyranosyl-D-glucose | 210 | $+56\cdot6° \rightarrow +40\cdot5°$ | 35 |
|  | 210 | $+15\cdot8° \rightarrow +39\cdot7°$ | 36, 37 |
| 6-*O*-α-L-Arabinofuranosyl-D-glucose | 163—165 | $-15° \ \rightarrow -40°$ | 100 |
| 6-*O*-β-L-Arabinofuranosyl-D-glucose | | $+73°$ | 100 |
| Primeverose | 203—205 |  |  |
| 6-*O*-β-D-xylopyranosyl-D-glucose | 208 | $+24° \ \rightarrow -3\cdot4°$ | 40, 42 |
|  |  | $+23\cdot8° \rightarrow -0\cdot2°$ | 41, 43 |
|  | 209 | $+24° \ \rightarrow -3\cdot4°$ | 38, 39 |
|  | 208—210 | $+24° \ \rightarrow -3\cdot3°$ | 44 |
| Isoprimeverose |  |  |  |
| 6-*O*-α-D-xylopyranosyl-D-glucose | 200·5 | $+151\cdot3° \rightarrow +121\cdot3°$ | 102 |
|  |  | $+70°$ | 103 |
| 6-*O*-β-D-Xylopyranosyl-D-galactose | 194—196 | $-23\cdot6° \rightarrow -3\cdot6°$ | 43 |
| 5-*O*-β-D-Xylopyranosyl-L-arabinose |  | $-34°$ | 104—106 |
|  |  | $-47°$ | 84 |

* For some comments regarding the purity of this substance see Ref. 34.

** A fructobiose with β,1→2 linkage has been reported as one of the hydrolysis products of lycorisin. As the physical constants [m. p. 98—99°C, $[\alpha]_D$ —60·8° (H₂O)] are slightly different from those of inulobiose, it is very difficult to regard both substances as identical; see T. Mizuno, Kagaku (Tokyo) *31*, 146 (1961); Chem. Abstr. *55*, 27099 (1961).

*** This substance, i. e. laevanbiose, has been obtained in purer form with $[\alpha]_D$ —22° (H₂O), see G. Avigad and R. Zelikson, Bull. Res. Council Israel *11 A*, 253 (1963).

## REFERENCES

1. G. O. Phillips and G. J. Moody, J. Chem. Soc. *1958*, 3534.
2. A. Georg and A. Pictet, Helv. Chim. Acta *9*, 912 (1926).
3. A. Georg, Compt. rend. soc. phys. et hist. nat. Genève *47*, 94 (1930).

4. M. L. Wolfrom, L. W. Georges, and I. L. Miller, J. Am. Chem. Soc. *71*, 125 (1949).
5. M. L. Wolfrom, A. O. Pittet, and I. C. Gillam, Proc. Natl. Acad. Sci. U.S. *47*, 700 (1961); Chem. Abstr. *55*, 23352 (1961).
6. R. W. Jones, D. J. Dimler, and C. E. Rist, J. Am. Chem. Soc. *77*, 1659 (1955).
7. T. Tamura and S. Suzuki, Shokuryo Kenkyusho Kenkyu Hokoku No. 13, 55 (1955); Chem. Abstr. *57*, 6193 (1962).
8. W. Charlton, W. N. Haworth, and W. J. Hickinbottom, J. Chem. Soc. *1927*, 1567.
9. W. N. Haworth and B. Wylam, J. Chem. Soc. *123*, 3120 (1923).
10. S. Sharpe, F. H. Stodola, and H. J. Koepsell, J. Org. Chem. *25*, 1062 (1960).
11. R. Weidenhagen and S. Lorenz, Angew. Chem. *69*, 641 (1957).
12. R. Weidenhagen and S. Lorenz, Z. Zuckerind. *82*, 533 (1957).
13. W. N. Haworth, J. V. Loach, and C. W. Long, J. Chem. Soc. *1927*, 3146.
14. P. Witonsky and F. Smith, J. Org. Chem. *24*, 124 (1959).
15. F. J. Bates, *Polarimetry, Saccharimetry and the Sugars*, National Bureau of Standards, Washington 1942, p. 474.
16. M. Polonovski and A. Lespagnol, Compt. rend. *192*, 1319 (1931).
17. M. Polonovski and A. Lespagnol, Compt. rend. *195*, 465 (1932).
18. M. Polonovski and A. Lespagnol, Bull. soc. chim. biol. *15*, 320 (1933).
19. B. Helferich and G. Sparmberg, Ber. *66*, 806 (1933).
20. M. Masamune and S. Kamiyama, Tôhoku J. Exptl. Med. *60*, 43 (1957); Chem. Abstr. *52*, 8974 (1958).
21. B. Helferich and H. Rauch, Ber. *59*, 2655 (1926).
22. J. H. Pazur, C. L. Tipton, T. Budovich, and J. M. Marsh, J. Am. Chem. Soc. *80*, 119 (1958).
23. D. French, G. M. Wild, B. Young, and W. J. James, J. Am. Chem. Soc. *75*, 709 (1953).
24. R. J. Suhadolnik, D. French, and L. A. Underkofler, Science *117*, 100 (1953).
25. L. Hough, J. K. N. Jones, and E. L. Richards, J. Chem. Soc. *1954*, 295.
26. T. R. Ingle and B. V. Bhide, J. Indian Chem. Soc. *31*, 943 (1954).
27. T. R. Ingle and B. V. Bhide, J. Indian Chem. Soc. *35*, 516 (1958).
28. C. N. Turton, A. Bebbington, S. Dixon, and E. Pacsu, J. Am. Chem. Soc. *77*, 2565 (1955).
29. H. Weinland, Hoppe-Seyler's Z. physiol. Chem. *305*, 87 (1956).
30. A. de Grandchamp-Chaudun, J. E. Courtois, P. Le Dizet, Bull. soc. chim. biol. *42*, 227 (1960).
31. J. H. Pazur and A. L. Gordon, J. Am. Chem. Soc. *75*, 3458 (1953).
32. H. H. Schlubach and A. Scheffler, Ann. *588*, 192 (1954).
33. D. S. Feingold and G. Avigad, Biochim. et Biophys. Acta *22*, 196 (1956).
34. K. Holzer, H. Wittmann-Zinke, and A. Zinke, Monatsh. Chem. *88*, 268 (1957).
35. G. Bertrand and G. Weissweiler, Compt. rend. *150*, 182 (1910).
36. B. Helferich and H. Bredereck, Ann. *465*, 166 (1928).
37. K. Wallenfels and D. Beck, Ann. *630*, 46 (1960).
38. A. Goris, M. Mascré, and C. Vischniac, Bull. sci. pharmacol. *19*, 577 (1912).
39. A. Goris, M. Mascré, and C. Vischniac, Bull. sci. pharmacol. *19*, 648 (1912).
40. M. Bridel, Compt. rend. *179*, 780 (1924); Chem. Abstr. *19*, 817 (1925).
41. B. Helferich and H. Rauch, Ann. *455*, 168 (1937).
42. D. Richter, J. Chem. Soc. *1936*, 1701.
43. D. H. Ball and J. K. N. Jones, J. Chem. Soc. *1957*, 4871.
44. G. Zemplén and R. Bognár, Ber. *72*, 47 (1939).
45. H. J. Dauben and W. L. Evans, J. Am. Chem. Soc. *60*, 886 (1938).
46. R. L. Whistler and D. Durso, J. Am. Chem. Soc. *73*, 4189 (1951).

47. J. E. Courtois and F. Petek, Bull. soc. chim. biol. *39*, 715 (1957).
48. M. E. Henderson, L. Hough, and T. J. Painter, J. Chem. Soc. *1958*, 3519.
49. H. Meier, Acta Chem. Scand. *14*, 749 (1960).
50. E. A. Talley, D. D. Reynolds, and D. L. Evans, J. Am. Chem. Soc. *65*, 575 (1943).
51. P. A. J. Gorin and A. S. Perlin, Can. J. Chem. *37*, 1930 (1959).
52. P. A. J. Gorin and A. S. Perlin, Can. J. Chem. *39*, 2474 (1961).
53. P. A. J. Gorin, Can. J. Chem. *40*, 275 (1962).
54. K. V. Giri, K. Saroja, R. Venkataraman, and P. L. N. Rao, Arch. Biochem. Biophys. *51*, 62 (1954); Chem. Abstr. *48*, 10826 (1954).
55. G. Avigad, Biochem. J. *73*, 587 (1959).
56. P. S. O'Colla, E. E. Lee, and D. McGrath, J. Chem. Soc. *1962*, 2730.
57. A. J. Charlson and A. S. Perlin, Can. J. Chem. *34*, 1804 (1956).
58. S. Peat, W. J. Whelan, and H. G. Lawley, J. Chem. Soc. *1958*, 729.
59. I. J. Goldstein and W. J. Whelan, J. Chem. Soc. *1962*, 170.
60. A. Jeanes, C. A. Wilham, R. W. Jones, H. M. Tsuchiya, and C. E. Rist, J. Am. Chem. Soc. *75*, 5911 (1953).
61. S. A. Barker and T. R. Carrington, J. Chem. Soc. *1953*, 2588.
62. M. Abdullah, I. J. Goldstein, and W. J. Whelan, J. Chem. Soc. *1962*, 176.
63. R. Kuhn and H. H. Baer, Chem. Ber. *87*, 1560 (1954).
64. F. J. Bates, *Polarimetry, Saccharimetry and the Sugars*, National Bureau of Standards, Washington 1942, p. 722.
65. E. Bourquelot, H. Hérissey, and J. Coirre, Compt. rend. *157*, 732 (1913).
66. R. Kuhn and A. Kolb, Chem. Ber. *91*, 2408 (1948).
67. M. L. Wolfrom, A. Thompson, and A. M. Brownstein, J. Am. Chem. Soc. *80*, 2015 (1958).
68. J. C. Sowden and A. S. Spriggs, J. Am. Chem. Soc. *78*, 2503 (1956).
69. S. Peat, W. J. Whelan, and T. E. Edwards, J. Chem. Soc. *1958*, 3862.
70. S. Peat, W. J. Whelan, and K. A. Hinson, Nature *170*, 1056 (1952).
71. K. Freudenberg, A. Wolf, E. Knopf, and S. H. Zaheer, Ber. *61*, 1743 (1928).
72. P. A. J. Gorin and J. F. T. Spencer, Can. J. Chem. *39*, 2282 (1961).
73. K. Freudenberg, A. Noë, and E. Knopf, Ber. *60*, 239 (1927).
74. B. Helferich and H. Bredereck, Ann. *465*, 166 (1928).
75. B. Helferich and R. Steinpreis, Chem. Ber. *91*, 1794 (1958).
76. E. Pacsu, E. J. Wilson, and L. Graf, J. Am. Chem. Soc. *61*, 2675 (1939).
77. P. Brigl and O. Widmaier, Ber. *69*, 1219 (1936).
78. J. K. N. Jones and W. H. Nicholson, J. Chem. Soc. *1958*, 27.
79. S. Peat, W. J. Whelan, and T. E. Edwards, J. Chem. Soc. *1961*, 29.
80. P. A. J. Gorin and A. S. Perlin, Can. J. Chem. *39*, 2474 (1961).
81. A. K. Mukherjee, D. Choudhury, and P. Bagchi, Can. J. Chem. *39*, 1408 (1961).
82. K. Nishida and H. Hachima, J. Dept. Agr. Kyushu Imp. Univ. *2*, 277 (1930); Chem. Abstr. *25*, 498 (1931).
83. H. Meier, Acta Chem. Scand. *16*, 2275 (1962).
84. F. Smith and A. M. Stephen, J. Chem. Soc. *1961*, 4892.
85. A. M. Stephen, S. Kirkwood, and F. Smith, Can. J. Chem. *40*, 151 (1962).
86. D. W. Drummond and E. Percival, J. Chem. Soc. *1961*, 3908.
87. A. Ballio and S. Russi, Tetrahedron *9*, 125 (1960).
88. H. Bouveng and B. Lindberg, Acta Chem. Scand. *10*, 1515 (1956).
89. G. O. Aspinall, B. J. Auret, and E. L. Hirst, J. Chem. Soc. *1958*, 4408.
90. B. O. Lindgren, Acta Chem. Scand. *11*, 1365 (1957).
91. J. H. Pazur, J. Biol. Chem. *208*, 439 (1954).

92. J. H. Pazur, C. L. Tipton, T. Budovich, and J. M. Marsh, J. Am. Chem. Soc. *80*, 119 (1958).

93. A. Wickström, J. E. Courtois, P. Le Dizet, and A. Archambault, Bull. soc. chim. France *1958*, 1410.

94. H. C. Srivastava and F. Smith, J. Am. Chem. Soc. *79*, 982 (1957).

95. I. J. Goldstein, F. Smith, and H. C. Srivastava, J. Am. Chem. Soc. *79*, 3858 (1957).

96. J. S. D. Bacon, Biochem. J. *57*, 320 (1954).

97. W. J. Whelan and D. M. Jones, Biochem. J. *54*, XXXIV (1953).

98. L. M. White and G. E. Secor, Arch. Biochem. Biophys. *36*, 490 (1952).

99. P. Andrews, L. Hough, and D. B. Powell, Chem. & Ind. (London) *1956*, 658.

100. P. A. J. Gorin, Can. J. Chem. *40*, 275 (1962).

101. A. M. Stephen, J. Chem. Soc. *1957*, 1919.

102. G. Zemplén and R. Bognár, Ber. *72*, 1160 (1939).

103. O. Perila and C. T. Bishop, Can. J. Chem. *39*, 815 (1961).

104. J. K. N. Jones, J. Chem. Soc. *1953*, 1672.

105. P. Andrews, D. H. Ball, and J. K. N. Jones, J. Chem. Soc. *1953*, 4090.

106. D. H. Ball and J. K. N. Jones, J. Chem. Soc. *1957*, 4871.

107. A. Assarson and O. Theander, Acta Chem. Scand. *12*, 1319 (1958).

## C. REDUCING DISACCHARIDES WITH A 1→2 LINKAGE

This group does not contain any substances of special significance. Attention has been paid to kojibiose (2-*O*-α-D-glucopyranosyl-D-glucose, I), which was several times isolated from natural sources and also obtained by synthesis.[1-8] In the last investigations of its synthesis,[8] kojibiose was obtained in three different crystalline forms corresponding to the β-anomer, the α-anomer and the monohydrate of the latter.

The isomer of kolibiose, namely sophorose, 2-*O*-β-D-glucopyranosyl-D-glucose (II), was likewise several times isolated from natural materials or synthesized.[9-16]

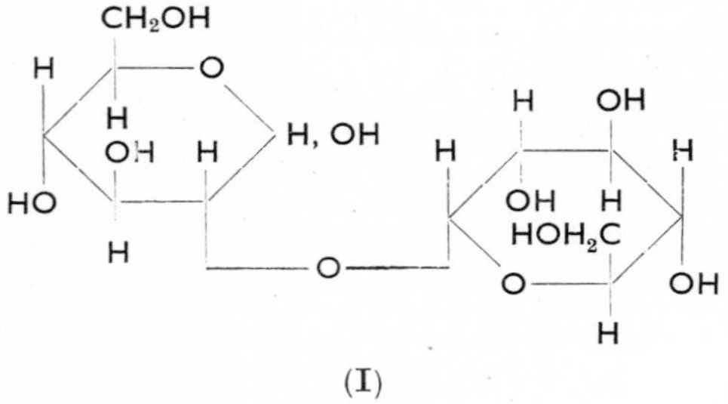

(I)

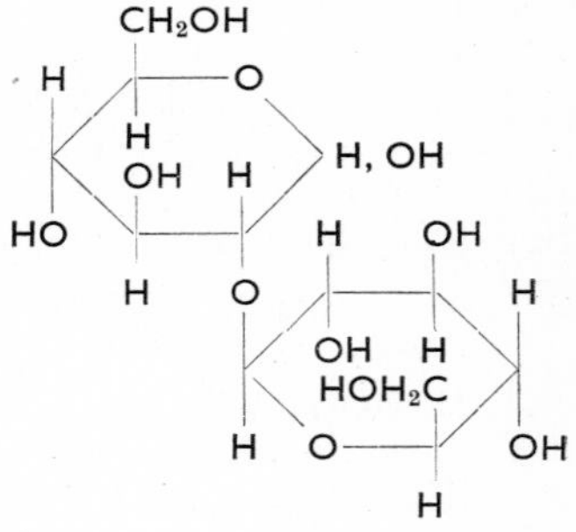

(II)

Most of the other substances whose physical constants are summarized in Table XXXIV were either isolated in particular cases from natural material or obtained by syntheses.

## Table XXXIV

Physical Properties of Reducing Disaccharides
Disaccharides with a 1→2 Bond

| Disaccharide | Melting Point °C | $[\alpha]_D(H_2O)$ | References |
|---|---|---|---|
| Kojibiose | | | |
| 2-O-α-D-glucopyranosyl-D-glucose | syrup | | 17 |
| | | $+140° \to +134°$ | 1—4 |
| | | $+121°$ | 5 |
| | | $+133°$ | 6 |
| | 187—188 | $+162° \to +137°$ | 7 |
| | 195 | $+134·6°$ | 8 |
| Sophorose | | | |
| 2-O-β-D-glucopyranosyl-D-glucose | 180 | $+34·5° \to +19·9°$ | 9—12, 14 |
| | 194—195 | $+\ 20°$ | 13, 15 |
| | 188—190 | $+33·4° \to +21·2°$ | 16 |
| | 198—200 | $+28°\ \ \to\ +16°$ | 18 |
| | | $+\ 18·4°$ | 19 |
| 2-O-β-D-Glucopyranosyl-D-xylose | 200—202 | $\pm\ \ \ 0°$ | 20 |
| 2-O-α-D-Glucopyranosyl-D-erythrose | 141 | $+\ 87·5°$ | 21, 22 |
| 2-O-β-D-Glucopyranosyl-D-erythrose | 150 | $+\ 36·8°$ | 23, 24 |
| 2-O-α-D-Mannopyranosyl-D-mannose | | $+\ 40°$ | 25, 26 |
| 2-O-?-D-Mannopyranosyl-D-mannose | 141—143 | $+\ 24·5°$ | 27 |
| 2-O-α-D-Galactopyranosyl-D-glucose | 120 | $+145°$ | 28 |
| 2-O-α-D-Galactopyranosyl-L-arabinose | 155 (dec.) | $+161° \to +153°$ | 29 |
| 2-O-β-D-Galactopyranosyl-D-xylose | | $+40°$ | 30 |
| 2-O-β-D-Galactopyranosyl-D-erythrose | syrup | $+18°$ | 31 |
| | 155 | $+22·5°$ | 32 |
| 2-O-β-L-Arabinopyranosyl-D-glucose | 210—220 (dec.) | $+165° \to +151°$ | 29 |
| 2-O-α-D-Xylopyranosyl-D-xylose | | | 33 |
| 2-O-β-D-Xylopyranosyl-L-arabinose* | | $+39·8°$ | 34 |
| anhydrous | 167—168 | $+32·9°$ | 35—38 |
| monohydrate | 80—81 | $+47·0° \to +32·5°$ | 38 |
| trihydrate | 97—99 | $+53·7° \to +33·2°$ | 37, 38 |

* This compound was originally described as the 2-O-α-isomer.[34,35]

## REFERENCES

1. S. Haq and W. J. Whelan, Nature *178*, 1224 (1956).
2. A. Sato and K. Aso, Nature *180*, 984 (1957).
3. K. Matsuda, Nature *180*, 985 (1957).
4. T. Watanabe and K. Aso, Nature *183*, 1740 (1959).
5. S. A. Barker, A. Gómez-Sánchez, and M. Stacey, J. Chem. Soc. *1959*, 3264.
6. R. W. Bailey, S. A. Barker, E. J. Bourne, P. M. Grant, and M. Stacey, J. Chem. Soc. *1958*, 1895.
7. F. Yamauchi and K. Aso, Nature *189*, 753 (1961).
8. K. Takiura and K. Koizumi, J. Pharm. Soc. Japan *82*, 852 (1962); Chem. Abstr. *58*, 6911 (1963).

9. K. Freudenberg and K. Soff, Ber. *69*, 1245 (1936).
10. J. Rabaté and J. Dussy, Bull. soc. chim. biol. *20*, 467 (1938).
11. J. Rabaté, Bull. soc. chim. France (5) *7*, 565 (1940).
12. K. Freudenberg, H. Knauer, and F. Cramer, Chem. Ber. *84*, 144 (1951).
13. R. Kuhn, I. Löw, and H. Trischmann, Chem. Ber. *90*, 203 (1957).
14. A. M. Gakhokidze, Zhur. Obshcheĭ Khim. *11*, 117 (1941); Chem. Abstr. *35*, 5467 (1941).
15. M. J. Clancy, J. Chem. Soc. *1960*, 4213.
16. B. Coxon and H. G. Fletcher, J. Org. Chem. *26*, 2892 (1961).
17. K. Matsuda, Tôhoku J. Agr. Research *6*, 271 (1956); Chem. Abstr. *50*, 13366 (1956).
18. P. A. J. Gorin, J. F. T. Spencer, and D. W. S. Westlake, Can. J. Chem. *39*, 1067 (1961).
19. S. Peat, W. J. Whelan, and K. A. Hinson, Nature *170*, 1056 (1952).
20. J. K. N. Jones and P. E. Reid, Can. J. Chem. *38*, 944 (1960).
21. A. M. Gakhokidze, Zhur. Obshcheĭ Khim. *20*, 116 (1950); Chem. Abstr. *44*, 5819 (1950).
22. G. Zemplén, Ber. *60*, 1563 (1927).
23. G. Zemplén, Ber. *59*, 1265 (1926).
24. A. M. Gakhokidze, Zhur. Obshcheĭ Khim. *20*, 289 (1950); Chem. Abstr. *44*, 6822 (1950).
25. P. A. J. Gorin and A. S. Perlin, Can. J. Chem. *35*, 262 (1957).
26. P. A. J. Gorin and A. S. Perlin, Can. J. Chem. *34*, 1796 (1956).
27. A. M. Gakhokidze and M. Kutidze, Zhur. Obshcheĭ Khim. *22*, 247 (1952); Chem. Abstr. *46*, 11117 (1952).
28. A. Wickström, Acta Chem. Scand. *11*, 1473 (1957).
29. J. Lehmann and D. Beck, Ann. *630*, 56 (1960).
30. G. O. Aspinall and J. Baillie, J. Chem. Soc. *1963*, 1702.
31. G. Zemplén, Ber. *59*, 2402 (1926).
32. A. M. Gakhokidze, Zhur. Obshcheĭ Khim. *20*, 120 (1950); Chem. Abstr. *44*, 5819 (1950).
33. D. H. Ball and J. K. N. Jones, J. Chem. Soc. *1958*, 33.
34. R. L. Whistler and D. I. McGilvray, J. Am. Chem. Soc. *77*, 1884 (1955).
35. R. L. Whistler and W. M. Corbett, J. Am. Chem. Soc. *77*, 3822 (1955).
36. G. O. Aspinall and R. J. Ferrier, Chem. & Ind. (London) *1957*, 819.
37. G. O. Aspinall and R. J. Ferrier, J. Chem. Soc. *1957*, 4188.
38. G. O. Aspinall and R. J. Ferrier, J. Chem. Soc. *1958*, 1501.

## D. REDUCING DISACCHARIDES WITH A 1→3 LINKAGE

This group contains several noteworthy oligosaccharides. A relatively short time ago, 3-*O*-α-D-glucopyranosyl-D-glucose (I) was found among natural products and described; it was termed nigerose[1-9] and also sakébiose.[3] Nowadays the first name is consistently employed since it was found[10,11] that nigerose and sakébiose are identical. The previously isolated disaccharides "*x*"[5] and "*y*"[9] were also nigerose, though probably not quite pure. This substance was evidently synthesized[12,13] prior to its isolation from nigeran (see Chapters VI and X).

Laminaribiose, 3-*O*-β-D-glucopyranosyl-D-glucose (II), is likewise frequently encountered among natural products.[12,14-20]

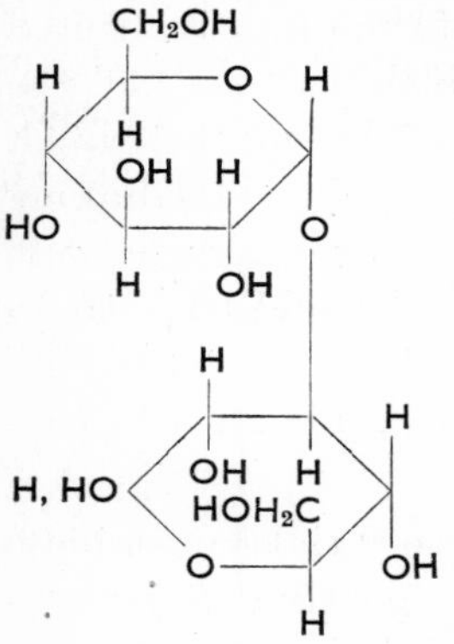

CH₂OH

(I) 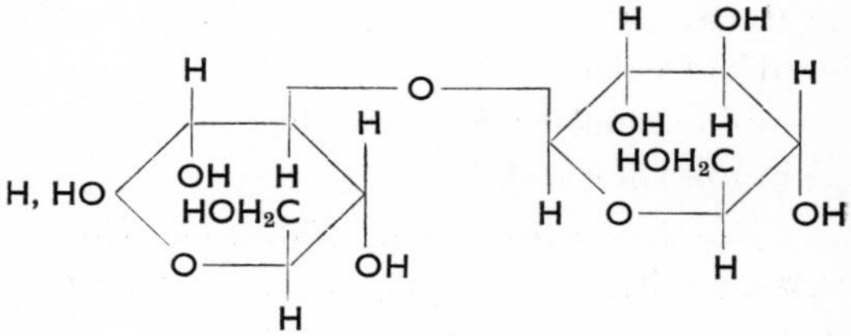                                                      (II)

Another product obtained from natural material, in particular by the hydrolysis of gums, is 3-*O*-β-D-galactopyranosyl-D-galactose (III),[21-27] but the substance known for the longest time in this group is turanose,* 3-*O*-α-D-gluco-

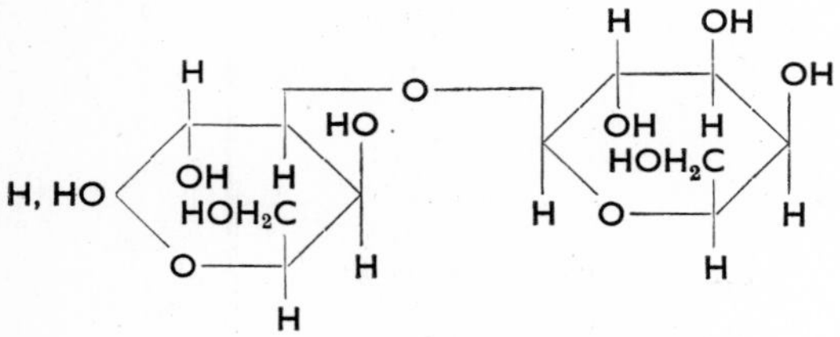

(III)

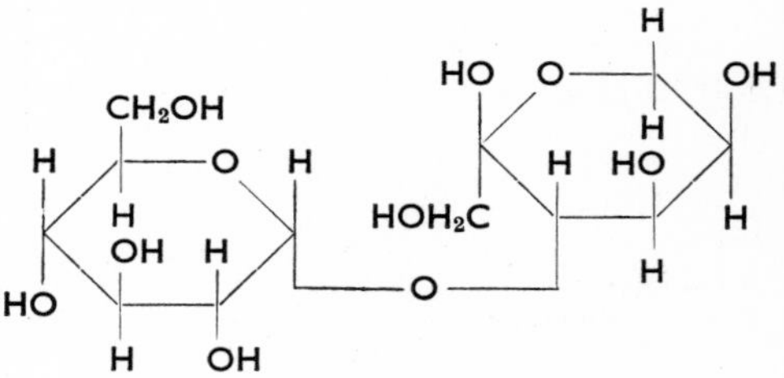

CH₂OH

(IV)

pyranosyl-D-fructose (IV).[16,28-34] Tanret found in 1906[30] that turanose is split by α-glucosidase with the formation of D-glucose and D-fructose, and must therefore be an α-glucoside. This disaccharide is not oxidized by alkaline hypoiodi-

---

* For a review see C. S. Hudson, Advances in Carbohydrate Chem. *2*, 2 (1946).

*References see p. 243*

te and, consequently, the free hemiacetal group must belong to D-fructose. Since turanose gives a phenylosazone,[31,32] D-glucose cannot be linked to D-fructose at C-1 nor at C-2. Moreover, as a result of the observed properties, mainly mutarotation of its solution, its existence in the form of a substituted fructofuranose or fructopyranose must be possible, which means that the hydroxyl groups at C-5 and C-6 of the fructose unit must be unsubstituted. Consequenty, only the hydroxyl groups at C-3 or C-4 are available for linking D-glucose to the D-fructose unit; if the glycosidically linked hydroxyl group were located at C-4, the phenylosazone obtained from turanose would have to be identical with maltose phenylosazone; however, this is not the case.[31] The only possible structure is that with a glycosidic 1→3 linkage, and this was confirmed in another way.[33]

Further reducing 1→3 disaccharides, such as solabiose,[35] rhodymenabiose [36,37] and other, not specially denominated and sometimes poorly defined substances are listed with their physical constants in Table XXXV.

## Table XXXV

Physical Properties of Reducing Disaccharides
Disaccharides with a 1→3 Bond

| Disaccharide | Melting Point °C | $[\alpha]_D(H_2O)$ | References |
|---|---|---|---|
| Nigerose[1,2], sakébiose[3]  3-*O*-α-D-glucopyranosyl-D-glucose |  | + 87° | 1, 2 |
|  |  | +135° | 4 |
|  |  | + 84° | 25, 26 |
|  | 162 | + 84·8° | 3 |
|  | 152—154 | + 83° | 38 |
| Laminaribiose  3-*O*-β-D-glucopyranosyl-D-glucose | 204—206 | +24·9° → +18·6° | 15, 17, 39 |
|  | 198—201 | −27° (MeOH) | 40 |
|  | 188—192 | +7·5° → +19·4° | 41 |
|  | 190—192 | +39·2° | 21 |
|  | 182—186 | +19·1° | 16, 19, 20 |
|  |  | +20·8° | 18 |
|  |  | +20·3° | 42 |
|  |  | +16·7° | 43 |
| Solabiose  3-*O*-β-D-glucopyranosyl-D-galactose | 175—200 (dec.) | +40·7° | 35 |
|  |  | +35° | 44 |
| Turanose  3-*O*-α-D-glucopyranosyl-D-fructose | 157 | +27·3° → +75·8° | 34 |
|  | 168 | +74·7° | 16 |
| 3-*O*-α-D-Glucopyranosyl-D-arabinose | syrup | +72° | 45 |
|  | 172 | +16·5° | 46—48 |
|  | 121 | +47° | 49, 50 |
|  |  | +48° | 51 |
| 3-*O*-α-D-Glucopyranosyl-D-xylose |  | +87·5° | 52 |

*Table XXXV - continued*

| Disaccharide | Melting Point °C | $[\alpha]_D(H_2O)$ | References |
|---|---|---|---|
| 3-*O*-β-D-Glucopyranosyl-D-xylose | 120 | $-$ 6·4° | 53, 54 |
| 3-*O*-α-D-Mannopyranosyl-D-mannose | | $+50°$ | 55 |
| | | $+53·6° \to +57·6°$ | 56 |
| 3-*O*-α-D-Galactopyranosyl-D-galactose | amorphous | $+155°$ | 57 |
| 3-*O*-β-D-Galactopyranosyl-D-galactose | 200 (dec.) | $-54°$ (?) | 58 |
| | 169—170 | $+84° \to +61°$ | 59 |
| | 163—170 | $+75° \to +60°$ | 25 |
| | | $+49·2° \to +54·1°$ | 23, 24 |
| | 165 | $+84° \to +64°$ | 60 |
| | 159—160 | $+62°$ | 21, 22, 27 |
| | 151—152 | $+69° \to +55°$ | 26 |
| | 150—151 | $+58°$ | 61 |
| | | $+52°$ | 62 |
| 3-*O*-β-D-Galactopyranosyl-D-glucose | 204—206 | $+76·7° \to +41·2°$ | 18, 63 |
| 3-*O*-β-D-Galactopyranosyl-D-fructose | 197—199 | $-14·6° \to -27·1°$ | 18 |
| 3-*O*-β-D-Galactopyranosyl-D-arabinose | 166—168 | $-50·3° \to -63·1°$ | 64, 65 |
| | 165 | $-55·1°$ | 66, 67 |
| | 165—166 | | 68 |
| | 162—169 | $-54·5° \to -62°$ | 69, 70 |
| | 168 | $-50·2° \to -63°$ | 49 |
| 3-*O*-α-D-Galactopyranosyl-L-arabinose | amorphous | $+152°$ | 71, 72 |
| 3-*O*-β-D-Galactopyranosyl-L-arabinose | 204—205 | $+97° \to +67°$ | 59 |
| | 200—201 | $+$ 60° | 61 |
| | 202—203 | $+$ 62° | 26 |
| 3-*O*-α-L-Arabinofuranosyl-L-arabinose | | $+$ 89° | 27 |
| | | $+$ 94° | 58, 73 |
| 3-*O*-β-L-Arabinopyranosyl-L-arabinose | | $+220°$ | 56, 74—77 |
| | | $+200°$ | 78 |
| 3-*O*-α-L-Arabinopyranosyl-D-glucose | 176·5—178·5 | $+$ 85°, $\to +$ 54·4° | 79 |
| 3-*O*-α-D-Xylopyranosyl-D-xylose | 178 | $+106° \to +118°$ | 80 |
| Rhodymenabiose | | | |
| 3-*O*-β-D-xylopyranosyl-D-xylose | | $-18·4°$ | 81 |
| | 192—193 | $-35° \to -22°$ | 82 |
| 3-*O*-α-D-Xylopyranosyl-L-arabinose | 123 | $+173°$ | 74, 83—85 |
| | 117—119 | $+175° \to +183°$ | |

## REFERENCES

1. J. H. Pazur and T. Budovich, J. Am. Chem. Soc. *78*, 1885 (1956).
2. J. H. Pazur, T. Budovich, and C. L. Tipton, J. Am. Chem. Soc. *79*, 625 (1957).
3. K. Matsuda and K. Aso, J. Fermentation Technol. *31*, 211 (1953); Chem. Abstr. *47*, 7731 (1953).
4. S. Haq and W. J. Whelan, J. Chem. Soc. *1958*, 1342.
5. S. A. Barker, E. J. Bourne, and M. Stacey, J. Chem. Soc. *1953*, 3084.
6. S. A. Barker, E. J. Bourne, D. M. O'Mant, and M. Stacey, J. Chem. Soc. *1957*, 2448.
7. K. Matsuda, Chem. & Ind. (London) *1958*, 1627.
8. K. Matsuda and T. Sekiguchi, Tôhoku J. Agr. Research *9*, 263 (1959); Chem. Abstr. *53*, 21677 (1959).

9. A. Thompson, K. Anno, M. L. Wolfrom, and M. Inatome, J. Am. Chem. Soc. *76*, 1309 (1954).

10. K. Matsuda, G. Hiroshima, K. Shibasaki, and K. Aso, Tôhoku J. Agr. Research *5*, 239 (1954); Chem. Abstr. *50*, 4043 (1956).

11. K. Matsuda, G. Hiroshima, K. Shibasaki, and K. Aso, J. Fermentation Technol. *32*, 498 (1954); Chem. Abstr. *49*, 8554 (1955).

12. A. M. Gakhokidze, Zhur. Obshcheĭ Khim. *16*, 9123 (1946); Chem. Abstr. *41*, 6210 (1947).

13. A. M. Gakhokidze, Zhur. Obshcheĭ Khim. *19*, 571 (1949).

14. V. C. Barry, Sci. Proc. Roy. Dublin *22*, 423 (1941).

15. P. Bächli and E. G. V. Percival, J. Chem. Soc. *1952*, 1243.

16. W. M. Corbett and J. Kenner, J. Chem. Soc. *1954*, 3274.

17. A. Sato, K. Watanabe, and K. Aso, Chem. & Ind. (London) *1958*, 887.

18. R. Kuhn and H. H. Baer, Chem. Ber. *87*, 1560 (1954).

19. S. Peat, W. J. Whelan, and H. G. Lawley, J. Chem. Soc. *1958*, 724.

20. S. Peat, W. J. Whelan, and H. G. Lawley, J. Chem. Soc. *1958*, 729.

21. E. L. Hirst and A. S. Perlin, J. Chem. Soc. *1954*, 2622.

22. A. S. Perlin, Anal. Chem. *27*, 396 (1955).

23. H. Weinland, Hoppe Seyler's Z. physiol. Chem. *305*, 87 (1956).

24. B. O. Lindgren, Acta Chem. Scand. *11*, 1365 (1957).

25. D. H. Ball and J. K. N. Jones, J. Chem. Soc. *1958*, 905.

26. G. O. Aspinall, B. J. Auret, and E. L. Hirst, J. Chem. Soc. *1958*, 4408.

27. G. O. Aspinall, E. L. Hirst, and A. Nicholson, J. Chem. Soc. *1959*, 1697.

28. C. S. Hudson and E. Pacsu, Science *69*, 278 (1929).

29. C. S. Hudson and E. Pacsu, J. Am. Chem. Soc. *52*, 2519 (1930).

30. G. Tanret, Bull. soc. chim. France (3) *25*, 816 (1906).

31. H. S. Isbell and W. Pigman, J. Research Natl. Bur. Standards *20*, 773 (1938).

32. E. Pacsu, E. J. Wilson, and L. Graf, J. Am. Chem. Soc. *61*, 2675 (1939).

33. H. S. Isbell, J. Research Natl. Bur. Standards *26*, 35 (1941).

34. J. F. Bates, *Polarimetry, Saccharimetry and the Sugars*, National Bureau of Standards, Washington 1942, p. 758.

35. R. Kuhn, I. Löw, and H. Trischmann, Chem. Ber. *88*, 1492 (1955).

36. B. H. Howard, Biochem. J. *67*, 643 (1957).

37. E. J. C. Curtis and J. K. N. Jones, Can. J. Chem. *38*, 1305 (1960).

38. I. J. Goldstein and W. J. Whelan, J. Chem. Soc. *1962*, 170.

39. H. Ono and M. Dazai, Nature *183*, 1055 (1959).

40. K. Fujimoto, K. Matsuda, and K. Aso, Tôhoku J. Agr. Research *13*, 55 (1962); Chem. Abstr. *57*, 15211 (1962).

41. K. Freudenberg and K. Oertsen, Ann. *574*, 37 (1951).

42. S. Peat, W. J. Whelan, and K. A. Hinson, Nature *170*, 1056 (1952).

43. P. S. O'Colla, E. E. Lee, and D. McGrath, J. Chem. Soc. *1962*, 2730.

44. P. A. J. Gorin and J. F. T. Spencer, Can. J. Chem. *39*, 2282 (1961).

45. G. Zemplén, Ber. *60*, 1555 (1927).

46. M. Gakhokidze, Zhur. Obshcheĭ Khim. *18*, 60 (1948); Chem. Abstr. *42*, 42 (1948).

47. M. Doudoroff, W. Z. Hassid, and H. A. Barker, J. Biol. Chem. *168*, 733 (1947).

48. W. Z. Hassid, M. Doudoroff, A. L. Potter, and H. A. Barker, J. Am. Chem. Soc. *70*, 307 (1948).

49. R. L. Whistler and K. Yagi, J. Org. Chem. *26*, 1050 (1961).

50. J. D. Moyer and H. S. Isbell, Abstracts of Papers, 126th Meeting Amer. Chem. Soc., New York 1954, p. 245I.

51. A. J. Charlson and A. S. Perlin, Can. J. Chem. *34*, 1804 (1956).
52. S. A. Barker, M. Stacey, and D. B. E. Stroud, Nature *189*, 138 (1961).
53. S. A. Barker, E. J. Bourne, G. C. Hewitt, and M. Stacey, J. Chem. Soc. *1957*, 3541.
54. W. A. M. Duncan, D. J. Manners, and J. L. Thompson, Biochem. J. *73*, 295 (1959).
55. A. Jeanes, J. E. Pittsley, P. R. Watson, and J. H. Sloneker, Can. J. Chem. *40*, 2256 (1962).
56. J. K. N. Jones and W. H. Nicholson, J. Chem. Soc. *1958*, 27.
57. K. Morgan and A. N. O'Neill, Can. J. Chem. *37*, 1201 (1959).
58. F. Smith and A. M. Stephen, J. Chem. Soc. *1961*, 4892.
59. G. O. Aspinall and T. B. Christensen, J. Chem. Soc. *1961*, 3461.
60. A. M. Stephen, S. Kirkwood, and F. Smith, Can. J. Chem. *40*, 151 (1962).
61. D. W. Drummond and E. Percival, J. Chem. Soc. *1961*, 3908.
62. P. A. J. Gorin and J. F. T. Spencer, Can. J. Chem. *39*, 2282 (1961).
63. J. H. Pazur, C. L. Tipton, T. Budovich, and J. M. Marsh, J. Am. Chem. Soc. *80*, 119 (1958).
64. G. Zamplén, Ber. *59*, 2402 (1926).
65. G. Zemplén, Ber. *60*, 1309 (1927).
66. P. A. Levene and O. Wintersteiner, J. Biol. Chem. *75*, 315 (1927).
67. A. M. Gakhokidze, Zhur. Obshcheĭ Khim. *16*, 1907 (1946); Chem. Abstr. *41*, 6208 (1947).
68. F. Zilliken, P. N. Smith, R. M. Tomarelli, and P. György, Arch. Biochem. Biophys. *54*, 398 (1955).
69. R. Kuhn and W. Kirschenlohr, Ann. *600*, 135 (1956).
70. H. L. Frush and H. S. Isbell, J. Research Natl. Bur. Standards *50*, 133 (1953).
71. F. Smith, J. Chem. Soc. *1939*, 744.
72. A. J. Charlson, J. R. Nunn, and A. M. Stephen, J. Chem. Soc. *1955*, 269.
73. P. Andrews, L. Hough, and D. B. Powell, Chem. & Ind. (London) *1956*, 658.
74. P. Andrews and J. K. N. Jones, J. Chem. Soc. *1954*, 4134.
75. J. K. N. Jones, J. Chem. Soc. *1953*, 1672.
76. P. Andrews and J. K. N. Jones, J. Chem. Soc. *1955*, 583.
77. P. Andrews, D. H. Ball, and J. K. N. Jones, J. Chem. Soc. *1953*, 4090.
78. H. Bouveng and B. Lindberg, Acta Chem. Scand. *10*, 1515 (1956).
79. L. Wallenfels and D. Beck, Ann. *630*, 46 (1960).
80. D. H. Ball and J. K. N. Jones, J. Chem. Soc. *1958*, 33.
81. B. H. Howard, Biochem. J. *67*, 643 (1957).
82. E. J. C. Curtis and J. K. N. Jones, Can. J. Chem. *38*, 1305 (1960).
83. R. Montgomery, F. Smith, and H. C. Srivastava, J. Am. Chem. Soc. *79*, 698 (1957).
84. R. L. Whistler and W. M. Corbett, J. Am. Chem. Soc. *77*, 6328 (1955).
85. H. C. Srivastava and F. Smith, J. Am. Chem. Soc. *79*, 982 (1957).

## E. REDUCING DISACCHARIDES WITH A 1→4 LINKAGE

Maltose, 4-$O$-α-D-glucopyranosyl-D-glucose (I), is a very important disaccharide forming the basic structural element of starch, from which it is usually obtained by hydrolysis. It may be prepared in the form of its β-anomer, either as the monohydrate[1,2] or anhydrous,[3] as well as in the form of the less common α-anomer, again as the monohydrate[3] or anhydrous.[3] Anhydrous maltose is best prepared from the monohydrate by boiling with absolute alcohol.[4]

*References see p. 253*

The structure of maltose (I) has been established by the investigation of the hydrolysis of the per-*O*-methylated derivative (II).[5] Acid hydrolysis of methyl hepta-*O*-methylmaltoside (II) yields 2,3,4,6-tetra-*O*-methyl-D-gluco-pyranose (III) as well as 2,3,6-tri-*O*-methyl-D-glucose (IV). The structure of the latter compound was not known at the time when the constitution of maltose was investigated. The product obtained by the hydrolysis of the per-*O*-methyl derivative (II) yielded with phenylhydrazine a phenylhydrazone but no phenylosazone. From this it follows that the hydroxyl groups in positions 2,3,4 or 2,3,6 or 2,4,6 could be transformed into etheric linkages. The problem was solved by oxidizing tri-*O*-methyl-D-glucopyranose (IV) with nitric acid to di-*O*-methyl-L-tartaric acid (V), from which it is obvious that the splitting product (IV) must have the structure of 2,3,6-tri-*O*-methyl-D-glucose. This, however, does not elucidate the attachment of the second D-glucose molecule in the maltose molecule, because it might be linked in the reducing part either in position 4 or, less probably, in position 5.

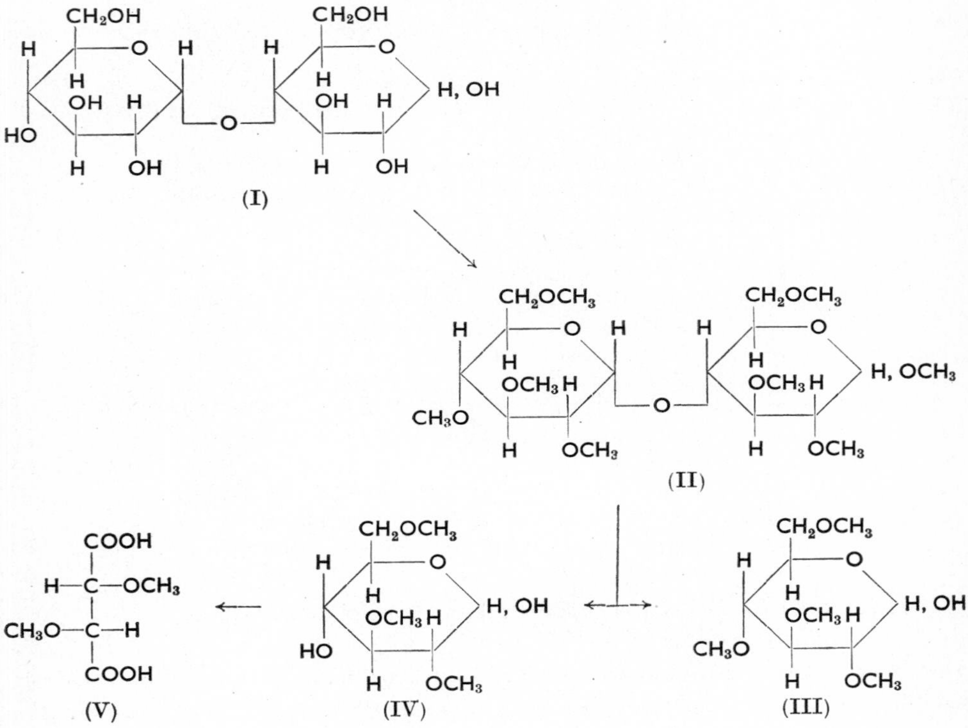

(I)

(II)

(V)          (IV)          (III)

This question was solved by oxidizing maltose to the corresponding carboxylic acid, namely maltobionic acid (VI).[6] The latter compound can be methylated to form the methyl ether (VII), which on hydrolysis, besides 2,3,4,6-

tetra-*O*-methyl-D-glucopyranose (III), also yields 2,3,5,6-tetra-*O*-methyl-D-gluconic acid (VIII). The structure of this acid follows clearly from the fact that its lactone is identical with the methylation product of D-gluconic acid γ-lactone (IX).

(I) ⟶

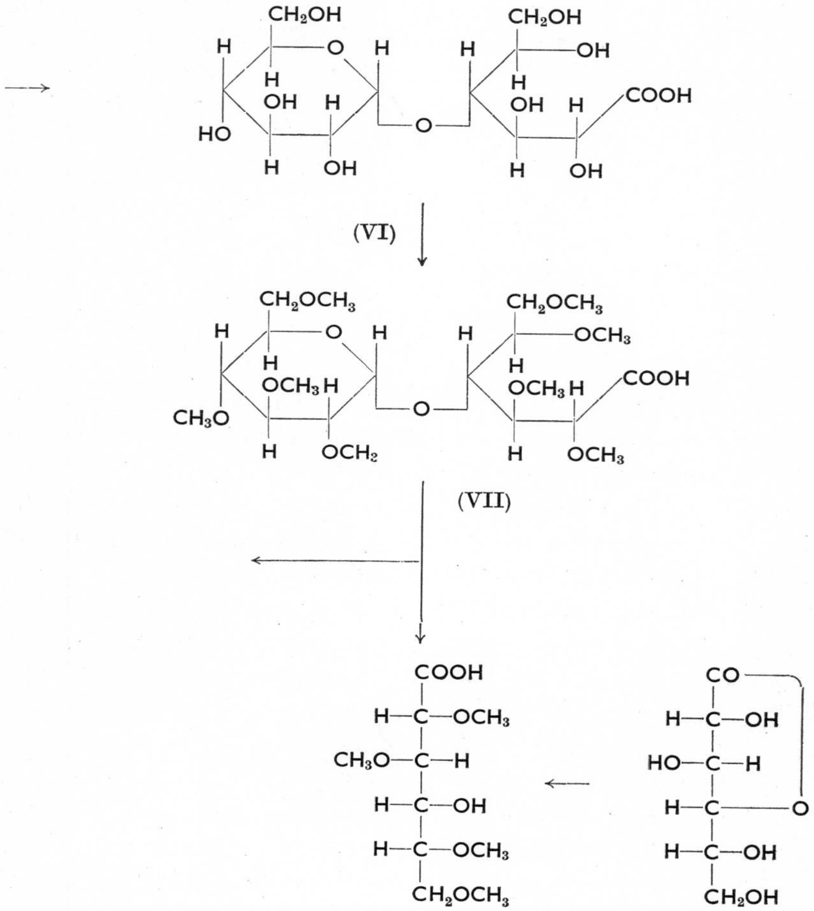

(VI)

(VII)

(III) ←

The question whether the glycosidic linkage in the maltose molecule is α or β was solved by enzymic splitting. Maltose is split by the same enzymes (α-glucosidases) as is methyl α-D-glucopyranoside. This problem was recently re-examined.[7]

Of late, attention has also been paid to the influence of radiation on maltose[8] (see also Chapter VIII), to the relative acidity of the hydroxyl groups[9] and to the complex of maltose with ferric ions.[10]

*References see p. 253*

Cellobiose, 4-$O$-$\beta$-D-glucopyranosyl-D-glucose (X), is the basic structural element of cellulose, from which it is also usually obtained by acetolysis. The structure of cellobiose has been established, similarly to the case of maltose, from the course of the splitting of the per-$O$-methylated derivative,[11–13] and the nature of the glycosidic linkage follows from the capability of being split by emulsin[14] which attacks $\beta$-glycosides.

(X)

The kinetics of the hydrolysis of cellobiose has been investigated,[15–17] and the problem of the arrangement of both D-glucose units in the cellobiose molecule has been studied by means of X-rays.[18,19]

The existence of isocellobiose, reportedly isolated as the octa-$O$-acetyl derivative besides the octa-$O$-acetyl derivative of cellobiose in the acetolysis of cotton,[20–22] is, according to recent findings, very doubtful.[23]

Structurally connected with both the above mentioned disaccharides are cellobiulose, (4-$O$-$\beta$-D-glucopyranosyl-D-fructose)[24] and maltulose, (4-$O$-$\alpha$-D-glucopyranosyl-D-fructose); they are less frequently encountered.[25–29]

Lactose,* 4-$O$-$\beta$-D-galactopyranosyl-D-glucose (XI), is likewise known in the forms of its two anomers. The $\alpha$-anomer crystallizes as a monohydrate,[30–34] from which the anhydrous compound[31,32,35] can be obtained by heating to 125—130°C,[35] or *in vacuo*.[31,32] The $\beta$-anomer crystallizes usually as the anhydrous product.[36–38] A modification is also known composed of five molecules of the $\alpha$-anomer for every three molecules of the $\beta$-anomer,[39] and obtained by crystallization from methanolic hydrogen chloride. The crystallography of $\alpha$-lactose monohydrate is the subject of a paper from recent years.[40]

The structure of lactose (XI) is evident from the following findings.

Lactose is hydrolysed into a molecule of D-galactose and a molecule of D-glucose. The latter is here the reducing part, because lactobionic acid (XII), formed by oxidation of lactose with bromine water (see Chapter XXXI), yields on hydrolysis D-galactose (XIII) and D-gluconic acid (XIV).[41]

---

* For a review see J. R. Clamp, L. Hough, J. L. Hickson, and R. L. Whistler, Advances in Carbohydrate Chem. *16*, 159 (1961).

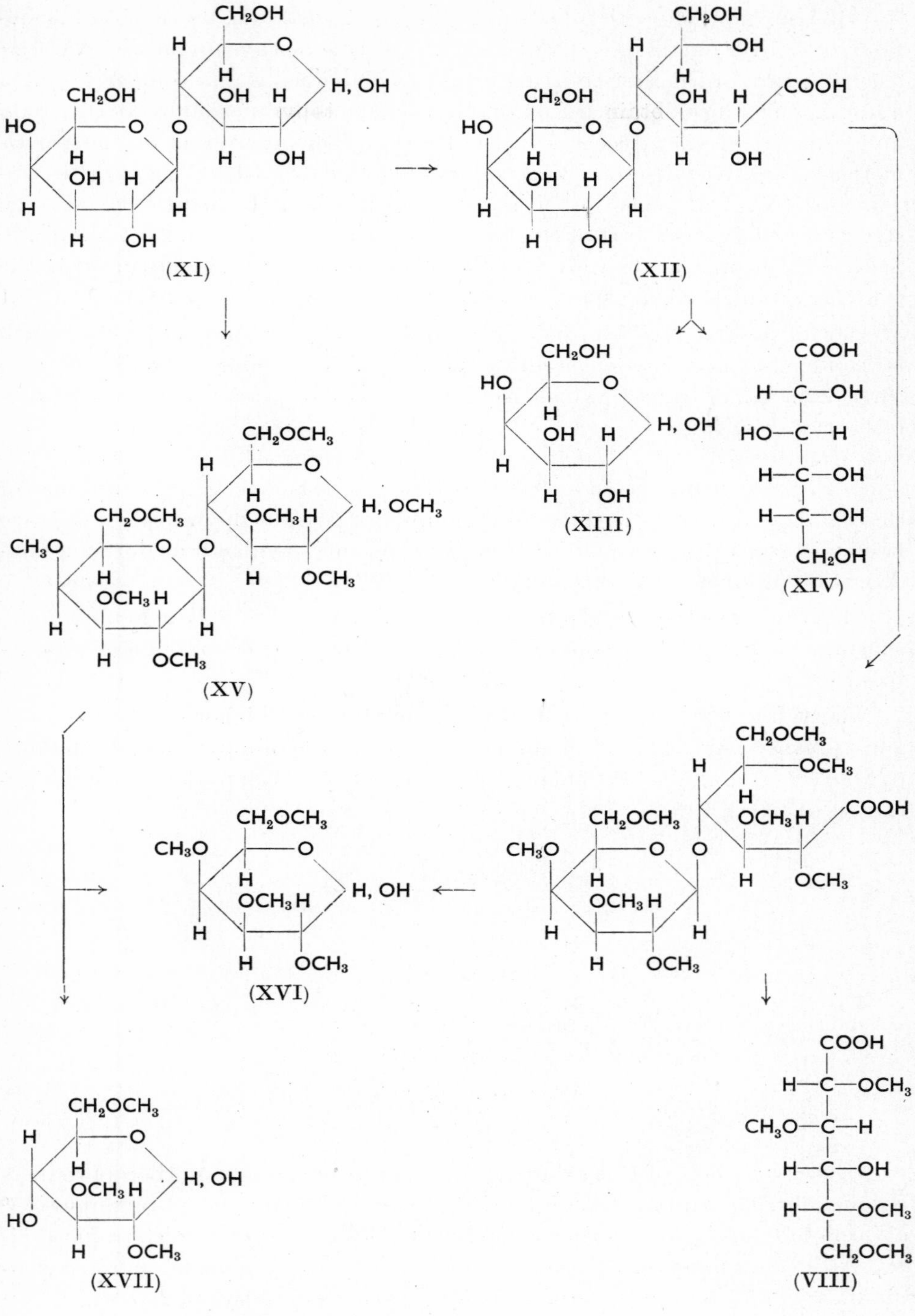

(XI)

(XII)

(XIII)

(XIV)

(XV)

(XVI)

(XVII)

(VIII)

*References see p. 253*

Methyl hepta-$O$-methyl-lactoside (XV), on hydrolysis, yields both 2,3,4,6-tetra-$O$-methyl-D-galactose (XVI) and 2,3,6-tri-$O$-methyl-D-glucose (XVII).[42] The structure of the first splitting product is obvious from a comparison with a known substance obtained from methyl D-galactopyranoside by methylation and removal of the glycosidic methyl group. The hydrolysis of the per-$O$-methyl derivative of lactobionic acid leads likewise to 2,3,4,6-tetra-$O$-methyl-D-galactose (XVI). By means of these reactions it is possible to establish also the structure of the other part of the lactose molecule, because the 2,3,5,6-tetra-$O$-methyl-D-gluconic acid (VIII)[43] obtained in this way is identical with the splitting product of maltobionic acid per-$O$-methyl ether (see p. 247).

From the practical viewpoint, the formation of complexes of lactose with ferric ions has been investigated[10] as well as the darkening of lactose in mixtures with amine salts,[44] which is of considerable importance in the manufacture of drug tablets.

Lactose is a suitable material for the preparation of D-galactosan (1,6-anhydro-$\beta$-D-galactopyranose);[45,46] the pyrolysis of lactose yields a mixture of this compound with laevoglucosan (1,6-anhydro-$\beta$-D-glucopyranose), but these two substances can be easily separated, since only D-galactosan forms a condensation product with acetone.[45,46]

Lactulose, 4-$O$-$\beta$-D-galactopyranosyl-D-fructose,[25,47-50] is a less common substance, and the same applies to lycobiose, 4-$O$-$\beta$-D-glucopyranosyl-D-galactose.[51,52]

Very frequently occuring hydrolysis products of higher oligosaccharides and polysaccharides are mannobiose, 4-$O$-$\beta$-D-mannopyranosyl-D-mannopyranose[53-60] and, in particular, xylobiose, 4-$O$-$\beta$-D-xylopyranosyl-D-xylopyranose (XVIII).[61-69]

(XVIII)

Other members of this group having special names are synthetic products throughout. This applies to *epi*-maltose (4-$O$-$\alpha$-D-glucopyranosyl-D-mannose),[70] *epi*-cellobiose (4-$O$-$\beta$-D-glucopyranosyl-D-mannose),[53,54,59,60,71-78] celtrobiose (4-$O$-$\beta$-D-glucopyranosyl-D-altrose),[79,80] *epi*-lactose (4-$O$-$\beta$-D-galactopyranosyl-D-mannose),[34,81,82] and *neo*-lactose (4-$O$-$\beta$-D-galactopyranosyl-D-altrose).[83,84]

## Table XXXVI

Physical Properties of Reducing Disaccharides
Disaccharides with a 1→4 Bond

| Disaccharide | Melting Point °C | $[\alpha]_D(H_2O)$ | References |
|---|---|---|---|
| Maltose | | | |
| 4-*O*-α-D-glucopyranosyl-D-glucose | | | |
| α-anomer | 108 | +173° | 3 |
| hydrate | 103 | +158° | 3 |
| β-anomer | 108 | +118° → +136° | 1, 85 |
| | 118—120 | +109° → +129° | 86 |
| hydrate | 103 | +112° → +130° | 2 |
| | | +118° → +131° | 87 |
| | 99—101 | +129° | 88 |
| | | +130° | 89 |
| [1-¹⁴C]-Maltose | | | 90 |
| Cellobiose | | | |
| 4-*O*-β-D-glucopyranosyl-D-glucose | 225 | +14·2° → +34·6° | 91 |
| | | +24·4° → +35·2° | 13, 92—95 |
| | 227 | +28° → +19° | 76 |
| | | +24° | 96 |
| | 229—231 | +15·2° → +36·7° | 106 |
| | 228—229 | +33·3° | 88, 97 |
| | 234 | +26·7° → +35·1° | 53 |
| | | +18·5° | 98 |
| | 234—235 | +35° | 99 |
| | 235—242 | | 59 |
| | | +34·5° | 89, 100 |
| *epi*-Maltose | | | |
| 4-*O*-α-D-glucopyranosyl-D-mannose | 216 (dec.) | +97° → +115° | 70 |
| *epi*-Cellobiose | | | |
| 4-*O*-β-D-glucopyranosyl-D-mannose | | +47° | 89 |
| α-anomer | 176 | +20° → +12·5° | 71 |
| | 135—138 | +18° → +15° | 54 |
| | 137 | +14·5° → + 5·9° | 77 |
| | 138 | +11° → + 6° | 96 |
| | | +15° | 74 |
| | 135—137 | +16° | 60 |
| β-anomer | 205 | −6·5° → +6·5° | 72, 73 |
| | 179—182 | +6° | 59 |
| | 169—172 | +5·7° → +6·6° | 105 |
| monohydrate | 134—137 | + 10° | 99 |
| | 135—136 | + 5·8° | 74, 75 |
| | 139—140° | + 5·8° | 59, 78 |
| | 133 | + 5·5° | 53, 58, 101 |
| | 134—139 | + 4·7° | 76 |
| 4-*O*-α-D-Glucopyranosyl-D-galactose | | +140° | 102 |
| Lycobiose | | | |
| 4-*O*-β-D-glucopyranosyl-D-galactose | 246—247 | +70° → +41·5° | 51, 52 |
| Celtrobiose | | | |
| 4-*O*-β-D-glucopyranosyl-D-altrose | 131—148 | +13·6° | 79, 80 |
| Maltulose | | | |
| 4-*O*-α-D-glucopyranosyl-D-fructose | | | |
| hydrate | 113—115 | +56·2° | 25—27 |
| | | +52·8° | 28, 29 |
| | | +60° | 103 |

*References see p. 253*

*Table XXXVI — continued*

| Disaccharide | Melting Point °C | $[\alpha]_D(H_2O)$ | References |
|---|---|---|---|
| Cellobiulose | | | |
| 4-*O*-β-D-glucopyranosyl-D-fructose | | −60·1° | 24 |
| 4-*O*-α-D-Glucopyranosyl-D-xylose | 58—78 | +97·5° → +94·5° | 104 |
| Mannosylglucose | | | |
| 4-*O*-β-D-mannopyranosyl-D-glucose | syrup | +29° | 99 |
| | | +27° | 96 |
| | | +20·1° | 53 |
| | | +12° | 101 |
| | | + 5·5° | 58 |
| | 202—203 | +30° → +19° | 76, 105 |
| | 203 | +35° → +18° | 54, 106 |
| | 201—203 | +18° | 59, 60, 76 |
| 4-*O*-α-D-Mannopyranosyl-D-mannose | | +49° | 58, 105 |
| Mannobiose | | | |
| 4-*O*-β-D-mannopyranosyl-D-mannose | syrup | −8° → −7° | 107 |
| | | −8·5° | 57 |
| | | −6° | 89 |
| | 208—209 | −8·1° → −7·4° | 53 |
| | 204 | −5° → −8° | 54 |
| | 202—203 | −5·2° → −8·2° | 58 |
| | 209—210 | −8° | 99 |
| | 204—206 | −8° | 59 |
| | 203—204 | −7° | 60 |
| | | −5·3° | 105 |
| | 201 | −8·5° | 96 |
| | 194 | −7·7° | 56 |
| | 190—191 | −8·5° | 101 |
| | 125—140 | −7·9° | 108 |
| | 122—124 | | 101 |
| 4-*O*-α-D-Galactopyranosyl-D-galactose | 210—211 | +177° | 109 |
| | | +186° → +173° | 110 |
| Galactobiose | | | |
| 4-*O*-β-D-galactopyranosyl-D-galactose | 209—213 | +67° | 111 |
| | 210—212 | +67° | 112 |
| | 208—210 | | 59 |
| | 204 | +68° | 113 |
| | 185 | +57·7° | 114 |
| Lactose | | | |
| 4-*O*-β-D-galactopyranosyl-D-glucose | 208—210 | | 115 |
| α-anomer | 223 | | 35 |
| monohydrate | 202 | +85·0° → +52·6° | 30—34 |
| | 201—202 | +86·3° → +58·1° | 116 |
| β-anomer | 252 | +34·9° → +55·4° | 36—38 |
| | | +67·9° | 39 |
| [1-¹⁴C]-Lactose | | | 117 |
| *epi*-Lactose | | | |
| 4-*O*-β-D-galactopyranosyl-D-mannose | | | |
| α-anomer | 150—160 | +38° → +27° | 81 |
| β-anomer | 196—197 | +23° → +30° | 34, 82 |
| *neo*-Lactose | | | |
| 4-*O*-β-D-galactopyranosyl-D-altrose | syrup | +34·7° | 83, 84 |

4-*O*-β-D-Mannnopyranosyl-L-gulose has been described with m. p. 201—203°C and $[\alpha]_D$-23,2° (H₂O), see E. L. Hirst, E. Percival, and J. K. Wold, J. Chem. Soc. *1964*, 1493.

*Table XXXVI — continued*

| Disaccharide | Melting Point °C | $[\alpha]_D(H_2O)$ | References |
|---|---|---|---|
| Lactulose | | | |
| 4-O-β-D-galactopyranosyl-D-fructose | 158 | $-23\cdot8° \to -51\cdot8°$ | 47 |
| | | $-50\cdot7°$ | 48 |
| | | $-49\cdot1°$ | 25 |
| | 165 | $-34\cdot3° \to -49\cdot8°$ | 50 |
| | 163 | $-50\cdot4°$ | 49 |
| 4-O-β-D-Galactopyranosyl-D-psicose | not given | not given | 49 |
| 4-O-β-D-Galactopyranosyl-D-xylose | 210—211 | $-1° \to +15°$ | 65, 118 |
| Xylobiose | | | |
| 4-O-β-D-xylopyranosyl-D-xylose | | $-25°$ | 89 |
| | | $-22°$ | 119 |
| | | $-15\cdot2°$ | 120 |
| | 195—197 | $-40° \to -27°$ | 66, 67 |
| | 194—196 | $-16°$ | 121 |
| | 188—189 | $-24\cdot8°$ | 122 |
| | 186—187 | $-32° \to -25\cdot5°$ | 63 |
| | 183—187 | $-30° \to -23°$ | 64, 65 |
| | 185 | $-32° \to -25\cdot5°$ | 61, 62 |
| | | $-25°$ | 123 |
| 4-O-β-L-Arabinopyranosyl-L-arabinose | not given | not given | 124 |
| 4-O-α-L-Arabinopyranosyl-D-glucose | syrup | $+41\cdot9°$ | 125 |

4-O-β-D-Gulopyranosyl-D-glucose has $[\alpha]_D +40\cdot7° \to +11\cdot5°$ ($H_2O$); 4-O-α-D-allopyranosyl-D-glucose and α-D-allopyranosyl β-D-fructofuranoside have been described without details of physical constants, see M. J. Bernaerts, J. Furnelle, and J. De Ley, Biochim. et Biophys. Acta *69*, 322 (1963).

## REFERENCES

1. E. Parcus and B. Tollens, Ann. *257*, 160 (1890).
2. J. Gillis, Natuurwetenschappelijk Tijdskr. *12*, 193 (1930); Chem. Abstr. *25*, 1805 (1931).
3. C. S. Hudson and E. Yanowski, J. Am. Chem. Soc. *39*, 1013 (1917).
4. Lobry de Bruyn and F. H. van't Lent, Rec. trav. chim. *13*, 220 (1894).
5. W. N. Haworth, J. V. Loach, and C. W. Long, J. Chem. Soc. *1927*, 3146.
6. W. N. Haworth and S. Peat, J. Chem. Soc. *1926*, 3094.
7. E. Ben-Gersham and J. Leibowitz, Enzymologia *20*, 148 (1958).
8. S. V. Starodubtsev, M. P. Tikhomolova, E. L. Aizenshtat, and K. Tashmukhamedova, Zhur. Obshcheĭ Khim. *31*, 3115 (1961).
9. V. A. Derevitskaya, G. S. Smirnova, and Z. A. Rogovin, Doklady Akad. Nauk S.S.S.R. *141*, 1090 (1961).
10. S. Ali Hasnain Zaidi, S. Ashfaq Husaina, and S. Mahdi-Hassan, Pakistan J. Sci. Ind. Research *5*, 43 (1962).
11. W. N. Haworth and E. L. Hirst, J. Chem. Soc. *119*, 193 (1921).
12. W. N. Haworth, C. W. Long, and J. H. G. Plant, J. Chem. Soc. *1927*, 2809.
13. P. A. Levene and M. L. Wolfrom, J. Biol. Chem. *77*, 671 (1928).
14. N. K. Richtmyer and C. S. Hudson, J. Am. Chem. Soc. *61*, 1834 (1939).
15. K. Freudenberg, W. Kuhn, W. Dürr, F. Bolz, and G. Steinbrunn, Ber. *63*, 1510 (1930).

16. K. Freudenberg and G. Blomquist, Ber. *68*, 2070 (1935).
17. G. N. La Diega, Chim. e ind. (Milan) *41*, 408 (1959); Chem. Abstr. *54*, 2733 (1960).
18. T. Petitpas and J. Méring, Compt. rend. *243*, 47 (1956); Chem. Abstr. *50*, 17423 (1956).
19. R. A. Jacobson, J. A. Wunderlich, and W. N. Lipscomb, Nature *184*, suppl. 22, 1719 (1959).
20. H. Ost and R. Prosiegel, Angew. Chem. *33*, 100 (1920).
21. H. Ost and G. Knoth, Papierfabr. Beibl. *3*, 25 (1922); Chem. Zentr. *1922*, III, 127.
22. H. Ost, Angew. Chem. *39*, 1117 (1926).
23. G. Bertrand and S. Benoit, Compt. rend. *177*, 85 (1923).
24. W. M. Corbett and J. Kenner, J. Chem. Soc. *1955*, 1431.
25. W. M. Corbett and J. Kenner, J. Chem. Soc. *1954*, 1789.
26. I. C. MacWilliam and A. W. Phillips, Chem. & Ind. (London) *1959*, 364.
27. J. W. White, Arch. Biochem. Biophys. *80*, 386 (1959).
28. S. Peat, P. J. P. Roberts, and W. J. Whelan, Biochem. J. *51*, XVII (1952).
29. L. Hough, J. K. N. Jones, and E. L. Richards, J. Chem. Soc. *1953*, 2005.
30. H. Trey, Z. phys. Chem. *46*, 620 (1903).
31. J. Gillis, Rec. trav. chim. *39*, 88 (1920).
32. J. Gillis, Rec. trav. chim. *39*, 677 (1920).
33. H. S. Isbell and W. Pigman, J. Research Natl. Bur. Standards *18*, 158 (1937).
34. W. T. Haskins, R. M. Hann, and C. S. Hudson, J. Am. Chem. Soc. *64*, 1852 (1942).
35. M. Schmoeger, Ber. *13*, 1920 (1880).
36. C. Tanret, Bull. soc. chim. France (3) *15*, 357 (1896).
37. C. S. Hudson and F. C. Brown, J. Am. Chem. Soc. *30*, 964 (1908).
38. R. Verschuur, Rec. trav. chim. *47*, 123 (1928).
39. R. C. Hockett and C. S. Hudson, J. Am. Chem. Soc. *53*, 4455 (1931).
40. H. Seifert and G. Labrot, Naturwissenschaften *48*, 691 (1961).
41. E. Fischer and J. Meyer, Ber. *22*, 361 (1889).
42. W. N. Haworth and G. C. Leitch, J. Chem. Soc. *113*, 192 (1918).
43. W. N. Haworth and C. W. Long, J. Chem. Soc. *1927*, 544.
44. R. A. Castello and A. M. Nattocks, J. Pharm. Sci. *51*, 106 (1962); Chem. Abstr. *56*, 13018 (1962).
45. R. M. Hann and C. S. Hudson, J. Am. Chem. Soc. *63*, 1484 (1941).
46. N. N. Shorygina and G. V. Davydova, Izvest. Akad. Nauk S.S.S.R., Otdel. Khim. Nauk *1961*, 728; Chem. Abstr. *55*, 23349 (1961).
47. E. Montgomery and C. S. Hudson, J. Am. Chem. Soc. *52*, 2101 (1930).
48. F. J. Bates, *Polarimetry, Saccharimetry and the Sugars*, National Bureau of Standards, Washington P. 1942, 467.
49. J. P. L. Bots, Rec. trav. chim. *76*, 515 (1957).
50. R. Kuhn and G. Krüger, Ann. *628*, 240 (1959).
51. R. Kuhn and I. Löw, Chem. Ber. *86*, 1027 (1953).
52. R. Kuhn, I. Löw, and H. Trischmann, Chem. Ber. *90*, 203 (1957).
53. J. K. Hamilton and H. W. Kircher, J. Am. Chem. Soc. *80*, 4703 (1958).
54. J. K. N. Jones and I. J. Painter, J. Chem. Soc. *1957*, 669.
55. A. J. Charlson, P. A. J. Gorin, and A. S. Perlin, Can. J. Chem. *34*, 1811 (1956).
56. R. L. Whistler and J. Z. Stein, J. Am. Chem. Soc. *73*, 4187 (1951).
57. J. K. N. Jones and W. H. Nicholson, J. Chem. Soc. *1958*, 27.
58. G. O. Aspinall, R. B. Rashbrook, and J. Kessler, J. Chem. Soc. *1958*, 215.
59. H. Meier, Acta Chem. Scand. *14*, 749 (1960).
60. A. Tymynski and T. E. Timell, J. Am. Chem. Soc. *82*, 2823 (1960).

61. R. L. Whistler, J. Bachrach, and Chen Chuan Tu, J. Am. Chem. Soc. *74*, 3059 (1952).
62. R. L. Whistler and Chen Chuan Tu, J. Am. Chem. Soc. *74*, 3609 (1952).
63. R. L. Whistler and Chen Chuan Tu, J. Am. Chem. Soc. *73*, 1389 (1951).
64. G. O. Aspinall, M. E. Carter, and M. Los, J. Chem. Soc. *1956*, 4807.
65. H. C. Srivastava and F. Smith, J. Am. Chem. Soc. *79*, 982 (1957).
66. D. H. Ball and J. K. N. Jones, J. Chem. Soc. *1958*, 33.
67. M. Ewald and A. S. Perlin, Can. J. Chem. *37*, 1254 (1959).
68. C. T. Bishop, Can. J. Chem. *33*, 1073 (1955).
69. D. V. Myhre and F. Smith, J. Org. Chem. *26*, 4609 (1961).
70. W. N. Haworth, E. L. Hirst, and R. J. W. Reynolds, J. Chem. Soc. *1934*, 302.
71. W. N. Haworth, E. L. Hirst, H. R. L. Streight, H. A. Thomas, and J. I. Webb, J. Chem. Soc. *1930*, 2636.
72. H. S. Isbell, J. Research Natl. Bur. Standards *7*, 1115 (1931).
73. H. S. Isbell, Proc. Natl. Acad. Sci. *16*, 704 (1930); Chem. Abstr. *25*, 1223 (1931).
74. M. Bergmann and H. Schotte, Ber. *54*, 1564 (1921).
75. W. T. Haskins, R. M. Hann, and C. S. Hudson, J. Am. Chem. Soc. *63*, 1725 (1941).
76. F. Smith and H. C. Srivastava, J. Am. Chem. Soc. *78*, 1404 (1956).
77. H. S. Isbell, J. Research Natl. Bur. Standards *5*, 1185 (1930).
78. D. H. Brauns, J. Am. Chem. Soc. *48*, 2784 (1926).
79. N. K. Richtmyer and C. S. Hudson, J. Am. Chem. Soc. *57*, 1716 (1935).
80. N. K. Richtmyer and C. S. Hudson, J. Am. Chem. Soc. *58*, 2534 (1936).
81. W. N. Haworth, E. L. Hirst, M. M. T. Plant, and R. J. W. Reynolds, J. Chem. Soc. *1930*, 2644.
82. M. Bergmann, R. Schotte, and E. Rennert, Ann. *434*, 94 (1923).
83. A. Kunz and C. S. Hudson, J. Am. Chem. Soc. *48*, 1978 (1926).
84. A. Kunz and C. S. Hudson, J. Am. Chem. Soc. *48*, 2435 (1926).
85. W. J. Whelan, J. M. Bailey, and P. J. P. Roberts, J. Chem. Soc. *1953*, 1293.
86. H. O. Bouveng, H. Kiessling, B. Lindberg, and J. McKay, Acta Chem. Scand. *16*, 615 (1962).
87. J. K. N. Jones, R. A. Wall, and A. O. Pittet, Can. J. Chem. *38*, 2285 (1960).
88. J. C. Sowden and A. S. Spriggs, J. Am. Chem. Soc. *78*, 2503 (1956).
89. A. J. Charlson and A. S. Perlin, Can. J. Chem. *34*, 1804 (1956).
90. H. S. Isbell and R. Schaffer, J. Am. Chem. Soc. *78*, 1887 (1956).
91. F. C. Peterson and C. C. Spencer, J. Am. Chem. Soc. *49*, 2822 (1927).
92. A. P. N. Franchimont, Ber. *12*, 1941 (1879).
93. Z. Skraup, Ber. *32*, 2413 (1899).
94. W. T. Haskins, R. M. Hann, and C. S. Hudson, J. Am. Chem. Soc. *64*, 1289 (1942).
95. V. E. Gilbert, F. Smith, and M. Stacey, J. Chem. Soc. *1946*, 622.
96. A. J. Mian and T. E. Timell, Can. J. Chem. *38*, 1511 (1960).
97. A. Beélik and J. K. Hamilton, J. Org. Chem. *26*, 5074 (1961).
98. E. T. Reese, E. Smakula, and A. S. Perlin, Arch. Biochem. Biophys. *85*, 171 (1959).
99. M. O. Gyaw and T. E. Timell, Can. J. Chem. *38*, 1957 (1960).
100. S. Peat, W. J. Whelan, and K. A. Hinson, Nature *170*, 1056 (1952).
101. O. Perila and C. T. Bishop, Can. J. Chem. *39*, 815 (1961).
102. J. K. N. Jones and M. B. Perry, J. Am. Chem. Soc. *79*, 2787 (1957).
103. G. Avigad, Biochem. J. *73*, 587 (1959).
104. E. W. Putman, C. F. Litt, and W. Z. Hassid, J. Am. Chem. Soc. *77*, 4351 (1955).
105. G. O. Aspinall, R. Begbie, and J. E. McKay, J. Chem. Soc. *1962*, 214.
106. M. E. Henderson, L. Hough, and T. J. Painter, J. Chem. Soc. *1958*, 3519.

107. A. K. Mukherjee, D. Choudhury, and P. Bagchi, Can. J. Chem. *39*, 1408 (1961).
108. K. Nishida and H. Hashima, J. Dept. Agr. Kyushu Imp. Univ. *2*, 277 (1930); Chem. Abstr. *25*, 498 (1931).
109. R. L. Whistler and H. E. Conrad, J. Am. Chem. Soc. *76*, 1673 (1954).
110. J. K. N. Jones and W. W. Reid, J. Chem. Soc. *1955*, 1890.
111. H. Meier, Acta Chem. Scand. *16*, 2275 (1962).
112. H. O. Bouveng and H. Meier, Acta Chem. Scand. *13*, 1884 (1959).
113. J. K. Gilham, A. S. Perlin, and T. E. Timell, Can. J. Chem. *36*, 1741 (1958).
114. M. Masamune and S. Kamiyama, Tôhoku J. Exptl. Med. *66*, 43 (1957); Chem. Abstr. *52*, 8974 (1958).
115. P. Andrews, L. Hough, and D. B. Powell, Chem. & Ind. (London) *1956*, 658.
116. E. J. C. Curtis and J. K. N. Jones, Can. J. Chem. *37*, 358 (1959).
117. H. G. Wood, P. Siu, and P. Schambye, Arch. Biochem. Biophys. *69*, 390 (1957).
118. R. Montgomery, F. Smith, and H. C. Srivastava, J. Am. Chem. Soc. *79*, 698 (1957).
119. G. O. Aspinall and K. M. Ross, J. Chem. Soc. *1961*, 3674.
120. D. V. Myhre and F. Smith, J. Org. Chem. *26*, 4609 (1961).
121. K. Hunt and J. K. N. Jones, Can. J. Chem. *40*, 1266 (1962).
122. C. T. Bishop, Can. J. Chem. *33*, 1073 (1955).
123. D. J. Howard, Biochem. J. *67*, 643 (1957).
124. D. H. Ball, J. K. N. Jones, W. H. N. Nicholson, and T. J. Painter, Tappi *39*, 438 (1956); Chem. Abstr. *50*, 12469 (1956).
125. K. Wallenfels and D. Beck, Ann. *630*, 46 (1960).

## F. REDUCING DISACCHARIDES WITH A 1→5 LINKAGE

This group of substances with a linkage that at the first glance seems very unusual contains only a few compounds, one of which, leucrose (5-*O*-β-D-glucopyranosyl-D-fructose),[1-3] is a natural product. Its physical properties together with those of the other members of this group are presented in Table XXXVII.

### Table XXXVII

Physical Properties of Reducing Disaccharides
Disaccharides with a 1→5 Bond

| Disaccharide | Melting Point °C | $[\alpha]_D (H_2O)$ | References |
|---|---|---|---|
| Leucrose<br>5-*O*-α-D-glucopyranosyl-D-fructose | 161—162 | — 6·8°<br>— 8° | 1, 2<br>3 |
| 5-*O*-β-D-Glucopyranosyl-D-glucose | syrup | —22·3°<br>—23·9° | 4, 5<br>6 |
| 5-*O*-β-D-Galactofuranosyl-D-galactose | syrup | —65° | 7 |

### REFERENCES

1. F. H. Stodola, H. J. Koepsell, and E. S. Sharpe, J. Am. Chem. Soc. *74*, 3202 (1952).
2. F. H. Stodola, E. S. Sharpe, and H. J. Koepsell, J. Am. Chem. Soc. *78*, 2514 (1956).
3. A. J. Charlson and A. S. Perlin, Can. J. Chem. *34*, 1804 (1956).
4. J. C. Sowden and A. S. Spriggs, J. Am. Chem. Soc. *78*, 2503 (1956).
5. R. W. Bailey and E. J. Bourne, Nature *184*, Suppl. 12, 904 (1959).
6. K. Freudenberg and K. Oertsen, Ann. *574*, 37 (1951).
7. P. A. J. Gorin and J. F. T. Spencer, Can. J. Chem. *37*, 499 (1959).

## G. DISACCHARIDES OF UNKNOWN CONSTITUTION

It would be possible to list a number of substances characterized as di-saccharides of various composition and unknown structure. The usually in-sufficient quantity of the material obtained has not permitted more than chro-matographic determination of their components after hydrolysis and, in some cases, of their ratio also.

A larger number of reducing disaccharides contain a molecule of D-glucose and a molecule of D-fructose; however, they are different from turanose (see Chapter XII, 1,D). At present it cannot be stated with certainty that the sub-stance designated [1-3] as 6-*O*-β-D-fructofuranosyl-D-glucose was correctly des-cribed by this name; a further isomer probably is the reducing D-fructosyl-D-glucose, described by Edelman,[4] and another isomer is D-fructosyl-D-glucose, having a specific rotation $[\alpha]_D$ +21°, referred to under the name ceratose.[5]

Mention has also been made of D-fructosyl-D-fructoses of uncertain struc-ture,[1] and of another compound of this type designated as sogdianose[6] (m. p. 156—158°C, $[\alpha]_D$ —16.4°). The structures of disaccharides containing a mole-cule of D-glucose and a molecule of D-galactose[7,8] or two molecules of D-ga-lactose,[7-9] have likewise not been elucidated in detail.

Disaccharides, formed as products of polysaccharide hydrolysis, containing two molecules of L-arabinose,[10] one molecule of L-arabinose and D-xylose[11] and two molecules of D-xylose[11] have been described. Disaccharides yielding D-galactose and L-arabinose after hydrolysis have been obtained, too.[11]

D-Mannosyl-D-glucose and D-glucosyl-D-mannose, m. p. 139—140°C, $[\alpha]_D$ +6.1° (H₂O), of unknown constitution have been described by T. E. Timell, Tappi *45*, 799 (1963); Chem. Abstr. *59*, 2922 (1963).

### REFERENCES

1. W. J. Whelan and D. M. Jones, Biochem. J. *54*, XXXIV (1953).
2. L. M. White and G. E. Secor, Arch. Biochem. Biophys. *36*, 490 (1952).
3. J. S. D. Bacon, Biochem. J. *57*, 320 (1954).
4. J. Edelman, Biochem. J. *57*, 22 (1954).

5. K. Wallenfels and J. Lehmann, Chem. Ber. *90*, 1000 (1957).

6. S. M. Strepkov, Zhur. Obshcheĭ Khim. *28*, 3143 (1958); Chem. Abstr. *53*, 10053 (1959).

7. K. Wallenfels, Naturwissenschaften *38*, 306 (1951).

8. K. Wallenfels, E. Bernt, and G. Limberg, Ann. *579*, 113 (1953).

9. K. Wallenfels, E. Bernt, and G. Limberg, Ann. *584*, 63 (1953).

10. P. Andrews and J. K. N. Jones, J. Chem. Soc. *1954*, 4134.

11. K. Hunt and J. K. N. Jones, Can. J. Chem. *40*, 1266 (1962).

## 2. TRISACCHARIDES

### A. NON-REDUCING TRISACCHARIDES

This group comprises a large number of more important compounds, which have been obtained by direct isolation as well as by hydrolytic processes, and in some cases by enzymic syntheses. They can be classified as substances containing in their molecule two D-glucose units and one D-fructose unit (gentianose, trisaccharide Z, erlose, and melezitose), further substances containing in their molecule one D-glucose unit and two D-fructose units (kestose, isokestose, *neo*-kestose and impatiose). Some non-reducing oligosaccharides containing D-glucose and D-fructose cannot at present be classified;[1] it is possible, however, that some of these compounds are identical with some of those given above, but whose structure has so far not been established.

Further non-reducing trisaccharides are composed of one unit of D-glucose, one of D-galactose and one of D-fructose (raffinose, umbelliferose and planteose); labiose contains two units of D-fructose and one unit of D-galactose. A smaller number of non-reducing trisaccharides have so far not been given trivial names.

Gentianose, *O*-β-D-glucopyranosyl-(1→6)-*O*-α-D-glucopyranosyl-(1→2) β-D-fructofuranoside, also termed $6^G$-β-glucosylsucrose (I),[2] is a non-reducing trisaccharide obtainable from various gentian roots by extraction with 90% ethanol.[3] The structure of gentianose follows from the identification of its splitting products. In acid solution it gives rise to a molecule of D-fructose and a molecule of gentiobiose (II),[4] while the action of emulsin leads to one molecule each of D-glucose and sucrose (III). From this it is evident that the D-glucose molecule must be attached by a β-linkage to position 6 of the glucose part of sucrose.

The trisaccharide Z, *O*-α-D-glucopyranosyl-(1→6)-*O*-α-D-glucopyranosyl-(1→2) β-D-fructofuranoside, also named $6^G$-α-D-glucosylsucrose,[2] is less common.[5] A more frequently occurring, though also rarer, trisaccharide is erlose,*

---

* Erlose is identical with the trisaccharide C (α-maltosyl β-D-fructofuranoside) isolated from *Panax ginseng* by K. Takiura and J. Nakagawa, J. Pharm. Soc. Japan (Yakugaku Zasshi) *83*, 305 (1963).

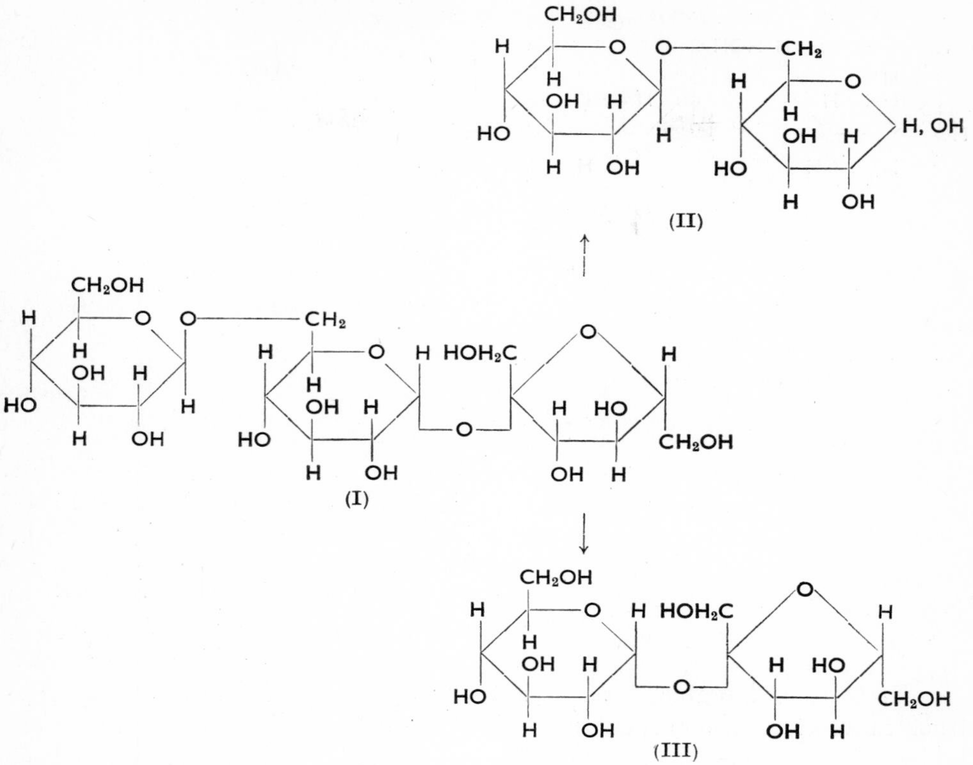

(II)

(I)

(III)

$O$-α-D-glucopyranosyl-$(1\rightarrow4)$-$O$-α-D-glucopyranosyl-$(1\rightarrow2)$  β-D-fructofuranoside, also designated as $4^G$-α-D-glucosylsucrose[2] or glucosucrose.[6] This substance has been described several times,[7-9] usually as a product of enzymic syntheses (see Chapter VI, 5) and less frequently as constituent of honey.[7]

Melezitose,*    $O$-α-D-glucopyranosyl-$(1\rightarrow3)$-$O$-β-D-fructofuranosyl-$(2\rightarrow1)$ α-D-glucopyranoside, also termed $3^F$-α-glucosylsucrose (IV), can be obtained from various mannas[10] (see Chapter IX). The structure has been established from the following findings: Acid hydrolysis gives rise to two molecules of D-glucose and one molecule of D-fructose,[11] while partial hydrolysis in acid solution[12] leads to a molecule of D-glucose and a molecule of the disaccharide turanose (V). Since the structure of turanose (3-$O$-α-D-glucopyranosyl-D-fructose) was known and melezitose is a non-reducing trisaccharide, it was clear that its constituents are D-glucose and turanose, but there remained the question of how these two parts are linked together. In the enzymic cleavage of melezitose the D-glucose molecule is liberated with the formation of one molecule of sucrose (III); thus the attachment of D-glucose to turanose is established.[13]

* For reviews see C. S. Hudson, Advances in Carbohydrate Chem. *2*, 2, (1946); E. J. Hehre, Advances in Carbohydrate Chem. *8*, 277 (1954).

*References see p. 265*

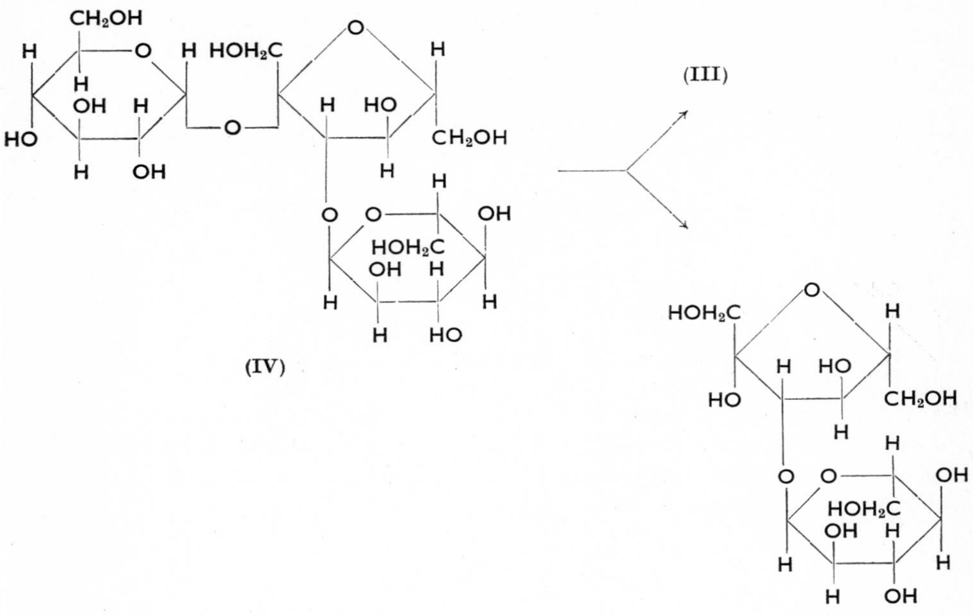

(III)

(IV)

(V)

Kestose, $O$-$\alpha$-D-glucopyranosyl-(1→2)-$O$-$\beta$-D-fructofuranosyl-(6→2) $\beta$-D-fructofuranoside, also termed 6-kestose[14] or $6^F$-fructosylsucrose[14] (VI), is an interesting non-reducing trisaccharide produced by enzymic processes from sucrose[15] and isolated in a number of cases[16-18] from plant material (see Chapters IX and X). The structure has been derived by identification of the hydrolysis products of kestose per-$O$-methyl ether.

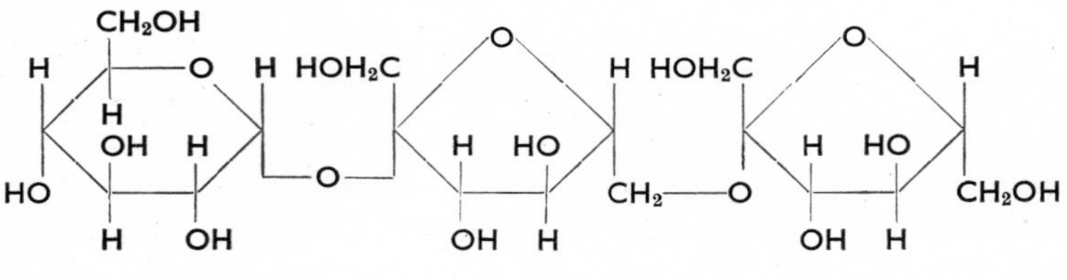

(VI)

Isokestose, $O$-$\alpha$-D-glucopyranosyl-(1→2)-$O$-$\beta$-D-fructofuranosyl-(1→2) $\beta$-D-fructofuranoside, also named 1-kestose,[14,19-21] $1^F$-fructosylsucrose[14] or 1-inulobiosyl-D-glucose[22] (VII), is likewise a frequently isolated product of enzymic conversions of sucrose;[21-27] it is also a splitting product in the hydrolysis of inulin[20] and a substance directly isolated from some plants.[16,17] Its structure has also been established by methylation analysis.[21]

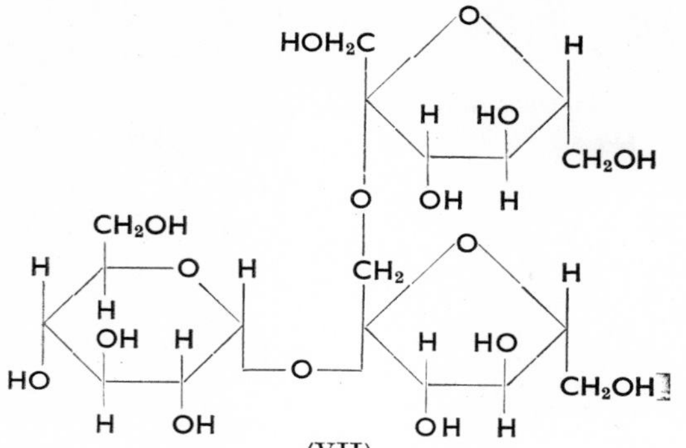

(VII)

*neo*-Kestose, $O$-$\beta$-D-fructofuranosyl-(2→6)-$O$-$\alpha$-D-glucopyranosyl-(1→2) $\beta$-D-fructofuranoside, also termed $6^G$-fructosylsucrose[2,14,16] (VIII), is another isomer of both foregoing compounds. The structure of this less common substance[18,28,29] has likewise been established by methylation analysis.

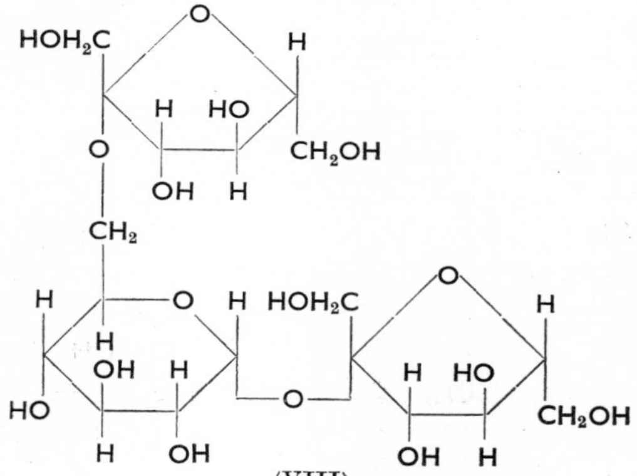

(VIII)

The structure of a further fructosylsucrose, namely impatiose,[30] is not known.

Raffinose,* $O$-$\alpha$-D-galactopyranosyl-(1→6)-$O$-$\alpha$-D-glucopyranosyl-(1→2) $\beta$-D-fructofuranoside, also named $6^G$-$\alpha$-galactosylsucrose[2,14] (older names are gossypose[31] and melitose,[32,33] or melitriose; the identity of all these substances was proved by Tollens),[34] has been found as a constituent of molasses.[35] It has also been found in raw sugar[36] and obtained by the enzymic hydrolysis of lychnose[37] and stachyose.[38-40] Its structure (IX) has been derived from the fact that acid hydrolysis leads to a mixture of D-glucose, D-galactose and D-fructose, while in a weakly acid medium D-fructose and melibiose (X) are formed.[41] Enzymic splitting of raffinose by emulsin produces D-galactose and sucrose (III),[42] whereby the structure of raffinose (IX) is established. Sucrose may also

---

* D. French, Advances in Carbohydrate Chem. *9*, 149 (1955).

*References see p. 265*

be obtained from the raffinose molecule by selective degradation of the galactose unit.[43] Other proofs, such as hydrolysis of the per-*O*-methylated derivative
and the course of potassium periodate oxidation, are in full agreement with
this structure.

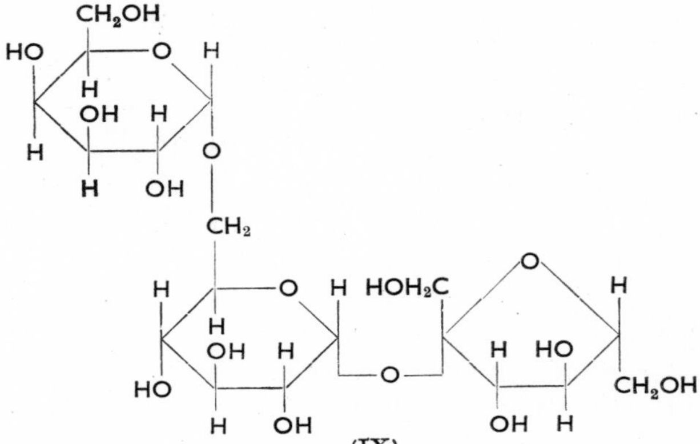

(IX)

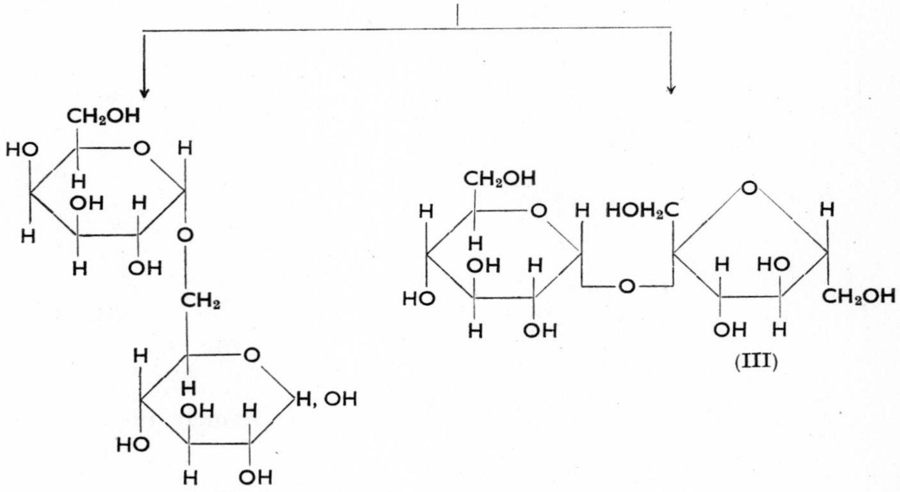

(X)

(III)

The isomer of raffinose designated as isoraffinose or better as umbelliferose,[44] *O*-α-D-galactopyranosyl-(1→2)-*O*-α-D-glucopyranosyl-(1→2) β-D-fructofuranoside, or also $2^G$-α-galactosylsucrose, is less frequently encountered.

A further isomer, namely planteose, *O*-α-D-galactopyranosyl-(1→6)-*O*-
β-D-fructofuranosyl-(2→1) α-D-glucopyranoside, or $6^F$-α-galactosylsucrose,[14]
is a commoner substance.[45-49] The structure (XI) follows from the fact that
hydrolysis leads to a mixture of D-glucose, D-galactose and D-fructose, while in
a moderately acidic medium planteose is split into D-glucose and the reducing
disaccharide planteobiose, and by emulsin into D-galactose and sucrose.[45]

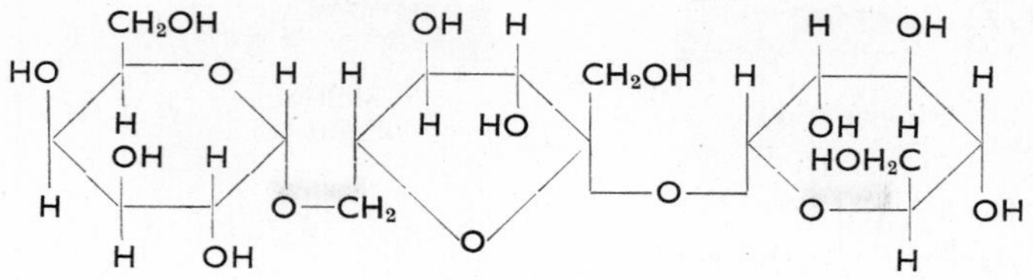

(XI)

The structure of difructosylgalactoside, designated as labiose,[50] has as yet not been elucidated.

The physical constants of these and further non-reducing trisaccharides are summarized in Table XXXVIII.

### Table XXXVIII

Physical Properties of Non-reducing Trisaccharides

| Trisaccharide | Melting Point °C | $[\alpha]_D(H_2O)$ | References |
|---|---|---|---|
| Erlose[7] $\alpha$-maltosyl $\beta$-D-fructofuranoside $4^G$-$\alpha$-glucosylsucrose[2] glucosucrose[6] $O$-$\alpha$-D-glucopyranosyl-(1→4)-$O$-$\alpha$-D-glucopyrano-syl-(1→2) $\beta$-D-fructofuranoside | amorphous 118—124 (dec.) | +121·8° + 98·3° | 8 9 75 |
| Gentianose $6^G$-$\beta$-glucosylsucrose[2] $O$-$\beta$-D-glucopyranosyl-(1→6)-$O$-$\alpha$-D-glucopyrano-syl-(1→2) $\beta$-D-fructofuranoside | 209—211 | + 33·4° | 51 |
| Trisaccharide Z $6^G$-$\alpha$-glucosylsucrose[2] $O$-$\alpha$-D-glucopyranosyl-(1→6)-$O$-$\alpha$-D-glucopyrano-syl-(1→2) $\beta$-D-fructofuranoside | 118—120 | +102·5° | 5 |
| Melezitose $3^F$-$\alpha$-glucosylsucrose[14] $O$-$\alpha$-D-glucopyranosyl-(1→3)-$O$-$\beta$-D-fructofurano-syl-(2→1) $\alpha$-D-glucopyranoside dihydrate | 153—154 148 | + 88·2° + 88·8° + 85·5° | 52—56 57—59 60 |
| monohydrate anhydro compound | | + 88·5° + 91·7° | 60 60 |
| Kestose 6-kestose[14] $6^F$-fructosylsucrose[14] $O$-$\alpha$-D-glucopyranosyl-(1→2)-$O$-$\beta$-D-fructofurano-syl-(6→2) $\beta$-D-fructofuranoside | 145 | + 27·3° | 15, 61–63 |
| Isokestose 1-kestose[14] $1^F$-fructosylsucrose[14,64] | | | |

*References see p. 265*

*Table XXXVIII - continued*

| Trisaccharide | Melting Point °C | $[\alpha]_D(H_2O)$ | References |
|---|---|---|---|
| 1-*O*-inulobiosyl D-glucoside[22] *O*-α-D-glucopyranosyl-(1→2)-*O*-β-D-fructotofura- nosyl-(1→2) β-D-fructofuranoside | syrup | + 28° | 20, 64 |
| | | + 29·2° | 23 |
| | | + 25·2° | 21, 24, 27 |
| | 195—197 | + 29° | 26 |
| | 189—190 | + 29° | 25 |
| | 148 | + 29·3° | 61 |
| | 105—110 | + 25·4° | 22 |
| hydrate | 90—92 | | 22 |
| *neo*-Kestose 6$^G$-β-fructosylsucrose[2,14,64] *O*-β-D-fructofuranosyl-(2→6)-*O*-α-D-glucopyrano- syl-(1→2) β-D-fructofuranoside | amorphous | + 22·2° | 29 |
| | | + 21·6° | 62, 63 |
| | | + 19° | 64 |
| Impatiose ?-fructosylsucrose | not given | not given | 30 |
| Raffinose 6$^G$-α-galactosylsucrose[2,14] *O*-α-D-galactopyranosyl-(1→6)-*O*-α-D-glucopyra- nosyl-(1→2) β-D-fructofuranoside | 118—120° | +123·1° | 65 |
| | | +122·8° | 66 |
| | | +111° | 67 |
| pentahydrate | 80 | +105·2° | 68, 69 |
| | 135—138 | +106° | 74 |
| Umbelliferose isoraffinose 2$^G$-α-galactosylsucrose *O*-α-D-galactopyranosyl-(1→2)-*O*-α-D-glucopyra- nosyl-(1→2) β-D-fructofuranoside | | +125·3° | 44 |
| *O*-α-D-Galactopyranosyl-(1→3)-*O*-α-D-glucopyrano- syl-(1→2) β-D-fructofuranoside | | + 90·5° | 70 |
| Lactsucrose α-lactosyl β-D-fructofuranoside[2] *O*-β-D-galactopyranosyl-(1→4)-*O*-α-D-glucopyra- nosyl-(1→2) β-D-fructofuranoside | 150—181 | + 59° | 2 |
| Planteose 6$^F$-α-galactosylsucrose[14] *O*-α-D-galactopyranosyl-(1→6)-*O*-β-D-fructofura- nosyl-(2→1) α-D-glucopyranoside | 123—124 | +125·2° | 46 |
| | | +129° | 45 |
| | | +130·5° | 47 |
| | | +127·2° | 48 |
| | | +123° | 49 |
| *O*-α-D-Glucopyranosyl-(1→2)-*O*-β-D-fructofurano- syl-(3→1) α-D-galactoside 3$^F$-galactosylsucrose | | + 28·5° | 67, 71–73 |
| *O*-α-D-Glucopyranosyl-(1→2)-*O*-β-D-fructofurano- syl-(1→1) α-D-galactoside 1$^F$-galactosylsucrose | | | 67, 72, 73 |
| Labiose difructosyl galactoside | 126—128 | +136·7° | 50 |

## REFERENCES

1. E. H. Fischer, L. Kohtés, and J. Fellig, Helv. Chim. Acta *34*, 1132 (1952).
2. G. Avigad, J. Biol. Chem. *229*, 121 (1957).
3. M. Bridel and M. Desmarest, J. pharm. chim. *9*, 465 (1929); Chem. Abstr. *23*, 5544 (1929).
4. E. Bourquelot and H. Hérissey, Compt. rend. *135*, 399 (1902).
5. S. A. Barker, E. J. Bourne, and O. Theander, J. Chem. Soc. *1957*, 2064.
6. J. P. Wolf and W. H. Ewart, Arch. Biochem. Biophys. *58*, 365 (1955).
7. S. Goldschmidt and H. Burkert, Hoppe-Seyler's Z. physiol. Chem. *300*, 188 (1955).
8. J. W. White and J. Maher, J. Am. Chem. Soc. *75*, 1259 (1953).
9. H. E. Gray and G. Fraenkel, Science *118*, 304 (1953); Chem. Abstr. *48*, 895 (1954).
10. C. S. Hudson and S. F. Sherwood, J. Am. Chem. Soc. *42*, 116 (1920).
11. G. Tanret, Bull. soc. chim. France (3) *35*, 817 (1906).
12. C. S. Hudson and E. Pacsu, J. Am. Chem. Soc. *52*, 2522 (1930).
13. E. J. Hehre and A. S. Carlson, Arch. Biochem. Biophys. *36*, 158 (1952).
14. S. Hestrin, D. S. Feingold, and G. Avigad, Biochem. J. *64*, 340 (1956).
15. N. Albon, D. J. Bell, P. H. Blanchard, D. Gross, and J. T. Rundell, J. Chem. Soc. *1953*, 24.
16. J. S. D. Bacon, Biochem. J. *73*, 507 (1959).
17. H. H. Schlubach and H. O. A. Koehn, Ann. *614*, 126 (1958).
18. H. H. Schlubach and J. Berndt, Ann. *647*, 41 (1961).
19. P. J. Allen and J. S. D. Bacon, Biochem. J. *63*, 200 (1956).
20. D. S. Feingold and G. Avigad, Biochim et Biophys. Acta *22*, 196 (1956).
21. J. S. D. Bacon and D. J. Bell, J. Chem. Soc. *1953*, 2528.
22. F. Kurasawa, Y. Yamamoto, I. Igaue, and Y. Nakamura, J. Agr. Chem. Soc. Japan *30*, 624 (1956); Chem. Abstr. *52*, 20376 (1958).
23. S. A. Barker, E. J. Bourne, and T. R. Carrington, J. Chem. Soc. *1954*, 2125.
24. I. R. Rominskiĭ, A. S. Shuskova, and A. V. Il'ina, Ukrain. Khim. Zhur. *24*, 236 (1958); Chem. Abstr. *52*, 15663 (1958).
25. S. Russi and A. Ballio, Gazz. chim. ital. *86*, 476 (1956); Chem. Abstr. *52*, 3922 (1958).
26. S. Russi and A. Ballio, Boll. soc. ital. biol. sperim. *31*, 1362 (1955); Chem. Abstr. *50*, 10885 (1956).
27. S. A. Barker and T. R. Carrington, J. Chem. Soc. *1953*, 3588.
28. H. H. Schlubach and F. Lederer, Ann. *635*, 154 (1960).
29. D. Gross, P. H. Blanchard, and D. J. Bell, J. Chem. Soc. *1954*, 1727.
30. M. Zimmermann, Experientia *8*, 424 (1952); Chem. Abstr. *47*, 3411 (1953).
31. R. Böhm, Arch. Pharm. (3), *22*, 159 (1884).
32. J. F. W. Johnston, Phil. Mag. (3) *23*, 14 (1843).
33. M. Berthelot, Ann. chim. phys. (3) *46*, 66 (1856).
34. B. Tollens, Ber. *18*, 26 (1885).
35. T. S. Harding, Sugar *25*, 308 (1923).
36. D. Gross and H. Albon, Analyst *78*, 191 (1953).
37. A. Archambault, J. E. Courtois, A. Wickström, and P. Le Dizet, Bull. soc. chim. biol. *38*, 1133 (1956).
38. D. French, P. M. Wild, and W. J. James, J. Am. Chem. Soc. *75*, 3664 (1953).
39. J. E. Courtois, C. Anagnostopoulos, and F. Petek, Compt. rend. *238*, 2020 (1954).
40. J. E. Courtois, C. Anagnostopoulos, and F. Petek, Enzymologia *17*, 69 (1954).
41. C. Scheibler and H. Mittelmeier, Ber. *22*, 1680, 3120 (1889).
42. C. Neuberg, Biochem. Z. *3*, 528 (1907).

43. A. K. Mitra and A. S. Perlin, Can. J. Chem. *35*, 1079 (1957).
44. A. Wickström and A. B. Svendsen, Acta Chem. Scand. *10*, 1199 (1956).
45. D. French, G. M. Wild, D. Young, and W. J. James, J. Am. Chem. Soc. *75*, 709 (1953).
46. N. Wattiez and M. Hans, Bull. acad. roy. med. Belg. *8*, 386 (1943); Chem. Abstr. *39*, 4849 (1945).
47. L. S. I. Hatanaka, Arch. Biochem. Biophys. *82*, 188 (1959).
48. D. French, J. Am. Chem. Soc. *77*, 1024 (1955).
49. D. French, R. W. Youngquist, and A. Lee, Arch. Biochem. Biophys. *85*, 471 (1959).
50. S. M. Strepkov, Zhur. Obshchei Khim. *9*, 1489 (1939); Chem. Abstr. *34*, 2798 (1940).
51. R. Binaghi and P. Falqui, Ann. chim. appl. *15*, 386 (1925).
52. A. Villiers, Compt. rend. *84*, 35 (1877).
53. L. Maquenne, Compt. rend. *117*, 127 (1893).
54. L. Maquenne, Bull. soc. chim. France (3) *9*, 723 (1893).
55. E. O. Lippmann, Ber. *60*, 161 (1927).
56. R. Kuhn and G. E. Grundherr, Ber. *59*, 1655 (1926).
57. E. Bourquelot and H. Hérissey, J. pharm chim. (6) *4*, 385 (1896).
58. Alekhine, Ann. chim. phys. (6) *18*, 532 (1889).
59. C. S. Hudson and S. F. Sherwood, J. Am. Chem. Soc. *40*, 1456 (1918).
60. N. K. Richtmyer and C. S. Hudson, J. Org. Chem. *11*, 610 (1946).
61. H. H. Schlubach and H. O. A. Koehn, Ann. *614*, 126 (1958).
62. H. H. Schlubach and J. Bundt, Ann. *647*, 41 (1961).
63. H. H. Schlubach and F. Lederer, Ann. *635*, 154 (1960).
64. J. S. D. Bacon, Biochem. J. *73*, 507 (1959).
65. D. Loiseau, Compt. rend. *82*, 1058 (1876).
66. R. Kuhn and H. Grassner, Ann. *610*, 122 (1957).
67. J. E. Courtois and U. Ariyoshi, Bull. soc. chim. biol. *42*, 737 (1960).
68. C. Scheibler, Ber. *18*, 1409 (1885).
69. C. Scheibler, Ber. *19*, 2868 (1886).
70. A. M. MacLeod and H. McCorquodate, Nature *182*, 815 (1958).
71. J. E. Courtois, P. Le Dizet, and F. Petek, Bull. soc. chim. biol. *41*, 1261 (1959).
72. J. E. Courtois and U. Ariyoshi, Bull. soc. chim. biol. *44*, 31 (1962).
73. J. E. Courtois and U. Ariyoshi, Bull. soc. chim. biol. *44*, 23 (1962).
74. A. Assarson and O. Theander, Acta Chem. Scand. *12*, 1319 (1958).
75. K. Takiura and J. Nakagawa, J. Pharm. Soc. Japan (Yakugaku Zasshi) *83*, 305 (1963).

## B. REDUCING TRISACCHARIDES

A considerable part of the group of more important reducing trisaccharides is formed by substances which are logical continuations of some reducing
disaccharides. They are composed of regularly repeating structural elements
and have been obtained throughout by partial hydrolysis of higher oligosaccharides or polysaccharides (see Chapter X); in many cases, there are also
known higher oligosaccharides, derived from these types, so that di-, tri-,
tetra-, penta- and higher saccharides form a kind of homologous series.

One of these substances is maltotriose,[1-7] *O*-α-D-glucopyranosyl-(1→4)-*O*-α-
glucopyranosyl-(1→4)-D-glucose (I), also named amylotriose. This reducing

trisaccharide is the repeating unit of the starch macromolecule; it is obtainable from starch by enzymic cleavage.[4] The structure of maltotriose has been derived from the course of its methylation analysis.

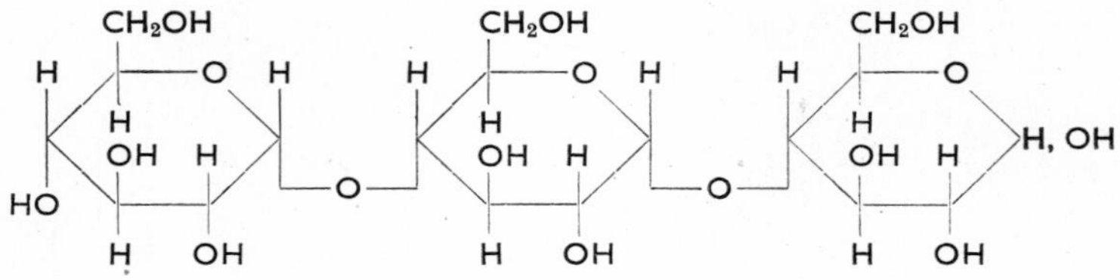

(I)

Cellotriose,[8-14] O-β-D-glucopyranosyl-(1→4)-O-β-D-glucopyranosyl-(1→4)-D-glucose (II), or procellose,[15] forms the analogous basic structure of cellulose. The constitution of cellotriose is obvious from the products of its degradation and enzymic splitting.[16]

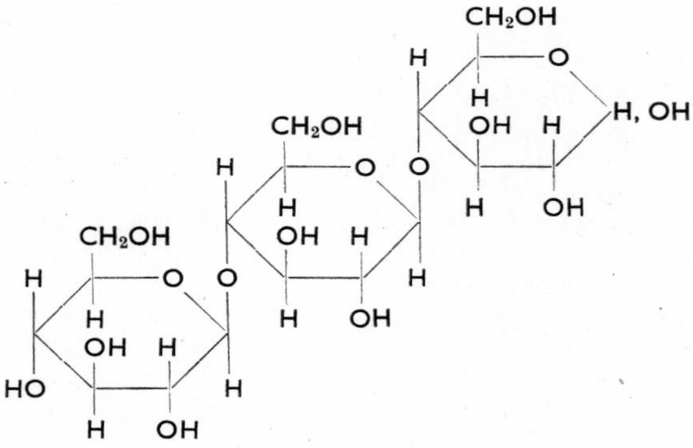

(II)

A trisaccharide very often mentioned in recent years is isomaltotriose,[17-19] O-α-D-glucopyranosyl-(1→6)-O-α-D-glucopyranosyl-(1→6)-D-glucose (III), also named dextrantriose,[17] 6-α-isomaltosyl-D-glucose or 6-α-D-glucopyranosylisomaltose; it is a product of the hydrolysis of the polysaccharide dextran[17,18] from which it is also formed by γ-irradiation[20] (see Chapter VIII). In this case, too, the structure is in agreement with the course of the hydrolysis.[21]

Reducing trisaccharides of similar structure are gentiotriose[22,23] O-β-D-glucopyranosyl-(1→6)-O-β-D-glucopyranosyl-(1→6)-D-glucose; kojitriose,[24,25] O-α-D-glucopyranosyl-(1→2)-O-α-D-glucopyranosyl-(1→2)-D-glucose; laminaritriose,[22,26-28] O-β-D-glucopyranosyl-(1→3)-O-β-D-glucopyranosyl-(1→3)-D-glu-

References see p. 274

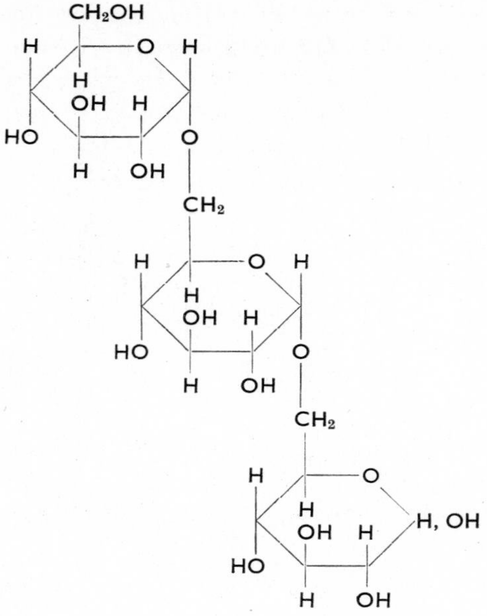

(III)

cose; mannotriose,[29-35] *O*-β-D-mannopyranosyl-(1→4)-*O*-β-D-mannopyranosyl-(1→4)-D-mannose; galactotriose,[32,36,37] *O*-β-D-galactopyranosyl-(1→4)-*O*-β-D-galactopyranosyl-(1→4)-D-galactose; and in particular xylotriose,[38-42] *O*-β-D-xylopyranosyl-(1→4)-*O*-β-D-xylopyranosyl-(1→4)-D-xylose (IV).

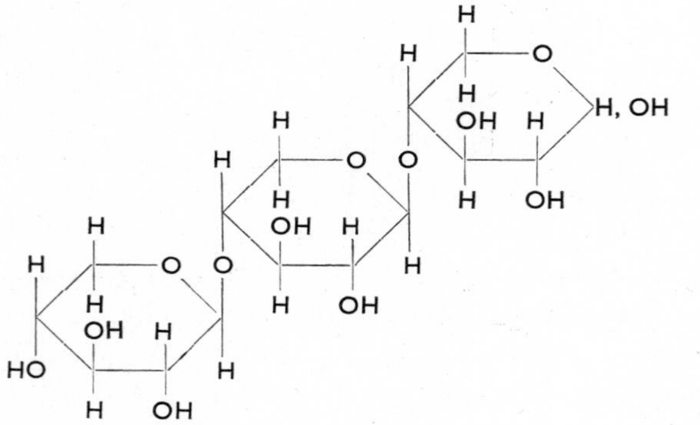

(IV)

Some trisaccharides obtained from natural material have a less regular structure, in particular manninotriose,[43-50] *O*-α-D-galactopyranosyl-(1→6)-*O*-α-D-galactopyranosyl-(1→6)-D-glucose. Less common trisaccharides are two fission products of the alkaloid tomatine, namely lycotriose *I*,[51,52] *O*-β-D-glucopyranosyl-$(1\rightarrow2)$-$O$-$\beta$-D-glucopyranosyl-$(1\rightarrow4)$-D-galactose and lycotriose *II*,[52] $O$-$\beta$-D-xylopyranosyl-$(1\rightarrow3)$-$O$-$\beta$-D-glucopyranosyl-$(1\rightarrow4)$-D-galactose.

Enzymic processes (see Chapter VI) lead to the very interesting reducing trisaccharide panose,[53-59] $O$-$\alpha$-D-glucopyranosyl-$(1\rightarrow6)$-$O$-$\alpha$-D-glucopyranosyl-$(1\rightarrow4)$-D-glucose or 4-$O$-$\alpha$-isomaltosyl-D-glucose or 6-$O$-$\alpha$-D-glucopyranosyl-maltose (V). The structure was in this case derived from the products of partial hydrolysis,[54,55] which yielded both maltose and isomaltose.

(V)

The results of methylation analysis of panose, see E. E. Smith and W. J. Whelan, J. Chem. Soc. *1963*, 3915, agree fully with the structure given above. The isomer of panose, $O$-$\alpha$-D-glucopyranosyl-$(1\rightarrow4)$-$O$-$\alpha$-D-glucopyranosyl-$(1\rightarrow6)$-D-glucose or 6-$O$-$\alpha$-maltosyl-D-glucose or 4-$O$-$\alpha$-D-glucopyranosylisomaltose isolated recently among products of partial hydrolysis of *Pullularia pullulans* glucan, see H. O. Bouveng, H. Kiessling, B. Lindberg, and J. McKay, Acta Chem. Scand. *17*, 797 (1963), was named isopanose.

Besides these substances, whose physico-chemical constants are given in Table XXXIX together with those of products of known constitution, a number of reducing trisaccharides have been described whose constitutions are not known. This applies to lactotriose (lactosyl-D-galactose or D-galactosyl-lactose),[60,61] a further D-galactosyl-lactose,[62] a trisaccharide containing three D-galactose molecules,[63] a trisaccharide composed of three D-glucose molecules,[64] prepared by the action of hydrochloric acid on laevoglucosan, and finally to a trisaccharide consisting of three L-arabinose molecules.[37] This group further contains a number of other, still less exactly defined compounds.

Enzymes of *Sporobolomyces singularis* synthesize from lactose a reducing trisaccharide, galactosyl-lactose, see P. A. J. Gorin, J. F. T. Spencer, and H. J. Phaff, Can. J. Chem. *42*, 1341 (1964); the structure of this compound has been determined to be $O$-$\beta$-D-galactopyranosyl-$(1\rightarrow4)$-$O$-$\beta$-D-galactopyranosyl-$(1\rightarrow4)$-D-glucose, m. p. 228° to 231°C, $[\alpha]_D + 68°_{\dot{5}} \rightarrow + 45°$ (H₂O). It is very difficult to say whether this compound could be identical with the galactosyl-lactose prepared by other authors.[62]

*References see p. 274*

## Table **XXXIX**

Physical Properties of Reducing Trisaccharides

| Trisaccharide | Melting Point °C | $[\alpha]_D(H_2O)$ | References |
|---|---|---|---|
| Kojitriose<br>$O$-$\alpha$-D-glucopyranosyl-(1→2)-$O$-$\alpha$-D-<br>glucopyranosyl-(1→2)-D-glucose | not given | not given | 24, 25 |
| Sophorotriose<br>$O$-$\beta$-D-glucopyranosyl-(1→2)-$O$-$\beta$-D-glu-<br>copyranosyl-(1→2)-D-glucose | 218—223 | $+16° \to +11°$ | 65 |
| Laminaritriose<br>$O$-$\beta$-D-glucopyranosyl-(1→3)-$O$-$\beta$-D-glu-<br>copyranosyl-(1→3)-D-glucose | 121 | $+ \ 2·2°$ | 22, 26–28 |
| Maltotriose, [1]amylotriose[2,3]<br>$O$-$\alpha$-D-glucopyranosyl-(1→4)-$O$-$\alpha$-D-glu-<br>copyranosyl-(1→4)-D-glucose | amorphous | $+160°$<br>$+152·8°$ | 1, 5, 6<br>66 |
| labelled | | $+157°$ | 3 |
| Cellotriose, procellose[15]<br>$O$-$\beta$-D-glucopyranosyl-(1→4)-$O$-$\beta$-D-glu-<br>copyranosyl-(1→4)-D-glucose | 238<br>225<br>224<br>210<br>205—209<br>206—212<br>203—214<br>205—207 | $+31·8° \to +23·2°$<br>$+14° \ \to +34·6°$<br>$+ \ 22·6°$<br>$+ \ 23°$<br>$+32° \to +23·9°$<br>$+22°$<br>$+32° \to +23°$<br>$+ \ 22·4°$ | 12<br>11<br>10<br>9<br>13<br>15<br>8<br>67 |
| Isomaltotriose, dextrantriose[17]<br>6-$O$-$\alpha$-isomaltosyl-D-glucose<br>6-$O$-$\alpha$-D-glucosylisomaltose | amorphous | $+145°$<br>$+134°$<br>$+146°$<br>$+136·1°$ | 18<br>17<br>68<br>69 |
| Gentiotriose<br>$O$-$\beta$-D-glucopyranosyl-(1→6)-$O$-$\beta$-D-glu-<br>copyranosyl-(1→6)-D-glucose | | $- \ 10·5°$<br>$+ \ 4·8°$ | 22<br>23 |
| 4-$O$-$\alpha$-Nigerosyl-D-glucose<br>$O$-$\alpha$-D-glucopyranosyl-(1→3)-$O$-$\alpha$-D-glu-<br>copyranosyl-(1→4)-D-glucose | | $+169·5°$ | 70 |
| 4-$O$-$\beta$-Laminaribiosyl-D-glucose<br>$O$-$\beta$-D-glucopyranosyl-(1→3)-$O$-$\beta$-D-gluco-<br>pyranosyl-(1→4)-D-glucose | 229—231 | $+18·7° \to +13·0°$ | 71 |
| 6-$O$-$\beta$-Laminaribiosyl-D-glucose<br>$O$-$\beta$-D-glucopyranosyl-(1→3)-$O$-$\beta$-D-glu-<br>copyranosyl-(1→6)-D-glucose | 216—217 | $-6·0°$ | 22, 26, 28 |
| 3-$O$-$\alpha$-Maltosyl-D-glucose<br>$O$-$\alpha$-D-glucopyranosyl-(1→4)-$O$-$\alpha$-D-glu-<br>copyranosyl-(1→3)-D-glucose | not given | not given | 70 |
| 3-$O$-$\beta$-Cellobiosyl-D-glucose<br>$O$-$\beta$-D-glucopyranosyl-(1→4)-$O$-$\beta$-D-glu-<br>copyranosyl-(1→3)-D-glucose | 236—239 | $+16·5° \to +11·7°$ | 71—73 |

*Table XXXIX — continued*

| Trisaccharide | Melting Point °C | $[\alpha]_D(H_2O)$ | References |
|---|---|---|---|
| 3-*O*-α-Isomaltosyl-D-glucose *O*-α-D-glucopyranosyl-(1→6)-*O*-α-D-glucopyranosyl-(1→3)-D-glucose | not given | not given +150° +151·9° | 74, 75 76 77 |
| 3-*O*-β-Gentiobiosyl-D-glucose *O*-β-D-glucopyranosyl-(1→6)-*O*-β-D-glucopyranosyl-(1→3)-D-glucose | | — 4·2° | 22, 26, 28 78 |
| Panose 4-*O*-α-isomaltosyl-D-glucose 6-*O*-α-D-glucopyranosylmaltose *O*-α-D-glucopyranosyl-(1→6)-*O*-α-D-glucopyranosyl-(1→4)-D-glucose | 213 (dec.) 218—219 (dec.) 221 222—224 225 | +154° +150° +163·4° → +153·3° +162° → +154° +155·9° → +153·9° +154° → +152·3° | 53, 54 56 69 57 59 58 |
| Isopanose *O*-α-D-glucopyranosyl-(1→4)-*O*-α-D-glucopyranosyl-(1→6)-D-glucose | | +152° +128° | 113 117 |
| 4-*O*-β-Gentiobiosyl-D-glucose *O*-β-D-glucopyranosyl-(1→6)-*O*-β-D-glucopyranosyl-(1→4)-D-glucose G-G-G | | + 10·3° + 9·45° + 99·4° | 23 79 80 |
| Lycotriose *I* 4-*O*-β-sophorosyl-D-galactose *O*-β-D-glucopyranosyl-(1→2)-*O*-β-glucopyranosyl-(1→4)-D-galactose | 261 251 | +21° → +13·1° +22° → +12·5° | 51 52 |
| 6-*O*-β-Cellobiosyl-D-galactose *O*-β-D-glucopyranosyl-(1→4)-*O*-β-D-glucopyranosyl-(1→6)-D-galactose | | +22·9° → + 9·3° | |
| 4-*O*-β-Cellobiosyl-D-mannose *O*-β-D-glucopyranosyl-(1→4)-*O*-β-D-glucopyranosyl-(1→4)-D-mannose | not given | not given | 32 |
| *O*-β-D-Glucopyranosyl-(1→4)-*O*-β-D-mannopyranosyl-(1→4)-D-mannose G-Man-Man | not given 217 | not given — 16° | 32, 82 83 |
| Isomaltotriulose 6-*O*-α-isomaltosyl-D-fructose *O*-α-D-glucopyranosyl-(1→6)-*O*-α-D-glucopyranosyl-(1→6)-D-fructose | | +118° | 68 |
| *O*-α-D-Mannopyranosyl-(1→2)-*O*-α-D-mannopyranosyl-(1→2)-D-mannose | | + 55° | 84 |
| *O*-α-D-Mannopyranosyl-(1→3)-*O*-α-D-mannopyranosyl-(1→3)-D-mannose | | + 79·8° | 85 |
| *O*-α-D-Mannopyranosyl-(1→4)-*O*-β-D-mannopyranosyl-(1→4)-D-mannose | 224—225 | +43° → +40° | 31 |

*References see p. 274*

*Table XXXIX — continued*

| Trisaccharide | Melting Point °C | $[\alpha]_D(H_2O)$ | References |
|---|---|---|---|
| Mannotriose | | | |
| $O$-$\beta$-D-mannopyranosyl-(1→4)-$O$-$\beta$-D-mannopyranosyl-(1→4)-D-mannose | syrup | −15° | 86, 87 |
| | 230 | −25° | 88 |
| | 208—212 | −12·9° | 114 |
| | 212—213 | −22° | 115 |
| | 165—169 | −25° | 33, 89 |
| | 155—169 | −23° | 82 |
| | 155—165 | −22° → −25° | 90 |
| | 165 | −16° | 30 |
| slowly heated | 169·5 | | 31 |
| rapidly heated | 135·5 | −15·7° → −20·2° | 31 |
| | 137 | −24·7° → −23·3° | 29, 32 |
| | 131—132·5 | −13·5° → −20·3° | 91 |
| $O$-$\alpha$-D-Mannopyranosyl-(1→6)-$O$-$\alpha$-D-mannopyranosyl-(1→6)-D-mannose | | +68° | 92 |
| 4-$O$-$\beta$-Mannobiosyl-D-glucose $O$-$\beta$-D-mannopyranosyl-(1→4)-$O$-$\beta$-D-mannopyranosyl-(1→4)-D-glucose | | − 7° | 31, 32, 82 |
| $O$-$\beta$-D-Mannopyranosyl-(1→4)-$O$-$\beta$-D-glucopyranosyl-(1→4)-D-glucose | | + 9·5° | 82 |
| $O$-$\beta$-D-Mannopyranosyl-(1→4)-$O$-$\beta$-D-glucopyranosyl-(1→4)-D-mannose | not given | not given | 32 |
| Inulotriose* 1-$O$-$\beta$-D-fructofuranosylinulobiose $O$-$\beta$-D-fructofuranosyl-(2→1)-$O$-$\beta$-D-fructofuranosyl-(2→1)-D-fructose | | − 41° | 93, 94 |
| $O$-$\beta$-D-Galactopyranosyl-(1→3)-$O$-$\alpha$-D-galactopyranosyl-(1→3)-D-galactose | 239 (dec.) | +146° | 95 |
| $O$-$\beta$-D-Galactopyranosyl-(1→3)-$O$-$\beta$-D-galactopyranosyl-(1→3)-D-galactose | 115—120 | + 39·0° | 96 |
| Galactotriose $O$-$\beta$-D-galactopyranosyl-(1→4)-$O$-$\beta$-D-galactopyranosyl-(1→4)-D-galactose | | + 58° | 32, 36 |
| $O$-$\beta$-D-Galactopyranosyl-(1→6)-$O$-$\beta$-D-galactopyranosyl-(1→6)-D-galactose | | + 20° | 97, 98 |
| | 158—163 | + 22° | 99 |
| | 148—150 | + 5° | 100 |
| Gal-Gal-Gal | | | 101 |
| 6-$O$-$\beta$-Lactosyl-D-galactose $O$-$\beta$-D-galactopyranosyl-(1→4)-$O$-$\beta$-D-glucopyranosyl-(1→6)-D-galactose | amorphous | + 22·2° | 81 |
| 6-$O$-$\beta$-Lactosyl-D-glucose $O$-$\beta$-D-galactopyranosy-(1→4)-$O$-$\beta$-D-glucopyranosyl-(1→6)-D-glucose | 257 (dec.) | +34·7° → +22·6° | 102 |

* Another fructotriose with $\beta$, 1→2 linkages has been prepared by hydrolysis of lycorisin; the identity of this fructotriose (m. p. 109—110°C, $[\alpha]_D$ −58·4°) with inulotriose is doubtful, see T. Mizuno, Kagaku (Tokyo) *31*, 146 (1961); Chem. Abstr. *55*, 27099 (1961).

*Table XXXIX — continued*

| Trisaccharide | Melting Point.°C | $[\alpha]_D(H_2O)$ | References |
|---|---|---|---|
| 6-O-β-D-Galactopyranosyl-lactose O-β-D-galactopyranosyl-(1→6)-O-β-D-galactopyranosyl-(1→4)-D-glucose | 187 | +34° | 103, 104 |
| O-D-Galactosyl-lactose Lactotriose | not given | not given | 62 |
| lactosyl-D-galactose or D-galactosyl-lactose | not given | not given | 60, 61 |
| Manninotriose O-α-D-galactopyranosyl-(1→6)-O-α-D-galactopyranosyl-(1→6)-D-glucose, trihydrate | amorphous | +167° +174·6° +140° → +150° +154·7° +158·9° | 43 44, 45 46, 47 48, 49 50 |
| O-β-D-Galactopyranosyl-(1→6)-O-β-D-galactopyranosyl-(1→6)-D-glucose | not given | not given | 103, 105 |
| O-α-D-Gagalactopyranosyl-(1→6)-O-α-D-galactopyranosyl-(1→1)-D-fructose | | +104·2° | 106 |
| O-α-D-Galactopyranosyl-(1→6)-O-α-D-galactopyranosyl-(1→6)-D-fructose | | +126·8° → +131·7° | 107 |
| O-α-D-Galactopyranosyl-(1→6)-O-α-D-galactopyranosyl-(1→6)-D-mannose | | +119° | 107 |
| O-α-D-Galactopyranosyl-(1→6)-O-α-D-mannopyranosyl-(1→6)-D-mannose | not given | not given | 32 |
| O-β-D-Galactopyranosyl-(1→6)-O-β-D-galactopyranosyl-(1→3)-L-arabinose | 190—191 | | 97, 98 |
| L-Ara-L-Ara-L-Ara | | −35° | 99 |
| O-?-L-Arabinofuranosyl-(1→3)-O-β-D-xylopyranosyl-(1→4)-D-xylose | amorphous | −19·3° −15·3° | 108 109 |
| Xylotriose 4-O-β-xylobiosyl-D-xylose O-β-D-xylopyranosyl-(1→4)-O-β-D-xylopyranosyl-(1→4)-D-xylose | 214 206 204·5 | +48°? −39·4° → −47° −44·4° −44° | 40 38 39 41, 110 |
| O-β-D-Xylopyranosyl-(1→3)-O-β-D-xylopyranosyl-(1→4)-D-xylose | 225 (dec.) | −52° → −47° | 110 |
| O-α-D-Xylopyranosyl-(1→6)-O-β-D-glucopyranosyl-(1→4)-D-glucose | 147—150 | +150° | 82 |
| Lycotriose II O-β-D-xylopyranosyl-(1→3)-O-β-D-glucopyranosyl-(1→4)-D-galactose | 175—180 | + 6° | 52 |
| O-β-D-Galactopyranosyl-(1→4)-O-β-D-xylopyranosyl-(1→2)-L-arabinose | | + 20° | 116 |
| O-?-L-Galactopyranosyl-(1→4)-O-?-D-xylopyranosyl-(1→2)-L-arabinose | 215 | − 38° | 111 |
| L-Ara-G-Man | not given | not given | 82 |
| L-Ara-L-Ara-Gal | not given | not given | 82 |
| L-Ara-L-Ara-Xyl | | +59° | 112 |
| L-Ara-L-Ara-Xyl | | +49° | 112 |

*References see p. 274*

## REFERENCES

1. J. M. Sugihara and M. L. Wolfrom, J. Am. Chem. Soc. *71*, 3357 (1949).
2. J. H. Pazur and T. Budovich, Science *121*, 702 (1955); Chem. Abstr. *49*, 11736 (1955).
3. J. H. Pazur, J. Am. Chem. Soc. *77*, 1015 (1955).
4. M. L. Wolfrom, L. W. Georges, A. Thompson, and I. L. Miller, J. Am. Chem. Soc. *71*, 2873 (1949).
5. D. French, M. L. Levine, J. H. Pazur, and E. Norberg, J. Am. Chem. Soc. *72*, 1746 (1950).
6. W. J. Whelan, J. M. Bailey, and P. J. P. Roberts, J. Chem. Soc. *1953*, 1293.
7. R. L. Whistler and J. H. Duffy, J. Am. Chem. Soc. *77*, 1017 (1955).
8. K. Hess and K. Dziengel, Ber. *68*, 1594 (1935).
9. R. Willstätter and L. Zechmeister, Ber. *62*, 722 (1929).
10. E. E. Dickey and M. L. Wolfrom, J. Am. Chem. Soc. *71*, 825 (1949).
11. M. L. Wolfrom and J. C. Dacons, J. Am. Chem. Soc. *74*, 5331 (1952).
12. L. Zechmeister and G. Tóth, Ber. *64*, 854 (1931).
13. E. T. Reese, E. Smakula, and A. S. Perlin, Arch. Biochem. Biophys. *85*, 171 (1959).
14. A. Beélik and J. K. Hamilton, J. Org. Chem. *26*, 5074 (1961).
15. G. Bertrand and S. Benoit, Bull. soc. chim. France (4) *33*, 1451 (1923).
16. N. K. Richtmyer and C. S. Hudson, J. Am. Chem. Soc. *61*, 1834 (1939).
17. J. H. Pazur and D. French, J. Biol. Chem. *196*, 265 (1952).
18. A. Jeanes, C. A. Wilham, J. K. N. Jones, H. M. Tsuchiya, and C. E. Rist, J. Am. Chem. Soc. *75*, 5911 (1953).
19. G. Avigad, Biochem. J. *73*, 587 (1959).
20. G. O. Phillips and G. J. Moody, J. Chem. Soc. *1958*, 3534.
21. R. W. Jones, D. J. Dimler, and C. E. Rist, J. Am. Chem. Soc. *77*, 1659 (1955).
22. S. Peat, W. J. Whelan, and T. E. Edwards, J. Chem. Soc. *1958*, 3862.
23. M. de Leizaola-Tripier, Compt. rend. *250*, 407 (1960).
24. K. Shibasaki, Tôhoku J. Agr. Research *6*, 47 (1955); Chem. Abstr. *50*, 11693 (1956).
25. K. Shibasaki, J. Agr. Chem. Soc. Japan *39*, 764 (1955); Chem. Abstr. *50*, 11693 (1956).
26. S. Peat, W. J. Whelan, and J. M. Evans, J. Chem. Soc. *1960*, 175.
27. S. Peat, W. J. Whelan, and H. G. Lawley, J. Chem. Soc. *1958*, 724.
28. S. Peat, W. J. Whelan, and H. G. Lawley, J. Chem. Soc. *1958*, 729.
29. R. L. Whistler and C. G. Smith, J. Am. Chem. Soc. *74*, 3795 (1952).
30. M. E. Henderson, L. Hough, and T. J. Painter, J. Chem. Soc. *1958*, 3519.
31. G. O. Aspinall, R. B. Rashbrook, and G. Kessler, J. Chem. Soc. *1958*, 215.
32. H. Meier, Acta Chem. Scand. *14*, 749 (1960).
33. A. Tymynski and T. E. Timell, J. Am. Chem. Soc. *82*, 2823 (1960).
34. J. K. N. Jones and T. J. Painter, J. Chem. Soc. *1957*, 669.
35. J. K. Hamilton and H. W. Kircher, J. Am. Chem. Soc. *80*, 4703 (1958).
36. H. O. Bouveng and H. Meier, Acta Chem. Scand. *13*, 1884 (1959).
37. F. Smith and A. M. Stephen, J. Chem. Soc. *1961*, 4892.
38. R. L. Whistler and Chen Chuan Tu, J. Am. Chem. Soc. *74*, 3609 (1952).
39. C. T. Bishop, Can. J. Chem. *33*, 1073 (1955).
40. J. K. N. Jones and L. E. Wise, J. Chem. Soc. *1952*, 2750.
41. M. Ewald and A. S. Perlin, Can. J. Chem. *37*, 1254 (1959).
42. P. J. Howard, Biochem. J. *67*, 643 (1957).
43. C. Tanret, Bull. soc. chim. France (3) *27*, 947 (1902).

44. M. Onuki, Sci. Papers Inst. Phys. Chem. Research *18*, 357 (1932).
45. M. Onuki, Sci. Papers Inst. Phys. Chem. Research *20*, 201 (1933); Chem. Abstr. *27*, 3454 (1933).
46. C. Neuberg and S. Lachmann, Biochem. Z. *24*, 174 (1910).
47. H. Bierry, Biochem. Z. *44*, 446 (1912).
48. J. E. Courtois, A. Wickström, and P. Le Dizet, Bull. soc. chim. biol. *34*, 1121 (1952).
49. J. E. Courtois, A. Wickström, and P. Le Dizet, Bull. soc. chim. biol. *35*, 1117 (1953).
50. J. E. Courtois, A. Wickström, P. Fleury, and P. Le Dizet, Bull. soc. chim. biol. *37*, 1009 (1955).
51. R. Kuhn and I. Löw, Chem. Ber. *86*, 1027 (1953).
52. R. Kuhn, I. Löw, and H. Trischmann, Chem. Ber. *90*, 203 (1957).
53. S. C. Pan, L. W. Nicholson, and C. Kolachow, J. Am. Chem. Soc. *73*, 2547 (1951).
54. D. French, Science *113*, 352 (1951).
55. M. L. Wolfrom, A. Thompson, and T. T. Galkowski, J. Am. Chem. Soc. *73*, 4093 (1951).
56. J. H. Pazur and D. French, J. Biol. Chem. *196*, 265 (1952).
57. M. Killey, R. J. Dimler, and J. E. Cluskey, J. Am. Chem. Soc. *77*, 3315 (1955).
58. S. A. Barker and T. R. Carrington, J. Chem. Soc. *1953*, 3588.
59. R. W. Bailey, S. A. Barker, E. J. Bourne, and M. Stacey, J. Chem. Soc. *1957*, 3536.
60. K. Wallenfels, E. Bernt, and G. Limberg, Ann. *584*, 63 (1953).
61. K. Wallenfels, E. Bernt, and G. Limberg, Ann. *579*, 113 (1953).
62. A. Ballio, E. B. Chain, and F. B. DiAccadia, Gazz. chim. ital. *87*, 194 (1957); Chem. Abstr. *52*, 13818 (1958).
63. P. A. J. Gorin and J. F. T. Spencer, Can. J. Chem. *37*, 499 (1959).
64. H. H. Schlubach and E. Lühre, Ann. *547*, 73 (1941).
65. P. A. J. Gorin, J. F. T. Spencer, and D. W. S. Westlake, Can. J. Chem. *39*, 1067 (1961).
66. R. L. Whistler and J. H. Duffy, J. Am. Chem. Soc. *77*, 1017 (1955).
67. A. Beélik and J. K. Hamilton, J. Org. Chem. *26*, 5074 (1961).
68. G. Avigad, Biochem. J. *73*, 587 (1959).
69. A. Sato, Y. Ito, and H. Ono, Chem. & Ind. (London) *1962*, 301.
70. S. A. Barker, E. J. Bourne, D. M. O'Mant, and M. Stacey, J. Chem. Soc. *1957*, 2448.
71. A. S. Perlin and S. Suzuki, Can. J. Chem. *40*, 50 (1962).
72. F. W. Parrish, A. S. Perlin, and E. T. Reese, Can. J. Chem. *38*, 2094 (1960).
73. H. Ono and M. Dazai, Nature *183*, 1055 (1959).
74. J. H. Pazur, T. Budovich, and C. L. Tipton, J. Am. Chem. Soc. *79*, 625 (1957).
75. I. J. Goldstein and W. J. Whelan, J. Chem. Soc. *1962*, 170.
76. M. Abdullah, I. J. Goldstein, and W. J. Whelan, J. Chem. Soc. *1962*, 176.
77. A. Sato and H. Ono, Chem. & Ind. (London) *1962*, 1536.
78. J. R. Turvey and J. M. Evans, J. Chem. Soc. *1960*, 2366.
79. S. A. Barker, E. J. Bourne, and M. Stacey, Chem. & Ind. (London) *1953*, 1287.
80. H. H. Schlubach and E. Lühre, Ann. *547*, 73 (1941).
81. K. Freudenberg, A. Wolf, E. Knopf, and S. H. Zaheer, Ber. *61*, 1743 (1928).
82. O. Perila and C. T. Bishop, Can. J. Chem. *39*, 815 (1961).
83. K. Nishida and H. Hashima, J. Dept. Agr. Kyushu Imp. Univ. *2*, 277 (1930); Chem. Abstr. *25*, 498 (1931).
84. P. A. J. Gorin and A. S. Perlin, Can. J. Chem. *35*, 262 (1957).
85. A. Jeanes, J. E. Pittsley, P. R. Watson, and J. H. Sloneker, Can. J. Chem. *40*, 2256 (1962).
86. J. K. Hamilton and H. W. Kircher, J. Am. Chem. Soc. *80*, 4703 (1958).

87. A. K. Mukherjee, D. Choudhury, and P. Bagchi, Can. J. Chem. *39*, 1408 (1961).
88. A. J. Mian and T. E. Timell, Can J. Chem. *38*, 1511 (1960).
89. M. O. Gyaw and T. E. Timell, Can. J. Chem. *38*, 1957 (1960).
90. J. K. N. Jones and T. J. Painter, J. Chem. Soc. *1957*, 669.
91. G. O. Aspinall, R. Begbie, and J. E. McKay, J. Chem. Soc. *1962*, 214.
92. S. Peat, W. J. Whelan, and T. E. Edwards, J. Chem. Soc. *1961*, 29.
93. S. Hestrin, D. S. Feingold, and G. Avigad, Biochem. J. *64*, 340 (1956).
94. D. S. Feingold and G. Avigad, Biochim. et Biophys. Acta *22*, 196 (1956).
95. K. Morgan and A. N. O'Neill, Can. J. Chem. *37*, 1201 (1959).
96. F. May and H. Weinland, Hoppe-Seyler's Z. physiol. Chem. *305*, 207 (1956).
97. G. O. Aspinall, B. J. Auret, and E. L. Hirst, J. Chem. Soc. *1958*, 4408.
98. G. O. Aspinall and T. B. Christensen, J. Chem. Soc. *1961*, 3461.
99. F. Smith and A. M. Stephen, J. Chem. Soc. *1961*, 4891.
100. H. Meier, Acta Chem. Scand. *16*, 2275 (1962).
101. P. A. J. Gorin and J. F. T. Spencer, Can. J. Chem. *37*, 499 (1959).
102. B. Helferich and W. Schäfer, Ann. *450*, 229 (1926).
103. J. H. Pazur, J. Biol. Chem. *208*, 439 (1954).
104. A. Ballio and S. Russi, Tetrahedron 9, 125 (1960).
105. J. H. Pazur, J. M. Marsh, and C. L. Tipton, J. Am. Chem. Soc. *80*, 1433 (1958).
106. A. Wickström, J. E. Courtois, P. Le Dizet, and A. Archambault, Bull. soc. chim. France *1959*, 871.
107. A. de Grandchamp-Chaudun, J. E. Courtois, and P. Le Dizet, Bull. soc. chim. biol. *42*, 227 (1960).
108. C. T. Bishop, J. Am. Chem. Soc. *78*, 2840 (1956).
109. G. O. Aspinall, I. M. Cairncross, R. J. Sturgeon, and K. C. B. Wilkie, J. Chem. Soc. *1960*, 3881.
110. P. J. Howard, Biochem. J. *67*, 643 (1957).
111. R. L. Whistler and W. M. Corbett, J. Am. Chem. Soc. *77*, 6328 (1955).
112. P. Andrews and J. K. N. Jones, J. Chem. Soc. *1954*, 4134.
113. H. O. Bouveng, H. Kiessling, B. Lindberg, and J. McKay, Acta Chem. Scand. *17*, 797 (1963).
114. T. E. Timell, Tappi *45*, 799 (1962); Chem. Abstr. *59*, 2922 (1963).
115. T. E. Timell, Svensk Papperstid *65*, 843 (1962); Chem. Abstr. *59*, 729 (1963).
116. G. O. Aspinall, I. M. Cairncross, and K. M. Ross, J. Chem. Soc. *1963*, 1721.
117. W. Sowa, A. C. Blackwood, and G. A. Adams, Can. J. Chem. *41*, 2314 (1963).

## C. BRANCHED REDUCING TRISACCHARIDES

The synthesis of branched reducing trisaccharides is undoubtedly possible; however, experiments in this respect were undertaken relatively late. They were probably initiated by the establishment of the structure of the branched reducing trisaccharide solanose (solatriose, see Chapter XXII). The first attempts to synthesize branched reducing trisaccharides were made with appropriately substituted glycosides of reducing trisaccharides[1,2] and led to derivatives of branched reducing trisaccharides.

Branched reducing trisaccharides as such were first obtained by enzymic syntheses.[3-5] Shortly afterwards, purely chemical syntheses were employed for the preparation of 3,6-di-$O$-$\beta$-D-glucopyranosyl-D-glucose,[6-8] identical with the trisaccharide Y from laminarin, as well as of 4-$O$-$\alpha$-6-$O$-$\beta$-di-D-glucopyranosyl-D-glucose[9,10] (I); it was found[11] that the hydrolysis of both glycosidic linkages of this trisaccharide proceeds more slowly than the splitting of both corresponding reducing disaccharides, namely maltose and gentiobiose.

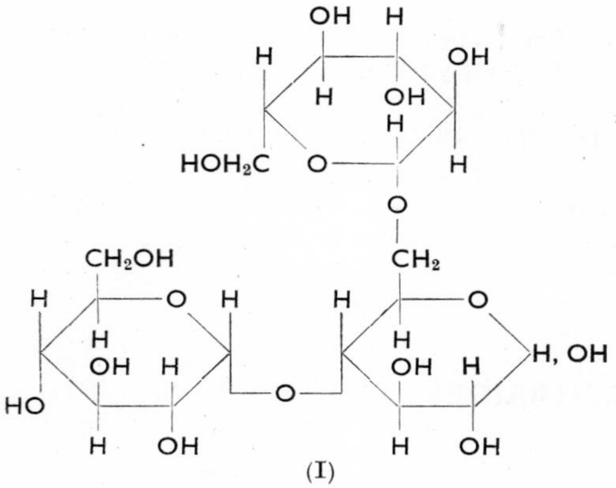

(I)

New branched reducing trisaccharides have been prepared by chemical syntheses. Thus, 3,5-di-$O$-$\beta$-D-glucopyranosyl-D-xylose has been described as a crisp, white, hygroscopic glass with $[\alpha]_D$ — 30° ($H_2O$), see J. K. N. Jones and P. E. Reid, Can. J. Chem. *41*, 2382 (1963). Another branched reducing trisaccharide, 4,6-di-$O$-$\alpha$-D-glucopyranosyl-D-glucose exhibits $[\alpha]_D$ + 125° ($H_2O$), see R. de Souza and I. J. Goldstein, Tetrahedron Letters *1964*, 1215.

**Table XL**

Physical Properties of Reducing Branched Trisaccharides

| Branched Trisaccharide | Melting Point °C | $[\alpha]_D (H_2O)$ | References |
|---|---|---|---|
| $O$-$\beta$-D-Glucopyranosyl-(1→4)-$O$-[$\alpha$-D-glucopyranosyl-(1→2)]-D-glucose | | + 93° | 4 |
| $O$-$\beta$-D-Galactopyranosyl-(1→4)-$O$-[$\alpha$-D-glucopyranosyl-(1→2)]-D-glucose labelled | | +103° | 3, 4 <br> 5 |
| $O$-$\beta$-D-Glucopyranosyl-(1→6)-$O$-[$\beta$-D-glucopyranosyl-(1→3)]-D-glucose laminarin trisaccharide X | | not given | 6 |
| 3,6-Di-$O$-$\beta$-D-glucopyranosyl-D-glucose $O$-$\beta$-D-glucopyranosyl-(1→6)-$O$-[$\beta$-D-glucopyranosyl-(1→3)]-D-glucose | 197—199 | —0·6° | 7, 8 |
| 4-$O$-$\alpha$-6-$O$-$\beta$-Di-D-glucopyranosyl-D-glucose $O$-$\alpha$-D-glucopyranosyl-(1→4)-$O$-[$\beta$-D-glucopyranosyl-(1→6)]-D-glucose | | +84° <br> +83° | 9 <br> 10 |

*References see p. 278*

### REFERENCES

1. A. Klemer, Chem. Ber. *89*, 2583 (1956).
2. A. Klemer, Angew. Chem. *69*, 638 (1957).
3. R. W. Bailey, S. A. Barker, E. J. Bourne, P. M. Grant, and M. Stacey, Nature *176*, 1164 (1955).
4. R. W. Bailey, S. A. Barker, E. J. Bourne, P. M. Grant, and M. Stacey, J. Chem. Soc. *1958*, 1895.
5. E. J. Bourne, J. Hartigan, and H. Weigel, J. Chem. Soc. *1959*, 2332.
6. J. R. Turvey and J. M. Evans, J. Chem. Soc. *1960*, 2366.
7. A. Klemer and K. Homberg, Chem. Ber. *93*, 1643 (1960).
8. A. Klemer and K. Homberg, Chem. Ber. *94*, 2747 (1961).
9. A. Klemer, Chem. Ber. *92*, 218 (1959).
10. I. J. Goldstein and B. Lindberg, Acta Chem. Scand. *16*, 383 (1962).
11. A. Klemer, Tetrahedron Letters *1960*, No. 22, 5.

## 3. TETRASACCHARIDES

### A. NON-REDUCING TETRASACCHARIDES

Stachyose,[*][1-20]    $O$-α-D-galactopyranosyl-(1→6)-$O$-α-D-galactopyranosyl-(1→6)-$O$-α-D-glucopyranosyl-(1→2) β-D-fructofuranoside (lupeose, manneotetrose, β-galactan, or also digalactosylsucrose, I),[1] is a tetrasaccharide known for a long time. Various procedures of its isolation from ash manna, from the rhizomes of *Stachys tuberifera* or powdered defatted soyabean meal have been very well described.[16,19]

Onuki in 1932 found by exact cryoscopic measurements[2,3] that this compound is a tetrasaccharide; other papers have shown[4-6,12] that the hydrolysis of stachyose definitely yields a molecule of D-fructose and a molecule of manninotriose. However, the first structure derived by Onuki[7,8] was incorrect at the place of the linkage between the central D-galactose unit and D-glucose; Onuki employed here his erroneously derived structure of manninotriose. The constitution of stachyose was correctly established as late as 1953[9] by methylation analysis, and these results are in full agreement with those of periodic acid oxidation.[10,11]

The other non-reducing tetrasaccharides have been isolated from *Lychnis dioica*.[**] These are first of all lychnose,[21-27] $O$-α-D-galactopyranosyl-(1→6)-$O$-α-D-glucopyranosyl-(1→2)-$O$-β-D-fructofuranosyl-(1→1) α-D-galactopyranoside (II) and, as well as this, isolychnose,[28] which was described later and differs from lychnose only in the linkage between the D-galactose and D-

---

\* For a review see D. French, Advances in Carbohydrate Chem. *9*, 174 (1954).

\*\* For a review see J. E. Courtois, Bull. soc. chim. biol. *42*, 1451 (1960).

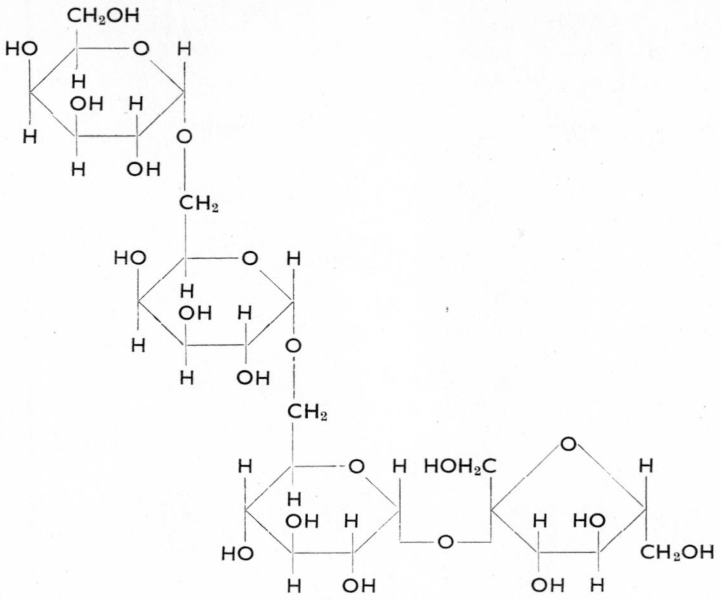


(I)

fructose units. The substance has the structure (III), i. e. *O*-α-D-galactopyranosyl-(1→6)-*O*-α-D-glucopyranosyl-(1→2)-*O*-β-D-fructofuranosyl-(3→1) α-D-galactopyranoside.

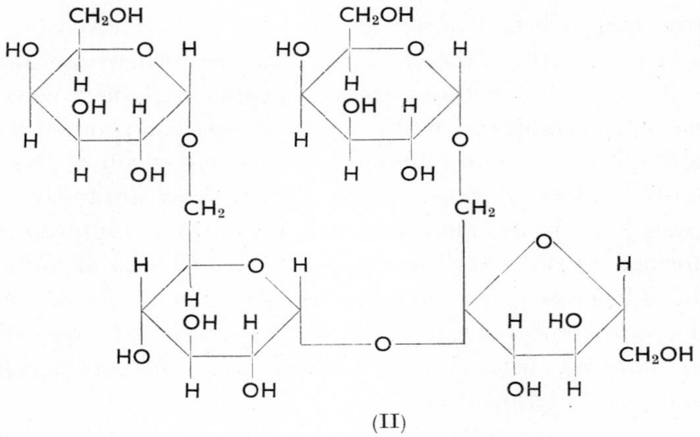


(II)

It is probable that a further tetrasaccharide, containing two D-galactose molecules, one D-glucose molecule and one D-fructose molecule, termed sesamose,[27] is isomeric with lychnose.[28] The structure of this substance was given

*References see p. 281*

(III)

as $O$-$\alpha$-D-galactopyranosyl-$(1\to6)$-$O$-$\alpha$-D-galactopyranosyl-$(1\to6)$-$O$-$\beta$-D-fructofuranosyl-$(2\to1)$ $\alpha$-D-glucopyranoside.[27] Another isomer may be a non-reducing tetrasaccharide obtained by enzymic synthesis,[29] which could be termed provisionally D-galactosylplanteose.

The structures of other described non-reducing tetrasaccharides are less clear. A tetrasaccharide is known which contains two D-fructose molecules, one D-galactose molecule and one D-glucose molecule; it was isolated from wheat flour[30] and named D-fructosylraffinose. Further, there are known substances with a still higher D-fructose content, several of them consisting of three D-fructose molecules and one D-glucose molecule. The product which was designated as fungitetraose[31] and whose structure was given as $O$-$\alpha$-D-glucopyranosyl-$(1\to2)$-$O$-$\beta$-D-fructofuranosyl-$(1\to2)$-$O$-$\beta$-D-fructofuranosyl-$(1\to2)$ $\beta$-D-fructofuranoside[31] may be identical with inulotriosyl-D-glucose;[32] another substance formed by an enzymic process from sucrose and containing three molecules of D-fructose per one molecule of D-glucose[33] may, according to its value of specific rotation, be identical with fungitetraose. The information available about a substance designated as di-D-fructosylsucrose[34] is not sufficient for an exact definition.

One non-reducing tetrasaccharide containing four D-fructose molecules is also known under the name scodorose,[35-37] with either $2\to2$, $6\to2$, $6\to2$ or $2\to6$, $2\to6$, $6\to2$ linkages.[37]

Still less exactly defined is a tetrasaccharide isolated from Jerusalem artichoke juice.[38]

## Table XLI
### Physical Properties of Non-reducing Tetrasaccharides

| Tetrasaccharide | Melting Point °C | $[\alpha]_D(H_2O)$ | References |
|---|---|---|---|
| Stachyose<br>di-*O*-D-galactosylsucrose<br>*O*-α-D-galactopyranosyl-(1→6)-*O*-α-D-galacto-<br>pyranosyl-(1→6)-*O*-α-D-glucopyranosyl-(1→2)<br>β-D-fructofuranoside | 170<br>152 | +146·3° | 4, 5, 13, 15<br>16 |
| | | +102° | 9 |
| pentahydrate | 105 | +131·3° | 17, 18, 20 |
| Lychnose<br>*O*-α-D-galactopyranosyl-(1→6)-*O*-α-D-glucopyra-<br>nosyl-(1→2)-*O*-β-D-fructofuranosyl-(1→1) α-D-<br>galactopyranoside | | +153°<br>+150° | 22, 23<br>24 |
| Isolychnose<br>*O*-α-D-galactopyranosyl-(1→6)-*O*-α-D-glucopyra-<br>nosyl-(1→2)-*O*-β-D-fructofuranosyl-(3→1) α-D-<br>galactopyranoside | | | 28 |
| Fungitetraose[31]<br>inulotriosylglucose[32]<br>*O*-α-D-glucopyranosyl-(1→2)-*O*-β-D-fructofurano-<br>syl-(1→2)-*O*-β-D-fructofuranosyl-(1→2) β-D-<br>fructofuranoside | 115<br>85 | + 25·4°<br>+ 17·9°<br>+ 16·7° | 31<br>31 |
| Scodorose (tetrafructoside) | | | 35 — 37 |
| Sesamose<br>*O*-α-D-galactopyranosyl-(1→6)-*O*-α-D-galactopy-<br>ranosyl-(1→6)-*O*-β-D-fructofuranosyl-(2→1)<br>α-D-glucopyranoside | | | 27 |
| Difructosylsucrose | | | 34 |
| Fructosylraffinose | | | 33 |
| Galactosylplanteose | | | 28 |
| Difructosylxylsucrose | | | 33 |

## REFERENCES

1. H. Hérissey, P. Fleury, A. Wickström, J. E. Courtois, and P. Le Dizet, Compt. rend. *239*, 824 (1954).
2. M. Onuki, Proc. Imp. Acad. (Tokyo) *8*, 496 (1932).
3. M. Onuki, Sci. Papers Inst. Phys. Chem. Research (Tokyo) *20*, 201 (1933).
4. C. Tanret, Compt. rend. *134*, 1586 (1902).
5. C. Tanret, Bull. soc. chim. France (3) *27*, 947 (1902).
6. C. Tanret, Bull. soc. chim. France (3) *29*, 888 (1903).
7. M. Onuki, J. Agr. Chem. Soc. Japan *8*, 445 (1932); Chem. Abstr. *26*, 4308 (1932).
8. M. Onuki, J. Agr. Chem. Soc. Japan *9*, 90 (1933); Chem. Abstr. *27*, 2138 (1933).
9. R. A. Laidlaw and C. B. Wylam, J. Chem. Soc. *1953*, 567.

10. H. Hérissey, A. Wickström, and J. E. Courtois, Bull. soc. chim. biol. *33*, 642 (1951).
11. H. Hérissey, A. Wickström, and J. E. Courtois, Bull. soc. chim. biol. *34*, 856 (1952).
12. L. Piault, Bull. pharm. chim. (7) *1*, 248 (1910).
13. H. Bierry, Biochem. Z. *44*, 446 (1912).
14. A. Planta and E. Schulze, Ber. *23*, 1692 (1890).
15. A. Planta and E. Schulze, Ber. *24*, 2705 (1891).
16. A. K. Mitra and A. S. Perlin, Can. J. Chem. *35*, 1079 (1957).
17. M. L. Wolfrom, R. C. Burrell, A. Thompson, and S. S. Furst, J. Am. Chem. Soc. *74*, 6299 (1952).
18. D. French, P. M. Wild and W. J. James, J. Am. Chem. Soc. *75*, 3664 (1953).
19. D. French, Advances in Carbohydrate Chem. *9*, 174 (1954).
20. R. S. Shallenberger, Chem. & Ind. (London) *1961*, 475.
21. A. Archambault, J. E. Courtois, A. Wickström, and P. Le Dizet, Compt. rend. *242*, 2875 (1956).
22. A. Archambault, J. E. Courtois, A. Wickström, and P. Le Dizet, Bull. soc. chim. biol. *38*, 1121 (1956).
23. A. Archambault, J. E. Courtois, A. Wickström, and P. Le Dizet, Bull. soc. chim. biol. *38*, 1133 (1956).
24. A. Wickström, J. E. Courtois, P. Le Dizet, and A. Archambault, Bull. soc. chim. France *1958*, 1410.
25. A. Wickström, J. E. Courtois, P. Le Dizet, and A. Archambault, Compt. rend. *246*, 1624 (1958); Chem. Abstr. *52*, 18230 (1958).
26. A. Archambault, J. E. Courtois, A. Wickström, and P. Le Dizet, Can. Pharm. J., Sci. Sect. *91*, 419 (1958); Chem. Abstr. *53*, 3603 (1959).
27. L. S. Hatanaka, Arch. Biochem. Biophys. *82*, 188 (1959).
28. A. Wickström, J. E. Courtois, P. Le Dizet, and A. Archambault, Bull. soc. chim. France *1959*, 871.
29. J. H. Pazur, J. M. Marsh, and C. L. Tipton, J. Biol. Chem. *233*, 277 (1958).
30. L. M. White and G. E. Secor, Arch. Biochem. Biophys. *44*, 244 (1953).
31. H. Kurasawa, Y. Yamamoto, I. Igaue, and Y. Nakamura, J. Agr. Chem. Soc. Japan *30*, 696 (1956); Chem. Abstr. *52*, 20376 (1958).
32. J. H. Pazur, J. Biol. Chem. *199*, 217 (1952).
33. S. A. Barker and T. R. Carrington, J. Chem. Soc. *1953*, 3588.
34. S. Hestrin, D. S. Feingold, and G. Avigad, Biochem. J. *64*, 340 (1956).
35. Y. Kihara, J. Agr. Chem. Soc. Japan *12*, 1044 (1936); Chem. Abstr. *31*, 3013 (1937).
36. Y. Kihara, J. Agr. Chem. Soc. Japan *13*, 363 (1937); Chem. Abstr. *31*, 8605 (1937).
37. Y. Kihara, J. Agr. Chem. Soc. Japan *15*, 348 (1939); Chem. Abstr. *34*, 385 (1940).
38. I. R. Rominskiĭ, A. S. Sushkova, and A. V. Il'ina, Ukrain. Khim. Zhur. *24*, 236 (1958); Chem. Abstr. *52*, 15663 (1958).

## B. REDUCING TETRASACCHARIDES

This group contains no substances of any great importance, requiring treatment in a special chapter. In the majority of cases, these tetrasaccharides are continuations of the homologous series of known disaccharides and trisaccharides. Such compounds are, for example, maltotetraose,[1-9] also named amylotetraose,[9] cellotetraose,[10-16] isomaltotetraose (dextrantetraose),[17] gentiotetraose,[18] laminaritetraose,[19] galactotetraose,[20,21] mannotetraose,[22-24] and xylotetraose.[25,26] More interesting among the other compounds is verbas-cotetraose,[27,28] *O*-α-D-galactopyranosyl-(1→6)-*O*-α-D-galactopyranosyl-(1→6)-*O*-α-D-galactopyranosyl-(1→6)-D-glucose, a splitting product of verbascose.

The structure of these substances was established by routine methods (methylation analysis, periodic acid oxidation, further splitting by acids and by means of enzymes). The physico-chemical constants of these compounds together with those of less exactly known tetrasaccharides and tetrasaccharides of unknown structure are listed in Table XLII.

Evidently, a new reducing tetrasaccharide has been prepared from lactose by the action of *Sporobolomyces singularis* enzymes, see P. A. J. Gorin, J. F. T. Spencer, and H. J. Phaff, Can. J. Chem. *42*, 1341 (1964). The compound in question, i. e. *O*-β-D-galacto-pyranosyl-(1→4)-*O*-β-D-galactopyranosyl-(1→4)-*O*-β-D-galactopyranosyl-(1→4)-D-glucose has been described with $[\alpha]_D + 43°$ ($H_2O$).

**Table XLII**

Physical Properties of Reducing Tetrasaccharides

| Tetrasaccharide | Melting Point °C | $[\alpha]_D$ ($H_2O$) | References |
|---|---|---|---|
| Sophorotetraose<br>*O*-β-D-glucopyranosyl-(1→2)-*O*-β-D-glucopyra-<br>nosyl-(1→2)-*O*-β-D-glucopyranosyl-<br>(1→2)-D-glucose | | + 10° | 29 |
| Laminaritetraose<br>*O*-β-D-glucopyranosyl-(1→3)-*O*-β-D-glucopyra-<br>nosyl-(1→3)-*O*-β-D-glucopyranosyl-<br>(1→3)-D-glucose | | − 5·9° | 19 |
| Maltotetraose, amylotetraose[9]<br>*O*-α-D-glucopyranosyl-(1→4)-*O*-α-D-glucopy-<br>ranosyl-(1→4)-*O*-α-D-glucopyranosyl-<br>(1→4)-D-glucose | | +165·5°<br>+177°<br>+176° | 4<br>5<br>7, 8 |
| Cellotetraose<br>*O*-β-D-glucopyranosyl-(1→4)-*O*-β-D-glucopy-<br>ranosyl-(1→4)-*O*-β-D-glucopyranosyl-<br>(1→4)-D-glucose | 253 (dec.)<br><br>256—257 | +11·3° → +17°<br>+ 8·4° → +16·5°<br>+ 11·6°<br>+ 16° | 10, 11<br>12<br>14<br>16 |
| Isomaltotetraose, dextrantetraose<br>*O*-α-D-glucopyranosyl-(1→6)-*O*-α-D-glucopy-<br>ranosyl-(1→6)-*O*-α-D-glucopyranosyl-<br>(1→6)-D-glucose | amorphous | +153° | 17 |
| Gentiotetraose<br>*O*-β-D-glucopyranosyl-(1→6)-*O*-β-D-glucopy-<br>ranosyl-(1→6)-*O*-β-D-glucopyranosyl-<br>(1→6)-D-glucose | | − 15·9° | 18 |
| 4-*O*-α-Isomaltotriosyl-D-glucose<br>4-*O*-α-dextrantriosyl-D-glucose<br>*O*-α D-glucopyranosyl(1→6)-*O*-α-D-gluco-<br>pyranosyl-(1→6)-*O*-α-D-glucopyranosyl-<br>(1→4)-D-glucose | | +134° | 17, 30, 31 |

*References see p. 285*

*Table XLII — continued*

| Tetrasaccharide | Melting Point °C | $[\alpha]_D(H_2O)$ | References |
|---|---|---|---|
| **3-O-β-Cellobiosylcellobiose** <br> O-β-D-glucopyranosyl-(1→4)-O-β-D-glucopy-pyranosyl-(1→3)-O-β-D-glucopyranosyl-(1→4)-D-glucose | 223—226 | | 32, 33 |
| **4-O-β-Laminaribiosylcellobiose** <br> O-β-D-glucopyranosyl-(1→3)-O-β-D-glucopyranosyl-(1→4)-O-β-D-glucopyranosyl-(1→4)-D-glucose | 187—188 | | 32, 33 |
| Mannotetraose <br> O-β-D-mannopyranosyl-(1→4)-O-β-D-mannopyranosyl-(1→4)-O-β-D-mannopyranosyl-(1→4)-D-mannose | 235—250 <br><br> 232—234 | -- 28° <br> — 31° <br> — 31° | 22 <br> 23 <br> 24, 34 |
| O-α-D-Mannopyranosyl-(1→6)-O-α-D-mannopyranosyl-(1→6)-O-α-D-mannopyranosyl-(1→6)-D-mannose | | + 70° | 35 |
| G-G-Man-Man | 237—238 | | 36 |
| Galactotetraose <br> O-β-D-galactopyranosyl-(1→4)-O-β-D-galactopyranosyl-(1→4)-O-β-D-galactopyranosyl-(1→4)-D-galactose | | + 53° | 20 |
| O-β-D-Galactopyranosyl-(1→6)-O-β-D-galactopyranosyl-(1→6)-O-β-D-galactopyranosyl-(1→6)-D-galactose | | + 14° <br> + 16° | 37 <br> 38, 39 |
| O-β-D-Galactopyranosyl-(1→6)-O-β-D-galactopyranosyl-(1→4)-O-β-D-galactopyranosyl-(1→6)-D-galactose | 132—140 <br> 176—178 | + 37° | 39 <br> 39 |
| Verbascotetraose <br> O-α-D-galactopyranosyl-(1→6)-O-α-D-galactopyranosyl-(1→6)-O-α-D-galactopyranosyl-(1→6)-D-glucose | | +191·4° | 27, 28 |
| O-β-D-Galactopyranosyl-(1→6)-O-β-D-galactopyranosyl-(1→6-O-β-D-galactopyranosyl-(1→3)-L-arabinose | 167—172 | | 37, 40 |
| Gal-Gal-Gal-Gal | | | 41 |
| Gal-Gal-Gal-G | | +161·0° | 42 |
| Inulotetraose* <br> O-β-D-fructofuranosyl-(2→1)-O-β-D-fructofuranosyl-(2→1)-O-β-D-fructofuranosyl-(2→1)-D-fructose | | | 43 |
| Xylotetraose <br> O-β-D-xylopyranosyl-(1→4)-O-β-D-xylopyranosyl-(1→4)-O-β-D-xylopyranosyl-(1→4)-D-xylose | 220 | −48·8° → −60° <br> −57·8° | 25 <br> 26 |
| O-β-D-Xylopyranosyl-(1→4)-O-β-D-xylopyranosyl-(1→3)-O-β-D-xylopyranosyl-(1→4)-D-xylose | | −56·7° | 44 |

* A tetrasaccharide containing D-fructose only has been described as one of the hydrolysis products of lycorisin. The compound with m. p. 115—117°C and $[\alpha]_D$ −43·7° may be identical with inulotetraose, see T. Mizuno, Kagaku (Tokyo) *31*, 146 (1961); Chem. Abstr. *55*, 27099 (1961).

## REFERENCES

1. B. Venkataraman and F. J. Reithel, Arch. Biochem. Biophys. *75*, 443 (1958); Chem. Abstr. *52*, 16502 (1958).
2. W. H. Fishman and Hsien-Gieh Sie, J. Am. Chem. Soc. *80*, 121 (1958).
3. J. Büchi and R. Gräub, Pharm. Acta Helv. *33*, 547 (1958).
4. R. L. Whistler and J. L. Hickson, J. Am. Chem. Soc. *76*, 1671 (1954).
5. W. J. Whelan, J. M. Bailey, and P. J. Roberts, J. Chem. Soc. *1953*, 1293.
6. R. L. Whistler and J. L. Hickson, J. Am. Chem. Soc. *76*, 1671 (1954).
7. D. French, Ch. L. Levine, and J. H. Pazur, J. Am. Chem. Soc. *71*, 356 (1949).
8. R. L. Whistler and J. H. Duffy, J. Am. Chem. Soc. *77*, 1017 (1955).
9. J. H. Pazur, J. Am. Chem. Soc. *77*, 1015 (1955).
10. R. Willstätter and L. Zechmeister, Ber. *62*, 722 (1929).
11. L. Zechmeister and G. Tóth, Ber. *64*, 854 (1931).
12. M. L. Wolfrom and J. C. Dacons, J. Am. Chem. Soc. *74*, 5331 (1952).
13. E. E. Dickey and M. L. Wolfrom, J. Am. Chem. Soc. *71*, 825 (1949).
14. W. M. Corbett and J. Kenner, J. Chem. Soc. *1955*, 1431.
15. R. Stack and T. K. Walker, Nature *180*, 201 (1957).
16. A. Beélik and J. K. Hamilton, J. Org. Chem. *26*, 5074 (1961).
17. K. Shibasaki, J. Agr. Chem. Soc. Japan *32*, 133 (1958); Chem. Abstr. *53*, 498 (1959).
18. S. Peat, W. J. Whelan, and T. E. Edwards, J. Chem. Soc. *1958*, 3862.
19. S. Peat, W. J. Whelan, and H. G. Lawley, J. Chem. Soc. *1958*, 724.
20. H. O. Bouveng and H. Meier, Acta Chem. Scand. *13*, 1884 (1959).
21. F. Smith and A. M. Stephen, J. Chem. Soc. *1961*, 4892.
22. H. Meier, Acta Chem. Scand. *14*, 749 (1960).
23. G. O. Aspinall, R. B. Rashbrook, and G. Kessler, J. Chem. Soc. *1958*, 215.
24. A. Tymynski and T. E. Timell, J. Am. Chem. Soc. *82*, 2823 (1960).
25. R. L. Whistler and Chen Chuan Tu, J. Am. Chem. Soc. *74*, 3609 (1952).
26. C. T. Bishop, Can. J. Chem. *33*, 1073 (1955).
27. S. Murakami, Acta Phytochim. *11*, 213 (1940).
28. S. Murakami, Acta Phytochim. *13*, 161 (1943).
29. P. A. J. Gorin, J. F. T. Spencer, and D. W. S. Westlake, Can. J. Chem. *39*, 1067 (1961).
30. J. H. Pazur and D. French, J. Biol. Chem. *196*, 265 (1952).
31. K. Shibasaki and K. Aso, J. Fermentation Technol. (Japan) *31*, 311 (1953); Chem. Abstr. *48*, 7109 (1954).
32. F. W. Parrish, A. S. Perlin, and E. T. Reese, Can. J. Chem. *38*, 2094 (1960).
33. A. S. Perlin and S. Suzuki, Can. J. Chem. *40*, 50 (1962).
34. M. O. Gyaw and T. E. Timell, Can. J. Chem. *38*, 1957 (1960).
35. S. Peat, W. J. Whelan, and T. E. Edwards, J. Chem. Soc. *1961*, 29.
36. A. J. Mian and T. E. Timell, Can. J. Chem. *38*, 1511 (1960).
37. G. O. Aspinall, D. J. Auret, and E. L. Hirst, J. Chem. Soc. *1958*, 4408.
38. F. Smith and A. M. Stephen, J. Chem. Soc. *1961*, 4892.
39. H. Meier, Acta Chem. Scand. *16*, 2275 (1962).
40. G. O. Aspinall and T. B. Christensen, J. Chem. Soc. *1961*, 3461.
41. P. A. J. Gorin and J. F. T. Spencer, Can. J. Chem. *37*, 499 (1959).
42. J. E. Courtois, A. Wickström, P. Fleury, and P. Le Dizet, Bull. soc. chim. biol. *37*, 1009 (1955).
43. J. H. Pazur and A. L. Gordon, J. Am. Chem. Soc. *75*, 3458 (1953).
44. B. H. Howard, Biochem. J. *67*, 643 (1957).

## C. BRANCHED TETRASACCHARIDES

This group contains some noteworthy compounds isolated in recent years from natural material. Lycotetraose (I)[1] is a branched reducing tetrasaccharide contained in the glycoalkaloid tomatine, where it is glycosidically bound to the aglycon tomatidine; this tetrasaccharide is composed of two D-glucose molecules, one D-galactose molecule and one D-xylose molecule. Its structure has been established by the investigation of the hydrolysis of the permethylated tomatine derivative.[1] It was found that lycotetraose is $O$-$\beta$-D-xylopyranosyl-$(1\rightarrow3)$-$O$-$[\beta$-D-glucopyranosyl-$(1\rightarrow2)]$-$O$-$\beta$-D-glucopyranosyl-$(1\rightarrow4)$-D-galactose.[1] This substance melts with decomposition at 188°C, and its specific optical rotation is $[\alpha]_D +2°$ ($H_2O$).

(I)

Some interesting branched non-reducing tetrasaccharides occurring as natural products have been described in recent years;[2-4] the tetrasaccharide bifurcose,[2-4] m. p. 156°C[2] and $[\alpha]_D +8.0°$[2,4] or $+8.3°$,[3,5] having the structure (II),[2-4] is a D-fructosyl derivative of the non-reducing trisaccharide kestose (see Chapter XII, 2, A). Its structure can be represented as $O$-$\alpha$-D-glucopyranosyl-$(1\rightarrow2)$-$O$-$[\beta$-D-fructofuranosyl-$(2\rightarrow1)]$-$O$-$\beta$-D-fructofuranosyl-$(6\rightarrow2)$ $\beta$-D-fructofuranoside.

Another, less well known branched non-reducing tetrasaccharide, namely *neo*-bifurcose (III), $[\alpha]_D +14.4°$, is a D-fructosyl derivative of the non-reducing trisaccharide *neo*-kestose (see Chapter XII, 2, A) and may be designated structurally as $O$-$\beta$-D-fructofuranosyl-$(2\rightarrow6)$-$O$-$[\beta$-D-fructofuranosyl-$(2\rightarrow2)]$-$O$-$\alpha$-D-glucopyranosyl-$(1\rightarrow2)$ $\beta$-D-fructofuranoside.

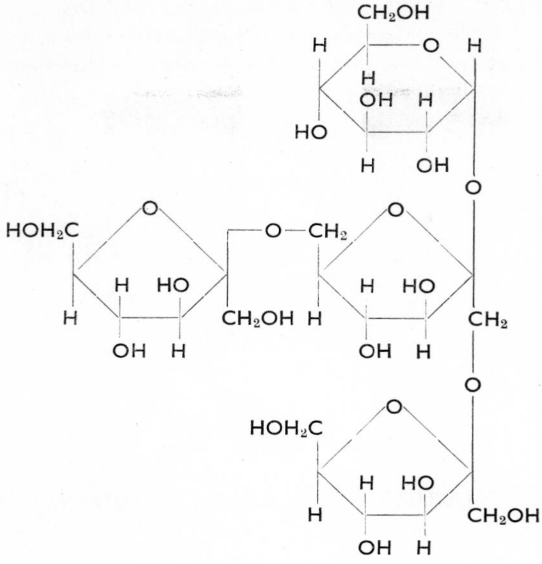

(II)

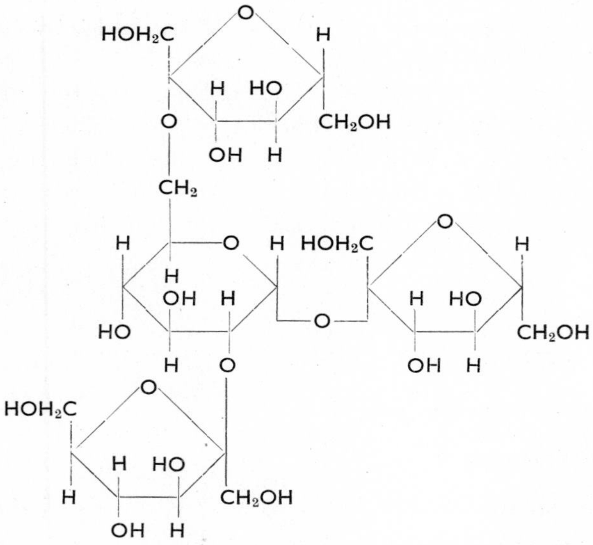

(III)

New branched reducing tetrasaccharides have been described recently. A. Klemer and F. Gundlach, Chem. Ber *96*, 1765 (1963), prepared synthetically 6,6'-di-*O*-β-D-glucopyranosylmaltose, $[\alpha]_D + 40°$ (H$_2$O). Another branched reducing tetrasaccharide,

*References see p. 288*

$O$-$\alpha$-L-arabinofuranosyl-$(1\rightarrow3)$-$O$-$[\beta$-D-xylopyranosyl-$(1\rightarrow4)]$-$O$-$\alpha$-D-xylopyranosyl-$(1\rightarrow4)$-D-xylose with $[\alpha]_D - 75°$ ($H_2O$) has been prepared from the soluble arabino-xylan of wheat via enzymic degradation by the action of a *Streptomyces* xylanase, see H. R. Goldschmid and A. S. Perlin, Can. J. Chem. *41*, 2272 (1963).

### REFERENCES

1. R. Kuhn, I. Löw, and H. Trischmann, Chem. Ber. *90*, 203 (1957).
2. H. H. Schlubach and H. O. A. Koehn, Ann. *614*, 126 (1958).
3. H. H. Schlubach and F. Lederer, Ann. *635*, 154 (1960).
4. H. H. Schlubach and J. Berndt, Ann. *647*, 41 (1961).
5. H. H. Schlubach, J. Berndt, and T. Chiemprasert, Ann. *665*, 191 (1963).

## 4. PENTASACCHARIDES, HEXASACCHARIDES, ETC.

### A. HOMOLOGOUS SERIES OF OLIGOSACCHARIDES

In the preceding chapters it was noted that some types of linkages observed in disaccharides occur repeatedly in the series of tri- and tetrasaccharides (see cellobiose, cellotriose, cellotetraose and, similarly, xylobiose, xylotriose, xylotetraose, etc.). These compounds are often obtained as hydrolytic products from regularly built higher oligosaccharides or polysaccharides, such as starch, cellulose, dextran and xylans, which on hydrolysis yield fragments of various molecular weights. This phenomenon is also noticeable in higher oligosaccharides, which may be divided into several distinctly separated groups.

### a) Homogeneous oligosaccharides

#### Substances containing D-glucose only

##### Homologous series of maltose

From the syrups remaining after the enzymic hydrolysis of starch may be obtained, besides maltose, also maltotriose (amylotriose, see Chapter XII, 2, B) and maltotetraose (see Chapter XII, 3, B). The syrup also contains, however, higher reducing oligosaccharides with $\alpha,1\rightarrow4$ linkages, such as maltopentaose (amylopentaose),[1-4] maltohexaose (amylohexaose)[1,4,5] and maltoheptaose.[4] The increases in the values of the specific rotations occur in this series as follows:

### Table XLIII

Homologous Series of Maltose

| Oligosaccharide | $[\alpha]_D(H_2O)$ | References |
|---|---|---|
| Maltose | +136·0° | 4 |
| Maltotriose | +152·0° | 3 |
| | +160·0° | 4 |
| Maltotetraose | +176·4° | 3 |
| | +177·0° | 4 |
| Maltopentaose | +180·3° | 4 |
| | +175·0° | 2 |
| | +179·4° | 3 |
| Maltohexaose | +184·7° | 4 |
| | +177·0° | 2 |
| | +182·0° | 5 |
| Maltoheptaose | +186·4° | 4 |
| | +178·5° | 2 |

#### Homologous series of cellobiose

Homologous reducing oligosaccharides with $\beta,1{\to}4$ linkages have been described by Wolfrom and Dacons,[6] who give exact constants for cellopentaose, cellohexaose and celloheptaose and state that the cellohexaose described by Zechmeister[7] corresponds in its composition to this substance, while Staudinger's cellohexaose[8] is in fact cellotetraose. The physico-chemical constants of the higher members in this group are:

### Table XLIV

Homologous Series of Cellobiose

| Oligosaccharide | Melting Point °C | $[\alpha]_D(H_2O)$ | References |
|---|---|---|---|
| Cellobiose | 228—229 | +33·3° | 9 |
| Cellotriose | 205—207 | +22·4° | 9 |
| Cellotetraose | 256—257 | +16° | 9 |
| Cellopentaose | 268·5 | +12·4° | 9 |
| | 266—268 | +8° → +11° | 6 |
| Cellohexaose* | 275—278 | +10° | 6 |
| Celloheptaose | 286 (dec.) | +7° ± 3° | 6 |

* A hexasaccharide from the human placenta, see S. Akiya and M. Tomoda, J. Pharm. Soc. Japan *76*, 1092 (1956); Chem. Abstr. *51*, 1406 (1957), is supposed to contain D-glucose, with $\beta,1{\to}4$ bonds only. However, it is very difficult to classify this compound as cellohexaose.

#### Homologous series of laminaribiose

Some members of the homologous series of laminaribiose are also known, namely D-glucose-containing reducing oligosaccharides with $\beta,1{\to}3$ linkages.[10] The physico-chemical constants of this series are:

*References see p. 294*

19 — The Oligosaccharides

**Table XLV**

Homologous Series of Laminaribiose

| Oligosaccharide | $[\alpha]_D (H_2O)$ | References |
|---|---|---|
| Laminaribiose | $+20 \cdot 4°$ | 10 |
| Laminaritriose | $+ 2 \cdot 4°$ | 10 |
| Laminaritetraose | $- 5 \cdot 9°$ | 10 |
| Laminaripentaose | $-10 \cdot 3°$ | 10 |

## Substances containing D-galactose only

Oligosaccharides of this group are less exactly defined. Besides a trisaccharide with $\beta, 1 \rightarrow 4$ linkages, termed galactotriose (see p. 268), the corresponding galactotetraose has been described.[11] Higher members named galactopentaose, [12,13] galactohexa-, galactohepta- and galacto-octaose,[13] have not been established with certainty.

## Substances containing D-xylose only

The homologous series of xylobiose* is well known, and higher oligosaccharides of this type have been described in two cases.[14,15] Their physical constants are:

**Table XLVI**

Homologous Series of Xylobiose

| Oligosaccharide | Melting Point °C | $[\alpha]_D (H_2O)$ | References |
|---|---|---|---|
| Xylotriose | 205—206 | $-39 \cdot 4° \rightarrow -47°$ | 14 |
| | 204—205 | $-44 \cdot 4°$ | 15 |
| | 215—216 | $-48 \cdot 1°$ | 53 |
| Xylotetraose | 219—220 | $-48 \cdot 8° \rightarrow -60°$ | 14 |
| | | $-57 \cdot 8°$ | 15 |
| | 224—225 | $-61 \cdot 9°$ | 53 |
| Xylopentaose ($\frac{1}{2}$ $H_2O$) | 231—232 | $-66°$ | 14 |
| | | $-62 \cdot 4°$ | 15 |
| | 240—242 | $-72 \cdot 9°$ | 53 |
| Xylohexaose (2 $H_2O$) | 236—237 | $-72 \cdot 8°$ | 14 |
| | | $-70°$ | 15 |
| | 237—238 | $-78 \cdot 5°$ | 53 |
| Xyloheptaose | 240—242 | $-71 \cdot 3°$ | 15 |
| Xylooctaose** | | $-25 \cdot 2°$ | 15 |

* For a review see A. Roudier, Bull. soc. chim. biol. *42*, 1493 (1960).
** Xylooctaose contains[14] some different glycosidic bonds.

## b) Heterogeneous oligosaccharides

### D-*Galactosyl derivatives of* D-*glucose*

As indicated by Murakami,[16–18] the D-fructose molecule can be hydrolytic-ally eliminated from the molecule of the D-galactosyl derivative of sucrose with the formation of D-galactosyl derivatives of D-glucose; this is obvious, for example, in the formation of verbascotetraose from verbascose. The galactosyl derivatives of sucrose[19] can be degraded in this way to the corresponding ga-lactosyl derivatives of D-glucose,[20] as proved using oligosaccharides from *Verbascum thapsiforme.** The substances isolated, together with manninotriose, which genetically belongs to this group, form a series with very distinctly rising values of specific rotation.[21]

### Table XLVII

Homologous Series of D-Galactosyl Derivatives of D-Glucose

| Oligosaccharide | $[\alpha]_D(H_2O)$ | References |
|---|---|---|
| Manninotriose (di-D-galactosyl-D-glucose) | $+158 \cdot 9°$ | 21 |
| Tri-D-galactosyl-D-glucose | $+161 \cdot 0°$ | 21 |
| Tetra-D-galactosyl-D-glucose | $+172 \cdot 4°$ | 21 |
| Penta-D-galactosyl-D-glucose | $+181 \cdot 1°$ | 21 |
| Hexa-D-galactosyl-D-glucose | $+190 \cdot 4°$ | 21 |

### D-*Galactosyl derivatives of sucrose*

#### Genetic series of raffinose**

Besides the non-reducing trisaccharide raffinose (D-galactopyranosylsucro-se) and the tetrasaccharide stachyose (di-D-galactopyranosylsucrose),[22] higher oligosaccharides also are known containing three, four and more molecules of D-galactose linked to the sucrose molecule.

Verbascose (tri-D-galactosylsucrose, I), $O$-α-D-galactopyranosyl-$(1\rightarrow6)$-$O$-α-D-galactopyranosyl-$(1\rightarrow6)$-$O$-α-D-galactopyranosyl-$(1\rightarrow6)$-$O$-α-D-glucopy-ranosyl-$(1\rightarrow2)$ β-D-fructofuranoside, is a non-reducing pentasaccharide, which was obtained in 1910 from the roots of the mullein (*Verbascum thapsus*).[23] Its constitution was investigated as late as 1940 by Murakami,[16–18] who, on the basis of cryoscopic measurements, defined the product as a pentasaccharide and determined its character by means of methylation analysis. Murakami then succeeded in the hydrolytic elimination of the D-fructose molecule and obtained the reducing tetrasaccharide verbascotetraose (II), $O$-α-D-galactopyranosyl-

---

* For a review see J. E. Courtois, Bull. soc. chim. biol. *42*, 1451 (1960).
** For a review see D. French, Advances in Carbohydrate Chem. *9*, 149 (1954).

*References see p. 294*

$(1 \rightarrow 6)$-*O*-α-D-galactopyranosyl-$(1 \rightarrow 6)$-*O*-α-D-galactopyranosyl-$(1 \rightarrow 6)$-D-glu-cose.

(I)                                                                      (II)

By a systematic investigation of the oligosaccharides in *Verbascum thapsus*, French chemists[24] arrived at the conclusion that this source contains five su-crose galactosides, namely digalactosylsucrose, i. e. stachyose, trigalactosyl-sucrose, i. e. verbascose, tetragalactosylsucrose, i. e. ajugose, pentagalactosyl-sucrose and hexagalactosylsucrose.

Of these compounds, tetragalactosylsucrose[24-27] is identical with ajugose[25] isolated by Murakami from *Ajuga nipponensis*; the identity of both these sub-stances was recently proved with certainty.[28] The same oligosaccharide is con-tained in *Vicia sativa*,[20-29] in *Salvia pratensis*[29] and in *Ajuga nipponensis*.[30]

The question of higher oligosaccharides of this type is less clear; probably they are D-galactosyl derivatives of sucrose with a regular *O*-α-D-galactopyra-nosyl-$(1 \rightarrow 6)$ linkage.[31] Substances of the type of pentagalactosylsucrose,[24,29,32] hexagalactosylsucrose[27],[29] and heptagalactosylsucrose [33] have as yet been classified in general only. The properties of all these substances are given in the following Table XLVIII:

**Table XLVIII**

Homologous Series of D-Galactosyl Derivatives of Sucrose

| Oligosaccharide | $[\alpha]_D(H_2O)$ | References |
|---|---|---|
| D-Galactosylsucrose, raffinose | see Table XXXVIII | |
| Di-D-galactosylsucrose, stachyose | see Table XLI | |
| Tri-D-galactosylsucrose, verbascose | $+169 \cdot 9°$ | 23 |
|   m. p. 219°C,[23] 253°C[17] | $+170°$ | 17 |
| | $+148°$ | 20 24, 34 |
| Tetra-D-galactosylsucrose, ajugose | $+161 \cdot 3°$ | 24 |
| | $+160 \cdot 5°$ | 27, 32 |
| | $+190 \cdot 8°$ | 25 |
| Penta-D-galactosylsucrose | $+169 \cdot 1°$ | 24 |
| | $+167 \cdot 5°$ | 32 |
| | $+168°$ | 29 |
| Hexa-D-galactosylsucrose | $+168 \cdot 7°$ | 24 |

### Genetic series of lychnose and isolychnose

The oligosaccharides isolated from *Lychnis dioica* also form a homologous series, connected to the tetrasaccharides lychnose and isolychnose.[34-38] The situation is here rather unclear because the oligosaccharides contained in the plant often vary depending on the season.[31] A pentasaccharide of $[\alpha]_D +180.4°$, isolated recently,[37] has the structure $O$-α-D-galactopyranosyl-$(1{\rightarrow}6)$-$O$-α-D-glucopyranosyl-$(1{\rightarrow}2)$-$O$-β-D-fructofuranosyl-$(1{\rightarrow}1)$-$O$-α-D-galactopyranosyl-$(6{\rightarrow}1)$ α-D-galactopyranoside.

Higher oligosaccharides (from penta- to octasaccharides) of the same type were recently isolated from *Cucubalus baccifer*[39],[40] and *Dianthus caryophyllus*.[41]

### Genetic series of D-fructosyl derivatives of sucrose

The D-fructosyl derivatives of sucrose, for which the name oligofructosides* was created, will evidently form the basis of a new series of non-reducing oligosaccharides. Bifurcose[42-44] and *neo*-bifurcose[44] are connected to the known initial members of this new series, kestose and *neo*-kestose (see p. 260). Besides them, the papers in question mention briefly the corresponding pentasaccharide,[42],[43] hexasaccharide[43] and higher members.[43]

---

\* For a review see J. S. D. Bacon, Bull. soc. chim. biol. *42*, 1441 (1960).

*References see p. 294*

## 5. HIGHER OLIGOSACCHARIDES OF UNKNOWN STRUCTURE

In addition to the compounds mentioned, many others are known in less detail. This applies to 4-$O$-α-isomaltotetraosyl-D-glucose,[45] maltotriosyl- and maltotetraosylsucrose,[46] D-fructosylsucrose[47] and tri-D-fructosylxylsucrose.[47] Acid hydrolysis of gum ghatti yields higher reducing oligosaccharides containing two to four D-galactose molecules per one L-arabinose molecule.[11]

Less information is available about other oligosaccharides; arctose[48] is said to be a non-reducing hexafructoside, and asparagose[49] is regarded as a fructoside with seven or eight D-fructose units, probably in cyclic linkage.

Hemicelluloses are believed to be potential sources of oligosaccharides.* It is also known that a number of oligosaccharides (di-, tri- up to hepta-), containing D-xylose and L-arabinose can be isolated from wheat straw xylan.[50] The constitutions of two members only of this series have as yet been established.

Golden apple gum may be autohydrolysed to a mixture of oligosaccharides. The structures of two of them, 3-$O$-β-L-arabinopyranosyl-L-arabinose and 3-$O$-β-D-xylopyranosyl-L-arabinose have been established; from the other golden apple gum oligosaccharides, three, on hydrolysis, yield L-arabinose only. Another two trisaccharides contain two molecules of L-arabinose and one molecule of D-xylose each.[51] A homologous series of oligosaccharides of the type $O$-β-D-galactopyranosyl-[$(1 \rightarrow 6)$-$O$-β-D-galactopyranosyl]$_n$-$(1 \rightarrow 3)$-L-arabinose has been obtained recently from *Anogeissus shimperi* gum.[52] Oligosaccharides with $n = 0$ to 3 were isolated.[11,52]

### REFERENCES

1. J. H. Pazur, J. Am. Chem. Soc. *77*, 1015 (1955).
2. J. H. Pazur and T. Budovich, J. Biol. Chem. *220*, 25 (1956).
3. R. L. Whistler and J. H. Duffy, J. Am. Chem. Soc. *77*, 1017 (1955).
4. W. J. Whelan, J. M. Bailey, and P. J. P. Roberts, J. Chem. Soc. *1953*, 1293.
5. R. L. Whistler and B. F. Moy, J. Am. Chem. Soc. *77*, 5761 (1955).
6. M. L. Wolfrom and J. C. Dacons, J. Am. Chem. Soc. *74*, 5331 (1952).
7. L. Zechmeister and G. Tóth, Ber. *64*, 854 (1931).
8. H. Staudinger and E. O. Leopold, Ber. *67*, 479 (1934).
9. A. Beélik and J. K. Hamilton, J. Org. Chem. *26*, 5074 (1961).
10. S. Peat, W. J. Whelan, and H. G. Lawley, J. Chem. Soc. *1958*, 724.
11. G. O. Aspinall, D. J. Auret, and E. L. Hirst, J. Chem. Soc. *1958*, 4408.
12. P. A. J. Gorin and J. F. Spencer, Can. J. Chem. *37*, 499 (1959).
13. H. O. Bouveng and H. Meier, Acta Chem. Scand. *13*, 1884 (1959).
14. R. L. Whistler and Chen Chuan Tu, J. Am. Chem. Soc. *74*, 3609 (1952).
15. C. T. Bishop, Can. J. Chem. *33*, 1073 (1955).
16. S. Murakami, Acta Phytochim. *11*, 213 (1940).

---

* For a review see A. Roudier, Bull. soc. chim. biol. *42*, 1493 (1960).

17. S. Murakami, Proc. Imp. Acad. Tokyo *16*, 12 (1940); Chem. Abstr. *34*, 3694 (1940).
18. S. Murakami, Acta Phytochim. *13*, 161 (1943).
19. A. Wickström, Medd. Norsk Farm. Selskap *18*, 129 (1956); Chem. Abstr. *51*, 17210 (1957).
20. J. E. Courtois, A. Archambault, and P. Le Dizet, Bull. soc. chim. biol. *38*, 351 (1956).
21. J. E. Courtois, A. Wickström, P. Fleury, and P. Le Dizet, Bull. soc. chim. biol. *37*, 1009 (1955).
22. D. French, Advances in Carbohydrate Chem. *9*, 149 (1954).
23. E. Bourquelot and M. Bridel, Compt. rend. *151*, 760 (1910).
24. H. Hérissey, P. Fleury, A. Wickström, J. E. Courtois, and P. Le Dizet, Compt. rend. *239*, 824 (1943); Chem. Abstr. *49*, 11565 (1955).
25. S. Murakami, Acta Phytochim. *12*, 97 (1941).
26. J. E. Courtois, A. Archambault, and P. Le Dizet, Bull. soc. chim. biol. *38*, 359 (1956).
27. A. Archambault, J. E. Courtois, A. Wickström, and P. Le Dizet, Bull. soc. chim. biol. *38*, 1121 (1956).
28. J. E. Courtois, G. Dillemann, and P. Le Dizet, Ann. pharm. franç. *18*, 17 (1960); Chem. Abstr. *54*, 13549 (1960).
29. H. Hérissey, P. Fleury, A. Wickström, J. E. Courtois, and P. Le Dizet, Bull. soc. chim. biol. *36*, 1507 (1954).
30. J. E. Courtois, G. Dillemann, and P. Le Dizet, Ann. pharm. franç. *18*, 17 (1960).
31. J. E. Courtois, Bull. soc. chim. biol. *42*, 1451 (1960).
32. J. E. Courtois, A. Archambault, and P. Le Dizet, Bull. soc. chim. biol. *38*, 1117 (1956).
33. S. Hattori and S. Hatanaka, The Botanical Magazine (Tokyo) *71*, 417 (1958).
34. J. E. Courtois, A. Archambault, and P. Le Dizet, Bull. soc. chim. biol. *38*, 1121 (1956).
35. A. Wickström, J. E. Courtois, P. Le Dizet, and A. Archambault, Compt. rend. *247*, 1911 (1958); Chem. Abstr. *53*, 11527 (1959).
36. J. E. Courtois, P. Le Dizet, and A. Wickström, Bull. soc. chim. biol. *40*, 1059 (1958).
37. A. Wickström, J. E. Courtois, P. Le Dizet, and A. Archambault, Bull. soc. chim. France *1959*, 871.
38. J. E. Courtois, P. Le Dizet, and J. Davy, Bull. soc. chim. biol. *42*, 351 (1960).
39. J. E. Courtois and U. Ariyoshi, Bull. soc. chim. biol. *42*, 737 (1960).
40. J. E. Courtois, and U. Ariyoshi, Bull. soc. chim. biol. *44*, 31 (1962).
41. J. E. Courtois and U. Ariyoshi, Bull. soc. chim. biol. *44*, 23 (1962).
42. H. H. Schlubach and H. O. A. Koehn, Ann. *614*, 126 (1958).
43. H. H. Schlubach and F. Lederer, Ann. *635*, 154 (1960).
44. H. H. Schlubach and J. Berndt, Ann. *647*, 41 (1961).
45. K. Shibasaki, J. Agr. Chem. Soc. Japan *32*, 133 (1958); Chem. Abstr. *53*, 498 (1959).
46. J. P. Wolf and W. H. Ewart, Arch. Biochem. Biophys. *58*, 365 (1955); Chem. Abstr. *50*, 2883 (1956).
47. S. Hestrin, D. S. Feingold, and G. Avigad, Biochem. J. *64*, 340 (1956).
48. S. Murakami, Acta Phytochim. *15*, 105 (1949); Chem. Abstr. *43*, 8451 (1949).
49. S. Murakami, Acta Phytochim. *10*, 43 (1937); Chem. Abstr. *31*, 8570 (1937).
50. C. T. Bishop and D. R. Whitaker, Chem. & Ind. (London) 1955, 119.
51. P. Andrews and J. K. N. Jones, J. Chem. Soc. *1954*, 4134.
52. G. O. Aspinall and T. B. Christensen, J. Chem. Soc. *1961*, 3461.
53. R. H. Marchessault and T. E. Timell, J. Polymer. Sci. Pt. C. No 2, 49 (1963); Chem. Abstr. *59*, 8847 (1963)

# XIII

# Esters of Oligosaccharides and Organic Acids

As in the monosaccharide series,[1] esters of various organic acids are also very important in the oligosaccharide group. These esters are usually crystalline compounds with a fairly sharp melting point and can be utilized for identifying even syrupy oligosaccharides. The commonest and most easily obtainable esters are those of acetic acid, in particular per-$O$-acetylated compounds.

## 1. ACETYL DERIVATIVES OF OLIGOSACCHARIDES

### A. PER-$O$-ACETYL DERIVATIVES

Substances of this type are very frequently encountered in the chemistry of oligosaccharides; they are obtainable by various procedures, mainly by direct acetylation of oligosaccharides. In the series of non-reducing oligosaccharides, the acetylation can be carried out by any of the usual procedures, namely by the action of acetic anhydride in the presence of anhydrous sodium acetate, zinc chloride, or pyridine;[2-4] thus it is possible to acetylate, for instance, sucrose[4] or trehalose[5] in the cold; however, difficulties are often caused by the low solubility of some oligosaccharides in pyridine, in which case the acetylation is accelerated either by an addition of dimethylformamide,[6] or by acetylating the non-reducing oligosaccharide in a warmed medium of pyridine and acetic anhydride.[7] This method appears to be more advantageous for sucrose and higher non-reducing oligosaccharides than the recommended acetylation with acetic anhydride in the presence of anhydrous sodium acetate.[4,8-14] A more recent paper also recommends the acetylation of sucrose with acetic anhydride in the presence of Amberlite IR-120[15] by heating the reaction mixture to 55—60°C for 6 hours.

According to a paper by P. S. O'Colla, E. E. Lee, and D. McGrath, Sci. Proc. Roy. Dublin Soc. Ser. A *1*, 337 (1963); Chem. Abstr. *60*, 10768 (1964), acetylation of maltose on Amberlite IR-120 gives the corresponding octa-$O$-acetate in a fairly good yield.

In the series of reducing oligosaccharides, appropriate reaction conditions must be selected for producing either α- or β-anomers. In principle, the acetylation is here governed by the same rules as the formation of per-$O$-acetyl derivatives of monosaccharides;[1] so the reaction with acetic anhydride in the presence of sodium acetate leads to the $\beta$-anomers (see the acetylation of gentiobiose,[16] maltose,[17-19] melibiose,[14,20] lactose,[21] etc.), while acetylation with acetic anhydride in the presence of zinc chloride yields the $\alpha$-anomers (see the acetylation of turanose[22]). The reaction of reducing oligosaccharides with acetic anhydride in pyridine usually gives rise to a mixture of per-$O$-acetyl derivatives,[23-25] although even this method has been successfully applied for the preparation of one of both expected isomers in pure state.[26,27]

Analogously as in the monosaccharide series,[1] the per-$O$-acetyl derivatives of reducing oligosaccharides of the $\beta$-series can be converted into those of the $\alpha$-series by heating with acetic anhydride in the presence of anhydrous zinc chloride. This has been demonstrated using the per-$O$-acetyl derivatives of gentiobiose,[16] cellobiose,[17] maltose[17] and lactose.[21] In the case of the per-$O$-acetyl derivative of *epi*-gentiobiose, such an anomerization has also been achieved[28] in the presence of perchloric acid.

A certain number of per-$O$-acetyl derivatives of oligosaccharides have been obtained in various syntheses (see Chapter VI) from simpler compounds. The splitting of higher oligosaccharides, polysaccharides and heterosides in acetic anhydride under suitable reaction conditions (see Chapters X and XI) likewise gives rise to per-$O$-acetyl derivatives of oligosaccharides. For example, gentiobiose is produced by the action of acetic anhydride and zinc chloride on some heterosides[29-31] or trisaccharides.[32] The acetolysis of polysaccharides is usually carried out with a mixture of acetic anhydride and concentrated sulphuric acid, and this method has been employed for preparing a number of per-$O$-acetyl derivatives of oligosaccharides, such as kojibiose,[33] 3-$O$-$\alpha$-D-galactopyranosyl-D-galactose,[34] 2-$O$-$\alpha$-D-mannopyranosyl-D-mannose,[35] 4-$O$-$\beta$-D-galactopyranosyl-3,6-anhydro-D-galactose,[36] 4-$O$-$\beta$-D-glucopyranosyl-D-mannose,[37] and of some trisaccharides.[34,35] The most important application of this reaction, however, is the several times described acetolysis of cellulose, which leads to the octa-$O$-acetyl derivative of cellobiose.[38-47]

In a few cases it was possible to prepare even a new per-$O$-acetyl derivative from an existing one, namely by anomerization at C-1 of the non-reducing part; this reaction, which was studied mainly by Lindberg[48-50] (see Chapter VI), offers the possibility of converting octa-$O$-acetyl-6-$O$-$\beta$-D-galactopyranosyl-D-glucose (I) by the action of titanium tetrachloride into octa-$O$-acetyl-6-$O$-$\alpha$-D-galactopyranosyl-D-glucose (II) (i. e. a melibiose derivative).[50] The reaction is more complicated, however, because, besides anomerization, it involves the replacement of the hemiacetal acetoxy group by a chlorine atom, which in turn must be replaced by a new acetoxy group by reacting with mercuric acetate. New per-$O$-acetyl derivatives may also be obtained by epimerization (see

Chapter VI), or by a double Walden inversion (see Chapter VI) of other per-*O*-acetyl derivatives.

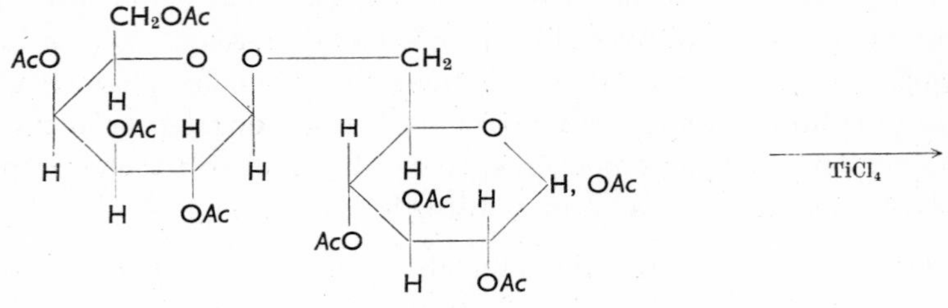

(I)

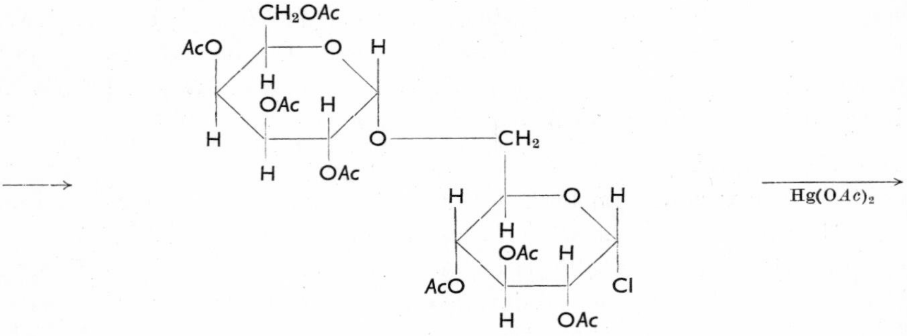

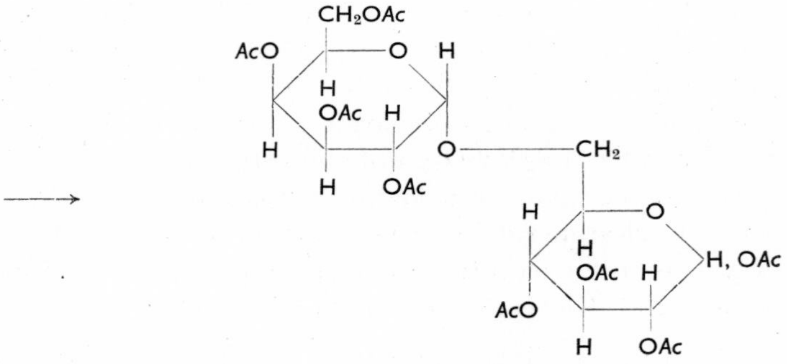

(II)

A less common procedure is that of Brauns,[25] according to which hepta-*O*-acetyl-4-*O*-α-D-glucopyranosyl-α-D-mannopyranosyl chloride is converted into the corresponding α-per-*O*-acetyl derivative by heating with acetic anhydride and zinc chloride.

Although the per-*O*-acetyl derivatives of oligosaccharides are compounds of considerable molecular weight, some of them can be distilled under a high vacuum.[51]

The conversion of per-$O$-acetyl derivatives of oligosaccharides into free oligosaccharides is usually not difficult; the deacetylation of per-$O$-acetyl derivatives of non-reducing oligosaccharides can easily be carried out by the Zemplén method, i. e. by the action of sodium methoxide in methanol,[52-54] or by the reaction with an ethanolic ammonia solution.[55] Per-$O$-acetyl derivatives of reducing oligosaccharides can be converted into free oligosaccharides by application of the Zemplén method in the cold[56,57] or, more advantageously, by using a solution of barium methoxide in methanol,[58-61] or by deacetylation with methanol acidified with concentrated hydrochloric acid.[62]

Oligosaccharide per-$O$-acetates undergo cleavage by the action of perchloric acid in acetic acid with the formation of per-$O$-acetyl derivatives of the corresponding monosaccharides, see H. Bredereck, A. Wagner, G. Hagellock, and G. Faber, Chem. Ber. *91*, 515 (1958).

The reaction of reducing disaccharide per-$O$-acetates with methanolic ammonia has been followed by J. O. Deferrari and R. A. Cadenas, J. Org. Chem. *28*, 1070 (1963), and R. A. Cadenas and J. O. Deferrari, J. Org. Chem. *28*, 1072 (1963). From both lactose and cellobiose acetates the corresponding glycosylamines, their $N$-acetyl and per-$O$-acetyl derivatives have been obtained.

Another paper by R. A. Cadenas and J. O. Deferrari, J. Org. Chem. *28*, 2613 (1963), reports the reaction of maltose octa-$O$-acetate with ammonia.

The per-$O$-acetyl derivatives of reducing oligosaccharides are very important intermediates for various syntheses. They are easily convertible into acetylated halogenoses, from which in turn other substances may be obtained, such as glycosides, thioglycosides, anhydro derivatives, unsaturated products, etc. Acetylated phenyl glycosides (see Chapter XVI) may be directly obtained from per-$O$-acetyl derivatives of reducing oligosaccharides by heating with phenol (Helferich reaction) in the presence of catalysts.

In a weakly acidic medium, per-$O$-acetyl derivatives of reducing oligosaccharides react with primary aromatic amines to form the per-$O$-acetyl derivatives of the corresponding $N$-arylglycosylamines (see Chapter XXIII). According to another communication, octa-$O$-acetyl-$\alpha$-cellobiose reacts directly with aniline.[63]

## B. PARTIALLY ACETYLATED OLIGOSACCHARIDE DERIVATIVES

One of the substances of this group has been isolated from a material which may be regarded as natural to a certain extent; xylobiose (4-$O$-$\beta$-D-xylopyranosyl-D-xylose) monoacetate has been obtained from waste liquor of a birch sulphite cook.[64] Investigation of the course of periodic acid oxidation has revealed that the acetoxy group is located at C-2 of the non-reducing part of the molecule.

*References see p. 313*

The most important substances in this group, however, are undoubtedly the partially acetylated derivatives of reducing oligosaccharides with a free hemiacetal hydroxyl group. These compounds are formed, as in the mono-saccharide series,[65] by the reaction of peracetylated halogenoses with silver carbonate in aqueous acetone. This reaction, usually leading to β-anomers, has been studied using a number of reducing oligosaccharides, such as celtrobiose,[66] gentiobiose,[67] lactose,[68,69] maltose,[68–71] melibiose,[72] *neo*-lactose,[73] turanose,[74] 4-*O*-β-D-glucopyranosyl-D-mannose,[24] and others. In some cases it was possible to isolate both anomers of the last compound mentioned.[66,73]

The less easily obtainable α-anomers can be prepared from acylated halo-genoses by the action of diethylamine in chloroform[75] or by the usual reaction with silver nitrate in a suitable solvent.[75]

Hydrolytic elimination of the halogen atom from the acetylated halogenose by means of an aqueous sodium acetate solution[69] is a reaction slightly differing from the course assumed.[69] Hepta-*O*-acetyl-α-cellobiosyl bromide yields under the reaction conditions given above 1,3,6,2',3',4',6'-hepta-*O*-acetyl-α-D-cellobiose, see B. Helferich and J. Zirner, Chem. Ber. *96*, 385 (1963).

Of interest is the course of the reaction of hepta-*O*-acetyl-4-*O*-β-D-gluco-pyranosyl-α-D-mannopyranosyl bromide (III) with silver carbonate in various solvents. This substance (III) is converted in aqueous acetone into the expected hepta-*O*-acetyl-4-*O*-β-D-glucopyranosyl-D-mannose (IV). However, if the reaction with silver carbonate is carried out in methanol, it leads, as in the monosaccharide series,[76] to a mixture of two anomeric acetylated methyl gly-cosides (V) and (VI) and, in addition to this, to the orthoacetate of hexa-*O*-acetyl-4-*O*-β-D-glucopyranosyl-D-mannopyranose of the structure (VII). The action of methanolic hydrogen chloride on this compound (VII) gives rise to hexa-*O*-acetyl-4-*O*-β-D-glucopyranosyl-D-mannose (VIII).

Moreover, there are known incompletely acetylated derivatives of other types, as in the series of reducing oligosaccharides, for example, derivatives with an unsubstituted primary alcoholic group (obtained from per-*O*-acetylated trityl ethers, see Refs 77 and 78). Other noteworthy substances are penta-*O*-acetyl derivatives of sucrose,[79] where interesting re-arrangements of the acetyl groups have been observed (see p. 305). Finally, acetylation of sucrose with acetic anhydride in pyridine yielded a mono-*O*-acetyl derivative[80] not estab-lished in detail.

According to a very recent paper by Y. Z. Frohwein and J. Leibowitz, Bull. Res. Council Israel Ser. A *11*, 330 (1963); Chem. Abstr. *59*, 15363 (1963), cold acetonic potassium hydroxide solution will preferentially set free secondary alcoholic groups; thus, from oligosacharide per-*O*-acetates, derivatives esterified in the primary alcoholic groups only can be obtained. Maltose 6,6'-di-*O*-acetate and sucrose 6,6'-di-*O*-acetate and 6,1',6'-tri-*O*-acetate have been prepared.

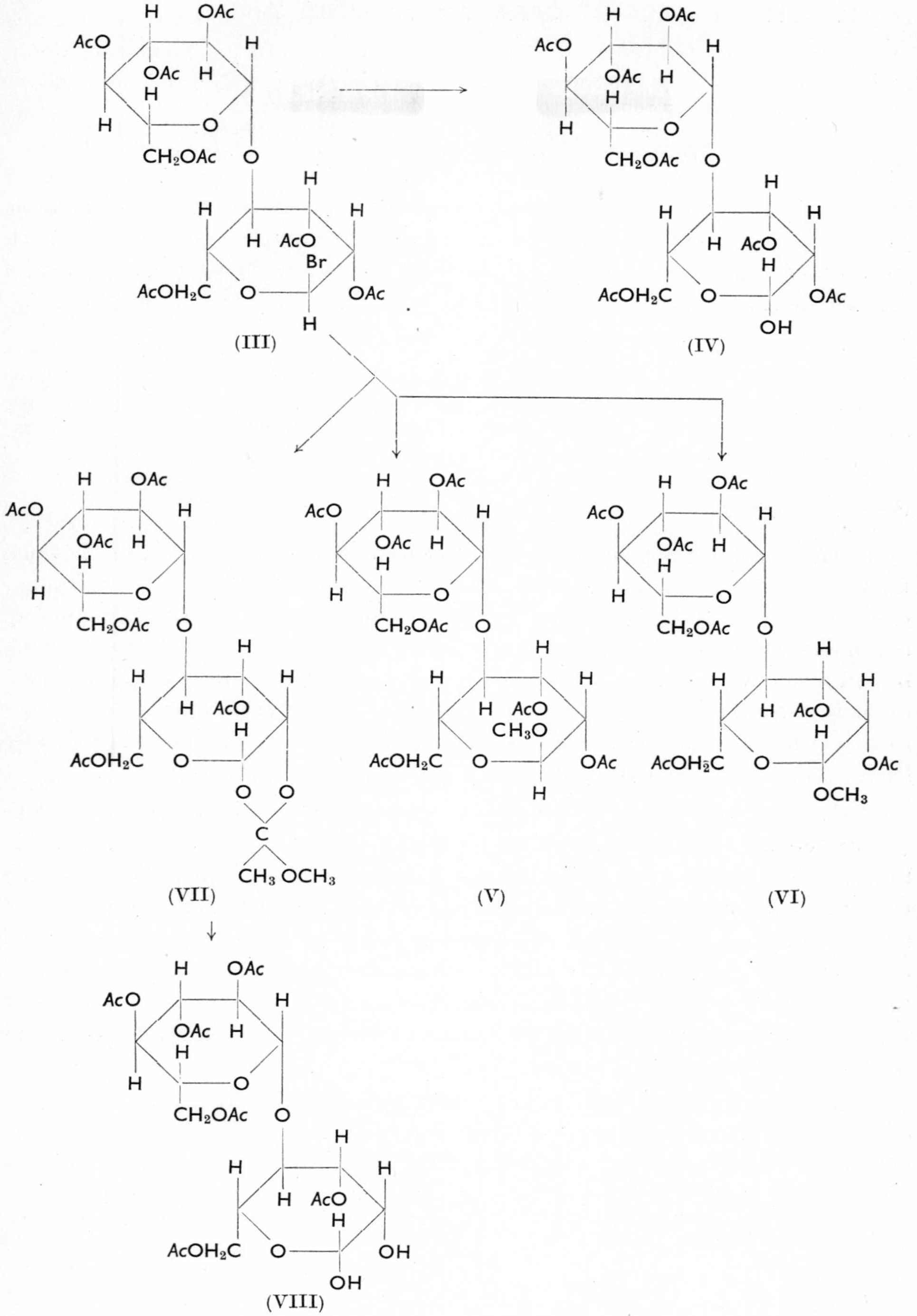

(III)

(IV)

(VII)

(V)

(VI)

(VIII)

References see p. 313

## 2. OTHER ESTERS OF CARBOXYLIC ACIDS AND OLIGOSACCHARIDES

Trehalose has been reported to occur as a fatty-acid ester in *Mycobacterium phlei*, see M. J. Pangborn and R. J. Anderson, J. Biol. Chem. *101*, 105 (1933); R. J. Anderson and M. S. Newman, J. Biol. Chem. *101*, 499 (1933).

Benzoylated oligosaccharides are known, but they are of relatively little significance. *p*-Bromobenzoyl,[81] *p*-nitrobenzoyl,[81,82] and *p*-aminobenzoyl derivatives[82] of oligosaccharides have also been prepared, in particular those of sucrose and lactose.

Re-esterification has been used recently for the preparation of sucrose esters with amino acids, see R. M. Ismail and H. Simonis, Angew. Chem. *75*, 1102 (1963). Even sucrose acetoacetates have been prepared from sucrose by the action of diketene, see L. K. Dalton, J. Appl. Chem. *13*, 277 (1963); Chem. Abstr. *59*, 10218 (1963).
β-D-Ribofuranosyl β-D-ribofuranoside hexa-*O*-benzoate, m. p. 143—144°C, $[\alpha]_D$ + 35·2° (CHCl₃) has been prepared synthetically by J. A. Zderic, Experientia *20*, 48 (1964).

Other esters of oligosaccharides, especially of sucrose, have been obtained by the action of variously substituted isocyanates.[83-87] *O*-Alkyloxycarbonyl derivatives obtained from sucrose by its reaction with alkyl chloroformates[88,89] polymerize, with elimination of diethyl carbonate and ethanol, to form cross-linked resins when heated in the presence of an alkaline catalyst;[90] the reaction of sucrose with carbonyl chloride in the presence of pyridine, or more conveniently with diphenyl carbonate in the presence of an alkaline catalyst, also leads to poly (sucrose carbonates).[91]

Attention has recently been paid to esters of oligosaccharides with long-chain carboxylic acids.* Lactose reacts with chlorides of higher aliphatic acids in pyridine to form esters containing about seven acyl groups per lactose molecule.[92] Far more important, however, are esters of higher aliphatic acids and non-reducing oligosaccharides. Trehalose is easily converted[93] into octa-*O*-acyl derivatives of this type, but favourable conditions have also been established under which trehalose yields physiologically important mono-,[94,95] di-[94] and tri-*O*-acyl derivatives[94] by its reaction with various acids. Hendeca-*O*-acyl derivatives of raffinose have also been prepared.[81,96]

Of special interest, however, are esters of higher aliphatic acids and sucrose. The first attempts[97] to prepare such esters by heating sucrose with stearic acid were unsuccessful, but it is no problem to prepare octa-*O*-acyl derivatives of sucrose by acylation with chlorides of higher aliphatic acids in an appropriate solvent, usually pyridine,[96-98] less usually in quinoline[99] or γ-butyrolactone.[100]

---

* For reviews see G. R. Ames, Chem. Revs *60*, 451 (1960); D. Mori and W. Watanabe, Yûki Gôsei Kagaku Kyokaishi *18*, 401 (1960); Chem. Abstr. *54*, 16392 (1960).

This method was also employed for preparing esters with different acyl-groups.[101]

Of higher significance are sucrose esters with a smaller number of bound acyl groups, in particular mono- and diesters. They are obtainable by controlled action of the chloride of the respective acid upon sucrose in pyridine,[102-104] or by the action of the acid anhydride;[105] a more advantageous procedure, however, is the re-esterification using the methyl ester of the higher aliphatic acid in question, and sucrose, catalysed by a small amount of sodium methoxide and carried out either in dimethylformamide,[106-113] or in *N*-acyl derivatives of morpholine.[114-116] The properties of these substances, common additions to lubricating oils,[117] are the subject of a special study with particular regard to their surface activity.[118] Attention has also been paid to the gas chromatography of these products[119] and to their further utilization in condensations with anhydrides of dicarboxylic acids.[120]

For some new papers on sucrose higher-fatty acid esters see R. U. Lemieux and A. G. McInnes, Can. J. Chem. *40*, 2376 (1962); R. U. Lemieux and A. G. McInnes, Can. J. Chem. *40*, 2394 (1962); E. G. Bobalek, A. P. DeMendoza, A. G. Causa, W. J. Collins, and G. Kapo, Ind. Eng. Chem., Prod. Res. Develop. *2*, 9 (1963); Chem. Abstr. *58*, 6912 (1963); K. Kunugi, Chem. Pharm. Bull. (Tokyo) *11*, 482 (1963); K. Kunugi, Chem. Pharm. Bull. (Tokyo) *11*, 486 (1963); S. Komori, M. Okahara, and K. Okamoto, Kogyo Kagaku Zasshi *63*, 600 (1960); Chem. Abstr. *57*, 9933 (1962); U.S.S.R. Patent 143,381; Chem. Abstr. *57*, 11296 (1962); Japan. Patent 21,717'61; Chem. Abstr. *57*, 10088 (1962); Belg. Patent 612,041; Chem. Abstr. *58*, 1525 (1963); U.S. Patent 3,030,356; Chem. Abstr. *57*, 11296 (1962); U.S. Patent 3,075,965; Chem. Abstr. *59*, 4026 (1963); M. Okahara, S. Komori, and A. Shiusugi, Kogyo Kagaku Zasshi *66*, 222 (1963); Chem. Abstr. *59*, 12892 (1963); Pi-Feng Wang and Chiang Yang, Chemistry (Taipei) *1962*, 105; Chem. Abstr. *59*, 5245 (1963); Japan. Patent 18,710'62; Chem. Abstr. *59*, 12910 (1963); Belg. Patent 622,394; Chem. Abstr. *59*, 11645 (1963); Brit. Patent 925,718; Chem. Abstr. *59*, 11645 (1963); U. S. Patent 3,096,324; Chem. Abstr. *60*, 649 (1964); adsorption chromatography of sucrose palmitates has been followed, too, see H. Mima, N. Kitamori, and T. Kanzawa, J. Chem. Soc. Japan, Ind. Chem. Sect. *65*, 833 (1962); for the chromatographic differentiation of sucrose esters see F. Linow, H. Ruttloff, and K. Täufel, Naturwissenschaften *50*, 689 (1963).

## 3. ESTERS OF OLIGOSACCHARIDES AND SULPHONIC ACIDS

The number of substances described in this group is relatively small; in addition to per-*O*-mesylated and per-*O*-tosylated sucrose derivatives,[121] there has been prepared a di-*O*-tosyl derivative of trehalose,[122] a tri-*O*-tosyl derivative of sucrose,[121,123] and later also a di-*O*-tosyl derivative of sucrose.[124] In these cases, the tosylation always proceeds preferentially at the primary alcoholic groups of the oligosaccharides. Chromatographic investigation of the course of the tosylation has shown that the reaction under conditions favourable for

*References see p. 313*

the production of the tri-$O$-tosyl derivative is more complicated and leads to di-, tri-, tetra- and penta-$O$-tosyl derivatives of sucrose.[124]

The course of lactose and lactulose tosylation has been investigated in detail. Lactose forms a tri-$O$-tosyl derivative, lactulose a penta-$O$-tosyl derivative, see Z. B. Shaposhnikova, N. N. Lisovskaya, I. V. Alekseeva, and I. R. Rominskiĭ, Ukr. Khim. Zh. *28*, 858 (1962); Chem. Abstr. *59*, 2919 (1963). Thorough investigation revealed that lactose 6,1',6'-tri-$O$-tosylate and lactulose 6,1',2',3',5'-penta-$O$-tosylate have been obtained, see I. R. Rominskiĭ, Z. B. Shaposhnikova, N. N. Lisovskaya, and I. V. Alekseeva, Ukr. Khim. Zh. *29*, 420 (1963); Chem. Abstr. *59*, 7626 (1963).

The tosyl esters of oligosaccharides and their acetyl derivatives are usually employed for further syntheses, such as the preparation of anhydro compounds [123,125,126] (see Chapter XIX) or iododeoxy derivatives[2] (see Chapter XV), etc.


## 4. RE-ARRANGEMENTS OF ACYL GROUPS IN PARTIALLY ACYLATED OLIGOSACCHARIDE DERIVATIVES

In the chemistry of monosaccharides, re-arrangements of acyl groups are no rare phenomenon;[127] the migration of acyl groups is assumed to be made possible by the temporary existence of orthoesters. Similar processes in the oligosaccharide series were observed only quite recently. Two of them relate to the hydrolysis of per-$O$-acetylated halogenose derivatives of the oligosaccharide series,[75,128] where the reaction yields, besides the usual derivatives with a free hemiacetal hydroxyl group, also isomeric compounds with a free hydroxyl group at C-2.* For example, hepta-$O$-acetylceltrobiosyl bromide gives in addition to the expected substance also 1,3,6,-tri-$O$-acetyl-4-$O$-(tetra-$O$-acetyl-$\beta$-D-glucopyranosyl)-D-altropyranose.[128] An interesting observation was made in the hydrolysis of hepta-$O$-acetylcellobiosyl bromide (IX) by the action of a silver nitrate solution in dioxane.[75] Besides 2,3,6,2',3',4',6'-hepta-$O$-acetyl-$\alpha$-cellobiose (X) and the anomer of this compound, a further substance was isolated and identified as 1,3,6,2',3',4',6'-hepta-$O$-acetyl-$\alpha$-cellobiose (XI). It is noteworthy that this product is converted by the action of pyridine into the compound (X); in both these conversions, the existence of a 1,2-orthoester is assumed as a necessary intermediate.

Another interesting occurence was found in the case of $O$-acetyl derivatives of sucrose. The tritylation of sucrose must proceed at the primary alcoholic groups[129] with the formation of the tri-$O$-trityl derivative (XII), which on acetylation showed to yield the corresponding penta-$O$-acetyl derivative (XIII). Detitrylation of this compound should give rise to the 2,3,4,3',4'-penta-$O$-acetyl derivative of sucrose. However, the methylation of this substance and

---

* See also B. Helferich and J. Zirner, Chem. Ber. *96*, 385 (1983).

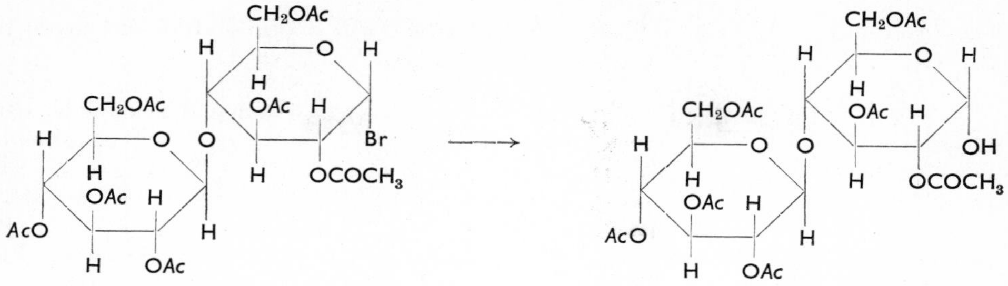

(IX)          $\longrightarrow$          (X)

$\uparrow$ $C_5H_5N$

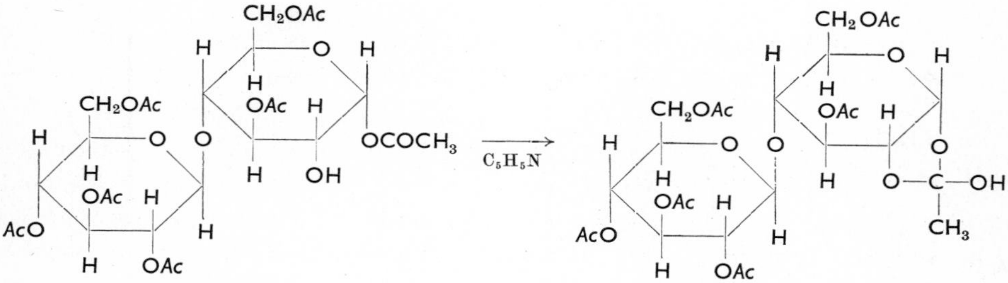

(XI)      $\xrightarrow{C_5H_5N}$

the following deacetylation did not lead to the 6,1′,6′-tri-*O*-methyl ether of sucrose but to 4,1′,6′-tri-*O*-methylsucrose.[129] Since the position of the methyl groups is evidently not in agreement with the original position of the trityl groups, the acetyl group must have been shifted from C-4 to C-6 in some phase of these reaction, and the first assumption was that this shifting takes place during methylation.[130]

Other writers, however, state[126] that the penta-*O*-acetyl derivative of the preceding investigators[129,130] already has the structure of 2,3,6,3′,4′-penta-*O*-acetylsucrose and that the migration of the acetyl group must have taken place already during detritylation. Bredereck proved[79] that this is actually the case. He succeeded in preparing both the penta-*O*-acetylsucroses under consideration; the first detritylation product of the substance (XIII) is undoubtedly 2,3,4,3′,4′-penta-*O*-acetylsucrose (XIV), which, however, is very easily converted, already in acetic acid or in weakly alkaline solution, through the corresponding orthoester into 2,3,6,3′,4′-penta-*O*-acetylsucrose (XV), also named isopenta-*O*-acetylsucrose. Tritylation of this compound yields a substance differing from the initial product (XIII), namely a di-*O*-trityl derivative.

*References see p. 313*

20 — The Oligosaccharides

(XII)

(XIII)

(XIV)

(XV)

### Table XLIX

Physical Properties of Oligosaccharide

Per-*O*-acetyl Derivatives

| Per-*O*-acetyl Derivative | Melting Point °C | $[\alpha]_D$(CHCl$_3$) | References |
|---|---|---|---|
| Hexa-*O*-acetyl- | | | |
| 2-*O*-β-D-galactopyranosyl-D-erythrose | 140 | | 131 |
| 2-*O*-α-D-glucopyranosyl-D-erythrose | 127 | | 132 |
| α-D-glucopyranosyl D-erythroside | 148 | | 133 |
| α-D-arabinopyranosyl α-D-arabinopyranoside | 116 | + 21° | 134 |
| β-L-arabinopyranosyl β-L-arabinopyranoside | 232 | +232° | 135 |
| β-xylobiose | 156 | − 76° | 64, 136–139, 306 |
| α-D-xylopyranosyl α-D-xylopyranoside | 242−250 | +159° | 140 |
| | 249−251 | +166·4° | 141 |
| α-D-xylopyranosyl β-D-xylopyranoside | 163 | + 24° | 69 |
| | 175−176·5 | + 39·7° | 141 |
| β-D-xylopyranosyl β-D-xylopyranoside | 137·5−139 | −107·4° | 141 |
| Hepta-*O*-acetyl- | | | |
| isoprimeverose | 110 | + 82·3° | 142 |
| primeverose | 217 | − 26·2° | 142−144 |
| vicianose | 159 | + 9·4° | 143, 145 |
| 2-*O*-β-L-arabinopyranosyl-D-glucose | syrup | | 146 |
| β-6-*O*-α-L-arabinofuranosyl-D-glucose | 108−109 | − 20° | 147 |
| 6-*O*-β-D-ribofuranosyl-D-glucose | 108−110 | + 3° | 147 |
| 6-*O*-β-D-xylopyranosyl-D-glucose | 216 | − 23·1° | 69 |
| α-D-xylopyranosyl β-D-galactopyranoside | 190 | +157° | 69 |
| α-D-xylopyranosyl β-D-fructofuranoside | amorphous | | 148 |
| 2-*O*-?-D-glucopyranosyl-D-arabinose | 139 | | 133 |
| 3-*O*-β-D-glucopyranosyl-D-arabinose | 196 | − 16·9° | 42 |
| | 161 | − 50·2° | 42 |
| | 106 | + 12·0° | 42 |
| 3-*O*-α-D-glucopyranosyl-L-arabinose | | +111° | 149 |
| 5-*O*-β-D-glucopyranosyl-D-arabinofuranose | 162 | − 14·4° | 150 |
| | 133 | + 23·1° | 150 |
| β-D-glucopyranosyl ?-D-arabinoside | 168−180 | − 21·5° | 151 |
| α-D-glucopyranosyl β-D-xylulofuranoside | 181 | + 22° | 152 |
| α-D-galactopyranosyl β-D-xylopyranoside | 181 | +140·5° | 69 |
| ?-D-mannopyranosyl β-D-arabinoside | 147−149 | | 153 |
| Octa-*O*-acetyl- | | | |
| α-cellobiose | 224−227 | +38·4° ± 3° | 31 |
| | 229 | + 42° | 17, 137, 154−158 |
| | 227−230 | + 35·3° | 159 |
| β-cellobiose | 188 | − 5·4° | 160 |
| | 192 | − 15·2° | 161−163 |
| | 192·5 | − 6·1° | 164 |
| | 193 | − 11·6° | 47 |
| | 197·3 | − 15·7° | 159 |
| | 200 | − 13·8° | 165 |
| | 202 | − 14·6° | 17 |
| | 221 | | 166, 167 |
| α-*epi*-cellobiose | 199−200 | + 36·5° | 58, 168 |
| | 202−203 | + 36·5° | 25, 169 |
| | 200−202 | + 34·9° | 170 |

*References see p. 313*

*Table XLIX — continued*

| Per-*O*-acetyl Derivative | Melting Point °C | [α]$_D$(CHCl$_3$) | References |
|---|---|---|---|
| | 203 | + 34° | 160 |
| | 203—204 | + 36° | 171, 172 |
| α-celtrobiose | 112 | | 66 |
| | 129—130 | + 48° | 66 |
| β-celtrobiose | 103—105 | | 66 |
| | 113—114 | — 13·0° | 66 |
| galactobiose | 172—173 | + 57·3° | 57 |
| α-gentiobiose | 186—189 | + 50·3° | 29 |
| | 188—189 | + 52·4° | 16, 30, 173 |
| | 187—190 | + 50·3° | 31 |
| | 190 | + 52° | 174 |
| | 191—192 | + 51° | 159 |
| | 191—192 | + 51·6° | 32, 175, 176 |
| | 190—191 | | 161 |
| | 192 | | 28 |
| | 193—194 | | 165 |
| β-gentiobiose | 187 | — 4·5° | 177 |
| | 185—188 | — 4·23° | 178 |
| | 191—193 | — 4·6° | 179 |
| | 191—193 | — 5·5° | 159, 180, 181 |
| | 193 | — 5·1° | 164 |
| | 194—195 | — 5·8° | 182 |
| | 195—196 | — 5·35° | 174 |
| | | — 4·4° | 183 |
| | 196 | — 5·4° | 16, 167, 175 |
| | | | 184—186 |
| α-*epi*-gentiobiose | 110—112 | + 24·5° | 28 |
| | 114 | + 26° | 187, 188 |
| | 142—143 | + 26° | 187, 188 |
| β-*epi*-gentiobiose | 132 | — 20·6° | 28, 187 |
| inulobiose* | | — 6·5° | 189 |
| β-isomaltose | 90 | + 97·5° | 190 |
| | 143 | + 96·9° | 191 |
| | | + 99° | 192 |
| | 143—144 | + 96·9° | 48, 49, 193, 194 |
| | 142—144 | + 95° | 179 |
| | 140—146 | + 98·4° | 165, 195 |
| | 145—146 | + 96·1° | 177, 182 |
| | 146—147 | + 96·1° | 159, 180 |
| | 143—145 | | 196 |
| | 144 | | 197 |
| | 146 | | 161 |
| | 148 | | 198 |
| isosucrose | 131—132 | + 19·2° | 199—202 |
| | | + 30·2° | 53 |
| isotrehalose | 181 | — 18·6° | 203—205 |
| | 182 | — 17·2° | 54, 159 |
| | 178 | — 18·3° | 53, 164 |
| | 189 | — 17·6° | 166 |

* A fructobiose octa-*O*-acetate, m.p. 67—68°C, [α]$_D$ —51·8° (CHCl$_3$), has been described by T. Mizuno, Kagaku (Tokyo) *31*, 146 (1961); Chem. Abstr. *55*, 27099 (1961). The compound with β,1→2 linkages could be identical with fructobiose, however, the properties are slightly different.

*Table XLIX — continued*

| Per-*O*-acetyl Derivative | Melting Point °C | $[\alpha]_D(CHCl_3)$ | References |
|---|---|---|---|
| α-kojibiose | syrup | | 206 |
| | 166 | +150° | 207—211 |
| | 168·5 | +152·2° | 212 |
| β-kojibiose | 118 | +112° | 207—210 |
| α-lactose | 152 | + 53·6° | 21 |
| β-lactose | 88—90 | — 4·5° | 60 |
| | 90 | — 25·8° | 21 |
| | 140 | — 4·0° | 213 |
| | 86 | | 8 |
| | 95—100 | | 214 |
| | 106 | | 215 |
| α-*epi*-lactose | 96—97 | + 41·2° | 59, 60 |
| α-*neo*-lactose | 178 | + 53·4° | 224, 225 |
| β-*neo*-lactose | 148 | — 7·1° | 224, 225 |
| lactulose | 138 | — 6·6° | 216, 217 |
| α-laminaribiose | 77—78 | + 20° | 218 |
| β-laminaribiose | 160 | — 29·3° | 219, 220 |
| | 160—161 | — 28·8° | 164, 180, 218, 221, 222 |
| | 160·5—161·5 | — 27·5° | 223 |
| lycobiose | 165—166 | + 26·8° | 26 |
| α-maltose | 125 | +122·8° | 8, 17, 18 |
| β-maltose | 159—161 | + 62·6° | 8, 17, 19, 159 166, 226—234 |
| | 158 | | 161, 165 |
| α-*epi*-maltose | 157 | +117° | 235 |
| α-melibiose | amorphous | +147·3° | 4 |
| β-melibiose | 172—173 | + 97·2° | 145 |
| | 173—174 | +102° | 50 |
| | 177 | +102·5° | 4, 20, 236 |
| | 178 | +103·2° | 237 |
| β-nigerose, sakébiose | 111—113 | | 231 |
| | 140—145 | + 80° | 195, 238 |
| | 149 | + 41·3° | 133 |
| | 150 | + 79·4° | 219 |
| | 151 | + 75·9° | 211 |
| | 151—152 | + 84·0° | 239 |
| | 152—154 | + 83° | 192 |
| | 155—157 | + 78° | 159 |
| sogdianose | 94—95 | — 28·7° | 246 |
| solabiose | 75 | + 27° | 27 |
| β-sophorose | 189·5° | —3° ± 2° | 164 |
| | 191—192 | — 3·8° | 159 |
| | 192 | — 32·5° | 247—249 |
| | 189 | — 40·5° (toluene) | 151 |
| | 186 | | 161 |
| sucrose | 68—69 | + 59·8° | 4, 14 |
| | 70—75 | + 59·4° | 13 |
| | 73·5 | + 60·6° | 15 |
| | 72—73 | + 59·6° | 8, 10, 240 |
| | 81—86 | + 62·5° | 241 |
| | 84 | + 60·2° | 51 |

*References see p. 313*

*Table XLIX — continued*

| Per-O-acetyl-Derivative | Melting Point °C | [α]$_D$(CHCl$_3$) | References |
|---|---|---|---|
|  | 86 | + 60·7° | 242 |
|  | 89—90 | + 60° | 243 |
|  | 89—93 | + 59° | 7 |
|  | 87 |  | 11, 116 |
|  | 85—88 |  | 244 |
| "sucrose C" | 125 | + 20·3° | 12, 245 |
| "sucrose D" | 113—114 | — 60·8° | 12 |
| trehalose (α,α) | 100 | +162° | 166 |
|  | 100—102 | +162·3° | 2, 4 |
|  | 100—102 | +164·5° | 5 |
|  | 97—98 |  | 165 |
| neo-trehalose (α,β) | 68—70 | + 68·1° | 250 |
|  | 118 | + 64° | 52 |
|  | 140 | + 80° | 54, 251 |
|  | 140 | + 82° | 252 |
|  | 140 | + 64·4° | 53 |
| α-turanose (furanose) | 158 | +107·0° | 253 |
| α-turanose (pyranose) | 194—195 | +103·2° | 22, 253 |
| β-turanose (furanose) |  | + 67·4° | 22, 253 |
| β-turanose (pyranose) | 216—217 | + 20·5° | 22 |
| xylotriose | 109—110 | — 85° | 136,138,254, 306 |
| α-2-O-α-D-glucopyranosyl-D-galactose | 168 | +141·5° | 212 |
| 4-O-β-D-glucopyranosyl-D-mannose | 165 | — 13° | 24 |
|  | 205 | + 36° | 37, 255, 256 |
| 6-O-α-D-mannopyranosyl-D-glucose* | 90 | + 38·9° | 257 |
| 6-O-α-D-mannopyranosyl-D-mannose* | 152—153 | + 19·6° | 257, 258 |
|  | 148—149 | + 24·2° | 262 |
| 2-O-?-D-mannopyranosyl-D-mannose | 153 | + 19·2° | 153 |
| α-D-mannopyranosyl α-D-mannopyranoside | 126 | + 65° | 259 |
| α-D-mannopyranosyl β-D-mannopyranoside |  | + 19° | 259 |
| β-D-fructopyranosyl α-D-galactopyranoside | 170 | — 41·4° | 69 |
| α-2-O-α-D-galactopyranosyl-D-galactose | 176—178 | +153° | 146, 212 |
| 4-O-β-D-galactopyranosyl-D-glucose | 88—90 | — 4·5° | 59, 60 |
| 6-O-α-D-galactopyranosyl-D-galactose |  | +186° | 263 |
| 6-O-β-D-galactopyranosyl-D-glucose | 166 | 0° | 260, 261 |
|  | 162 | + 20·7° | 57 |
| α-D-galactopyranosyl α-D-galactopyranoside | 225 | + 185° | 53 |
| α-D-galactopyranosyl β-D-galactopyranoside | 85 | + 58° | 52 |
|  | 82—83 | + 51·7° | 250 |
|  | 150 | + 96·9° | 212 |
| β-D-galactopyranosyl β-D-galactopyranoside | 164 | — 6° | 53, 69 |
| β-D-galactopyranosyl α-D-glucopyranoside | 171 | + 37·5° | 54 |
| Deca-O-acetyl-** xylotetraose | 201 | — 93·6° | 138, 264, 306 |
| Hendeca-O-acetyl-*** cellotriose | 223—224 | + 22·6° | 265—268 |
| erlose |  | + 86° | 269 |

* These compounds have recently been considered to be 6-α-O-derivatives.[258]

** O-α-L-Arabinofuranosyl-(1→3)-O-[β-D-xylopyranoxyl-(1→4)]-O-β-D-xylopyranosyl-(1→4)-D-xylose deca-O-acetate, m. p. 179—180°C, [α]$_D$ — 85° (CHCl$_3$), has been described by H. R. Goldschmid and A. S. Perlin, Can. J. Chem. *41*, 2272 (1963).

*** A fructotriose hendeca-O-acetate, m. p. 73—74°C, [α]$_D$ —40·1° (CHCl$_3$), has been described by T. Mizuno, Kagaku (Tokyo) *31*, 146 (1961); Chem. Abstr. *55*, 27099 (1961).

*Table XLIX — continued*

| Per-O-acetyl Derivative | Melting Point °C | $[\alpha]_D(CHCl_3)$ | References |
|---|---|---|---|
| gentianose | 75 | + 36·4° | 7 |
| gentiotriose | 221 | — 8° | 28, 270, 271 |
| | 215 | — 9·4° | 272 |
| labiose | 88 | +122·5° | 273 |
| laminaritriose | 121 | — 40·3° | 61, 180, 221, 272 |
| lycotriose | 120 | + 17·8° | 26 |
| maltotriose (amylotriose) | 134—136 | + 89·5° | 274 |
| melezitose | 117 | +103·6° | 275, 276 |
| planteose | 135 | + 97° | 277, 278 |
| raffinose | 99 | +101° | 51 |
| | 101 | +105·8° | 51 |
| | | + 92·2° | 20 |
| | | +100·3° | 279 |
| O-D-galactosyl-lactose | 120—122 | | 280 |
| 3,6-di-O-β-D-glucopyranosyl-D-glucose | 237 | — 2·56° | 281, 282 |
| 12-O-β-D-mannopyranosyl-epi-gentiobiose | 111—113 | + 11·2° | 283 |
| 12-O-β-D-mannopyranosylgentiobiose | 117—119 | + 20·2° | 283 |
| 3-O-β-cellobiosyl-D-glucose | 182·5 | — 21·7° | 222 |
| 6-O-β-cellobiosyl-D-glucose | 246·5 | — 10·9° | 270, 284 |
| | 240 | — 12·2° | 28 |
| 6-O-β-cellobiosyl-D-mannose | 120—126 | — 18·4° | 284 |
| 6-O-β-gentiobiosyl-D-mannose | 122—123 | — 21° | 186, 188 |
| | 118—120 | — 21° | 28 |
| 3-O-α-isomaltosyl-D-glucose | 117—120 | +121° | 285 |
| | 119—120 | +117° | 192, 286 |
| 6-O-β-lactosyl-D-glucose | 198 | — 2·5° | 270, 287 |
| 4-O-β-laminaribiosyl-D-glucose | 121—123 | | 288 |
| 6-O-β-laminaribiosyl-D-glucose | 216—217 | — 27·4° | 61, 180, 172 |
| 6-O-β-laminaribiosyl-D-mannose | 218 | — 27° | 272 |
| α-6-O-β-maltosyl-D-glucose | 174—176 | + 80·4° | 289 |
| β-6-O-β-maltosyl-D-glucose | 242·7 | + 42·5° | 284 |
| 6-O-β-maltosyl-D-mannose | 110—115 | + 58·6° | 284 |
| O-α-D-galactopyranosyl-(1→3)-O-α-D-galacto-pyranosyl-(1→3)-D-galactose | 275 | +105·5° | 34 |
| O-α-D-mannopyranosyl-(1→6)-O-?-D-manno-pyranosyl ?-D-mannopyranoside | | + 58° | 259 |
| O-α-D-mannopyranosyl-(1→6)-O-α-D-manno-pyranosyl-(1→6)-D-mannose | 162—163 | + 43·7° | 262 |
| G-Man-Man | 95—110 | + 18° | 290 |
| G-G-G | | + 95° | 291 |
| Dodeca-O-acetyl-xylopentaose | 248—249 | — 97·5° | 136, 138, 306 |
| Tetradeca-O-acetyl-* | | | |
| cellotetraose | 230—234 | + 13·4° | 266, 267 |
| laminaritetraose | 122—123 | — 46·2° | 221 |
| scodorose | 85—90 | — 28·5° | 292 |
| xylohexaose | 260—261 | —102° | 136 |
| | 257—259 | —103° | 138 |

* A fructotetraose tetradeca-O-acetate, m. p. 80—81°C, $[\alpha]_D$ —38·1° (CHCl_3), and a fructopentaose heptadeca-O-acetate, m. p. 84—86°C, $[\alpha]_D$ —32·7° (CHCl_3), have been described by T. Mizuno, Kagaku (Tokyo) *31*, 146 (1961); Chem. Abstr. *55*, 27099 (1961).

*References see p. 313*

*Table XLIX — continued*

| Per-*O*-acetyl Derivative | Melting Point °C | [α]$_D$(CHCl$_3$) | References |
|---|---|---|---|
| 12-β-cellobiosylgentiobiose | 239—240 | — 19·6° | 293 |
| 12-β-gentiobiosylgentiobiose | 207—209 | — 11·1° | 271 |
| maltosylmaltose | 105 | +105·4° | 250 |
| Hexadeca-*O*-acetyl- xyloheptaose | | —105° | 138 |
| Heptadeca-*O*-acetyl- cellopentaose | 240—241 | + 4·2° | 267 |
| verbascose | 132 | +130·4° | 294 |
| Octadeca-*O*-acetyl- xylooctaose | | — 56·8° | 138 |
| Eicosa-*O*-acetyl- cellohexaose | 252—253 | — 0·23° | 267 |
| arctose | 108 | — 36·5° | 296 |
| Tricosa-*O*-acetyl- celloheptaose | 263—266 | — 4·4° | 268 |
| sessilifolan | 73—75 | — 28·3° | 296 |

**Table L**

Physical Properties of Reducing Oligosaccharide Acetyl Derivatives
with a Free Hemiacetal Group

| Oligosaccharide Derivative | Melting Point °C | [α]$_D$(CHCl$_3$) | References |
|---|---|---|---|
| Hexa-*O*-acetyl- | | | |
| 2-*O*-α-D-glucopyranosyl-D-arabinose | 142 | +25·8° | 297 |
| 3-*O*-α-D-glucopyranosyl-D-arabinose | 153 | —42° | 298 |
| 3-*O*-β-D-glucopyranosyl-D-arabinose | 159 | —54° | 299 |
| 3-*O*-β-D-galactopyranosyl-D-arabinose | 154 | —80·8° (EtOH) | 300 |
| Hepta-*O*-acetyl- | | | |
| α-cellobiose | 218 | +35° | 75 |
| β-cellobiose | 204 | —2·4° → +22·5° | 68, 301, 302 |
| | 199 | + 3° | 69 |
| | 203 | —11·2° | 75 |
| β-*epi*-cellobiose | 110 | +11·7° | 229 |
| α-celtrobiose | 130—131 | +22·4° → +15·1° | 66 |
| β-celtrobiose | | + 3·9° → +15·1° | 66 |
| α-gentiobiose | 178 | +35·1° → +31·6° | 67 |
| β-lactose | 83 | — 0·3° | 68 |
| | | +1·0° | 69 |
| α-*neo*-lactose | 85—95 | +23·3° → +21° | 73 |
| β-*neo*-lactose | 135—136 | +10·0° → +21° | 73 |
| β-maltose | 181 | +67·8° → +110° | 68, 70, 71 303 |
| | 183 | +70° | 69 |
| β-melibiose | 193 | +119° → +125·8° | 72 |
| β-turanose | 147 | +38·7° → +41·7° | 74 |

## Table LI

Physical Properties of Some Other Oligosaccharide
Acetyl Derivatives

| Acetyl Derivative | Melting Point °C | $[\alpha]_D$ (CHCl$_3$) | References |
|---|---|---|---|
| 4-$O$-$\beta$-(2-$O$-Acetyl-D-xylopyranosyl)-D-xylose | 195—196 | −15° (H$_2$O) | 64 |
| 2,3,4,3′,4′-Penta-$O$-acetylsucrose | 122 | +31·2° | 79 |
| 2,3,6,3′,4′-Penta-$O$-acetylsucrose | 156 | +22·3° | 79, 129, 130 |
| 3,6,2′,3′,4′,6′-Hexa-$O$-acetyl-$epi$-cellobiose | 171 | +21·7° | 24 |
| 2,3,4,2′,3′,4′-Hexa-$O$-acetyltrehalose | 93—95 | +158·3° | 2 |
| 1,2,4,2′,3′,4′-Hexa-$O$-acetyl-laminaribiose | | + 2·0° | 304 |
| 1,3,6,2′,3′,4′,6′-Hepta-$O$-acetylcellobiose | 211 | +36·1° | 305 |
| 1,2,3,2′,3′,4′,6′-Hepta-$O$-acetyl-$\beta$-cellobiose | 202—203 | −22° | 307 |
| 1,2,3,2′,3′,4′,6′-Hepta-$O$-acetylmaltose | 140—141 | +65° | 230 |

## Table LII

Physical Properties of Oligosaccharide Sulphonic Acid Esters and Their Acetyl Derivatives

| Oligosaccharide Derivative | Melting Point °C | $[\alpha]_D$ (CHCl$_3$) | References |
|---|---|---|---|
| 6-$O$-Tosyl-1,2,3,2′,3′,4′,6′-hepta-$O$-acetylmaltose | 141 | + 50° | 230 |
| 6,6′-Di-$O$-tosyltrehalose | 118 | +110° | 122 |
| 2,3,4,2′,3′,4′-hexa-$O$-acetate | 170—172 | +136·1° | 2, 122 |
| Octa-$O$-mesylsucrose | 86—94 | + 43·7° | 121 |
| 6,6′-Di-$O$-tosylsucrose | 108—110 | + 54° | 124 |
| 6,1′,6′-Tri-$O$-tosylsucrose | 66—69 | + 41·3° | 121, 123 |
| 2,3,4,3′,4′-penta-$O$-acetate | 85—91 | | 126 |
| Octa-$O$-tosylsucrose | 82—86 | + 41·8° | 121 |

## REFERENCES

1. J. Staněk, M. Čərný, J. Kocourek, and J. Pacák, *The Monosaccharides*, Acad. Press New York 1963, 175.
2. H. Bredereck, Ber. *63*, 959 (1930).
3. L. Maquenne, Compt. rend. *112*, 947 (1891).
4. C. S. Hudson and J. M. Johnson, J. Am. Chem. Soc. *37*, 2748 (1915).
5. B. Stjernholm, Acta Chem. Scand. *12*, 646 (1958).
6. H. H. Schlubach and K. Repenning, Angew. Chem. *71*, 193 (1959).
7. J. Staněk and J. Černá, Monatsh. Chem. *94*, 239 (1963).
8. A. Herzfeld, Ber. *13*, 267 (1880).
9. W. Koenigs and E. Knorr, Ber. *34*, 4347 (1901).
10. P. Brigl and W. Scheyer, Hoppe-Seyler's Z. physiol. Chem. *160*, 214 (1926).
11. M. Frèrejacque, Compt. rend. *203*, 731 (1936).
12. A. Pictet and H. Vogel, Helv. Chim. Acta *11*, 901 (1928).
13. A. Pictet, Helv. Chim. Acta *13*, 698 (1930).
14. G. J. Cox, J. H. Ferguson, and M. L. Dodds, Ind. Eng. Chem. *25*, 968 (1933).

15. G. M. Christensen, J. Org. Chem. *27*, 1442 (1962).
16. C. S. Hudson and J. M. Johnson, J. Am. Chem. Soc. *39*, 1272 (1917).
17. C. S. Hudson and J. M. Johnson, J. Am. Chem. Soc. *37*, 1276 (1915).
18. A. Herzfeld, Ann. *220*, 215 (1883).
19. A. Herzfeld, Ber. *28*, 440 (1895).
20. C. Scheibler and H. Mittelmeier, Ber. *23*, 1438 (1890).
21. C. S. Hudson and J. M. Johnson, J. Am. Chem. Soc. *37*, 1270 (1915).
22. E. Pascu, J. Am. Chem. Soc. *54*, 3649 (1932).
23. M. Bergmann and H. Schotte, Ber. *54*, 1570 (1921).
24. H. S. Isbell, J. Research Natl. Bur. Standards *7*, 1115 (1931).
25. D. H. Brauns, J. Am. Chem. Soc. *48*, 2776 (1926).
26. R. Kuhn and I. Löw, Chem. Ber. *86*, 1027 (1953).
27. R. Kuhn, I. Löw, and H. Trischmann, Chem. Ber. *88*, 1492 (1955).
28. H. Bredereck, A. Wagner, H. Kuhn, and H. Ott, Chem. Ber. *93*, 1201 (1960).
29. A. Rheiner, A. Hunger, and T. Reichstein, Helv. Chim. Acta *35*, 687 (1952).
30. W. Rittel and T. Reichstein, Helv. Chim. Acta *37*, 1361 (1954).
31. A. Okano, Chem. Pharm. Bull. (Tokyo) *6*, 178 (1958).
32. J. C. Hess, A. Hunger, and T. Reichstein, Helv. Chim. Acta *35*, 2202 (1952).
33. K. Aso, K. Shibasaki, and M. Nakamura, Nature *182*, 1303 (1958).
34. K. Morgan and A. N. O'Neill, Can. J. Chem. *37*, 1201 (1959).
35. P. A. J. Gorin and A. S. Perlin, Can. J. Chem. *35*, 262 (1957).
36. J. Painter, Chem. & Ind. (London) *1959*, 1488.
37. T. Koshijima and I. Tachi, Bull. Agr. Chem. Soc. Japan *22*, 11 (1958).
38. A. P. N. Franchimont, Ber. *12*, 1241 (1879).
39. Z. Skraup, Ber. *32*, 2413 (1899).
40. F. Klein, Z. angew. Chem. *25*, 1409 (1912).
41. K. Freudenberg, Ber. *54*, 767 (1921).
42. G. Zemplén, Ber. *59*, 1254 (1926).
43. F. J. Bates, *Polarimetry, Saccharimetry and the Sugars*, Natl. Bur. Standards, Washington 1942, p. 459.
44. Org. Reactions, Coll. Vol. *2*, 124 (1946).
45. G. Jayme and W. Demmig, Chem. Ber. *88*, 434 (1955).
46. G. Jayme and W. Demmig, Chem. Ber. *93*, 356 (1960).
47. J. Staněk and J. Kocourek, Chem. listy *47*, 697 (1953); Chem. Abstr. *49*, 190 (1955).
48. B. Lindberg, Nature *164*, 706 (1949).
49. B. Lindberg, Acta Chem. Scand. *3*, 1355 (1949).
50. B. Lindberg, Acta Chem. Scand. *5*, 340 (1951).
51. H. Bredereck and G. Höschele, Chem. Ber. *86*, 47 (1953).
52. V. E. Sharp and M. Stacey, J. Chem. Soc. *1951*, 285.
53. H. Bredereck, G. Höschele, and K. Ruck, Chem. Ber. *86*, 1277 (1953).
54. B. Helferich and K. Weiss, Chem. Ber. *89*, 314 (1956).
55. R. U. Lemieux and H. F. Bauer, Can. J. Chem. *32*, 340 (1954).
56. M. Barbier and O. Schindler, Helv. Chim. Acta *42*, 1484 (1937).
57. H. Masamune and S. Kamiyama, Tôhoku J. Exptl. Med. *66*, 43 (1957); Chem. Abstr. *52*, 8974 (1958).
58. W. T. Haskins, R. M. Hann, and C. S. Hudson, J. Am. Chem. Soc. *63*, 1724 (1941).
59. W. T. Haskins, R. M. Hann, and C. S. Hudson, J. Am. Chem. Soc. *64*, 1289 (1942).
60. W. T. Haskins, R. M. Hann, and C. S. Hudson, J. Am. Chem. Soc. *64*, 1852 (1942).
61. S. Peat, W. J. Whelan, and J. M. Evans, J. Chem. Soc. *1960*, 175.
62. J. Staněk and J. Černá, Tetrahedron Letters *1963*, 35.

63. W. R. Moore and J. Russell, J. Appl. Chem. *4*, 369 (1954); Chem. Abstr. *49*, 5830 (1955).
64. J. Croon, Acta Chem. Scand. *16*, 827 (1962).
65. Ref. 1, p. 181.
66. N. K. Richtmyer and C. S. Hudson, J. Am. Chem. Soc. *58*, 2534 (1936).
67. M. Bergmann and W. Freudenberg, Ber. *62*, 2783 (1929).
58. C. S. Hudson and R. Sayre, J. Am. Chem. Soc. *38*, 1867 (1916).
69. B. Helferich and R. Steinpreis, Chem. Ber. *91*, 1794 (1958).
70. E. Fischer and H. Fischer, Ber. *43*, 2521 (1910).
71. P. Karrer and C. Naegeli, Helv. Chim. Acta *4*, 169 (1921).
72. B. Helferich and S. R. Petersen, Ber. *68*, 790 (1935).
73. N. K. Richtmyer and C. S. Hudson, J. Am. Chem. Soc. *57*, 1716 (1935).
74. E. Pacsu, J. Am. Chem. Soc. *55*, 2451 (1933).
75. W. M. Corbett, J. Kidd, and A. M. Liddle, J. Chem. Soc. *1960*, 616.
76. Ref. 1, p. 291.
77. L. Asp and B. Lindberg, Acta Chem. Scand. *6*, 941 (1952).
78. I. J. Goldstein and B. Lindberg, Acta Chem. Scand. *16*, 383 (1962).
79. H. Bredereck, H. Zinner, A. Wagner, G. Faber, W. Greiner, and W. Huber, Chem. Ber. *91*, 2824 (1958).
80. O. K. Kononenko and I. L. Kestenbaum, J. Appl. Chem. *11*, 7 (1961); Chem. Abstr. *55*, 12687 (1961).
81. S. Odén, Arkiv Kémi *7*, No. 15 (1918).
82. T. Ida, J. Pharm. Soc. Japan (Yakugaku Zasshi) *78*, 616 (1958); Chem. Abstr. *52*, 18227 (1958).
83. S. Komori and T. Agawa, Technol. Repts. Osaka Univ. *8*, 487 (1958); Chem. Abstr. *53*, 18873 (1959).
84. S. Komori, T. Agawa, S. Tonogai, and K. Nozaki, Kôgyô Kagaku Zasshi *61*, 1250 (1958); Chem. Abstr. *56*, 2503 (1962).
85. H. Bertsch, E. Ulsperger, W. Gerhardt, and M. Bock, J. prakt. Chem. *4*, 108 (1960).
86. H. Bertsch and E. Ulsperger, J. prakt. Chem. *4*, 115 (1960).
87. H. Bertsch, E. Ulsperger, and M. Bock, J. prakt. Chem. *13*, 138 (1961).
88. C. F. Allpress and W. N. Haworth, J. Chem. Soc. *125*, 1223 (1924).
89. R. S. Theobald, J. Chem. Soc. *1961*, 5359.
90. R. S. Theobald, J. Chem. Soc. *1961*, 5365.
91. R. S. Theobald, J. Chem. Soc. *1961*, 5370.
92. J. H. Schwartz and E. A. Talley, J. Am. Chem. Soc. *73*, 4490 (1951).
93. H. Willstaedt and M. Borggard, Bull. soc. chim. biol. *28*, 733 (1946).
94. J. Polonsky, G. Ferreol, R. Toubiana, and E. Lederer, Bull. soc. chim. France *1956*, 1471.
95. T. Gendre and E. Lederer, Bull. soc. chim. France *1956*, 1478.
96. K. Hess and E. Messmer, Ber. *54*, 499 (1921).
97. M. Berthelot, Ann. chim. phys. [*3*], *60*, 93 (1860).
98. M. Zief, J. Am. Chem. Soc. *72*, 1137 (1950).
99. K. Hess and E. Messmer, Ber. *54*, 499 (1921).
100. U.S. Patent 2,938,898; Chem. Abstr. *55*, 1468 (1961).
101. U.S. Patent 2,931,802; Chem. Abstr. *54*, 16401 (1960).
102. U.S. Patent 1,917,250; Chem. Abstr. *27*, 4600 (1933).
103. U.S. Patent 1,917,257; Chem. Abstr. *27*, 4601 (1933).
104. G. Nebbia, Ann. Chim. (Roma) *47*, 1280 (1957).
105. U.S. Patent 1,959,590; Chem. Abstr. *28*, 4432 (1934).

106. L. Osipow, F. Dee Snell, W. C. York, and A. Finchler, Ind. Eng. Chem. *48*, 1459 (1956).
107. L. Osipow, F. Dee Snell, and A. Finchler, J. Am. Oil Chemists' Soc. *34*, 185 (1957).
108. U.S. Patent 2,893,990; Chem. Abstr. *53*, 19422 (1959).
109. K. Mihara and K. Takaoka, J. Chem. Soc. Japan, Ind. Chem. Sect. *62*, 389 (1959).
110. K. Mihara and K. Takaoka, J. Chem. Soc. Japan, Ind. Chem. Sect. *62*, 393 (1959).
111. Brit. Patent 826,801; Chem. Abstr. *54*, 17282 (1960).
112. U.S. Patent 2,999,858; Chem. Abstr. *56*, 3557 (1962).
113. Brit. Patent 890,206; Chem. Abstr. *57*, 3554 (1962).
114. S. Komori, M. Okahara, and E. Shiusugi, Technol. Repts Osaka Univ. *8*, 497 (1958); Chem. Abstr. *53*, 18874 (1959).
115. S. Komori, M. Okahara, and E. Shiusugi, J. Chem. Soc. Japan *62*, 220 (1959).
116. S. Komori, M. Okahara, and E. Shiusugi, Kôgyô Kagaku Zasshi *62*, 240 (1959); Chem. Abstr. *55*, 27072 (1961).
117. U.S. Patent 2,700,022.
118. L. Osipow, F. Dee Snell, D. Marra, and W. C. York, Ind. Eng. Chem. *48*, 1462 (1956).
119. M. Gee and H. G. Walker, Chem. & Ind. (London) *1961*, 829.
120. Ger. Patent 1,040,525; Chem. Abstr. *55*, 1467 (1961).
121. R. C. Hockett and M. Zief, J. Am. Chem. Soc. *72*, 1839 (1950).
122. G. Ferréol-Brocheré and J. Polonsky, Bull. soc. chim. France *1958*, 714.
123. P. D. Bragg and J. K. N. Jones, Can. J. Chem. *37*, 575 (1959).
124. R. U. Lemieux and J. P. Barrette, Can. J. Chem. *38*, 656 (1960).
125. R. U. Lemieux and J. P. Barrette, Can. J. Chem. *37*, 1964 (1959).
126. R. U. Lemieux and J. P. Barrette, J. Am. Chem. Soc. *80*, 2243 (1958).
127. Ref. 1, p. 184.
128. W. A. Bonner, J. Org. Chem. *24*, 1388 (1959).
129. G. G. McKeown, R. S. E. Serenius, and L. D. Hayward, Can. J. Chem. *35*, 28 (1957).
130. G. G. McKeown and L. D. Hayward, Can. J. Chem. *35*, 992 (1957).
131. A. M. Gakhokidze, Zhur. Obshcheĭ Khim. *20*, 120 (1950); Chem. Abstr. *44*, 5819 (1950).
132. A. M. Gakhokidze, Zhur. Obshcheĭ Khim. *20*, 116 (1950); Chem. Abstr. *44*, 5819 (1950).
133. A. M. Gakhokidze, Zhur. Obshcheĭ Khim. *16*, 1923 (1946); Chem. Abstr. *41*, 6210 (1947).
134. F. A. H. Rice, J. Am. Chem. Soc. *78*, 6167 (1956).
135. J. K. N. Jones and W. H. Nicholson, J. Chem. Soc. *1958*, 27.
136. R. L. Whistler and C. C. Tu, J. Am. Chem. Soc. *74*, 4334 (1952).
137. R. L. Whistler, J. Bachrach, and C. C. Tu, J. Am. Chem. Soc. *74*, 3059 (1952).
138. C. T. Bishop, Can. J. Chem. *33*, 1073 (1955).
139. D. V. Myhre and F. Smith, J. Org. Chem. *26*, 4609 (1961).
140. D. H. Ball and J. K. N. Jones, J. Chem. Soc. *1958*, 33.
141. B. Helferich and W. Ost, Chem. Ber. *95*, 2616 (1962).
142. G. Zemplén and R. Bognar, Ber. *72*, 47 (1939).
143. C. M. McCloskey and G. H. Coleman, J. Am. Chem. Soc. *65*, 1778 (1943).
144. B. Helferich and H. Rauch, Ann. *455*, 168 (1927).
145. B. Helferich and H. Bredereck, Ann. *465*, 166 (1928).
146. J. Lehmann and D. Beck, Ann. *630*, 56 (1960).
147. P. A. J. Gorin, Can. J. Chem. *40*, 275 (1962).
148. G. Avigad, D. S. Feingold, and S. Hestrin, Biochim. et Biophys. Acta *20*, 129 (1956).

149. W. Z. Hassid, M. Doudoroff, A. L. Potter, and H. A. Barker, J. Am. Chem. Soc. *70*, 306 (1948).

150. N. S. MacDonald and W. L. Evans, J. Am. Chem. Soc. *64*, 2731 (1942).

151. A. M. Gakhokidze, Zhur. Obshcheĭ Khim. *11*, 117 (1941); Chem. Abstr. *35*, 3467 (1941).

152. W. Z. Hassid, M. Doudoroff, H. A. Barker, and W. H. Dore, J. Am. Chem. Soc. *68*, 1465 (1942).

153. A. M. Gakhokidze and M. Kutidze, Zhur. Obshcheĭ Khim. *22*, 247 (1952); Chem. Abstr. *46*, 11117 (1952).

154. Z. Skraup and J. König, Ber. *34*, 1115 (1901).

155. P. A. Levene and M. L. Wolfrom, J. Biol. Chem. *77*, 671 (1928).

156. K. Freudenberg and W. Nagai, Naturwissenschaften *20*, 578 (1932).

157. K. Freudenberg and W. Nagai, Ber. *66*, 27 (1933).

158. H. Friese and K. Hess, Ann. *456*, 38 (1927).

159. A. Thompson, K. Anno, M. L. Wolfrom, and M. Inatome, J. Am. Chem. Soc. *76*, 1309 (1954).

160. F. Smith and H. C. Srivastava, J. Am. Chem. Soc. *78*, 1404 (1956).

161. M. L. Wolfrom, A. Thompson, and R. B. Ward, J. Am. Chem. Soc. *81*, 4623 (1959).

162. L. Maquenne and W. Goodwin, Bull. soc. chim. France (3) *31*, 854 (1904).

163. W. Schliemann, Ann. *378*, 366 (1911).

164. S. Peat, W. J. Whelan, and K. A. Hinson, Nature *170*, 1056 (1952).

165. J. C. Sowden and A. S. Spriggs, J. Am. Chem. Soc. *78*, 2503 (1956).

166. H. Bredereck, H. Dürr, and K. Ruck, Chem. Ber. *87*, 526 (1954).

167. V. E. Gilbert, F. Smith, and M. Stacey, J. Chem. Soc. *1946*, 622.

168. M. Bergmann and H. Schotte, Ber. *54*, 1564 (1921).

169. H. S. Isbell, J. Research Natl. Bur. Standards *5*, 1185 (1930).

170. G. O. Aspinall, R. Begbie, and J. E. McKay, J. Chem. Soc. *1962*, 214.

171. A. Anthis, Tappi *39*, 401 (1956); Chem. Abstr. *50*, 12467 (1956).

172. J. K. N. Jones and T. J. Painter, J. Chem. Soc. *1957*, 669.

173. B. Helferich and H. Masamune, Ber. *64*, 1260 (1931).

174. H. Bredereck, A. Wagner, G. Faber, H. Ott, and J. Rauther, Chem. Ber. *92*, 1135 (1959).

175. D. D. Reynolds and W. L. Evans, J. Am. Chem. Soc. *60*, 2559 (1938).

176. H. A. Hardy, J. Am. Chem. Soc. *69*, 518 (1947).

177. A. Thompson, M. L. Wolfrom, and E. J. Quinn, J. Am. Chem. Soc. *75*, 3003 (1953).

178. G. Zemplén and L. Kisfaludy, Acta Chim. Acad. Sci. Hung. *4*, 79 (1954).

179. M. L. Wolfrom, A. Thompson, and A. M. Brownstein, J. Am. Chem. Soc. *80*, 2015 (1958).

180. S. Peat, W. J. Whelan, and H. G. Lawley, J. Chem. Soc. *1958*, 729.

181. H. Berlin, J. Am. Chem. Soc. *48*, 2627 (1926).

182. P. S. O'Colla, E. E. Lee, and D. McGrath, J. Chem. Soc. *1962*, 2730.

183. H. Berlin, J. Am. Chem. Soc. *48*, 1107 (1936).

184. G. Zemplén, Hoppe-Seyler's Z. physiol. Chem. *85*, 399 (1913).

185. B. Helferich and W. Klein, Ann. *450*, 219 (1926).

186. B. Helferich, K. Bäuerlein, and F. Wiegand, Ann. *477*, 27 (1926).

187. H. J. Dauben and W. L. Evans, J. Am. Chem. Soc. *60*, 886 (1938).

188. D. D. Reynolds and W. L. Evans, J. Am. Chem. Soc. *62*, 66 (1940).

189. J. H. Pazur and A. L. Gordon, J. Am. Chem. Soc. *75*, 3458 (1953).

190. K. V. Giri, K. Saroja, R. Venkataraman, and P. L. N. Rao, Arch. Biochem. Biophys. *51*, 62 (1954); Chem. Abstr. *48*, 10826 (1954).

191. S. Peat, J. R. Turvey and J. M. Evans, Nature *179*, 261 (1957).
192. J. I. Goldstein and W. J. Whelan, J. Chem. Soc. *1962*, 170.
193. M. L. Wolfrom, L. W. Georges, and I. L. Miller, J. Am. Chem. Soc. *71*, 125 (1949).
194. S. A. Barker and T. R. Carrington, J. Chem. Soc. *1953*, 3588.
195. M. L. Wolfrom and A. Thompson, J. Am. Chem. Soc. *78*, 4116 (1956).
196. K. Shibasaki and K. Aso, J. Ferment. Tech. (Japan) *31*, 354 (1953); Chem. Abstr. *48*, 7109 (1954).
197. E. E. Bacon and J. S. D. Bacon, Biochem. J. *58*, 396 (1954).
198. C. R. Ricketts and C. E. Rowe, J. Chem. Soc. *1955*, 3809.
199. J. C. Irvine, J. W. H. Oldham, and A. F. Skinner, J. Soc. Chem. Ind. *27*, 494 (1928).
200. J. C. Irvine, J. W. H. Oldham, and A. F. Skinner, J. Am. Chem. Soc. *51*, 1279 (1929).
201. J. C. Irvine and J. W. H. Oldham, J. Chem. Soc. *51*, 3609 (1929).
202. W. H. Binkley and M. L. Wolfrom, J. Am. Chem. Soc. *68*, 2171 (1946).
203. E. Fischer and K. Delbrück, Ber. *42*, 2776 (1909).
204. H. H. Schlubach and K. Schetelig, Hoppe-Seyler's Z. physiol. Chem. *213*, 83 (1932).
205. C. M. McClosky, R. E. Pyle, and G. H. Coleman, J. Am. Chem. Soc. *66*, 349 (1944).
206. K. Matsuda, Tôhoku J. Agr. Research *6*, 271 (1956); Chem. Abstr. *50*, 13366 (1956).
207. A. Sato and K. Aso, Nature *180*, 984 (1957).
208. K. Matsuda, Nature *180*, 985 (1957).
209. F. Yamauchi and K. Aso, Nature *189*, 753 (1961).
210. K. Aso, K. Shibasaki, and M. Nakamura, Nature *182*, 1303 (1958).
211. S. Peat, W. J. Whelan, and K. A. Hinson, Chem. & Ind. (London) *1955*, 385.
212. B. Helferich and J. Zirner, Chem. Ber. *95*, 2604 (1962).
213. R. Sasaki and K. Taniguchi, Nippon Nôgei Kagaku Kayshi *33*, 183 (1959); Chem. Abstr. *54*, 308 (1960).
214. M. Schmöger, Ber. *25*, 1452 (1892).
215. E. Fischer and E. F. Armstrong, Ber. *35*, 841 (1902).
216. H. L. Frush and H. S. Isbell, J. Research Natl. Bur. Standards *34*, 111 (1945).
217. J. P. L. Bots, Rec. trav. chim. *76*, 515 (1957).
218. P. Bächli and E. G. V. Percival, J. Chem. Soc. *1952*, 1243.
219. K. Matsuda, Chem. & Ind. (London) *1958*, 1627.
220. A. Sato, K. Watanabe, and K. Aso, Chem. & Ind. (London) *1958*, 887.
221. S. Peat, W. J. Whelan, and H. G. Lawley, J. Chem. Soc. *1958*, 724.
222. H. Ono and M. Dazai, Nature *183*, 1055 (1959).
223. A. Klemer and K. Homberg, Chem. Ber. *94*, 2747 (1961).
224. A. Kunz and C. S. Hudson, J. Am. Chem. Soc. *78*, 1978 (1926).
225. A. Kunz and C. S. Hudson, J. Am. Chem. Soc. *78*, 2435 (1926).
226. K. Freudenberg, H. Hochstein, and H. Engels, Ber. *58*, 667 (1925).
227. J. C. Irvine and I. M. A. Black, J. Chem. Soc. *1926*, 862.
228. A. R. Ling and J. L. Baker, J. Chem. Soc. *67*, 212 (1895).
229. A. R. Ling and J. L. Baker, Ber. *38*, 1019 (1895).
230. L. Asp and B. Lindberg, Acta Chem. Scand. *6*, 941 (1952).
231. S. A. Barker, E. J. Bourne, and M. Stacey, J. Chem. Soc. *1953*, 3588.
232. R. U. Lemieux, Can. J. Chem. *31*, 949 (1953).
233. J. J. Goldstein, Acta Chem. Scand. *16*, 383 (1962).
234. H. O. Bouveng, H. Kiessling, B. Lindberg, and J. McKay, Acta Chem. Scand. *16*, 615 (1962).
235. W. N. Haworth, E. L. Hirst, and R. J. W. Reynolds, J. Chem. Soc. *1934*, 302.
236. H. B. Wright and T. B. Walker, Chem. & Ind. (London) *1955*, 18.
237. P. A. Levene and E. Jorpes, J. Biol. Chem. *86*, 403 (1930).

238. M. L. Wolfrom and A. Thompson, J. Am. Chem. Soc. *77*, 6403 (1955).

239. S. Haq and W. J. Whelan, J. Chem. Soc. *1958*, 1342.

240. W. Z. Hassid, M. Doudoroff, and H. A. Barker, J. Am. Chem. Soc. *66*, 1416 (1944).

241. R. U. Lemieux and G. Huber, J. Am. Chem. Soc. *78*, 4117 (1956).

242. H. Bredereck, A. Wagner, G. Hagellock, and G. Faber, Chem. Ber. *91*, 515 (1958).

243. R. P. Linstead, A. Ruttenberg, W. G. Dauben, and W. L. Evans, J. Am. Chem. Soc. *62*, 3260 (1940).

244. J. B. Pridham, Biochem. J. *76*, 13 (1960).

245. A. Pictet and H. Vogel, Helv. Chim. Acta *11*, 436 (1928).

246. S. M. Strepkov, Zhur. Obshcheĭ Khim. *28*, 3143 (1958); Chem. Abstr. *53*, 10053 (1959).

247. K. Freudenberg and K. Soff, Ber. *69*, 1245 (1936).

248. K. Freudenberg, H. Knauer, and F. Cramer, Chem. Ber. *84*, 144 (1951).

249. J. Rabaté, Bull. soc. chim. France (5) *7*, 565 (1940).

250. H. V. Vogel and H. D. Debowska-Kurnicka, Helv. Chim. Acta *11*, 910 (1928).

251. F. Micheel and K. O. Hagel, Chem. Ber. *85*, 1087 (1952).

252. W. N. Haworth and W. J. Hickinbottom, J. Chem. Soc. *1931*, 2847.

253. F. B. Cramer and E. Pacsu, J. Am. Chem. Soc. *59*, 711 (1937)

254. G. O. Aspinall, M. E. Carter, and M. Los, J. Chem. Soc. *1956*, 4807.

255. T. Koshijima, K. Kitao, and I. Tachi, Mokuzai Kenkyu *19*, 19 (1958); Chem. Abstr. *52*, 21085 (1958).

256. A. Tymynski and T. E. Timell, J. Am. Chem. Soc. *82*, 2823 (1960).

257. E. A. Talley, D. D. Reynolds, and W. L. Evans, J. Am. Chem. Soc. *65*, 575 (1943).

258. P. A. J. Gorin and A. S. Perlin, Can. J. Chem. *37*, 1930 (1959).

259. F. Micheel and D. Borrmann, Chem. Ber. *93*, 1143 (1960).

260. B. Helferich and G. Sparmberg, Ber. *66*, 806 (1933).

261. B. Helferich and H. Rauch, Ber. *59*, 2655 (1926).

262. S. Peat, W. J. Whelan, and T. E. Edwards, J. Chem. Soc. *1961*, 29.

263. C. N. Turton, A. Bebbington, S. Dixon, and E. Pacsu, J. Am. Chem. Soc. *77*, 2565 (1955).

264. R. L. Whistler and C. C. Tu, J. Am. Chem. Soc. *74*, 3609 (1952).

265. K. Hess and K. Dziengel, Ber. *68*, 1594 (1935).

266. L. Zechmeister and G. Tóth, Ber. *64*, 854 (1931).

267. F. E. Dickey and M. L. Wolfrom, J. Am. Chem. Soc. *71*, 825 (1949).

268. M. L. Wolfrom and J. C. Dacons, J. Am. Chem. Soc. *74*, 5331 (1952).

269. J. W. White and J. Maher, J. Am. Chem. Soc. *75*, 1259 (1953).

270. B. Helferich and W. Schäfer, Ann. *450*, 229 (1926).

271. B. Helferich and R. Gootz, Ber. *64*, 109 (1931).

272. S. Peat, W. J. Whelan, and E. Edwards, J. Chem. Soc. *1958*, 3862.

273. S. M. Strepkov, Zhur. Obshcheĭ Khim. *9*, 1489 (1939); Chem. Abstr. *34*, 2798 (1940).

274. M. L. Wolfrom, L. W. Georges, A. Thompson, and I. L. Miller, J. Am. Chem. Soc. *71*, 2873 (1949).

275. A. Alekhin, Ann. chim. phys. (6) *18*, 532 (1889).

276. C. S. Hudson and S. F. Sherwood, J. Am. Chem. Soc. *40*, 1456 (1918).

277. N. Wattiez and M. Haus, Bull. acad. roy med. Belg. *8*, 386 (1943).

278. D. French, G. M. Wild, B. Young, and W. J. James, J. Am. Chem. Soc. *75*, 790 (1953).

279. C. Tanret, Bull. soc. chim. France *13*, 261 (1895).

280. K. Wallenfels, E. Bengt, and G. Limberg, Ann. *579*, 113 (1953).

281. A. Klemer and K. Homberg, Chem. Ber. *93*, 1643 (1960).

282. A. Klemer and K. Homberg, Chem. Ber. *94*, 2747 (1961).

283. E. A. Talley and W. L. Evans, J. Am. Chem. Soc. *65*, 573 (1943).

284. S. H. Nichols, W. L. Evans, and H. D. McDowell, J. Am. Chem. Soc. *62*, 1754 (1940).

285. M. Abdullah, I. J. Goldstein, and W. J. Whelan, J. Chem. Soc. *1962*, 176.

286. A. Sato and H. Ono, Chem. & Ind. (London) *1962*, 1536.

287. K. Miescher and C. Meystre, Helv. Chim. Acta *26*, 224 (1943).

288. A. S. Perlin and S. Suzuki, Can. J. Chem. *40*, 50 (1962).

289. A. Thompson and M. L. Wolfrom, J. Am. Chem. Soc. *77*, 3567 (1955).

290. K. Nishida and H. Hashima, J. Dept. Agr. Kyushu Imp. Univ. *2*, 277 (1930); Chem. Abstr. *25*, 498 (1931).

291. H. H. Schlubach and E. Lühre, Ann. *547*, 73 (1941).

292. Y. Kihara, J. Agr. Chem. Soc. Japan *12*, 1044 (1936); Chem. Abstr. *31*, 3013 (1937).

293. B. Helferich, H. Bredereck, W. Schäfer, and K. Bäuerlein, Ann. *465*, 174 (1928).

294. S. Murakami, Proc. Imp. Acad. Tokyo *16*, 12 (1940); Chem. Abstr. *34*, 3694 (1940).

295. S. Murakami, Acta Phytochim. *15*, 105 (1949); Chem. Abstr. *43*, 8451 (1949).

296. T. Sasaki, M. Mikami, and H. Ueda, J. Pharm. Soc. Japan (Yakugaku Zasshi) *81*, 626 (1961); Chem. Abstr. *56*, 7712 (1962).

297. A. M. Gakhokidze, Zhur. Obshcheĭ Khim. *19*, 2082 (1949); Chem. Abstr. *44*, 3194 (1950).

298. A. M. Gakhokidze, Zhur. Obshcheĭ Khim. *18*, 60 (1948); Chem. Abstr. *42*, 4948 (1948).

299. A. M. Gakhokidze, Zhur. Obshcheĭ Khim. *16*, 1914 (1946); Chem. Abstr. *41*, 6209 (1947).

300. A. M. Gakhokidze, Zhur. Obshcheĭ Khim. *16*, 1907 (1946); Chem. Abstr. *41*, 6208 (1947).

301. E. Fischer and G. Zemplén, Ber. *43*, 2536 (1910).

302. E. Fischer and G. Zemplén, Ann. *372*, 254 (1909).

303. H. Fischer and F. Kögl, Ann. *436*, 219 (1924).

304. J. R. Turvey and J. M. Evans, J. Chem. Soc. *1960*, 2366.

305. B. Helferich and J. Zirner, Chem. Ber. *96*, 385 (1963).

306. R. H. Marchessault and T. E. Timell, J. Polymer. Sci. Pt. C. No 2, 49 (1963); Chem. Abstr. *59*, 8847 (1963).

307. I. Johansson, B. Lindberg, and O. Theander, Acta Chem. Scand. *17*, 2019 (1963).

# XIV

# Acylated Halogenoses of Oligosaccharides

As in the monosaccharide series,[1] acylated halogenoses represent in the oligosaccharide series also a very important group of initial compounds for both the preparation of further derivatives (glycosides, thioglycosides, glycals, etc.) and the synthesis of higher oligosaccharides by various methods (see Chapter VI). However, the possibilities of synthesizing acylated oligosaccharide halogenoses[2] are limited in comparison with those available in the monosaccharide series.[1] In the majority of cases, the hemiacetal acyloxy group is replaced by a halogen atom, as a rule by the action of hydrogen halide, either in a solvent or without it. As is the case in the monosaccharide series, the stable anomers of acylated oligosaccharide halogenoses belong to the α-series.

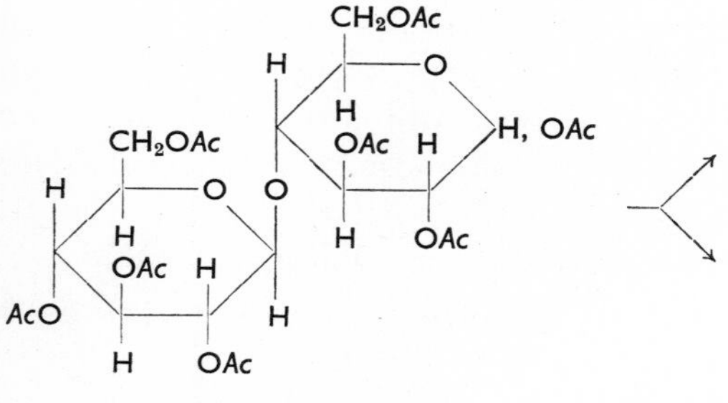

(I)

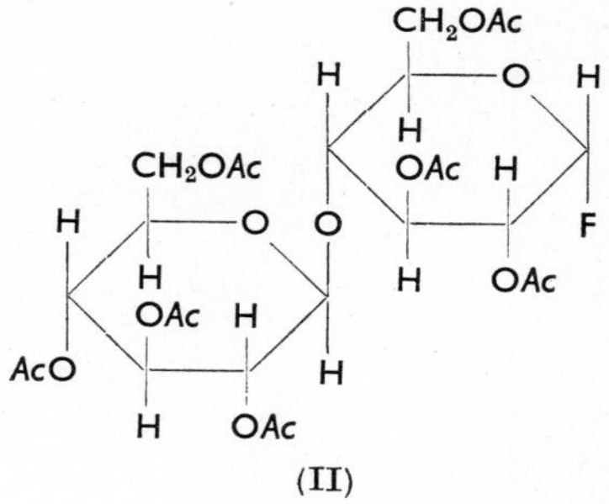

(II)

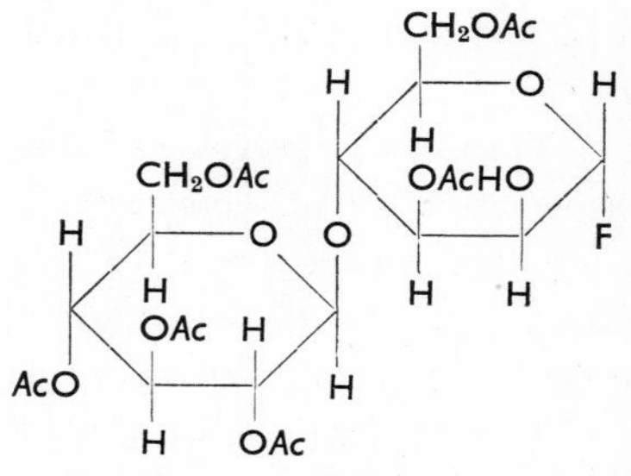

(III)

*References see p. 326*

Of the anhydrous hydrogen halides, hydrogen fluoride is almost exclusively employed in the oligosaccharide group;[3] however, the action of this reagent may lead to noteworthy changes in the molecule of the acylated oligosaccharide. For example, the reaction of octa-*O*-acetylcellobiose (I) with anhydrous hydrogen fluoride for 30 minutes gives rise to hepta-*O*-acetyl-α-cellobiosyl fluoride (II). If, however, the reaction time is extended to 5 hours, the acetoxy group adjacent to the C-F bond is deacetylated with simultaneous inversion of the configuration at C-2, so that the reaction product then is an *epi*-cellobiose derivative, namely 4-*O*-(2,3,4,6-tetra-*O*-acetyl-β-D-glucopyranosyl)-3,6-di-*O*-acetyl-α-D-mannopyranosyl fluoride (III).

The action of anhydrous hydrogen chloride also converts a per-*O*-acetylated derivative of a reducing oligosaccharide into the corresponding acetylated halogenose; octa-*O*-acetyl-β-maltose thus yields hepta-*O*-acetyl-α-maltosyl chloride.[4]

However, the reaction proceeds in another way when a solution of hydrogen chloride in ether is employed.[5–8] Octa-*O*-acetyl-β-maltose is thus converted into a substance isomeric with hepta-*O*-acetyl-α-maltosyl chloride, which has the character of an orthoacetate. It is assumed that this product corresponds in its structure to hexa-*O*-acetyl-1,2-*O*-(1-chloroethylidene)-maltose (IV).

(IV)

The method most frequently employed for the preparation of peracetylated halogenoses of oligosaccharides is the reaction of the peracetylated oligosaccharide with a solution of a hydrogen halide in acetic anhydride. This procedure may be utilized for obtaining the corresponding bromides,[9–11] as well as the less common iodides.[11] A rarely applied modification consists of blowing the gaseous hydrogen halide into the solution of the per-*O*-acetyl derivative as obtained after acetylation with acetic anhydride in the presence of perchloric acid.[12]

The most convenient method for preparing per-*O*-acetyl derivatives of halogenoses is the reaction of per-*O*-acetyl derivatives of reducing oligosaccharides with a mixture of red phosphorus and bromine in glacial acetic acid,[13,14] either with simultaneous addition of water[13] or without it.[14] The latter procedure seems to be more advantageous because it leads to higher yields.

The application of a mixture of phosphorus pentachloride and aluminium chloride in the group of per-*O*-acetyl derivatives of reducing oligosaccharides gives rise to acetylated halogenoses, however, at the cost of structural changes. Thus, octa-*O*-acetyllactose (V) yields, besides the expected hepta-*O*-acetyl-α-lactosyl chloride (VI), an almost equal amount of hepta-*O*-acetyl-α-*neo*-lactosyl chloride (VII), i. e. hepta-*O*-acetyl-4-*O*-β-D-galactopyranosyl-α-D-altropyranosyl chloride.[15-18]

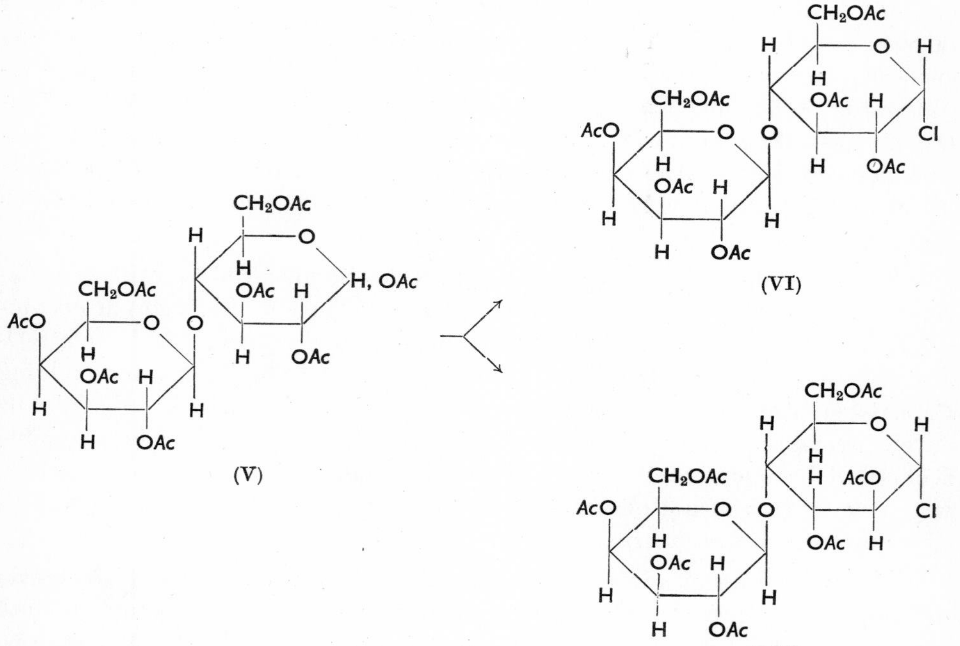

(V)

(VI)

(VII)

Similarly, octa-*O*-acetylcellobiose gives under these conditions not only the expected hepta-*O*-acetyl-α-cellobiosyl chloride but also hepta-*O*-acetyl-α-celtrobiosyl chloride.[16,18] In a similar way to that possible in the monosaccharide series, Soviet investigators[19] recently succeeded in converting octa-*O*-acetylcellobiose by the action of phosphorus pentachloride into hexa-*O*-acetyl-2-*O*-trichloroacetyl-β-cellobiosyl chloride (VIII).

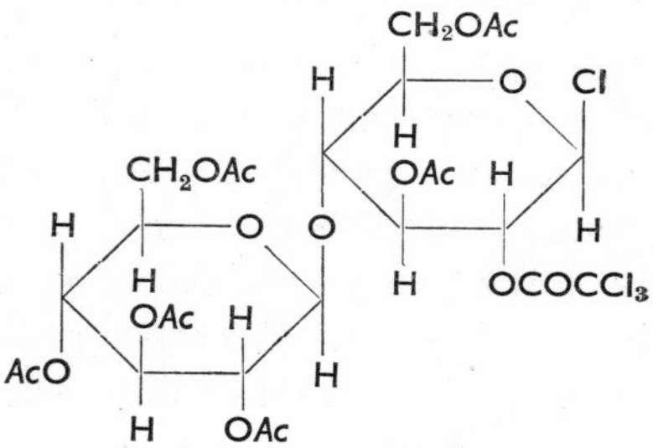

(VIII)

*References see p. 326*

21*

Titanium tetrachloride is very rarely employed for this purpose. Lindberg[20] converted the octa-$O$-acetyl derivative of 6-$O$-$\beta$-D-galactopyranosyl-D-glucose by its reaction with titanium tetrachloride into a per-$O$-acetylated halogenose, however, with simultaneous anomerization in the oligosaccharide molecule, so that in this case the resulting compound was hepta-$O$-acetylmelibiosyl chloride (a derivative of 6-$O$-$\alpha$-D-galactopyranosyl-D-glucose). In the group of oligosaccharides where the monosaccharides are mutually bound by $\alpha$-linkages such changes are not to be expected, and, in fact, according to Japanese investigators,[21,22] octa-$O$-acetylmaltose may be converted in this way into hepta-$O$-acetyl-$\alpha$-maltosyl chloride. Another possible way of preparing per-$O$-acetylated halogenoses may be the cleavage of the 1,6-anhydro ring by the action of titanium tetrachloride, as proved by Lindberg on maltosan hexa-$O$-acetate.[23]

The unstable acylated halogenoses of the $\beta$-series, derived from oligosaccharides, have been known for a short time only.[24,25] The action of anhydrous aluminium chloride on octa-$O$-acetyl-$\beta$-maltose in chloroform yields hepta-$O$-acetyl-$\beta$-maltosyl chloride.[24,25] In some cases, the possibility of interchanging the halogen atoms in acylated halogenoses may also be utilized; in principle the only conversion coming here into consideration is that of the easily accessible acetylated bromides of the $\alpha$-series into acetylated fluorides of the $\beta$-series, which are otherwise not obtainable. As usual, the reaction is carried out with silver fluoride in acetonitrile.[26]

The properties of acylated halogenoses derived from oligosaccharides do not in any way differ in principle from those of analogous compounds in the monosaccharide series. According to recent findings,[27] their instability may be removed by chromatography in anhydrous ether through silica gel.

As far as somewhat unusual reactions of acylated halogenoses are concerned, mention must be made of the migrations of acyl groups proceeding in the hydrolytic elimination of the halogen atom[28,29] (see Chapter XIII). The action of ammonia offers the possibility of replacing the halogen atom in the molecule of the acetylated halogenose by an amino group.[30] Reactions with secondary amines also proceed in a similar manner,[31,32] although here substances of the glycoseen type may be formed (see Chapter XXI).[32]

Much attention has recently been paid to the reaction of acylated halogenoses with tertiary amines.[33,34] Besides the usual formation of a quaternary ammonium salt, another, less clear reaction occurs;[33] thus, hepta-$O$-acetyl-$\alpha$-cellobiosyl bromide, on treatment with trimethylamine at $-180°$C, yields a product of the same elementary composition as that of the initial acetylated halogenose, but with different properties. For the time being it cannot be stated with certainty that this substance is the unstable $\beta$-anomer, although several repeated crystallizations lead to hepta-$O$-acetyl-$\alpha$-cellobiosyl bromide.

According to other writers, the alkyl halide molecule is liberated by the action of tertiary amines upon the acylated halogenose, and the products obtained in this way are identical with those formed by the reaction with secondary amines.[32,35]

## Table LIII

Physical Properties of Oligosaccharide Glycosyl Halides

| Oligosaccharide Derivative | Melting Point °C | $[\alpha]_D(H_2O)$ | References |
|---|---|---|---|
| α-Lactosyl fluoride | 180—195 (dec.) | +83·2° | 36 |
| β-Cellobiosyl fluoride | | + 7° | 26 |
| α-Gentiobiosyl fluoride | 215—220 (dec.) | +33·5° | 72 |

## Table LIV

Physical Properties of Acetylated Oligosaccharide Glycosyl Halides

| Oligosaccharide Derivative | Melting Point °C | $[\alpha]_D(CHCl_3)$ | References |
|---|---|---|---|
| 4-O-(2,3,4,6-Tetra-O-acetyl-β-D-glucopyranosyl)-3,6-di-O-acetyl-α-D-mannopyranosyl fluoride | 145 | + 20·8° | 38 |
| Hexa-O-acetyl- | | | |
| α-isoprimeverosyl chloride | 158—160 | +180·6° | 39 |
| α-isoprimeverosyl bromide | 155·3—157·8 | +186·6° | 39 |
| α-primeverosyl chloride | 186 | + 70·7° | 40 |
| | 201—203 | + 72·3° | 39 |
| α-primeverosyl bromide | 176—178 | + 96·5° | 39 |
| 2-O-trichloroacetyl-β-maltosyl chloride | 132—133 | + 80° | 41 |
| 2-O-trichloroacetyl-β-cellobiosyl chloride | 80 | + 28·2° | 19 |
| 2,3,2′,3′,4′,6′-α-cellobiosyl chloride | 231—232 | +79° | 82 |
| Hepta-O-acetyl- | | | |
| α-cellobiosyl fluoride | 187 | + 30·6° | 38 |
| β-cellobiosyl fluoride | 173 | — 4° | 26 |
| α-cellobiosyl chloride | 200—201 | + 73° | 38, 42—44 |
| α-cellobiosyl bromide | 180 (dec.) | + 95·8° | 11, 42—48 |
| | 182 | + 94·5° | 38, 83 |
| β-cellobiosyl bromide (?) | 157—158 | + 83·6° | 33 |
| α-cellobiosyl iodide | 160—170 | +125·7° | 38, 42—45 |
| α-epi-cellobiosyl fluoride | 155—156 | + 13·6° | 38 |
| α-epi-cellobiosyl chloride | 172 | + 51·2° | 38, 49 |
| α-epi-cellobiosyl bromide | 168—169 | + 77·9° | 9, 38, 50 |
| α-epi-cellobiosyl iodide | 140 (dec.) | +111·5° | 38 |
| α-celtrobiosyl chloride | 141—142 | + 64·2° | 51, 52 |
| α-gentiobiosyl fluoride | 168—169 | + 43·8° | 53 |
| α-gentiobiosyl chloride | 148 | + 80·5° | 38, 53 |
| | 142—143 | + 89·2° | 54 |
| | 137 | + 82·8° | 55 |
| α-gentiobiosyl bromide | 144 | +101·1° | 53, 56—58 |
| α-gentiobiosyl iodide | 134 (dec.) | +126·1° | 53 |
| α-isomaltosyl bromide | 131—133 | +202° | 59 |

*References see p. 326*

*Table LIV — continued*

| Oligosaccharide Derivative | Melting Point °C | $[\alpha]_D$ (CHCl$_3$) | References |
|---|---|---|---|
| α-lactosyl fluoride | amorphous | | 36 |
| α-lactosyl chloride | 120—121 | + 83·9° | 15, 54, 60, 61 |
| α-lactosyl bromide | 145 (dec.) | +108·7° | 15, 62—65 |
| | 138 | +104·2° | 66 |
| | 146—147 | +109° | 27 |
| | 149 | +107° | 67 |
| α-lactosyl iodide | 145 (dec.) | +136·9° | 15 |
| α-neo-lactosyl chloride | 182 (dec.) | + 71·2° | 16—18 |
| α-laminaribiosyl bromide | 180·5—181·5 | +185° | 10 |
| | 176—177 | | 57 |
| α-maltosyl fluoride | 174—176 | +111·1° | 68 |
| α-maltosyl chloride | 125 | +159·5° | 4, 21, 61, 68—70 |
| β-maltosyl chloride | 125 | + 57·4° | 24, 25 |
| α-maltosyl bromide | 112—113 | +180·1° | 27, 68, 71—73 |
| α-maltosyl iodide | 62—63 | | 72 |
| α-melibiosyl fluoride | 135 | +149·7° | 68 |
| α-melibiosyl chloride | 127 | +192·5° | 68 |
| α-melibiosyl bromide | 116 | +209·9° | 68 |
| α-sophorosyl bromide | 194 (dec.) | + 95·6° | 74 |
| | 190—191 | + 97·4° | 75 |
| α-turanosyl chloride | syrup | + 92·9° | 76, 77 |
| β-turanosyl chloride | 165 | — 0·44° | 76, 77 |
| α-turanosyl bromide | syrup | +117·4° | 76, 77 |
| β-turanosyl bromide | 133—134 | — 30·5° | 76, 77 |
| β-turanosyl iodide | 105—106 | — 54·2° | 76, 77 |
| 6-*O*-β-D-mannopyranosyl-α-D-gluco pyrano- syl bromide | 172 | +151·2° | 78 |
| Deca-*O*-acetyl- 6-*O*-β-cellobiosyl-α-D-glucopyrano syl chloride | 223—224 | + 48·4° | 55 |
| 6-*O*-β-cellobiosyl-α-D-glucopyranosyl bromide | 209 | + 63·8° | 55 |
| | 205 (dec.) | + 69·9° | 79 |
| cellotriosyl bromide | 183 (dec.) | + 58·0° | 34, 83 |
| 6-*O*-β-gentiobiosyl-α-D-glucopyrano syl bromide | 193—194 | + 63·3° | 80 |
| 6-*O*-β-lactosyl-α-D-glucopyranosyl bromide | 138—142 | | 81 |
| laminaritriosyl bromide | | + 44·8° | 57 |
| Trideca-*O*-acetyl- cellotetraosyl bromide | 182—183 (dec.) | + 36·8° | 34 |
| laminaritetraosyl bromide | | + 20·0° | 57 |

## REFERENCES

1. J. Staněk, M. Černý, J. Kocourek, and J. Pacák, *The Monosaccharides*, Acad. Press, New York 1963.
2. L. J. Haynes and F. H. Newth, Advances in Carbohydrate Chem. *10*, 207 (1955).
3. D. H. Brauns, J. Am. Chem. Soc. *45*, 833, 2388 (1923).
4. E. Fischer and E. F. Armstrong, Ber. *34*, 2885 (1901).

5. K. Freudenberg and O. Ivers, Ber. *55*, 941 (1922).
6. K. Freudenberg, H. Hochstetter, and H. Engels, Ber. *58*, 666 (1925).
7. K. Freudenberg, W. Dürr, and H. Hochstetter, Ber. *61*, 1740 (1928).
8. K. Freudenberg and H. Scholz, Ber. *63*, 1969 (1930).
9. W. T. Haskins, R. M. Hann, and C. S. Hudson, J. Am. Chem. Soc. *64*, 1289 (1942).
10. P. Bächli and E. G. V. Percival, J. Chem. Soc. *1952*, 1243.
11. E. Fischer and G. Zemplén, Ber. *43*, 2537 (1910).
12. S. D. Nicholas and F. Smith, Nature *161*, 349 (1948).
13. M. Barczai-Martos and F. Körösy, Nature *165*, 369 (1910).
14. P. G. Scheuer and F. Smith, J. Am. Chem. Soc. *76*, 3224 (1954).
15. C. S. Hudson and A. Kunz, J. Am. Chem. Soc. *47*, 2052 (1925).
16. A. Kunz and C. S. Hudson, J. Am. Chem. Soc. *48*, 1978 (1926).
17. A. Kunz and C. S. Hudson, J. Am. Chem. Soc. *48*, 2435 (1926).
18. N. K. Richtmyer and C. S. Hudson, J. Am. Chem. Soc. *57*, 1716 (1935).
19. S. N. Danilov, O. P. Kozmina, and A. N. Shirshova, Zhur. Obshcheĭ Khim. *27*, 945 (1957); Chem. Abstr. *52*, 3696 (1958).
20. B. Lindberg, Acta Chem. Scand. *5*, 340 (1951).
21. J. Karasawa, Doshiska Joshidaigaku *7*, 227 (1956); Chem. Abstr. *54*, 3216 (1960).
22. J. Karasawa, Doshiska Joshidaigaku *9*, 1 (1958); Chem. Abstr. *54*, 3217 (1960).
23. L. Asp and B. Lindberg, Acta Chem. Scand. *6*, 941 (1952).
24. W. Korytnyk and J. A. Mills, Chem. & Ind. (London) *1957*, 817.
25. W. Korytnyk and J. A. Mills, J. Chem. Soc. *1959*, 636.
26. F. Micheel, A. Klemer, and G. Baum, Chem. Ber. *88*, 475 (1955).
27. P. A. Finan and C. D. Warren, J. Chem. Soc. *1962*, 2823.
28. W. A. Bonner, J. Org. Chem. *24*, 1388 (1959).
29. W. M. Corbett, J. Kidd, and A. M. Liddle, J. Chem. Soc. *1960*, 616.
30. F. Micheel, R. Trier, E. Platz, and A. Hiller, Chem. Ber. *85*, 1092 (1952).
31. P. Karrer and J. C. Harloff, Helv. Chim. Acta *16*, 962 (1933).
32. G. Zemplén and Z. Bruckner, Ber. *61*, 2481 (1928).
33. W. M. Corbett and J. Kidd, J. Chem. Soc. *1959*, 1594.
34. W. M. Corbett and J. Kidd, J. Chem. Soc. *1959*, 2632.
35. G. Zemplén and Z. Bruckner, Ber. *61*, 927 (1928).
36. B. Helferich and R. Gootz, Ber. *62*, 2505 (1929).
37. B. Helferich, K. Bäuerlein, and F. Wiegand, Ann. *447*, 32 (1926).
38. D. H. Brauns, J. Am. Chem. Soc. *48*, 2776 (1926).
39. G. Zemplén and R. Bognár, Ber. *72*, 1160 (1939).
40. G. Zemplén and R. Bognár, Ber. *72*, 47 (1939).
41. P. Brigl and P. Mistele, Hoppe-Seyler's Z. physiol. Chem. *126*, 120 (1923).
42. Z. H. Skraup and J. M. Koenig, Ber. *34*, 1115 (1901).
43. Z. H. Skraup and J. M. Koenig, Monatsh. Chem. *22*, 1033 (1901).
44. Z. H. Skraup and E. Geiersperger, Monatsh. Chem. *26*, 1459 (1905).
45. E. Fischer and G. Zemplén, Ann. *372*, 254 (1909).
46. A. M. Gakhokidze, Zhur. Obshcheĭ Khim. *16*, 1914 (1946); Chem. Abstr. *41*, 6209 (1947).
47. K. Freudenberg and W. Nagai, Ann. *494*, 63 (1932).
48. J. Staněk and J. Kocourek, Chem. listy *47*, 697 (1953); Chem. Abstr. *49*, 190 (1955).
49. H. S. Isbell, J. Research Natl. Bur. Standards *7*, 1115 (1931).
50. W. N. Haworth, E. L. Hirst, H. R. L. Streight, H. A. Thomas, and J. I. Webb, J. Chem. Soc. *1930*, 2636.
51. C. S. Hudson, J. Am. Chem. Soc. *48*, 2002 (1926).
52. N. K. Richtmyer and C. S. Hudson, J. Am. Chem. Soc. *58*, 2534 (1936).

53. D. H. Brauns, J. Am. Chem. Soc. *49*, 3170 (1927).

54. E. Pacsu, Ber. *61*, 1508 (1928).

55. G. Zemplén and A. Gerecs, Ber. *64*, 1545 (1931).

56. R. Campbell and W. N. Haworth, J. Chem. Soc. *125*, 1337 (1924).

57. S. Peat, W. J. Whelan, and J. M. Evans, J. Chem. Soc. *1960*, 175 .

58. F. H. Newth and G. O. Phillips, J. Chem. Soc. *1953*, 2904.

59. M. L. Wolfrom, L. W. Georges, and I. L. Miller, J. Am. Chem. Soc. *71*, 125 (1949).

60. A. Bodart, Monatsh. Chem. *23*, 5 (1902).

61. E. Fischer and E. F. Armstrong, Ber. *35*, 833 (1902).

62. R. Ditmar, Ber. *35*, 1951 (1902).

63. R. Ditmar, Monatsh. Chem. *23*, 865 (1902).

64. E. Fischer and H. Fischer, Ber. *43*, 2521 (1910).

65. A. M. Gakhokidze, Zhur. Obshcheï Khim. *16*, 1907 (1946); Chem. Abstr. *41*, 6208 (1947).

66. R. Sasaki and K. Taniguchi, Nippon Nôgie Kagaku Kaishi *33*, 183 (1959); Chem. Abstr. *54*, 308 (1960).

67. F. J. Reithel and R. G. Young, J. Am. Chem. Soc. *74*, 4210 (1952).

68. D. H. Brauns, J. Am. Chem. Soc. *51*, 1820 (1929).

69. R. Foerg, Monath. Chem. *23*, 45 (1902).

70. G. Schliephacke, Ann. *377*, 184 (1910).

71. A. M. Gakhokidze, Zhur. Obshcheï Khim. *18*, 60 (1948); Chem. Abstr. *42*, 4948 (1948).

72. C. S. Hudson and E. P. Phelps, J. Am. Chem. Soc. *46*, 2591 (1924).

73. E. Fischer and E. F. Armstrong, Ber. *35*, 3153 (1902).

74. K. Freudenberg and K. Soff, Ber. *69*, 1245 (1936).

75. R. Coxon and H. G. Fletcher, J. Org. Chem. *26*, 2892 (1961).

76. E. Pacsu, J. Am. Chem. Soc. *54*, 3649 (1932).

77. E. Pacsu, E. J. Wilson, and L. Graf, J. Am. Chem. Soc. *61*, 2675 (1939).

78. E. A. Talley, D. D. Reynolds, and W. L. Evans, J. Am. Chem. Soc. *65*, 575 (1943).

79. B. Helferich, H. Bredereck, W. Schäfer, and K. Bäuerlein, Ann. *465*, 174 (1928).

80. B. Helferich and R. Gootz, Ber. *64*, 109 (1931).

81. K. Miescher and C. Meystre, Helv. Chim. Acta *26*, 224 (1943).

82. I. Johansson, B. Lindberg, and O. Theander, Acta Chem. Scand. *17*, 2019 (1963).

83. M. L. Wolfrom and S. Haq, Tappi *47*, 183 (1964); Chem. Abstr. *60*, 15967 (1964).

# XV

# Esters of Oligosaccharides and Inorganic Acids

### 1. PHOSPHATE ESTERS

The esters of phosphoric acid and sugars, which play such an important role in the chemistry of monosaccharides,[1] are only rarely encountered among natural substances of the oligosaccharide group. The information about sucrose monophosphate is rather incomplete;[2,3] it has been described as a syrup of $[\alpha]_D$ $+85.1°$. More exact data are available on trehalose monophosphate, which has been isolated[4] from the reaction mixture remaining after sugar fermentation, and has been prepared[5] in the form of its pure barium salt. Other phosphate esters allegedly isolated from rice cannot so far be classified, as the original literature is inaccessible.[6]

Trehalose 6-phosphate may also be regarded as naturally occuring. It has been synthesized[7,8] by transfer of a D-glucose molecule from UDPG (uridine diphospho-D-glucose) to D-glucose 6-phosphate according to the scheme:

UDPG $+$ D-glucose 6-phosphate $=$ trehalose phosphate $+$ UDP

Lactose 1-phosphate[9] has been synthesized analogously by the action of UDPGal upon D-glucose 1-phosphate.

Some other oligosaccharide phosphates have been obtained synthetically, mainly by the application of methods known from the chemistry of monosaccharides.[10] Thus, maltose 1-phosphate[11] has been prepared by the reaction of hepta-$O$-acetyl-$\alpha$-maltosyl bromide with silver phosphate.

Other investigators[12] succeeded in preparing both anomers of lactose 1-phosphate. The $\beta$-anomer is produced in the form of the corresponding hepta-$O$-acetyl derivative by the reaction of hepta-$O$-acetyl-$\alpha$-lactosyl bromide with $AgH_2PO_4$, while the $\alpha$-anomer is obtained from the same initial halogenose by the action of the silver salt of diphenylphosphoric acid and hydrogenolytic elimination of the aromatic residues.

Japanese investigators,[13] too, have studied the question of lactose 1-phosphate synthesis and report that the reaction of hepta-$O$-acetyl-$\alpha$-lactosyl bromide with silver diphenylphosphate gives rise to the corresponding $\beta$-anomer, while the use of silver dibenzylphosphate leads to the $\alpha$-anomer of lactose

*References see p. 331*

1-phosphate; both anomers are obtained, of course, after hydrogenolytic elimination of the blocking groups linked to phosphoric acid. According to other papers,[14,15] the lactose di- and triphosphates may be obtained from the reaction mixture produced by the action of phosphorus oxychloride on lactose in pyridine.

The preparation of sucrose octa-(diphenylphosphate) has been a subject of several patents, see Fr. Patent 1,309,244; Chem. Abstr. *58*, 14083 (1963); Ital. Patent 630,656; Chem. Abstr. *58*, 1252 (1963); Belg. Patent 611,292; Chem. Abstr. *57*, 16770 (1962).

The structure of "phosphomaltotetraose" [see T. A. Posternak, J. Biol. Chem. *188*, 317 (1951)] has recently been established [see F. W. Parrish and W. J. Whelan, Biochem. J. *79*, 19 *p* (1961)]; according to the suggestion of W. J. Whelan [see Ann. Rev. Biochem. *29*, 105 (1960)], phosphomaltotetraose is designated as maltotetraose 6³-phosphate.

## 2. ESTERS WITH HYDROGEN HALIDES

The commonest substances of this group are the hydrogen iodide esters which as a rule are obtainable from primary mesyl or tosyl esters by the reaction of sodium iodide in acetone in a sealed tube at 120°C. This method has been employed for derivatives of trehalose,[16,17] cellobiose,[18,19] maltose,[20,21] and sucrose.[22-24] In the last case it must be pointed out that the tosyl group linked to C-1 of the D-fructose molecule does not in any case react with sodium iodide.[22-24]

The hydrogen iodide esters are of special importance in the preparation of the corresponding deoxy compounds, because the iodine atom when bound to a primary carbon atom may be split off from the molecule, and this is achieved either by reduction with zinc in acetic acid,[20] in particular with platinum as catalyst,[19] or, more advantageously, on Raney nickel.[20] It is interesting to note that in these substances the iodine atom cannot be replaced by a fluorine atom by the action of silver fluoride. It has been reported several times that silver fluoride acts similarly to silver hydroxide, so that a hydrogen iodide molecule is split off and the reaction leads to an unsaturated compound[16,18] (see Chapter XXI).

An oligosaccharide derivative with a bromine atom at a primary carbon atom has also been described;[18,25] the bromine atom may be replaced by an iodine atom;[18] however, the action of silver fluoride here leads likewise to an unsaturated compound.[18,25]

## 3. ESTERS OF NITRIC ACID

The esters of nitric acid in the series of mono- and oligosaccharides are of far less significance than in the polysaccharide group. The octa-*O*-nitrate of sucrose[26-28] (m. p. 85·5°C, $[\alpha]_D$ +55·9°) has been described several times, but no remarkable properties have been found in comparison with similar substances.

It is known from the monosaccharide series that the per-$O$-acetyl derivatives of aldoses react with nitric acid to form analogues of acetylated halogenoses, i. e. acylated derivatives with esterically linked nitric acid at C-1; in this way, hepta-$O$-acetylmaltosyl nitrate (m. p. 93—95°C, $[\alpha]_D$ +149·3°) has been obtained by the action of nitric acid on octa-$O$-acetylmaltose.[29] In acylated halogenoses, the bromine atom may also be replaced by the –O–NO$_2$ group by the action of silver nitrate; in tetrahydrofuran solution, hepta-$O$-acetyl-$\alpha$-cellobiosyl nitrate has been prepared by this method.[30]

## 4. ESTERS FORMED BY THE ACTION OF SULPHURYL CHLORIDE ON OLIGOSACCHARIDES

The reactions taking place in the treatment of oligosaccharides with sulphuryl chloride have not as yet been elucidated in detail and seem to be very complicated. It is possible, however, that this reaction will lead to chlorodeoxy derivatives in a comparatively simple way. In the reaction with sulphuryl chloride some of the hydroxyl groups are replaced by chlorine atoms, while other hydroxyl groups are esterified by sulphuric acid; these ester linkages can easily be split hydrolytically. Trehalose[31] is thus converted into a tetrachlorotetradeoxy disulphate (decomp. at 175°C, $[\alpha]_D$ +152·3°) not established in detail, and sucrose[32] yields a mixture of dichlorodideoxy and trichlorotrideoxy derivatives.

### REFERENCES

1. L. F. Leloir, Fortschritte Chem. org. Naturstoffe 8, 47 (1951).
2. C. Neuberg, Z. Ver. deutsch. Zuckerind. 76, 463 (1926).
3. O. Meyerhoff and K. Lohmann, Biochem. Z. 185, 113 (1927).
4. R. Robison and W. T. J. Morgan, Boichem. J. 22, 1277 (1928).
5. R. Robison and W. T. J. Morgan, Biochem. J. 24, 119 (1930).
6. H. Kurasawa, I. Igaue, T. Hayakawa, and H. Ogami, J. Agr. Chem. Soc. Japan 33, 388 (1959).
7. L. F. Leloir and E. Cabib, J. Am. Chem. Soc. 75, 5445 (1953).
8. E. Cabib and L. F. Leloir, J. Biol. Chem. 231, 259 (1958).
9. J. E. Gander, W. E. Petersen, and P. D. Boyer, Arch. Biochem. Biophys. 69, 85 (1957).
10. J. Staněk, M. Černý, J. Kocourek, and J. Pacák, The Monosaccharides, Acad. Press, New York 1963.
11. W. R. Meagher and W. Z. Hassid, J. Am. Chem. Soc. 68, 2135 (1946).
12. F. J. Reithel and R. G. Young, J. Am. Chem. Soc. 74, 4210 (1952).

13. R. Sasaki and K. Taniguchi, J. Agr. Chem. Soc. Japan (Nippon Nôgei Kagaku Kaishi) *33*, 183 (1959); Chem. Abstr. *54*, 308 (1960).
14. Brit. Patent 819,359; Chem. Abstr. *54*, 7983 (1960).
15. Ger. Patent 1,011,870; Chem. Abstr. *54*, 12501 (1960).
16. H. Bredereck, Ber. *63*, 959 (1930).
17. B. Helferich and F. Stryk, Ber. *74*, 1794 (1941).
18. B. Helferich, E. Bohn, and S. Winkler, Ber. *63*, 989 (1930).
19. J. Compton, J. Am. Chem. Soc. *60*, 1203 (1938).
20. B. Helferich and W. Speicher, Ann. *579*, 106 (1953).
21. L. Asp and B. Lindberg, Acta Chem. Scand. *6*, 941 (1952).
22. R. U. Lemieux and J. P. Barrette, J. Am. Chem. Soc. *80*, 2243 (1958).
23. P. D. Bragg and J. K. N. Jones, Can. J. Chem. *37*, 575 (1959).
24. R. U. Lemieux and J. P. Barrette, Can. J. Chem. *38*, 656 (1960).
25. B. Helferich and H. Collatz, Ber. *61*, 1640 (1928).
26. W. Will and F. Lenze, Ber. *31*, 68 (1898).
27. E. J. Hoffmann and V. P. Hawse, J. Am. Chem. Soc. *41*, 235 (1919).
28. P. Lhoste, Mém-Poudres *39*, 191 (1937); Chem. Abstr. *52*, 21107 (1958).
29. W. Koenigs and E. Knorr, Ber. *34*, 4343 (1901).
30. W. M. Corbett, J. Kidd, and A. M. Liddle, J. Chem. Soc. *1960*, 616.
31. B. Helferich, A. Löwa, W. Nippe, and Riedel, Hoppe-Seyler's Z. physiol. Chem. *128*, 146 (1923).
32. P. D. Bragg, J. K. N. Jones, and J. C. Turner, Can. J. Chem. *37*, 1412 (1959).

# XVI

# Glycosides of Reducing Oligosaccharides*

The simplest method for preparing glycosides, employed in the mono-saccharide series and consisting of heating a suspension or solution of the mono-saccharide with the appropriate alcohol in the presence of hydrogen chloride, is not well suited to oligosaccharides, mainly with regard to the possibility of the glycosidic linkage of the oligosaccharide cleaving in acid solution. In a comprehensive review in 1957,[1] the possibility of such a preparation was excluded altogether; lately, however, in the methanolysis of the polysaccharide dextran, various fractions of methyl glycosides were obtained, corresponding to the homologous series of isomaltose.[2] Consequently, such a synthesis cannot be regarded as impossible even in the oligosaccharide series.

This is also supported by a Japanese paper,[3] reporting that methyl α-mal-toside may be obtained from maltose by heating this substance with 0·1% methanolic hydrogen chloride to 50°C for 42 hours.**

The most frequently employed method for preparing glycosides of reducing oligosaccharides is probably synthesis, which, however, usually leads to glyco-side derivatives, in particular per-O-acetylated compounds. Their conversion into free glycosides presents no problem; it may be carried out reliably in alka-line solution by the action of sodium methoxide (by the Zemplén method), as well as by means of an alcoholic ammonia solution,[4] or, as reported recently,[5] in a moderately acidic methanolic solution in the cold.

Acylated halogenoses were used as starting materials for the preparation of acylated methyl glycosides of cellobiose,[6-8] lactose,[9] maltose,[10-13] lamina-ribiose,[14] and various acylated glycosides of higher alcohols, as described, for example, for cellobiose.[15] The reaction may also be carried out by converting a per-O-acetyl derivative of a reducing disaccharide (such as maltose) into the per-O-acetyl derivative of the corresponding halogenose by the action of tita-

---

* For a review see J. Conchie, G. A. Levvy, and C. A. Marsh, Advances in Carbohydrate Chem. *12*, 157 (1957).

** The formation of oligosaccharide alkyl glycosides in a similar way is mentioned also by R. Montgomery, F. Smith, and H. C. Srivastava, J. Am. Chem. Soc. *79*, 698 (1957); H. C. Srivastava and F. Smith, J. Am. Chem. Soc. *79*, 982 (1957); S. A. Barker, M. Stacey, and D. B. E. Stroud, Nature *189*, 138 (1961).

*References see p. 341*

nium tetrachloride,[13],[16] whereupon the acylated glycoside is prepared by the action of alcohol in the presence of silver carbonate.

The reaction of acylated halogenoses of oligosaccharides with alcohols in the presence of mercuric acetate likewise gives rise to acylated glycosides of the β-series, as demonstrated on the reaction of hepta-O-acetyl-α-cellobiosyl bromide with methanol[12] and ethanol.[17] These reactions also proceed in a similar way in the presence of mercuric cyanide.[4]

Acylated β-phenyl glycosides of oligosaccharides, too, are readily formed by the reaction of acylated halogenoses of oligosaccharides with phenol in the presence of potassium hydroxide. This method was employed for preparing the phenyl β-glycosides of maltose,[18],[19] lactose[20] and cellobiose.[21],[22] Contrary to the original classical procedure,[18] viz. the reaction of, for instance, hepta-O-acetyl-α-maltosyl bromide with sodium phenoxide in absolute ether, such a reaction may be carried out easily in acetone with the use of the above-mentioned acylated halogenose, phenol and an aqueous sodium hydroxide solution.[20-22] The mother liquors arising in this operation may be subjected to further treatment for isolating even acylated derivatives of the anomeric phenyl α-glycosides.[19]

The reactions of acylated halogenoses with phenol in the presence of quinoline and silver oxide usually lead to a mixture of both corresponding anomeric acylated phenyl glycosides, which, moreover, are produced in bad yields. Acylated phenyl glycosides of the α-series, however, may be obtained, as demonstrated on cellobiose,[22-24] by the reaction of hepta-O-acetyl-α-cellobiosyl bromide with phenol in the presence of mercuric acetate and aluminium in benzene.[22] In chloroform solution, octa-O-acetylcellobiose is easily formed even in the presence of phenol.[22]

Quite a new procedure for preparing glycosides derived from maltose has been described by Helferich.[25] This is the reaction of hepta-O-acetyl-α-maltosyl bromide with benzyl alcohol, which may be carried out in the presence of zinc oxide and leads to the corresponding acetylated benzyl β-maltoside. A similar reaction between hepta-O-acetyl-α-cellobiosyl bromide and benzyl alcohol also takes place, in the presence of mercuric cyanide.[4]

Another possibility of preparing acylated phenyl glycosides is offered by the Helferich method, according to which the per-O-acetylated derivative of the reducing oligosaccharide is heated in an excess of phenol, in the presence of either zinc chloride (leading to α-anomers) or p-toluenesulphonic acid (leading to β-anomers). The reaction was examined on the octa-O-acetyl derivative of cellobiose, which readily reacts with phenol in the presence of zinc chloride to form phenyl hepta-O-acetyl-α-cellobioside.[22],[26],[27] Equally successful was the preparation of phenyl hepta-O-acetyl-α-maltoside;[3] in this case, in the presence of p-toluenesulphonic acid, also the corresponding phenyl hepta-O-acetyl-β-maltoside is produced,[19] while the preparation of the phenyl hepta-O-acetyl-β-cellobioside was impracticable.[22]

The Helferich reaction with the use of $p$-nitrophenol, applied to oligo-saccharides, is the subject of a paper by Jermyn.[28] Very little is known about possible anomerization; methyl hepta-$O$-acetyl-$\beta$-cellobioside is converted into the corresponding $\alpha$-anomer by the action of titanium tetrachloride;[8] no other experiments have been undertaken in this respect.

A new method elaborated by Helferich[29] seems to be very promising for the preparation of acylated $\alpha$-glycosides of reducing oligosaccharides. This in-vestigator sets out from acylated halogenoses and silver 2,4,6-trimethylben-zoate. As demonstrated on the example of cellobiose, the 2,4,6-trimethyl-benzoyl-$\beta$-cellobiose obtained in this way, when dissolved in methanol and subjected to the action of methanesulphonic acid for about 160 hours, yields methyl $\alpha$-cellobioside.

Among the syntheses of reducing oligosaccharides, we must also include enzymic procedures,[30-33] in which methyl glycosides of higher reducing oligo-saccharides are formed by the transfer of a mono- or oligosaccharide unit from another substance to methyl[30-32] or phenyl glycosides.[33] One investigator,[30] using methyl $\alpha$-D-glucopyranoside as substrate, succeeded in preparing a ho-mologous series of methyl $\alpha$-glycosides of the isomaltose group by enzymic transfer of a D-glucose molecule starting from sucrose and using dextran-sucrase.

Some methyl glycosides of reducing oligosaccharides have been obtained even by syntheses from methyl glycosides of monosaccharides, in particular from appropriately substituted methyl glycosides of monosaccharides by means of the Koenigs-Knorr reaction (see Chapter VI).[34-39]

Oligosaccharide glycosides may be converted by acid hydrolysis into free reducing oligosaccharides, although this method involves a certain risk of simultaneous hydrolysis of the glycosidic linkage itself in the oligosaccharide. For selective hydrolytic removal of the glycosidic methyl group it is recommend-ed that the methyl glycoside of the reducing oligosaccharide be heated for an hour to 90°C with 90% formic acid.[37]

Methyl glycosides of reducing oligosaccharides have also been used for structure correlation. For example, methyl $\beta$-lactoside and methyl $\beta$-cellobiosi-de, on oxidation with potassium periodate, must yield the same tetraldehyde (see Chapter III, 2).

### Thioglycosides of reducing oligosaccharides

Acylated halogenoses of the series of reducing oligosaccharides react with thiophenol in alkaline solution fo form the corresponding acylated phenyl $\beta$-thioglycosides. This reaction was described for thiophenol itself[40-44] and pro-ceeds similarly with other thiophenols.[41,45] The deacetylation of these products in alkaline solution presents no difficulties,[40,41,43,45] while in acid solution the glycosidic linkage of the oligosaccharide is split preferentially; thus, phenyl

$\beta$-thiolactoside gives rise to phenyl $\beta$-thio-D-glucoside,[40,41,45] and the splitting of phenyl $\beta$-thiomaltoside takes place analogously.[43,45]

The special significance of phenyl thioglycosides from the series of reducing oligosaccharides lies in the fact that these substances have contributed

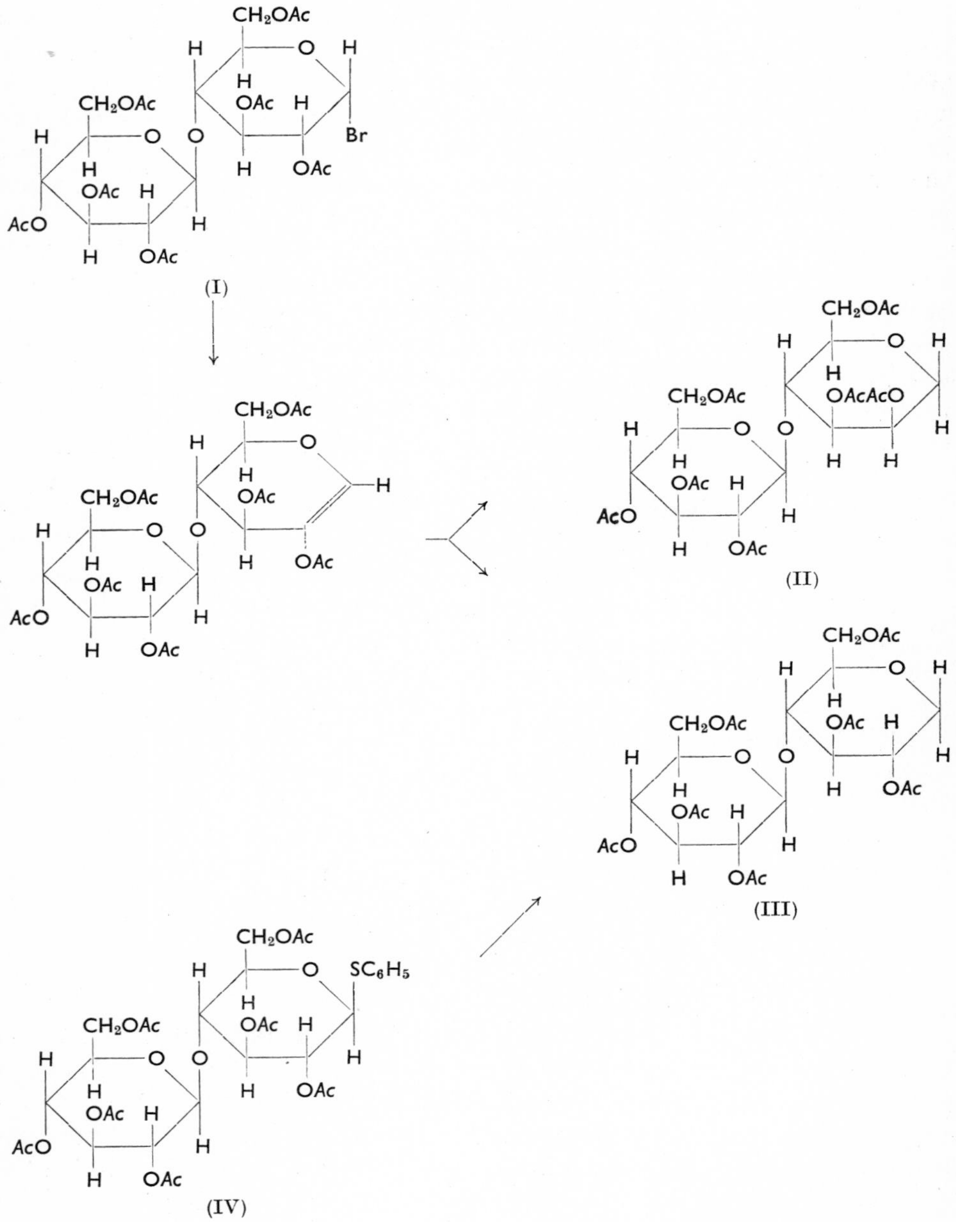

CH₂OAc
H — O H
H
OAc H
CH₂OAc
H — O O     Br
H
OAc H    H    OAc
AcO
H   OAc

(I)

CH₂OAc
H — O
H
OAc
CH₂OAc    H — H
H — O O
H      H   OAc
OAc H
AcO
H
H   OAc

CH₂OAc
H — O H
H
OAcAcO
CH₂OAc    H   H
H — O O
H
OAc H    H
AcO
H   OAc

(II)

CH₂OAc
H — O H
H
OAc H
CH₂OAc    H   OAc
H — O O
H
OAc H    H
AcO
H   OAc

(III)

CH₂OAc
H — O   SC₆H₅
H
OAc H
CH₂OAc    H
H — O O
H     H   OAc
OAc H
AcO
H
H   OAc

(IV)

to the elucidation of the structure of products formed by the action of diethylamine upon acylated halogenoses from the series of reducing oligosaccharides[46,47] and the following hydrogenation. Such a reaction may convert hepta-O-acetyl-α-cellobiosyl bromide (I) into a substance with L-configuration at C-2 (i. e. a styracitol derivative, II) or a compound with D-configuration at C-2 (a D-glucitol derivative, III). The authors of the first papers on this subject were convinced that they had obtained styracitol derivatives.[47] Desulphurization of phenyl hepta-O-acetyl-β-thiocellobioside (IV),[44] where the position of the acetoxy group at C-2 is exactly defined, leads to the same product as obtained by the action of diethylamine on hepta-O-acetyl-α-cellobiosyl bromide (I) and following hydrogenation. Consequently, the structure of the product cannot correspond to a styracitol derivative but only to a derivative of D-glucitol (III).

A similar procedure was employed[44] for correcting the structure of the product formed by the action of diethylamine on hepta-O-acetyl-α-gentiobiosyl bromide[47] and hydrogenation, and which was also regarded as a styracitol derivative,[47] while in fact it is a derivative of 6-O-β-D-glucopyranosyl-D-glucitol.[44] Similar desulphurizations are also desribed in another paper.[48]

**Table LV**

Physical Properties of Oligosaccharide Methyl Glycosides and Their Acetylated Derivatives

| Oligosaccharide Derivative | Melting Point °C | $[\alpha]_D$ | Solvent | References |
|---|---|---|---|---|
| Methyl | | | | |
| α-maltoside | 201—202 | +183° | $H_2O$ | 3, 31, 32 |
| hepta-O-acetate | 163—164 | +101·6° | $C_2H_2Cl_4$ | 49, 50 |
| β-maltoside | 155 | | | |
| monohydrate | 110 | + 78·8° | $H_2O$ | 34 |
| | 111 | + 81° | $H_2O$ | 12 |
| | | + 83·9° | $H_2O$ | 10 |
| | 113 | + 84·6° | $H_2O$ | 11 |
| hepta-O-acetate | 123—124 | | | 12, 13 |
| | 126—128 | | | 11, 51 |
| | 128—129 | + 53·5° | CHCl₃ | 10, 52, 53 |
| 6,6′-di-O-mesyl-penta-O-acetate | 175—176 | + 56·6° | CHCl₃ | 12 |
| α-cellobioside | 144—145 | + 96·8° | $H_2O$ | 8 |
| hepta-O-acetate | 185 | + 55·7° | CHCl₃ | 8 |
| | 186 | + 57·8° | CHCl₃ | 29 |
| β-cellobioside | 193 | — 19·1° | $H_2O$ | 6, 8, 17, 90 |
| | | — 19·7° | $H_2O$ | 11 |
| | 198 | — 30·0° | $H_2O$ | 12 |
| | 192·5 | — 19·4° | $H_2O$ | 54 |
| hepta-O-acetate | 187 | — 25·0° | CHCl₃ | 6, 17, 35, 90 |
| | | — 25·7° | CHCl₃ | 51 |
| | | — 26·5° | CHCl₃ | 7 |
| | 178—182 | | | 12 |
| 6,6′-di-O-tosyl derivative | 160—162 | — 2·9° | CHCl₃ | 7 |
| 6,6′-di-O-mesyl-penta-O-acetyl derivative | 197—198 | | | 12, 55 |

*References see p. 341*

*Table LV — continued*

| Oligosaccharide Derivative | Melting Point °C | $[\alpha]_D$ | Solvent | References |
|---|---|---|---|---|
| α-gentiobioside | 120 | + 65·5° | $H_2O$ | 34, 56 |
|    monohydrate | 100—102 | + 59·4° | $H_2O$ | 34, 56 |
|    hepta-O-acetate | 96 | + 64·5° | $CHCl_3$ | 56 |
| | 94 | + 72° | $CHCl_3$ | 57 |
|    2,3,4-tri-O-benzoyl-2′,3′,4′,6′-tetra-O-acetyl derivative | 173 | + 53·2° | $CHCl_3$ | 34 |
| | 190—191 | | | 84 |
|    2,3,4-tri-O-acetyl-2′,3′,4′,6′-tetra-O-benzoyl derivative | amorphous | + 73·2° | $CHCl_3$ | 57 |
|    hepta-O-benzoate | 192—193 | + 55° | $CHCl_3$ | 84 |
| β-gentiobioside | 98 | — 36° | $H_2O$ | 58 |
|    hepta-O-acetate | 82 | — 18·9° | $CHCl_3$ | 58, 84 |
| | 150—151 | — 23·7° | $CHCl_3$ | 59, 84 |
|    hepta-O-benzoate | 203 | + 2·0° | $CHCl_3$ | 60 |
| | 211 | + 8·3° | $CHCl_3$ | 84, 85 |
| α-isomaltoside | 110—111 | +177·4° | $H_2O$ | 30 |
| | | +169° | $H_2O$ | 61 |
|    hepta-O-benzoate | 188—189 | +108° | $CHCl_3$ | 85 |
| β-isomaltoside | | | | |
|    hepta-O-benzoate | 85 | + 54·7° | $CHCl_3$ | 60 |
| | 125 | + 56·4° | $CHCl_3$ | 85 |
| β-lactoside | 170—171 | | | 62, 63 |
| | 206 | + 5·6° | $H_2O$ | 64 |
|    hepta-O-acetate | 76—77 | — 5·9° | $CHCl_3$ | 63 |
| | 65—66 | + 6·4° | $CHCl_3$ | 62 |
| α-epi-lactoside | 207 | + 66° | $H_2O$ | 65 |
|    hepta-O-acetate | amorphous | + 36° | $CHCl_3$ | 65 |
| α-epi-cellobioside | 227—228 | + 46° | $H_2O$ | 66 |
|    hepta-O-acetate | 185 | + 29·3° | $CHCl_3$ | 66, 67 |
| β-epi-cellobioside | 229 | — 48·5° | $H_2O$ | 67 |
|    hepta-O-acetate | 178 | — 23·2° | $CHCl_3$ | 67 |
| β-laminaribioside | 165—166 | — 28° | $H_2O$ | 14 |
|    hepta-O-acetate | 179—180 | — 45° | $CHCl_3$ | 14 |
| β-melibioside | | | | |
|    hepta-O-acetate | 158—160 | + 92·7° | $CHCl_3$ | 68 |
| | 150 | + 90·5° | $CHCl_3$ | 69 |
| β-primeveroside | | | | |
|    hexa-O-acetate | 220 | — 37° | $CHCl_3$ | 70 |
| β-isoprimeveroside | | | | |
|    hexa-O-acetate | 124 | + 66° | $CHCl_3$ | 70 |
| β-sophoroside | 189—190 | — 28° | $H_2O$ | 83 |
| β-turanoside | 173—174 | + 3·5° | $H_2O$ | 8 |
|    hepta-O-acetate | 188—189 | + 27·5° | $CHCl_3$ | 8 |
| 3-O-β-D-glucopyranosyl-D-xylofuranoside | | | | 71 |
| 4-O-β-D-galactopyranosyl-D-xylopyranoside | 247—248 | — 18° | $H_2O$ | 72, 73 |
| α-maltotrioside | | +200° | $H_2O$ | 31, 32 |
| α-isomaltotrioside | 140—146 | +185·4° | $H_2O$ | 30 |
| | | +176·3° | $H_2O$ | 61 |
| 6-O-β-cellobiosyl-β-D-glucoside | | | | |
|    deca-O-acetate | 248—249 | — 23·5° | $CHCl_3$ | 74 |
| 6-O-β-cellobiosyl-α-D-glucoside | | | | |
|    deca-O-acetate | 235 | + 26·2° | $CHCl_3$ | 74 |
| 6-O-β-D-galactopyranosyl-α-D-glucoside | | | | |
|    hepta-O-acetate | 99 | + 65° | $CHCl_3$ | 84 |

*Table LV — continued*

| Oligosaccharide Derivative | Melting Point °C | $(\alpha)_D$ | Solvent | References |
|---|---|---|---|---|
| 6-O-α-D-mannopyranosyl-α-D-glucopyranoside | | | | |
| hepta-O-acetate | 137 | +111° | CHCl₃ | 84 |
| β-cellotrioside | 240—242 | − 13·7° | H₂O | 90 |
| deca-O-acetate | 198—199 | − 25·9° | CHCl₃ | 90 |
| β-cellotetraoside | 251—253 | − 10° | H₂O | 90 |
| trideca-O-acetate | 215—216 | − 25·2° | CHCl₃ | 90 |
| α-maltotetraoside | | +213° | H₂O | 31, 32 |
| α-isomaltotetraoside | 192—193 | +188·6° | H₂O | 30 |
| 6-O-β-gentiobiosyl-β-gentiobioside | 100 | − 30·3° | H₂O | 75 |
| trideca-O-acetate | 236 | − 16·4° | CHCl₃ | 75 |
| β-cellopentaoside | 255—258 | − 8·1° | H₂O | 90 |
| hexadeca-O-acetate | 224—226 | − 24·2° | CHCl₃ | 90 |
| α-isomaltopentaoside | 161—164 | +188·7° | H₂O | 30 |

**Table LVI**

Physical Properties of Oligosaccharide Phenyl Glycosides and Their Acetyl Derivatives

| Oligosaccharide Derivative | Melting Point °C | $[\alpha]_D$ | Solvent | References |
|---|---|---|---|---|
| Phenyl | | | | |
| α-maltoside | syrup | +198° | H₂O | 68 |
| | 202—204 | +211° | H₂O | 3 |
| hepta-O-acetate | 182 | +164° | CHCl₃ | 19 |
| | 184—185 | +170° | CHCl₃ | 3, 68 |
| β-maltoside | 96 | + 34° | H₂O | 18, 19 |
| hepta-O-acetate | 157—158 | + 42° | CHCl₃ | 18, 19 |
| α-cellobioside | 251 | +124° | H₂O | 26, 27, 76 |
| | 252—254 | +122° | H₂O | 22 |
| hepta-O-acetate | 217 | + 81·1° | CHCl₃ | 23, 24 |
| | 225 | + 78·7° | CHCl₃ | 22 |
| | 224 | + 77·9° | CHCl₃ | 77 |
| | 226 | + 83° | CHCl₃ | 26 |
| | 228 | | | 86 |
| β-cellobioside | 211—213 | − 60° | H₂O | 21 |
| dihydrate | 209 | − 53·1° | H₂O | 22 |
| hepta-O-acetate | 193 | | | 78 |
| | 206—208 | − 36° | CHCl₃ | 21 |
| β-gentiobioside | 190—193 | − 67° | H₂O | 26,33 |
| hepta-O-acetate | 194—195 | − 29° | CHCl₃ | 8 |
| α-lactoside | amorphous | + 88·7° | H₂O | 76 |
| hepta-O-acetate | amorphous | + 66·6° | CHCl₃ | 76 |
| β-lactoside | 191—192 | − 36° | H₂O | 20, 21 |
| hepta-O-acetate | 162 | − 23° | CHCl₃ | 20, 21 |

*References see p. 341*

22*

## Table LVII

Physical Properties of Some Other Oligosaccharide Glycosides and Their Acetylated Derivatives

| Oligosaccharide Derivative | Melting Point °C | $[\alpha]_D$ | Solvent | References |
|---|---|---|---|---|
| Ethyl β-maltoside | 168—169 | +79·2° | $H_2O$ | 79 |
| hepta-O-acetate | 132 | +48·9° | $CHCl_3$ | 79 |
| Benzyl β-maltoside | 142—145 | | | 25, 87 |
| | 148—149 | | | 89 |
| hepta-O-acetate | 121—123 | | | 25, 79, 89 |
| 2,3,2′,3′,4′-penta-O-acetyl derivative | 174—175 | +26° | $CHCl_3$ | 88 |
| 2,3,4,2′,3′,6′-hexa-O-acetyl derivative | 162—164 | +24·9° | $CHCl_3$ | 25 |
| 6-O-tosyl derivative | 135—137 | +35·4° | $CHCl_3$ | 25 |
| Ethyl α-cellobioside | | | | |
| hepta-O-acetate | 175·5 | +57·2° | $CHCl_3$ | 17 |
| Isopropyl α-cellobioside | | | | |
| hepta-O-acetate | 209 | +59·5° | $CHCl_3$ | 17, 23 |
| Isopropyl β-cellobioside | | | | |
| hepta-O-acetate | | −22·7° | $CHCl_3$ | 17 |
| n-Butyl α-cellobioside | | | | |
| hepta-O-acetate | 172 | +52·4° | $CHCl_3$ | 17 |
| n-Butyl β-cellobioside | 147—151 | −34·9° | $H_2O$ | 15 |
| hepta-O-acetate | | −24·6° | $CHCl_3$ | 17 |
| | 189—190·5 | −26·4° | $CHCl_3$ | 15 |
| Benzyl β-cellobioside | 187 | −35·6° | $H_2O$ | 4, 80 |
| hepta-O-acetate | 187 | | | 80 |
| | 190 | | | 4 |
| | 193 | −37·4° | $CHCl_3$ | 78 |
| Hexahydrobenzyl β-cellobioside | | | | |
| hepta-O-acetate | 186·5 | | | 81 |
| Benzyl β-xylobioside | syrup | −126° | $H_2O$ | 82 |
| Ethyl 6-O-β-cellobiosyl-α-D-glucopyranoside | | | | |
| deca-O-acetate | 212 | +23·6° | $CHCl_3$ | 74 |
| Benzyl 6-O-β-D-glucopyranosyl-β-maltoside | | | | |
| deca-O-acetate | 115 | +13·8° | $CHCl_3$ | 25 |

**Table LVIII**

Physical Properties of Some Oligosaccharide Thiglycosides and Their Acetylated Derivatives

| Oligosaccharide Derivative | Melting Point °C | $[\alpha]_D$ | Solvent | References |
|---|---|---|---|---|
| Phenyl | | | | |
| β-thiolactoside | 220 | −40·6° | $H_2O$ | 40, 41 |
| hepta-O-acetate | 164 | −17·6° | $CHCl_3$ | 40 |
| | 155—156 | −19·6° | $CHCl_3$ | 41 |
| β-thiocellobioside | 230 | −59·2° | $H_2O$ | 41 |
| hepta-O-acetate | 295 | −29·5° | $CHCl_3$ | 41 |
| β-thiomaltoside | | +38·1° | $H_2O$ | 43 |
| hepta-O-acetate | 95 | +48·6° | $CHCl_3$ | 43 |
| 2-Naphthyl | | | | |
| β-thiolactoside | 217 | −38·2° | $C_5H_5N$ | 45 |
| hepta-O-acetate | 142 | −16·0° | $CHCl_3$ | 45 |
| β-thiocellobioside | 185 | −58·3° | EtOH | 45 |
| hepta-O-acetate | 203 | −25·3° | $CHCl_3$ | 45 |
| β-thiomaltoside | | | | |
| hepta-O-acetate | 136 | +46·1° | $CHCl_3$ | 45 |

**REFERENCES**

1. J. Conchie, G. A. Levvy, and C. A. Marsh, Advances in Carbohydrate Chem. *12*, 157 (1957).
2. T. A. Scott and F. R. Senti, J. Am. Chem. Soc. *77*, 3816 (1955).
3. S. Matsubara, Bull. Chem. Soc. Japan *34*, 718 (1961); Chem. Abstr. *56*, 8823 (1962).
4. G. Jayme and W. Demmig, Chem. Ber. *93*, 356 (1960).
5. J. Staněk and J. Černá, Tetrahedron Letters *1963*, 35.
6. B. Helferich, A. Löwa, W. Nippe, and H. Riedel, Hoppe-Seyler's Z. physiol. Chem. *128*, 141 (1923).
7. B. Helferich, E. Bohn, and S. Winkler, Ber. *63*, 989 (1930).
8. E. Pacsu, J. Am. Chem. Soc. *52*, 2571 (1930).
9. R. Ditmar, Ber. *35*, 1951 (1902).
10. J. C. Irvine and I. M. A. Black, J. Chem. Soc. *1926*, 826.
11. T. J. Schoch, E. J. Wilson, and C. S. Hudson, J. Am. Chem. Soc. *64*, 2871 (1942).
12. F. H. Newth, S. D. Nicholas, F. Smith, and L. F. Wiggins, J. Chem. Soc. *1949*, 2550.
13. J. Karasawa, Dôshisha Joshidaigaku *7*, 227 (1956); Chem. Abstr. *54*, 3216 (1960).
14. P. Bächli and E. G. V. Percival, J. Chem. Soc. *1952*, 1243.
15. R. Hori, J. Pharm. Soc. Japan (Yakugaku Zasshi) *78*, 999 (1958); Chem. Abstr. *53*, 3573 (1959).
16. J. Karasawa and R. Onishi, Dôshisha Joshidaigaku *9*, 1 (1958); Chem. Abstr. *54*, 3217 (1960).
17. G. Zemplén and A. Gerecs, Ber. *63*, 2720 (1930).
18. E. Fischer and E. F. Armstrong, Ber. *35*, 3153 (1902).
19. L. Asp and B. Lindberg, Acta Chem. Scand. *6*, 941 (1952).
20. B. Helferich and R. Griebel, Ann. *544*, 191 (1940).
21. E. M. Montgomery, N. K. Richtmyer, and C. S. Hudson, J. Am. Chem. Soc. *65*, 1848 (1943).

22. J. Staněk and J. Kocourek, Chem. listy 47, 697 (1953); Chem. Abstr. 49, 190 (1955).
23. G. Zemplén, Ber. 62, 990 (1929).
24. G. Zemplén and Z. Szomolyai-Nagy, Ber. 63, 368 (1930).
25. B. Helferich and W. Speicher, Ann. 579, 106 (1953).
26. B. Helferich and F. Schmitz-Hillebrecht, Ber. 66, 378 (1933).
27. G. Jayme and W. Demmig, Chem. Ber. 88, 434 (1955).
28. M. A. Jermyn, Australian J. Chem. 8, 403 (1955).
29. B. Helferich and W. Pick, Ann. 623, 124 (1959).
30. R. W. Jones, A. Jeanes, C. S. Stringer, and H. M. Tsuchiya, J. Am. Chem. Soc. 78, 2499 (1956).
31. S. Peat, W. J. Whelan, and G. Jones, J. Chem. Soc. 1957, 2490.
32. J. H. Pazur, J. M. Marsh, and T. Ando, J. Am. Chem. Soc. 81, 2170 (1959).
33. T. Yamaka and C. E. Cardini, Arch. Biochem. Biophys. 86, 133 (1960).
34. B. Helferich and J. Becker, Ann. 440, 1 (1924).
35. B. Helferich and H. Bredereck, Ber. 64, 2411 (1931).
36. I. J. Goldstein, F. Smith, and H. C. Srivastava, J. Am. Chem. Soc. 79, 3858 (1957).
37. D. H. Ball and J. K. N. Jones, J. Chem. Soc. 1957, 4871.
38. G. O. Aspinall and R. J. Ferrier, Chem. & Ind. (London) 1957, 819.
39. G. O. Aspinall and R. J. Ferrier, J. Chem. Soc. 1958, 1501.
40. E. Fischer and K. Delbrück, Ber. 42, 1476 (1909).
41. C. B. Purves, J. Am. Chem. Soc. 51, 3619 (1929).
42. C. B. Purves, J. Am. Chem. Soc. 51, 3627 (1929).
43. C. B. Purves, J. Am. Chem. Soc. 51, 3631 (1929).
44. H. G. Fletcher and C. S. Hudson, J. Am. Chem. Soc. 70, 309 (1948).
45. W. T. Haskins, R. M. Hann, and C. S. Hudson, J. Am. Chem. Soc. 69, 1668 (1947).
46. K. Maurer, Ber. 63, 25 (1930).
47. K. Maurer and K. Plötner, Ber. 64, 281 (1931).
48. H. G. Fletcher, L. H. Koehler, and C. S. Hudson, J. Am. Chem. Soc. 71, 3679 (1949).
49. K. Freudenberg, H. Hochstetter, and H. Engels, Ber. 58, 666 (1925).
50. K. Freudenberg and H. Scholz, Ber. 63, 1963 (1930).
51. C. S. Hudson and R. Sayre, J. Am. Chem. Soc. 38, 1867 (1916).
52. E. Fischer and E. F. Armstrong, Ber. 34, 2896 (1901).
53. W. Koenigs and E. Knorr, Ber. 34, 4343 (1901).
54. A. Beélik and J. K. Hamilton, J. Org. Chem. 26, 5074 (1961).
55. B. Helferich and F. Stryk, Ber. 74, 1794 (1941).
56. B. Helferich, W. Klein, and W. Schäfer, Ann. 447, 19 (1926).
57. H. Bredereck, A. Wagner, H. Kuhn, and H. Ott, Chem. Ber. 93, 1201 (1960).
58. C. S. Hudson and J. M. Johnson, J. Am. Chem. Soc. 39, 1272 (1917).
59. B. Helferich and H. Masamune, Ber. 64, 1257 (1931).
60. G. Zemplén a Z. Bruckner, Ber. 64, 1852 (1931).
61. R. W. Bailey, S. A. Barker, E. J. Bourne, and M. Stacey, J. Chem. Soc. 1957, 3536.
62. R. Ditmar, Ber. 35, 1951 (1902).
63. R. Ditmar, Monatsh. Chem. 23, 870 (1902).
64. F. Smith and J. W. Van Cleve, J. Am. Chem. Soc. 74, 1912 (1952).
65. W. N. Haworth, E. L. Hirst, M. M. T. Plant, and R. J. W. Reynolds, J. Chem. Soc. 1930, 2644.
66. W. N. Haworth, E. L. Hirst, H. R. L. Streight, H. A. Thomas, and J. L. Webb, J. Chem. Soc. 1930, 2636.
67. H. S. Isbell, J. Research Natl. Bur. Standards 7, 1115 (1931).
68. B. Helferich and S. R. Petersen, Ber. 68, 790 (1935).

69. P. A. Levene and E. Jorpes, J. Biol. Chem. *86*, 403 (1930).

70. G. Zemplén and R. Bognár, Ber. *72*, 47 (1939).

71. S. A. Barker, M. Stacey, and D. B. E. Stroud, Nature *189*, 138 (1961).

72. R. Montgomery. F. Smith, and H. C. Srivastava, J. Am. Chem. Soc. *79*, 698 (1957).

73. H. C. Srivastava and F. Smith, J. Am. Chem. Soc. *79*, 982 (1957).

74. G. Zemplén, Z. Bruckner, and A. Gerecs, Ber. *64*, 744 (1931).

75. G. Zemplén and A. Gerecs, Ber. *64*, 2458 (1931).

76. C. R. Petersen, Ber. Verh. sächs. Akad. Wiss., Leipzig, Math. Phys. Kl. 85, 154 (1933).

77. G. Zemplén, Fortschr. Chemie org. Naturstoffe *1*, 14 (1938).

78. G. Zemplén, Ber. *53*, 1004 (1920).

79. H. Fischer and F. Kögl, Ann. *436*, 219 (1924).

80. K. Hess and G. Salzmann, Ann. *445*, 111 (1925).

81. M. Uenaka, Sci. Papers Osaka Univ. *27*, 17 (1951); Chem. Abstr. *46*, 8883 (1952).

82. G. O. Aspinall and K. M. Ross, J. Chem. Soc. *1961*, 3674.

83. P. A. Finan and C. D. Warren, J. Chem. Soc. *1963*, 5229.

84. H. Bredereck, A. Wagner, D. Geissel, P. Gross, U. Hutten, and H. Ott, Chem. Ber. *95*, 3056 (1962).

85. H. Bredereck, A. Wagner, D. Geissel, and H. Ott, Chem. Ber. *95*, 3064 (1962).

86. J. Karasawa and R. Onishi, Nippon Nogei Kagaku Kaishi *35*, 817 (1961); Chem. Abstr. *60*, 5611 (1964).

87. B. Helferich and A. Berger, Chem. Ber. *90*, 2492 (1957).

88. A. Klemer and F. Gundlach, Chem. Ber. *96*, 1765 (1963).

89. G. G. S. Dutton and K. N. Slessor, Can. J. Chem. *42*, 1110 (1964).

90. M. L. Wolfrom and S. Haq, Tappi *47*, 183 (1964); Chem. Abstr. *60*, 15967 (1964).

# XVII

## Oligosaccharide Orthoesters

Freudenberg and his co-workers prepared in the years 1922—1928[1-3] an isomer of hepta-*O*-acetyl-α-maltosyl chloride, and in 1930 it was found that its structure corresponds to that of the orthoester chloride (I),[4] namely hexa-*O*-acetyl-1,2-(1-chloroethylidene)-α-maltose. The action of methanol on this chloride leads to the corresponding methyl ester, likewise of orthoester structure (II).[2,5,6]

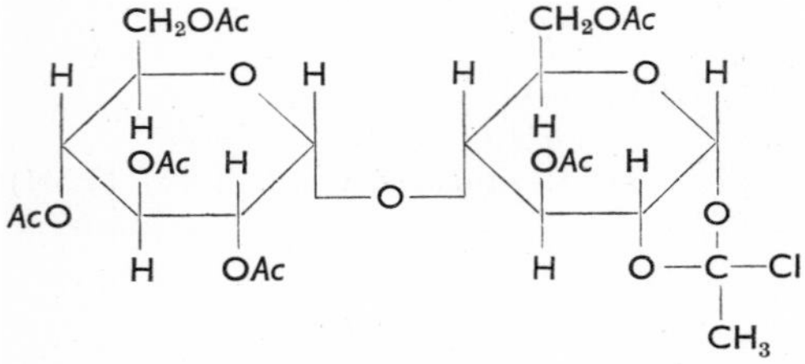

(I)

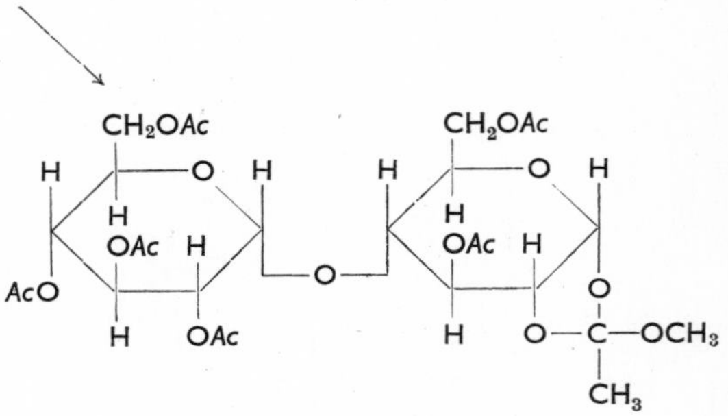

(II)

According to our present knowledge[7,8] it is obvious that the formation of orthoesters is limited for the greater part to those compounds, mainly acylated halogenoses in the series of sugars, in which the halogen atom at C-1 of aldoses or at C-2 of ketoses and the adjacent acyloxy group are in mutual *trans*-positions. In agreement with this, a substance of orthoester structure is formed by the reaction of hepta-*O*-acetyl-α-*epi*-cellobiosyl bromide with methanol,[9] and the reactions of derivatives of celtrobiose[10] and *neo*-lactose[11] proceed likewise. The hepta-*O*-acetyl derivative of 6-*O*-β-D-glucopyranosyl-α-D-mannopyranosyl halogenoses yields both possible isomers of the generating methyl orthoester.[12]

The decomposition of 2,3,4,6-tetra-*O*-acetyl-α-D-mannopyranosyl bromide in the presence of silver oxide gives rise to a new type of carbohydrate orthoesters. The substance formed contains three units of D-mannose linked together through the functional groups of a molecule of acetoacetic acid; for details see C. S. Giam, H. R. Goldschmid, and A. S. Perlin, Can. J. Chem. *41*, 3074 (1963).

Finally, turanose (3-*O*-α-D-glucopyranosyl-D-fructose), too, satisfies by its configuration at C-2 and C-3 the conditions for the formation of orthoesters, and, in fact, substances of orthoester type have been prepared in this case also.[13]

The orthoesters undoubtedly play an important role in a number of other reactions, in particular in migration of acyl groups (see Chapter XIII), as is the case, for example, in the formation of the 1,3,6,2',3',4',6'-hepta-*O*-acetyl derivatives of cellobiose[14] by the hydrolysis of hepta-*O*-acetylcellobiosyl bromide.

**Table LIX**

Physical Properties of Oligosaccharide Orthoesters

| Oligosaccharide Derivative | Melting Point °C | $[\alpha]_D$(CHCl$_3$) | References |
|---|---|---|---|
| 1,2-*O*-(1'-Chloroethylidene)-maltose hexa-*O*-acetate | 112—114 | +67·5° | 1—4 |
| 1,2-*O*-(1'-Methoxyethylidene)-maltose hexa-*O*-acetate | 161—162 | +98·8° | 5, 6 |
| | 164 | +101·6° (C$_2$H$_2$Cl$_4$) | 2 |
| 1,2-*O*-(1'-Methoxyethylidene)-*epi*-cellobiose hexa-*O*-acetate | 167 | — 12·7° | 9 |
| 1,2-*O*-(1'-Methoxyethylidene)-celtrobiose hexa-*O*-acetate | 216 | +110° | 10 |
| 1,2-*O*-(1'-Methoxyethylidene)-*neo*-lactose hexa-*O*-acetate | 122 | + 25·3° | 11 |
| 1,2-*O*-(1'-Methoxyethylidene)-6-*O*-β-D-glucopyranosyl-D-mannose hexa-*O*-acetate | | | |
| dextro-rotatory isomer | 169 | +171° | 12 |
| laevo-rotatory isomer | 174 | — 27·6° | 12 |
| 2,3-*O*-(1'-Methoxyethylidene)-turanose hexa-*O*-acetate | 137 | +114·6° (H$_2$O) | 13 |
| | 164 | + 80° | 13 |

**REFERENCES**

1. K. Freudenberg and O. Ivers, Ber. *55*, 941 (1922).
2. K. Freudenberg, H. Hochstetter, and H. Engels, Ber. *58*, 666 (1925).
3. K. Freudenberg, W. Dürr, and H. Hochstetter, Ber. *61*, 1740 (1928).

4. K. Freudenberg and H. Scholz, Ber. *63*, 1969 (1930).
5. E. Pascu and F. V. Rich, J. Am. Chem. Soc. *57*, 587 (1935).
6. W. Korytnyk and J. A. Mills, J. Chem. Soc. *1959*, 636.
7. J. Staněk, M. Černý, J. Kocourek, and J. Pacák, *The Monosaccharides*, Acad. Press, New York 1963.
8. E. Pascu, Advances in Carbonhydrate Chem. *1*, 78 (1945).
9. H. S. Isbell, J. Research Natl. Bur. Standards *7*, 1115 (1931); Chem. Abstr. *26*, 2173 (1932).
10. N. K. Richtmyer and C. S. Hudson, J. Am. Chem. Soc. *58*, 2534 (1936).
11. H. L. Frush and H. S. Isbell, J. Research Natl. Bur. Standards *27*, 413 (1941); Chem. Abstr. *36*, 1018 (1942).
12. E. L. Talley, D. D. Reynolds, and W. L. Evans, J. Am. Chem. Soc. *65*, 575 (1943).
13. E. Pacsu, J. Am. Chem. Soc. *55*, 2451 (1933).
14. W. M. Corbett, J. Kidd, and A. M. Liddle, J. Chem. Soc. *1960*, 616.

# XVIII

# Ethers of Oligosaccharides

## 1. METHYL ETHERS

The methyl ethers are probably the most important of the ethers derived from oligosaccharides. None of the substances contained in this group can be regarded as a genuinely naturally occuring product.

$O$-α-D-Glucopyranosyl-(1→6)-$O$-α-D-glucopyranosyl-(1 → 6)-3-$O$-methyl-D-glucose[1] and a similarly constituted tetrasaccharide[1] have been obtained by enzymic methods (see Chapter VI, 5); other methylated derivatives have been obtained by the splitting of per-$O$-methylated polysaccharides or higher oligosaccharides, for example, in the methanolysis of per-$O$-methylated agar from *Ahnfeltia plicata.*[2]

The per-$O$-methyl derivatives are of greatest significance for structural studies of oligosaccharides as the investigation of their hydrolysis and the identification of the splitting products usually offers a clear picture of the constitution of the oligosaccharide (see Chapter III, 1). For this reason, a relatively large number of per-$O$-methylated oligosaccharide derivatives is known, although their exact identification is impaired by the fact that these substances are as a rule obtainable in syrupy form only.

The older method of permethylation, known from the chemistry of mono-sacharides,[3] i. e. the action of methyl iodide in the presence of silver oxide, has practically fallen into disuse. The procedure recommended today consists of repeated methylation with dimethyl sulphate in an aqueous sodium hydroxide solution,[4-8] in particular combined with a subsequent  final methylation with methyl iodide in the presence of silver oxide.[9-11] Dioxane has been reported as a satisfactory solvent for methylation procedures.[12]

With regard to the many difficulties encountered, the problem involved in the permethylation of oligosaccharides was recently thoroughly re-examined,[13] and it is recommended that the reaction be carried out with methyl iodide in dimethylformamide, in the presence of strontium oxide. From the results obtained it is obvious that the course of the methylation is influenced by a number of factors including not only such expected items as the nature of the base added and the temperature, but also the amount of the solvent.[13]

*References see p. 351*

Dimethyl sulphoxide has been found to be a good solvent for methylation of oligo-saccharides, like sucrose and maltose, see H. C. Srivastava, S. N. Harshe, and P. P. Singh, Indian J. Chem. *1*, 304 (1963); Chem. Abstr. *59*, 14093 (1963). By the action of the same solvent on 2,3,4,6-tetra-*O*-methyl-D-glucose, octa-*O*-methyl derivatives of trehalose and *neo*-trehalose have been prepared, see F. Micheel, W. Nielinger, and F. Zerhusen, Tetra-hedron Letters *1963*, 1205.

Although it is an almost general rule that the glycosidic linkage is stable in alkaline solution (for exceptions see Chapter VII), unexpected complications may sometimes be encountered in constitutional studies by means of methyla-tion analysis; thus, the permethylation of raffinose yields besides other pro-ducts also a per-*O*-methyl derivative of melibiose, i. e. of a splitting product of raffinose.[14]

If the methylation is not carried out by an often repeated operation, the substances obtained sometimes give satisfactory analytical results, correspond-ing to incompletely methylated derivatives; however, the products of this type are probably no chemical individuals. In this way it was possible to obtain a hepta-*O*-methyl derivative of sucrose[15] and a hexa-*O*-methyl derivative of methyl *β*-cellobioside.[16,17] As is the case in the monosaccharide series, in the case of reducing oligosaccharides, too, the methyl group can be hydro-lytically removed from the hemiacetal group of the per-*O*-methyl deriva-tive of the reducing oligosaccharide with the formation of a product with reducing properties. The same substances are also obtainable by methylation of benzyl glycosides of oligosaccharides[18] and elimination of the benzyl group. This is best achieved by hydrogenation on palladium, whereas on platinum the aromatic nucleus of the benzyl group is hydrogenated prefe-rentially.[18]

Partially methylated derivatives of oligosaccharides are of minor impor-tance; they may be prepared from other appropriately substituted derivatives by methylation and subsequent removal of the blocking groups, as has been done, for instance, in the preparation of penta-*O*-methyl derivatives of sucro-se.[19,20] Other attempts to achieve partial methylation of an oligosaccharide by direct action of the methylation reagent have not been very promising. This is obvious from the case of sucrose,[21] where the methylation of the trisodium salt of sucrose with the methyl ester of *p*-toluenesulphonic acid gives rise to a mono-*O*-methyl derivative which, however, is evidently not homogeneous, as on mere hydrolysis it yields D-glucose, D-fructose, 5-*O*-methyl- and 2-*O*-methyl-D-glucose and, further, 1-*O*-methyl- and 3-*O*-methyl-D-fructose.

## Table LX

Physical Properties of Oligosaccharide Methyl Ethers

| Oligosaccharide Methyl Ether | Melting Point °C | $[\alpha]_D$ | Solvent | References |
|---|---|---|---|---|
| 6-$O$-$\alpha$-D-glucopyranosyl-3-$O$-methyl-D-glucose | | $+121°$ | $H_2O$ | 1 |
| $O$-$\alpha$-D-Glucopyranosyl-$(1\to6)$-$O$-$\alpha$-D-glucopyranosyl-$(1\to6)$-3-$O$-methyl-D-glucose | | $+130°$ | $H_2O$ | 1 |
| $O$-$\alpha$-D-Glucopyranosyl-$(1\to6)$-$O$-$\alpha$-D-glucopyranosyl-$(1\to6)$-$O$-$\alpha$-D-glucopyranosyl-$(1\to6)$-3-$O$-methyl-D-glucose | | $+129°$ | $H_2O$ | 1 |
| Mono-$O$-methylsucrose | | $+ 60·6°$ | $H_2O$ | 21 |
| 1′,4,6-Tri-$O$-methylsucrose | | | | 19, 20 |
| 2,3,2′,3′-Tetra-$O$-methyl-4-$O$-$\alpha$-D-xylopyranosyl-D-xylose | | | | 22 |
| Penta-$O$-methylsucrose | | $+ 28·3°$ | $CHCl_3$ | 19, 20 |
| Hepta-$O$-methylsucrose | b.p.195/0·001 | $+ 68·5°$ | MeOH | 15 |
| Octa-$O$-methylsucrose | b.p. 115/0·001 | $+ 70·1°$ | MeOH | 23 |
| | | $+ 29·5°$ | | 24 |
| Octa-$O$-methyltrehalose | b.p. 170/0·03 | $+199·8°$ | $C_6H_6$ | 25 |
| | | $+ 69·3°$ | MeOH | 15, 26, 27 |
| Hendeca-$O$-methylkestose | | $+ 25·8°$ | $H_2O$ | 12 |
| | | $+ 25°$ | | 28 |
| | | $+ 20·1°$ | $CHCl_3$ | 12 |
| Hendeca-$O$-methylisokestose | | $+ 27·7°$ | | 28 |
| | | $+ 27·9°$ | $CHCl_3$ | 29 |
| | | $+ 27·3°$ | $CHCl_3$ | 30 |
| Tetradeca-$O$-methylbifurcose | | $+ 3·0°$ | | 28 |
| Tetradeca-$O$-methyllychnose | | $+101°$ | $CHCl_3$ | 9 |
| Tetradeca-$O$-methylscodorose | 45 | $- 49·2°$ | $CHCl_3$ | 31 |
| Tetradeca-$O$-methylstachyose | | $+130°$ | $CHCl_3$ | 4 |
| Heptadeca-$O$-methylverbascose | | $+123·6°$ | | 32 |
| Hepta-$O$-methyl-$\alpha$-cellobiose | 103 | $+50·2° \to +44·1°$ | $H_2O$ | 18, 33, 34 |
| Hepta-$O$-methyl-$\beta$-cellobiose | 96—99 | $+42° \to +44·5°$ | $H_2O$ | 18 |

Crystalline per-$O$-methyl ethers of fructobiose, m.p. 76—77°C, $[\alpha]_D$ $-76·4°$, fructotriose, m.p. 89—91°C, $[\alpha]_D$ $-69·7°$, fructotetraose, m. p. 99—101°C, $[\alpha]_D$ $-61·4°$, and fructopentaose, m.p. 107—109°C, $[\alpha]_D$ $-50·9°$, have been obtained recently by T. Mizuno, Kagaku (Tokyo) *31*, 146 (1961); Chem. Abstr. *55*, 27099 (1961).

*References see p. 351*

**Table LXI**

Physical Properties of Methylated Oligosaccharide Glycosides

| Oligosaccharide Derivative | Melting Point °C | $[\alpha]_D$ | Solvent | References |
|---|---|---|---|---|
| Methyl | | | | |
| 2-*O*-(4-*O*-methyl-α-D-glucopyrano-syl)-D-xyloside | | + 95° | | 35 |
| penta-*O*-methyl-3-*O*-β-L-arabino-pyranosyl-L-arabinoside | | +128° | CHCl₃ | 36 |
| penta-*O*-methyl-3-*O*-α-D-xylopyra-nosyl-L-arabinoside | b.p. 160/0·3 | | | 37 |
| hexa-*O*-methyl-β-primeveroside | 220 | — 37° | | 38 |
| hexa-*O*-methyl-β-isoprimeveroside | 124 | + 66° | | 38 |
| hexa-*O*-methyl-β-cellobioside | 83—84 | — 7·7° | CHCl₃ | 16, 17 |
| hexa-*O*-methyl-5-*O*-β-D-galactopy-ranosyl-L-arabinoside | | — 45° | | 39 |
| hepta-*O*-methyl-β-maltoside | | + 88·1° | H₂O | 40 |
| | | + 78·9° | CHCl₃ | 40 |
| hepta-*O*-methyl-β-cellobioside | 86 | — 15·9° | H₂O | 16, 17, 41–43 |
| hepta-*O*-methyl-β-isomaltoside | | + 80·7° | | 44 |
| hepta-*O*-methyl-β-gentiobioside | 106 | — 33·9° | H₂O | 45, 46 |
| hepta-*O*-methyl-β-lactoside | 82 | — 5·2° | | 47, 48, 54 |
| | | — 16·9° | EtOH | 47, 48, 54 |
| hepta-*O*-methyl-β-melibioside | 107 | + 97·8° | H₂O | 14 |
| hepta-*O*-methyl-α-melibioside | 123 | | | 14 |
| hepta-*O*-methyl-α-galactobioside | | +116° | | 5 |
| hepta-*O*-methyl-?-sogdianoside | | — 40·3° | H₂O | 49 |
| hepta-*O*-methyl-4-*O*-α-D-glucopy-ranosyl-D-galactopyranoside | | + 52° | | 50 |
| hepta-*O*-methyl-6-*O*-β-D-galacto-pyranosyl-D-galactopyranoside | 68—70 | — 5·7° | MeOH | 7 |
| hepta-*O*-methyl-2-*O*-α-D-manno-pyranosyl-D-mannopyranoside | 43—46 | + 72° | EtOH | 6 |
| hepta-*O*-methyl-3-*O*-α-D-manno-pyranosyl-D-mannopyranoside | b.p. 197/0·3 | | | 36 |
| hepta-*O*-methyl-4-*O*-β-D-manno-pyranosyl-D-mannopyranoside | | — 12° | | 36 |
| hepta-*O*-methyl-6-*O*-α-D-manno-pyranosyl-D-mannopyranoside | b.p. 192/0·1 | | | 36 |
| hepta-*O*-methyl-6-*O*-β-D-manno-pyranosyl-D-mannopyranoside | | — 26° | | 36 |
| deca-*O*-methylmaltotrioside | | +122° | CHCl₃ | 51 |
| deca-*O*-methyl-*O*-β-D-galactopyrano-syl-(1→6)-*O*-β-D-galactopyrano-syl-(1→6)-D-galactopyranoside | 153 | — 18° | | 52 |
| deca-*O*-methyl-*O*-β-D-galactopy-ranosyl-(1→6)-*O*-β-D-galactopy-ranosyl-(1→3)-D-galactopyrano-side | 158—160 | — 10° | MeOH | 7 |
| Benzyl hepta-*O*-methylcellobioside | 72 | — 32·4° | CHCl₃ | 18, 53 |
| Hexahydrobenzyl hepta-*O*-methyl-cellobioside | 60 | — 15·4° | CHCl₃ | 18 |

## REFERENCES

1. S. A. Barker, E. J. Bourne, P. M. Grant, and M. Stacey, J. Chem. Soc. *1958*, 601.
2. K. Arai, J. Chem. Soc. Japan *82*, 1557 (1961).
3. J. Staněk, M. Černý, J. Kocourek, and J. Pacák, *The Monosaccharides*, Acad. Press, New York 1963.
4. R. A. Laidlaw and C. B. Wylam, J. Chem. Soc. *1953*, 567.
5. R. L. Whistler and H. E. Conrad, J. Am. Chem. Soc. *76*, 1673 (1954).
6. P. A. J. Gorin and A. S. Perlin, Can. J. Chem. *34*, 1796 (1956).
7. S. Haq and G. A. Adams, Can. J. Chem. *39*, 1563 (1961).
8. A. Klemer and K. Homberg, Chem. Ber. *93*, 1643 (1960).
9. A. Wickström, J. E. Courtois, P. Le Dizet, and A. Archambault, Bull. soc. chim. France *1958*, 1410.
10. Ch. Araki and K. Arai, Bull. Chem. Soc. Japan *29*, 339 (1956).
11. Ch. Araki and K. Arai, Bull. Chem. Soc. Japan *30*, 287 (1957).
12. N. Albon, D. J. Bell, P. H. Blanchard, D. Gross, and J. T. Rundell, J. Chem. Soc. *1953*, 24.
13. H. Egge, Bull. soc. chim. biol. *42*, 95 (1960).
14. W. Charlton, W. N. Haworth, and W. Hickinbottom, J. Chem. Soc. *1927*, 1527.
15. W. N. Haworth, J. Chem. Soc. *107*, 8 (1915).
16. P. Karrer and F. Widmer, Helv. Chim. Acta *4*, 174 (1921).
17. W. N. Haworth and E. L. Hirst, J. Chem. Soc. *119*, 198 (1921).
18. M. Uenaka, Sci. Papers Osaka Univ. *27*, 17 (1951).
19. G. G. McKeown, R. S. E. Serenius, and L. D. Hayward, Can. J. Chem. *35*, 28 (1957).
20. G. G. McKeown and L. D. Hayward, Can. J. Chem. *35*, 992 (1957).
21. W. A. P. Black, E. T. Dewar, and D. Rutherford, J. Chem. Soc. *1959*, 3073.
22. G. G. S. Dutton and T. G. Murata, Can. J. Chem. *39*, 1995 (1961).
23. H. Bredereck, O. Hagellock, and E. Hambsch, Chem. Ber. *87*, 35 (1954).
24. R. Kuhn and H. Grassner, Ann. *610*, 122 (1957).
25. H. H. Schlubach and K. Maurer, Ber. *58*, 1178 (1925).
26. T. Purdie and J. C. Irvine, J. Chem. Soc. *87*, 1022 (1905).
27. W. N. Haworth and J. G. Mitchell, J. Chem. Soc. *123*, 301 (1923).
28. H. H. Schlubach and H. O. A. Koehn, Ann. *614*, 126 (1958).
29. J. S. D. Bacon and D. J. Bell, J. Chem. Soc. *1953*, 2528.
30. S. A. Barker, E. J. Bourne, and T. R. Carrington, J. Chem. Soc. *1954*, 2125.
31. Y. Kihara, J. Agr. Chem. Soc. Japan *12*, 1044 (1936); Chem. Abstr. *31*, 3013 (1937).
32. S. Murakami, Proc. Imp. Acad. Tokyo *16*, 12 (1940); Chem. Abstr. *34*, 3694 (1940).
33. K. Freudenberg, C. C. Andersen, Y. Go, K. Friedrich, and N. K. Richtmyer, Ber. *63*, 1961 (1930).
34. K. Freudenberg and N. K. Richtmyer, Ber. *63*, 1965 (1930).
35. G. A. Adams, Can. J. Chem. *37*, 29 (1959).
36. J. K. N. Jones and W. H. Nicholson, J. Chem. Soc. *1958*, 27.
37. P. Andrews and J. K. N. Jones, J. Chem. Soc. *1954*, 4134.
38. G. Zemplén and R. Bognár, Ber. *72*, 47 (1939).
39. I. J. Goldstein, F. Smith, and H. C. Srivastava, J. Am. Chem. Soc. *79*, 3858 (1957).
40. J. C. Irvine and I. M. A. Black, J. Chem. Soc. *1926*, 862.
41. F. Micheel and O. Littman, Ann. *466*, 130 (1928).
42. G. Zemplén, Ber. *63*, 1820 (1930).
43. K. Hess and K. Dziengel, Ber. *68*, 1820 (1930).

44. M. L. Wolfrom, A. Thompson, and A. M. Brownstein, J. Am. Chem. Soc. *80*, 2015 (1958).

45. W. N. Haworth and B. Wylam, J. Chem. Soc. *123*, 3120 (1923).

46. G. Zemplén, Ber. *57*, 698 (1924).

47. W. N. Haworth and G. L. Leitch, J. Chem. Soc. *113*, 188 (1918).

48. R. Kuhn and H. H. Schlubach, Hoppe-Seyler's Z. physiol. Chem. *143*, 154 (1925).

49. S. M. Strepkov, Zhur. Obshcheĭ Khim. *28*, 3143 (1958); Chem. Abstr. *53*, 10053 (1959).

50. J. K. N. Jones and M. B. Perry, J. Am. Chem. Soc. *79*, 2787 (1957).

51. J. M. Sugihara and M. L. Wolfrom, J. Am. Chem. Soc. *71*, 3357 (1949).

52. F. Smith and A. M. Stephen, J. Chem. Soc. *1961*, 4892.

53. K. Hess and G. Salzmann, Ann. *445*, 111 (1925).

54. H. H. Schlubach and K. Moog, Ber. *56*, 1957 (1923).

## 2. TRITYL ETHERS*

Tritylation, i. e. introduction of the triphenylmethyl group, leads as a rule to a selective substitution on the primary alcoholic group.[1] Consequently, di-*O*-trityl derivatives are obtainable from trehalose,[2] maltose[3,4] and laminaribiose,[5,6] as well as from cellobiose and its glycosides.[7] For benzyl $\beta$-maltoside[8,9] and methyl $\beta$-cellobioside[10] it was found that mono-*O*-trityl derivatives are obtained in both cases by substitution on the primary alcoholic group in the original non-reducing part of the oligosaccharide.

Trityl derivatives of maltose have been dealt with in papers by A. Klemer and F. Gundlach, Chem. Ber. *96*, 1665 (1963), and by Y. Hirasaka, I. Matsunaga, K. Umemoto, and M. Sukegava, J. Pharm. Soc. Japan (Yakugaku Zasshi) *83*, 966 (1963); Chem. Abstr. *60*, 4232 (1964).

As may be expected, turanose yields a tri-*O*-trityl derivative,[11] and the same applies to raffinose[3,4] and sucrose.[3,4,11,12] Tritylation of scodorose leads to the corresponding hexa-*O*-trityl derivative.[14]

It is obviously possible to acetylate the free hydroxyl groups of the tritylated oligosaccharide and then to split off the trityl groups in acid solution,[5,7–10] and this has also been done in nearly all the cases reported. This operation unblocks the primary alcoholic hydroxyl groups, but may also lead to a migration of the acetyl groups in the molecule. This was demonstrated for sucrose,[12,13,15] where the removal of the trityl groups is accompanied by a shift of the acetyl group from C-4 to C-6 of the glucose part of the molecule.

Trityl ethers were utilized for synthesizing branched trisaccharides from maltose and cellobiose[9,10] (see Chapter VI).

---

\* For a review see B. Helferich, Advances in Carbohydrate Chem. *3*, 79 (1948).

**Table LXII**

Physical Properties of Oligosaccharide Trityl Ethers

| Trityl Derivative | Melting Point °C | $[\alpha]_D$ | Solvent | References |
|---|---|---|---|---|
| 6,6′-Di-O-trityltrehalose | 278—281 | +62·8° | $C_5H_5N$ | 2 |
| hexa-O-acetate | 235—238 | +115·7° | $CHCl_3$ | 2 |
| 6,6′-Di-O-trityllaminaribiose | 146—147 | +40·6° | $CHCl_3$ | 6 |
| hexa-O-acetate | | + 2·0° | $CHCl_3$ | 5 |
| 6,6′-Di-O-tritylmaltose | 137—139 | +78° | EtOH | 3, 4 |
| hexa-O-acetate | 116—119 | +91° | $CHCl_3$ | 3, 4 |
| Tri-O-tritylturanose | 105—115 | +30·9° | $CHCl_3$ | 11 |
| penta-O-acetate | amorphous | +75·9° | $CHCl_3$ | 11 |
| Tri-O-tritylsucrose | 127—129 | +43·4° | EtOH | 3, 4, 12 |
| | | +14·7° | | 13 |
| penta-O-acetate | 125—126 | +57° | $CHCl_3$ | 3, 4, 12, 13 |
| | 230 | +72·4° | $CHCl_3$ | 15 |
| penta-O-methyl ether | | +32·4° | $CHCl_3$ | 13 |
| Tri-O-tritylraffinose | 130 | +79° | EtOH | 3, 4 |
| octa-O-acetate | 123—125 | +66° | $C_5H_5N$ | 3, 4 |
| Hexa-O-tritylscodorose | 77 | —20·7° | $CHCl_3$ | 14 |
| Methyl 6-O-trityl-β-cellobioside 4′,6′-O-ethylidene-2,3,4′,6′-tetra-O-acetyl derivative | 125—130 | —23° | $CHCl_3$ | 10 |
| Methyl 6,6′-di-O-trityl-β-cellobioside | | —12·1° | $CHCl_3$ | 7 |
| penta-O-acetate | amorphous | +19° | $CHCl_3$ | 7 |
| Benzyl 6-O-trityl-β-maltoside hexa-O-acetate | 162—164 | +24·9° | $CHCl_3$ | 8 |

## REFERENCES

1. B. Helferich, Advances in Carbohydrate Chem. *3*, 79 (1948).
2. H. Bredereck, Ber. *63*, 959 (1930).
3. K. Josephson, Ann. *472*, 217 (1928).
4. K. Josephson, Ann. *472*, 230 (1929).
5. J. R. Turvey and J. M. Evans, J. Chem. Soc. *1960*, 2366.
6. A. Klemer and K. Homberg, Chem. Ber. *94*, 2747 (1962).
7. B. Helferich, E. Bohn, and S. Winkler, Ber. *63*, 989 (1930).
8. B. Helferich and W. Speicher, Ann. *579*, 106 (1953).
9. A. Klemer, Angew. Chem. *69*, 638 (1957).
10. A. Klemer, Chem. Ber. *89*, 2583 (1956).
11. E. Pacsu, J. Am. Chem. Soc. *53*, 3099 (1931).
12. G. G. McKeown, R. S. E. Serenius, and L. D. Hayward, Can. J. Chem. *35*, 28 (1957).
13. G. G. McKeown and L. D. Hayward, Can. J. Chem. *35*, 992 (1957).
14. Y. Kihara, J. Agr. Chem. Soc. Japan *12*, 1044 (1936); Chem. Abstr. *31*, 3013 (1937).
15. H. Bredereck, H. Zinner, A. Wagner, G. Faber, W. Greiner, and W. Huber, Chem. Ber. *91*, 2824 (1958).

## 3. OTHER OLIGOSACCHARIDE ETHERS

Other oligosaccharide ethers are materials prepared mainly from sucrose, mostly for technical purposes, to be utilized either as polymers or as plasticizers. In this field reactions have been carried out[1] with mono-, tri-, penta- and heptasodium saccharate and epichlorohydrin; hydroxyethyl ethers[2] and 2-hydroxypropyl ethers of sucrose[3] and further substances derived from them have been prepared. Products of ether character have also been obtained by the reaction of sucrose with 2,3-dihydropyran in dimethylformamide;[4] in this case, too, the many times repeated reaction leads to polymeric materials.

The preparation of mono-$O$-alkyl ethers of sucrose with higher alkyls (octyl-dodecyl) has been reported;[5] benzylation of sucrose in dimethylformamide by benzyl bromide under the presence of silver oxide and barium oxide leads to the octa-$O$-benzyl ether of sucrose.[6] Some other sucrose ethers have been prepared by the action of active unsaturated derivatives on sucrose.[7] From a mixture produced by repeated reaction of sucrose with acrylonitrile, octa-$O$-(2-cyanoethyl)sucrose was isolated.[7]

Octakis-(trimethylsilyl) ether of sucrose was prepared by treating sucrose in pyridine solution with trimethylchlorosilane at $80-85°C$.[8,9] Analogously, octakis-(trimethylsilyl) ether of maltose has been prepared;[10] trimethylsilyl groups undergo rapid hydrolysis in aqueous methanol under regeneration of the parent oligosaccharide.[11]

The action of triphenylchlorosilane on sucrose[7] yields a hexa-$O$-(triphenylsilyl)sucrose; obviously the bulky nature of the substituents prevents further substitution. Tricyclohexylchlorosilane may be regarded as a selective substituting agent,[7] as its reaction with sucrose permits the preparation of the corresponding 6,1′,6′-tri-$O$-(tricyclohexylsilyl)sucrose. Both triphenylsilyl and tricyclohexylsilyl groups were not readily hydrolysed in boiling aqueous methanol, and a mixture of ethanol, ether and 4N sodium hydroxide solution at 65°C was required to regenerate the sucrose.[7]

## REFERENCES

1. W. A. P. Black, E. T. Dewar, J. C. Paterson, and D. Rutherford, J. Appl. Chem. *9*, 256 (1959); Chem. Abstr. *53*, 19893 (1959).
2. U. S. Patent 2,927,919; Chem. Abstr. *54*, 14143 (1960).
3. U. S. Patent 2,908,681; Chem. Abstr. *54*, 14143 (1960).
4. S. A. Barker, J. S. Brimacombe, J. A. Jarvis, and J. M. Williams, J. Chem. Soc. *1962*, 3158.
5. F. Grundschober and V. Prey, Z. Zuckerind. *12*, 502 (1962); Chem. Abstr. *58*, 2496 (1963).
6. M. E. Tate and C. T. Bishop, Can. J. Chem. *41*, 1801 (1963).
7. S. A. Barker, J. S. Brimacombe, M. R. Harnden, and J. A. Jarvis, J. Chem. Soc. *1963*, 3403.
8. C. D. Chang and H. B. Haas, J. Org. Chem. *23*, 773 (1958).
9. F. A. Henglein, G. Abelsnes, H. Henecka, K. Lienhard, P. Nakhre, and K. Scheinost, Makromol. Chem. *24*, 1 (1957); Chem. Abstr. *52*, 4535 (1958).
10. E. J. Hedgley and W. G. Overend, Chem. & Ind. (London) *1960*, 378.

# XIX

# Anhydro Derivatives of Oligosaccharides

## 1. NATURAL SUBSTANCES

The number of anhydro derivatives of oligosaccharides encountered among natural products is very small. Free substances of this type have so far been described only by Strepkov,[1] who isolated the fructosan polygontin, $C_{18}H_{30}O_{15}$, from *Polygonatum sewertzowi*, and the fructosan alliuminoside, $C_{20}H_{12}O_{10}$, from *Allium sewertzowi*. Although in both cases the splitting products of the methylation analysis were isolated and identified, the structure of these substances, whose properties are given in Table LXIV, has so far remained unclear.

A larger number of anhydro derivatives of oligosaccharides has been obtained by splitting higher oligosaccharides and, in particular, polysaccharides. The first substance in this group was agarobiose (I), isolated by Japanese investigators from agar-agar, which is a gel-forming polysaccharide extracted from certain species of red seaweeds, especially *Gelidium amansii*.[2-7] Agarobiose was later obtained also from other sources,[8-10] and its isolation was carried out by various methods; thus, it was isolated after acid hydrolysis,[2-4,7] by methanolysis,[6,8-10] and by mercaptolysis.[5] The structure of this substance, i. e. 4-O-β-D-galactopyranosyl-3,6-anhydro-L-galactose, was established by methylation analysis.[4] It is a very interesting feature of agarobiose that its reaction with methanolic hydrogen chloride does not yield the corresponding methyl glycoside but an acyclic dimethyl acetal (see Chapter XXIX), which conceivably is isolated as primary product in the methanolysis of agar-agar.[6,8-10]

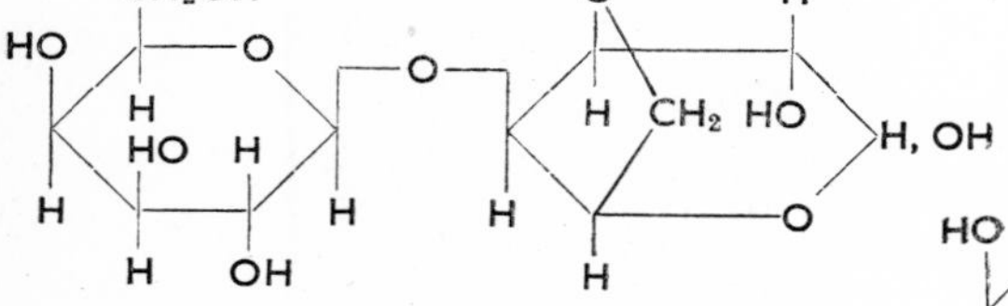

(I)

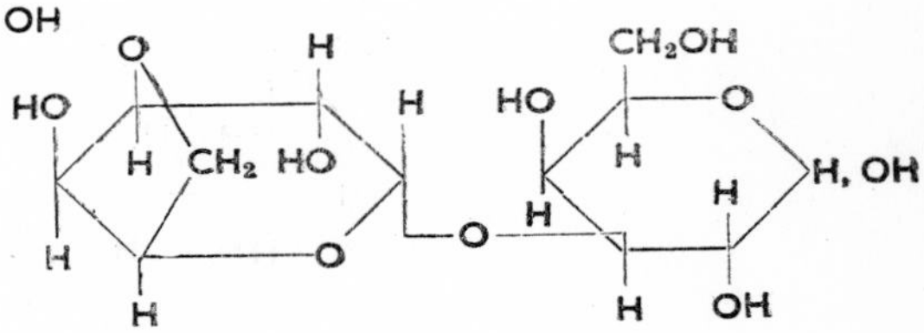

(II)

*References see p. 370*

23*

For some other communications on the isolation of agarobiose from agar-agar see M. Yoshikawa and K. Watanabe, Hyôgo Nôka Daigaku Kenkyû Hôkoku *3*, 53 (1957); Chem. Abstr. *52*, 19198 (1958); W. Yapke, Can. J. Microbiol. *5*, 589 (1960); Chem. Abstr. *54*, 6873 (1960). Some other authors described the isolation of agarobiose after hydrolysis of *Pterocladia tenuis* and *Bangia fusco-purpurea*, see Ya-Chen Wu and Hon-Kai Ho, J. Chinese Chem. Soc. (Taivan) *6*, 84 (1959); Chem. Abstr. *54*, 25092 (1960).

The enzymic hydrolysis of agar-agar proceeds in another way, leading to the disaccharide *neo*-agarobiose (II);[7,11] in this case, too, the structure, corresponding to 3-*O*-α-(3′,6′-anhydro-L-galactopyranosyl)-D-galactose, was established from the products of the methylation analysis.[11] Enzymic splitting of agar-agar produces also the tetrasaccharide *neo*-agarotetraose (III),[7] whose structure corresponds to the composition of *O*-(3,6-anhydro-α-L-galactopyranosyl)-(1 → 3)-*O*-β-D-galactopyranosyl-(1 → 4)-*O*-(3,6-anhydro-α-L-galactopyranosyl)-(1→3)-D-galactose.

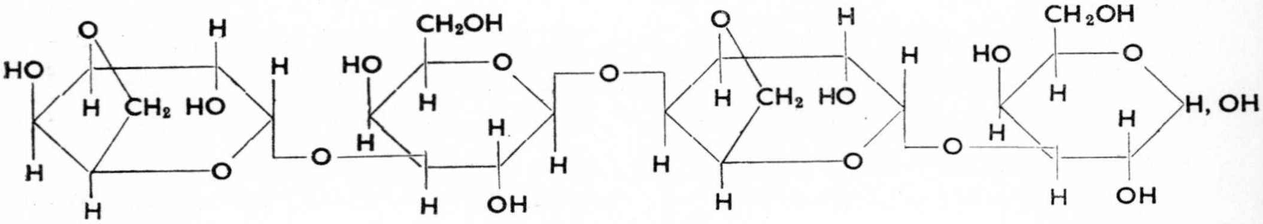

(III)

A further member of this group is 4-*O*-β-D-galactopyranosyl-3,6-anhydro-D-galactose (IV), which was isolated by mercaptolysis,[12,13] autohydrolysis[14] or methanolysis of natural polysaccharidic substrates.[15] The sources of these substances are given in Table LXIII and their properties in Table LXIV.

4-*O*-β-D-Galactopyranosyl-3,6-anhydro-D-galactose was obtained in the form of its dimethyl acetal from the *Chondrus ocellatus* mucilage several years ago, see Ch. Araki and S. Hirase, Bull. Chem. Soc. Japan *29*, 770 (1956); Chem. Abstr. *51*, 8015 (1957). The name carrabiose has been proposed for this substance. The structure of this compound agrees with the results of methylation analysis, see T. J. Painter, J. Chem. Soc. *1964*, 1396; the name carrobiose has been recommended.

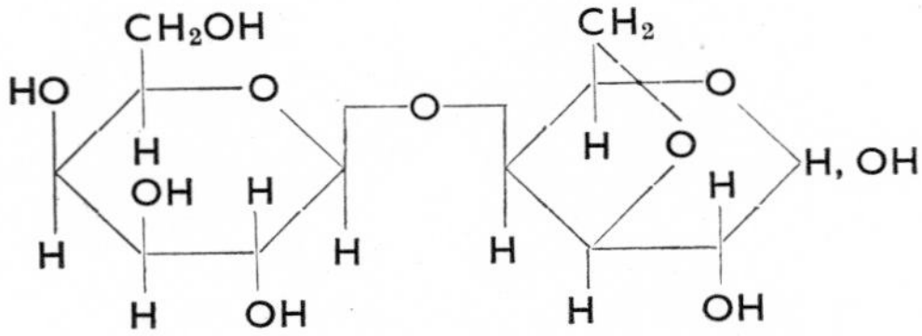

(IV)

## 2. SYNTHETIC DERIVATIVES

### A. ANHYDRO DERIVATIVES OF OLIGOSACCHARIDES OF THE GLYCOSAN TYPE

The first experiments on thermal polymerization of laevoglucosan (1,6-anhydro-$\beta$-D-glucopyranose)[16-20] led only to polymeric products, although in some cases it was possible to isolate oligosaccharides of the orders from tri- to octasaccharides[17,18] (see also Chapter VI). Only quite recently the thermal polymerization of laevoglucosan could be controlled so that four disaccharides and three trisaccharides were isolated in the form of their acetyl derivatives by chromatography on carbon and silica. The disaccharides were identified as 1,6-anhydromaltose (maltosan, 4-$O$-$\alpha$-D-glucopyranosyl-1,6-anhydro-$\beta$-D-glucopyranose), 1,6-anhydrocellobiose (cellobiosan, 4-$O$-$\beta$-D-glucopyranosyl-1,6-anhydro-$\beta$-D-glucopyranose), 1,6-anhydrokojibiose (kojibiosan, 2-$O$-$\alpha$-D-glucopyranosyl-1,6-anhydro-$\beta$-D-glucopyranose), and 1,6-anhydrosophorose (sophorosan, 2-$O$-$\beta$-D-glucopyranosyl-1,6-anhydro-$\beta$-D-glucopyranose). The structures of the trisaccharides prepared in this reaction have so far not been established.

Substances of this group are more easily obtainable by synthesis, which is in principle carried out in two ways. According to the first one, the acylated halogenose is condensed under the conditions of the Koenigs-Knorr reaction with an appropriately substituted derivative of a 1,6-anhydroaldohexose. For instance, the reaction of 2,3,4,6-tetra-$O$-acetyl-$\alpha$-D-glucopyranosyl bromide (V) with 2,3-$O$-isopropylidene-D-mannosan (VI) gives rise to the tetra-$O$-acetyl derivative of 4-$O$-$\beta$-D-glucopyranosyl-2,3-$O$-isopropylidene-D-mannosan (VII). A similar reaction has been carried out with 2,3-$O$-isopropylidene-D-mannosan and 2,3,4,6-tetra-$O$-acetyl-$\alpha$-D-galactopyranosyl bromide[23] and, according to another paper, the latter compound reacts with 2-$O$-acetyl-D-galactosan to form 4-$O$-(2,3,4,6-tetra-$O$-acetyl-$\beta$-D-galactopyranosyl)-2-$O$-acetyl-D-galactosan.[24]

(V)    (VI)    (VII)

According to the second method, phenyl $\beta$-lactoside (VIII) is converted by the action of aqueous potassium hydroxide solution into the lactosan (IX), i. e. 4-$O$-$\beta$-D-galactopyranosyl-1,6-anhydro-$\beta$-D-glucopyranose.[25] This substance is identical with the product obtained in a less pure state by the decomposition of hepta-$O$-acetyl-lactosyltrimethylammonium iodide in alkaline solution.[26]

(VIII)                                                                               (IX)

Analogously, phenyl $\beta$-cellobioside gives rise in alkaline solution to cellobiosan (4-$O$-$\beta$-D-glucopyranosyl-1,6-anhydro-$\beta$-D-glucopyranose).[25] This substance, too, has been obtained in a less pure state[26] in the decomposition of hepta-$O$-acetylcellobiosyltrimethylammonium iodide in alkaline solution. Cellobiosan is also formed by the action of an aqueous barium hydroxide solution on $\beta$-cellobiosyl fluoride.[27]

In the same way, phenyl $\beta$-maltoside in alkaline solution is converted into maltosan (i. e. 4-$O$-$\alpha$-D-glucopyranosyl-1,6-anhydro-$\beta$-D-glucopyranose), which, however, has been isolated only in the form of the hexa-$O$-acetyl derivative.

1,6-Anhydrocellobiose hexa-$O$-acetate has been converted by treatment with titanium tetrachloride in chloroform to 2,3,2',3',4',6'-hexa-$O$-acetyl-$\alpha$-cellobiosyl chloride, see I. Johansson, B. Lindberg, and O. Theander, Acta Chem. Scand. *17*, 2019 (1963).

## B. OTHER ANHYDRO DERIVATIVES

Derivatives of methyl $\beta$-cellobioside and methyl $\beta$-maltoside with mesyl groups in positions 6,6' are converted by the action of sodium hydroxide into the corresponding 3,6:3',6'-dianhydro derivatives.[10] Greater attention has been paid to the trianhydro derivatives of sucrose, which are formed from the tri-$O$-tosyl derivatives of sucrose in alkaline solution and exhibit phenomena very interesting from the theoretical viewpoint.

The known 6,1',6'-tri-$O$-tosylsucrose,[30-32] on heating with an ethanolic solution of sodium ethoxide, yields a trianhydro derivative.[33,34] This substance gives a di-$O$-methyl ether and a di-$O$-tosyl derivative, and its constitution is given by the fact[34] that the latter does not react with sodium iodide in acetone

solution under pressure, from which it is evident that both substituted hydroxyl groups are secondary alcoholic groups.

The isolated trianhydro derivative is remarkably labile in acid solution, in
which it is hydrolysed about 200 times as fast as sucrose. The product of this
hydrolysis, which reduces Fehling solution, has so far not been isolated in a
crystalline state. Nevertheless, its structure was derived in the same indirect
way as that of trianhydrosucrose.[34] The elucidation of the constitution was
supported, on the one hand, by periodic acid oxidation and, on the other hand,
in particular by the identification of the products obtained on reduction of the
labile compound with sodium borohydride and following hydrolysis. According
to this, sucrose yields a 6,1',6'-tri-$O$-tosyl derivative (X) which, in alkaline solution, is converted into 1',2:3,6:3',6'-trianhydrosucrose (XI). Acid hydrolysis
splits the glycosidic linkages with the formation of a hitherto not isolated substance of the structure (XII).

An isomer of the above-mentioned tri-*O*-tosylsucrose, namely 4,1′,6′-tri-*O*-tosylsucrose, obtainable in the form of its penta-*O*-acetyl derivative,[33] yields likewise a trianhydro derivative which is unstable in acid solution. In this case, 4,1′,6′-tri-*O*-tosylpenta-*O*-acetylsucrose (XIII) is converted into 3,6-anhydro-α-D-galactopyranosyl 1,4:3,6-dianhydro-β-D-fructofuranoside (XIV). The formation of both anhydro rings in the fructofuranose part is not surprising, a special feature, however, is the inversion of the configuration at C-4 in the aldose part of the molecule. The authors of the paper in question[33] explain this phenomenon by the assumption that first the 3,4-anhydro ring is formed with inversion of the configuration at C-4, whereupon the anhydro ring

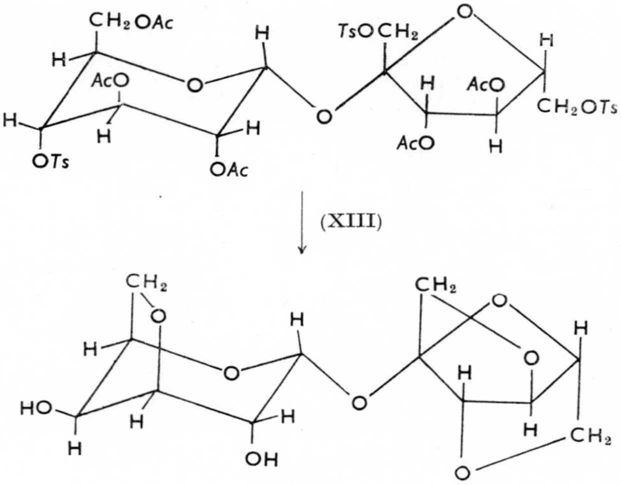

(XIII)

(XIV)

shifts from the positions 3,4 to the positions 2,3 with simultaneous inversion of the configuration at C-3. The hydroxyl group at C-4 now has the L configuration. The formation of the 3,6-anhydro ring from the 2,3-anhydro ring is accompanied by a further inversion of the configuration at C-3, where the hydroxyl group is then likewise in position L.

## C. ANHYDRO DERIVATIVES WITH DOUBLED MONOSACCHARIDE MOLECULES

An interesting reaction was observed[35] in an attempt to detritylate 1,2,3-tri-*O*-acetyl-5-*O*-trityl-D-ribofuranose (XV); contrary to expectations, the reaction product was not 1,2,3-tri-*O*-acetyl-D-ribofuranose, but a substance containing one molecule of acetic acid less, which was first stated to be 2,3-di-*O*-acetyl-1,5-anhydro-D-ribofuranose (XVI). Other writers,[36] when reproducing these experiments, obtained a product which they regarded as another substance in consequence of the great difference in the values of specific rotations (later it was found that Bredereck's data of specific rotations contain a numerical error). The product of the detritylation of the substance (XV) has a doubled molecule, and its structure[36,37] corresponds to 2,3,2′,3′-tetra-*O*-acetyl-1,5′:1′,5-dianhydro-di-D-ribofuranose (XVII).

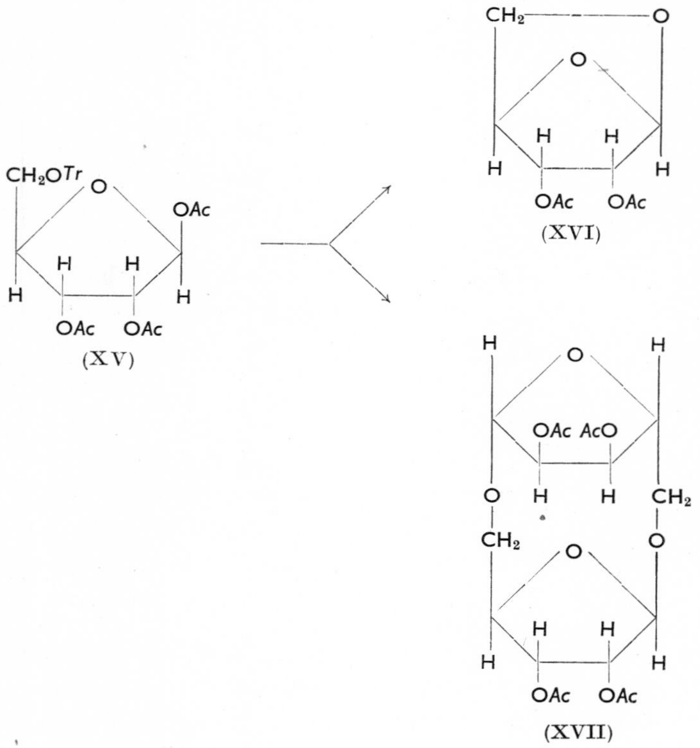
CH₂OTr
O
OAc
H
H
H
H
OAc
OAc
(XV)
CH₂
O
O
H
H
H
H
OAc
OAc
(XVI)
H
O
H
OAc AcO
O
H
H
CH₂
CH₂
O
O
H
H
H
H
OAc
OAc
(XVII)

A substance of the same type was also obtained[38] in the condensation of D-ribose with benzaldehyde which, besides 2,3-*O*-benzylidene-*β*-D-ribofuranose, yields as a by-product also di-(2,3-*O*-benzylidene-D-ribofuranose)-1,5′:1′,5-dianhydride (XVIII),[38] whose hydrogenolysis leads to di-D-ribofuranose-1,5′-1′,5-dianhydride.

Anhydro derivatives of doubled monosaccharide molecules may usually be obtained by the action of hydrochloric acid on ketohexoses. The treatment of L-sorbose with concentrated hydrochloric acid at —5°C gives rise to two products.[39] The first of them, designated as diheterosorbosan *I*, has the structure of 2,1′:1,2′-dianhydro-di-L-sorbopyranose (XIX), while the structure of the

*References see p. 370*

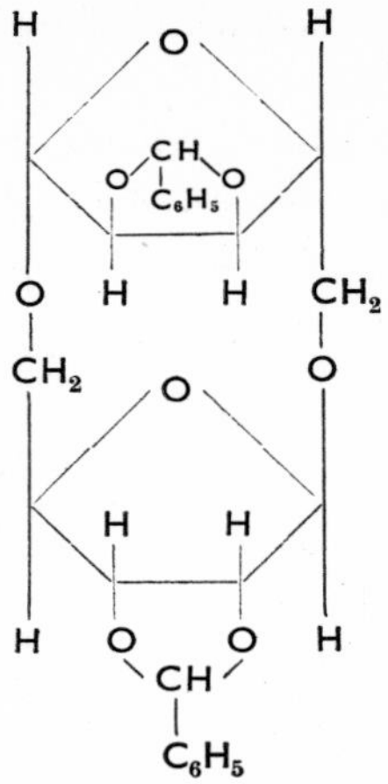

(XVIII)

second product, diheterosorbosan *II*, has not been established with certainty.
It is either 2,1':3,2'-dianhydro-di-L-sorbopyranose (XX) or 2,1':1,2'-dianhydro-
L-sorbofuranosyl-L-sorbopyranose (XXI).

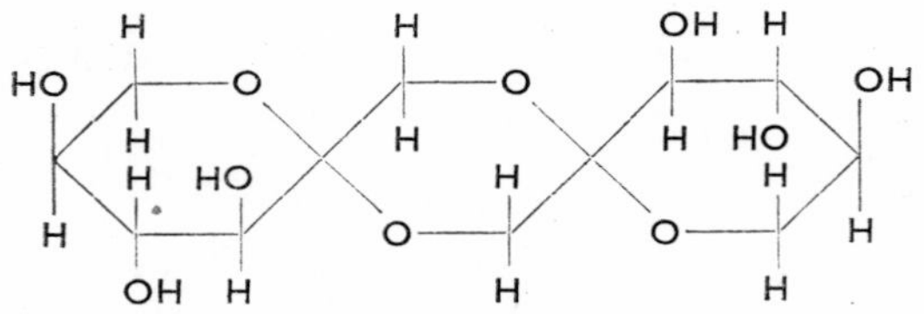

(XIX)

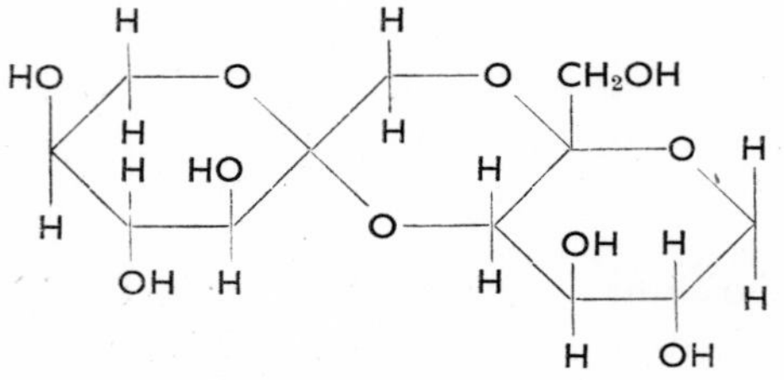

(XX)

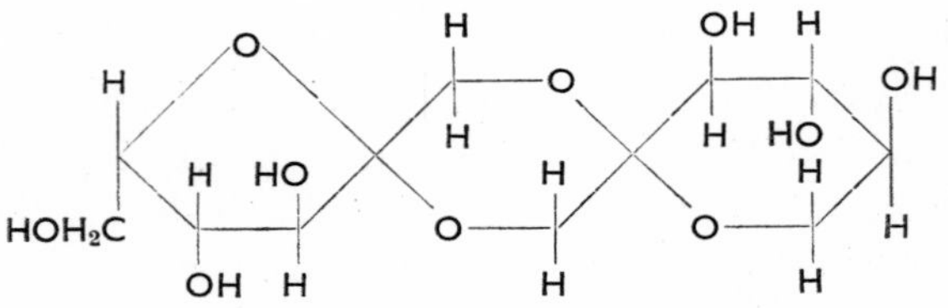

(XXI)

Various dianhydro derivatives composed of two D-fructose molecules are formed by diverse reactions, such as the direct action of acids, usually hydrochloric acid on D-fructose,[40–45] or acid hydrolysis of inulin,[46–50] the action of nitric acid in chloroform on per-*O*-acetyl derivatives of inulin[51–54] or of polyfructosans.[55] Moreover, the nitration of D-fructose with nitronium sulphate[56,57] gives rise to nitric esters of dianhydro derivatives which may be converted by hydrogenation into substances of the above-mentioned type.[57] Heating of D-fructose in absolute ethanol[58] likewise yields products of this class. Finally, methyl ethers of these dianhydrides may be obtained from per-*O*-methyl ethers of inulin.[59]

The identification of these dianhydrides was facilitated by chromatographic methods.[60]

Diheterolaevulosan *I*, 1,2':2,1'-dianhydride of di-D-fructopyranose, is formed by the action of concentrated hydrochloric acid on D-fructose[40] or by the treatment of this monosaccharide with gaseous hydrogen chloride in a sealed tube.[41] It is produced, together with other substances, by heating D-fructose in ethanolic solution[58] and has also been found in the unfermentable constituents of sugar beet molasses.[61,62] The assumption that it might be a monomeric anhydride of D-fructose[40,61] was disproved. The structure was then established by methylation analysis; the hexa-*O*-methyl ether of diheterolaevulosan *I* yielded on hydrolysis, though with difficulty, D-fructose tri-*O*-methyl ether, which may be converted into a phenylosazone, and from this it follows that the hydroxyl groups at C-1 and C-2 are unsubstituted. From the highly negative rotation of diheterolaevulosan *I* it was correctly deduced that both fructose units are linked by hydroxyl groups from C-1 to C-2 and that they are bound in the molecule in the form of pyranoses. This structure (XXII) was then fully confirmed.[42,43] Diheterolaevulosan *I* is also encountered among the products obtained[57] after hydrogenation of the reaction mixture formed by nitration of D-fructose.

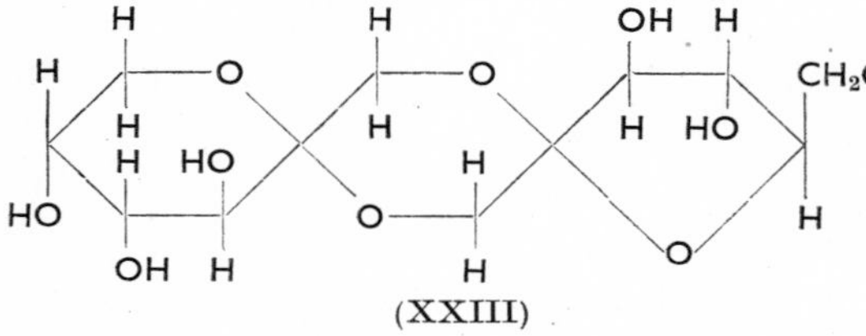

(XXII)

(XXIII)

*References see p. 370*

Diheterolaevulosan *II* is formed either by the action of hydrochloric acid on D-fructose[43,44] or by the hydrogenation of products obtained by the reaction of D-fructose with nitric acid,[57] or, along with other products, by heating D-fructose in ethanol.[58] It is supposed to be 1,2′:2,1′-dianhydro-D-fructopyranosyl-D-fructofuranose (**XXIII**).[43,44,57] Diheterolaevulosan *III*, likewise found among the products of the reaction between D-fructose and hydrochloric acid,[45] is either an anomeric form of the foregoing substance or corresponds in its structure to the 1,2′-3′,2-dianhydride of di-D-fructopyranose.

Di-D-fructose dianhydride *I* has been obtained as a by-product in the acid hydrolysis of inulin;[46−48] it is also formed by the action of nitric acid in chloroform on the per-*O*-acetyl derivative of inulin[51−54] or of polyfructosans[55] and, analogously, the action of nitric acid in chloroform on the per-*O*-methyl derivative of inulin yields the per-*O*-methyl derivative of di-D-fructose dianhydride *I*.[59]

The structure of this product (**XXIV**) was determined by investigating the course of the methylation analysis,[63] whereby the hexa-*O*-methyl derivative of the dianhydride of di-D-fructose *I* yielded 3,4,6-tri-*O*-methyl-D-fructofuranose; from this it follows that the product must have the formula (**XXIV**), i. e. 1,2′:1′,2-dianhydro-di-D-fructofuranose. This substance was also found among the products of the nitration and subsequent hydrogenation of D-fructose,[57] as well as among the products formed by heating D-fructose in ethanol.[58]

The constitution and conformation of di-D-fructose dianhydride *I* has been dealt with in a recent paper by R. U. Lemieux and R. Nagarajan, Can. J. Chem. *42*, 1270 (1964).

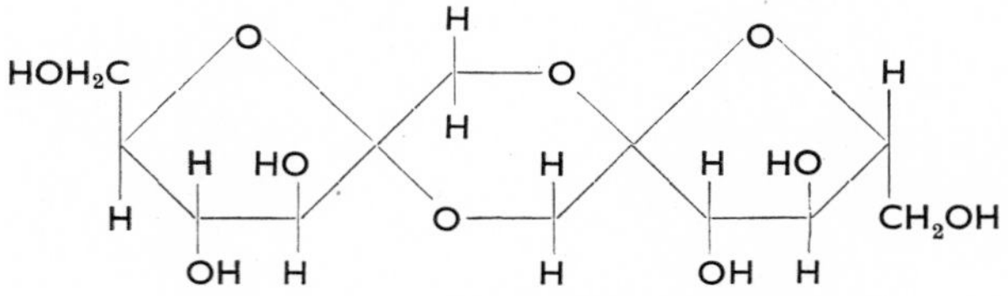

(**XXIV**)

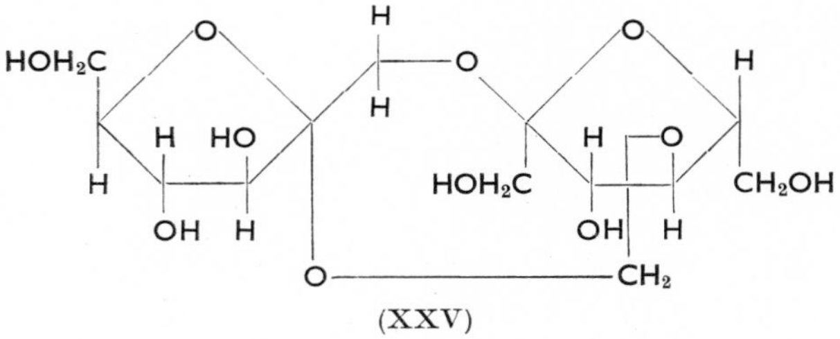

(**XXV**)

Di-D-fructose dianhydride *II*, which always accompanies the foregoing isomer, may be converted into the hexa-*O*-methyl derivative, which on hydrolysis yields two tri-*O*-methyl ethers of D-fructose.[49] The structure of this dianhydride has not been established with certainty, however, the results of periodic acid oxidation seem to prove[64] that it has the structure (XXV), i. e. 2,1':4,2'-dianhydride of di-D-fructose, whereas other writers do not exclude the possibility[45] that this substance and the product dealt with in the following paragraph might differ only in the anomeric arrangement.

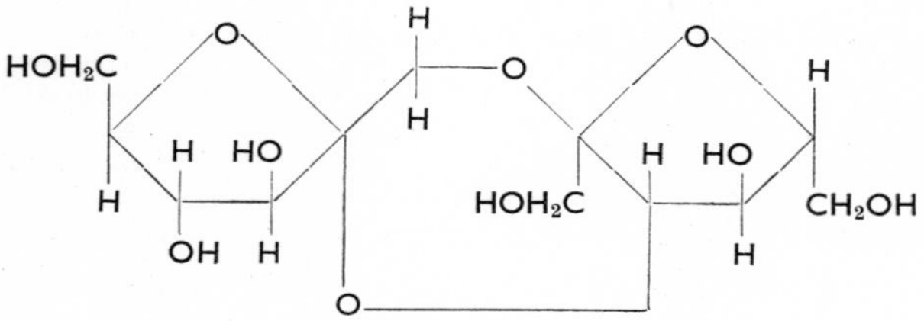

(XXVI)

The structure of the third substance of this group, namely di-D-fructose dianhydride *III*, is not exactly known.[48,49] Since the hydrolysis of the per-*O*-methyl ether yields 3,4,6-tri-*O*-methyl- and 1,4,6-tri-*O*-methyl-D-fructose and the unsubstituted substance gives a tri-*O*-trityl ether, this anhydride must be assumed to have the structure (XXVI) corresponding to the 1,2':2,3'-dianhydride of di-D-fructose.

*References see p. 370*

**Table LXIII**

Anhydro Oligosaccharides Obtained from Higher Oligosaccharides or from Polysaccharides

| Oligosaccharide | Natural Material | Method of Isolation | References |
|---|---|---|---|
| Agarobiose. 4-*O*-β-D-galactopyranosyl-3,6-anhydro-L-galactose | *Gelidium amansii* | acid | 2—4 |
| | | mercaptolysis | 5 |
| | | methanolysis | 6 |
| | *neo*-agarotetraose | acid | 7 |
| | *Gloiopeltis fuscata* | methanolysis | 8 |
| | *Gracilaria confervoides* | methanolysis | 9 |
| | *Ahnfeltia plicata* | methanolysis | 10 |
| *neo*-Agarobiose 3-*O*-(3′,6′-anhydro-α-L-galactopyrano-syl)-D-galactose | *Gelidium amansii* | enzym. | 11 |
| | *neo*-agarotetraose | enzym. | 7 |
| *neo*-Agarotetraose *O*-(3,6-anhydro-α-L-galactopyranosyl)-(1→3)-*O*-β-D-galactopyranosyl-(1→4)-*O*-(3,6-anhydro-α-L-galacto-pyranosyl)-(1→3)-D-galactose | *Gelidium amansii* | enzym. | 7 |
| Carrabiose 4-*O*-β-D-galactopyranosyl-3,6-anhydro-D-galactose | ϰ-carrageenin | mercaptolysis | 12 |
| | *Furcillaria fastigiata* | autohydrolysis | 14 |
| | | mercaptolysis | 13 |
| | *Hypnea specifera* | methanolysis | 15 |
| | *Chondrus ocellatus* | methanolysis | 68 |

**Table LXIV**

Properties of Natural Anhydro Oligosaccharides and Their Derivatives

| Oligosaccharide | Melting Point °C | $[\alpha]_D$ | Solvent | References |
|---|---|---|---|---|
| Polygontin | 207—208 | −52·9° | $H_2O$ | 1 |
| nona-*O*-acetate | 84—85 | −38·4° | $CHCl_3$ | 1 |
| nona-*O*-methyl ether | | −34·8° | $CHCl_3$ | 1 |
| Alliuminoside | 92—93 | −23·8° | $H_2O$ | 1 |
| hexa-*O*-acetate | 98—99 | −29·3° | $CHCl_3$ | 1 |
| hexa-*O*-methyl ether | | −39·7° | $CHCl_3$ | 1 |

## Table LXV

Properties of Anhydro Oligosaccharides Obtained by Hydrolysis

| Oligosaccharide | Melting Point °C | $[\alpha]_D$ | Solvent | References |
|---|---|---|---|---|
| Agarobiose | amorphous | $-21 \cdot 5° \rightarrow$ | | |
| | | $\rightarrow -16 \cdot 4°$ | $H_2O$ | 5 |
| neo-Agarobiose | 202—203 | $+25° \rightarrow$ | | |
| | | $\rightarrow +22 \cdot 5°$ | $H_2O$ | 7 |
| | 207—208 | $+34 \cdot 4° \rightarrow$ | | |
| | | $\rightarrow +20 \cdot 3°$ | $H_2O$ | 11 |
| hexa-O-acetate | 112 | $+1 \cdot 57°$ | $CHCl_3$ | 11 |
| methyl penta-O-methyl-β-glycoside | 127—128 | $-22°$ | $CHCl_3$ | 11 |
| neo-Agarotetraose | 214—218 (dec.) | $-3 \cdot 9°$ | $H_2O$ | 7 |
| dihydrate | 104—107 | $-2 \cdot 8°$ | $H_2O$ | 7 |
| deca-O-acetate | 121 | $-15 \cdot 8°$ | $CHCl_3$ | 7 |
| methyl nona-O-methyl-β-glycoside | 167 | $-87 \cdot 6°$ | $CHCl_3$ | 7 |
| Carrabiose | 211—213 | $+110° \pm 8°$ | $H_2O$ | 13, 14 |
| | | $+15 \cdot 6°$ | $H_2O$ | 68 |

## Table LXVI

Physical Properties of Anhydro Oligosaccharides Prepared by Syntheses

| Anhydro Oligosaccharide | Melting Point °C | $[\alpha]_D$ | Solvent | References |
|---|---|---|---|---|
| Maltosan<br>1,6-anhydromaltose<br>4-O-α-D-glucopyranosyl-1,6-anhydro-β-D-glucopyranose | | | | |
| hexa-O-acetate | 182—183 | $+48°$ | $CHCl_3$ | 28, 65 |
| | 183 | $+49 \cdot 5°$ | $CHCl_3$ | 21 |
| Cellobiosan<br>1,6-anhydrocellobiose<br>4-O-β-D-glucopyranosyl-1,6-anhydro-β-D-glucopyranose | 122 | $-75 \cdot 0°$ | $H_2O$ | 26 |
| | | $-73 \cdot 0°$ | $H_2O$ | 27 |
| hexa-O-acetate | 145—146 | $-54 \cdot 4°$ | $CHCl_3$ | 25 |
| | 144 | $-46°$ | $CHCl_3$ | 26, 27 |
| | 142 | | | 21 |
| second modification | 94—96 | $-52°$ | $CHCl_3$ | 21 |
| 2,3,2′,3′,4′-penta-O-acetate | 156—157 | $-133°$ | $CHCl_3$ | 66 |
| 6′-O-trityl derivative | 119—120 | $-50°$ | $CHCl_3$ | 66 |
| Kojibiosan<br>1,6-anhydrokojibiose<br>2-O-α-D-glucopyranosyl-1,6-anhydro-β-D-glucopyranose | | | | |
| hexa-O-acetate | syrup | $+58°$ | $CHCl_3$ | 21 |
| Sophorosan<br>1,6-anhydrosophorose<br>3-O-β-D-glucopyranosyl-1,6-anhydro-β-D-glucopyranose | | | | |
| hexa-O-aectate | 170—171·5 | $-40 \cdot 6°$ | $CHCl_3$ | 21 |

*References see p. 370*

*Table LXVI — continued*

| Anhydro Oligosaccharide | Melting Point °C | $[\alpha]_D$ | Solvent | References |
|---|---|---|---|---|
| *epi*-Cellobiosan | | | | |
| 1,6-anhydro-*epi*-cellobiose | | | | |
| 4-O-β-D-glucopyranosyl-1,6-anhydro-β-D-mannose | | | | |
| 2,3,4,6-tetra-O-acetate | 192—193 | — 69·8° | CHCl₃ | 22 |
| 2,3,4,6,2′,3′-hexa-O-acetate | 131—132 | — 69·8° | CHCl₃ | 22 |
| 2,3,4,6-tetra-O-acetyl-2′,3′-O-isopropylidene derivative | 176 | — 50·0° | CHCl₃ | 22 |
| Lactosan | | | | |
| 1,6-anhydrolactose | | | | |
| 4-O-β-D-galactopyranosyl-1,6-anhydro-β-D-glucose | 140—144 | — 53·5° | H₂O | 25 |
| monohydrate | 128—130 | — 50·6° | H₂O | 25 |
| hexa-O-acetate | 206—208 | — 40·8° | CHCl₃ | 25 |
| | | — 38·9° | CHCl₃ | 26 |
| *epi*-Lactosan | | | | |
| 1,6-anhydro-*epi*-lactose | | | | |
| 4-O-β-D-galactopyranosyl-1,6-anhydro-β-D-mannose | | | | |
| hexa-O-acetate | 193—194 | — 62·7° | CHCl₃ | 23 |
| Anhydrotrisaccharide *I* | | | | |
| nona-O-acetate | 256 | + 20° | CHCl₃ | 21 |
| Anhydrotrisaccharide *II* | | | | |
| nona-O-acetate | 209·5 | + 26° | CHCl₃ | 21 |
| Anhydrotrisaccharide *III* | | | | |
| nona-O-acetate | 230·5 | — 47° | CHCl₃ | 21 |
| Methyl 3,6:3′,6′-dianhydro-β-cellobioside | 182—183 | —201° | H₂O | 29 |
| tri-O-acetate | 155—156 | —127° | CHCl₃ | 29 |
| Methyl 3,6:3′,6′-dianhydro-β-maltoside | | | | |
| monohydrate | 95—101 | — 66° | H₂O | 29 |
| tri-O-acetate | 218—219 | + 25·4° | CHCl₃ | 29 |
| 1′,2:3,6:3′,6′-Trianhydrosucrose | 163—164·5 | +117° | H₂O | 33, 34 |
| di-O-tosyl derivative | 164·5—166 | | | 34 |
| di-O-methyl ether | 179—181 | +140° | CHCl₃ | 34 |
| 3,6-Anhydro-α-D-galactosyl 1,4:3,6-dianhydro-β-D-fructofuranoside | 191—192·5 | +137·5° | | 33 |
| di-O-acetate | 157·5—158·5 | + 94·3° | CHCl₃ | 33 |
| di-O-tosylate | 158—159 | | | 33 |
| di-O-methyl ether | 105—106 | + 48·5° | CHCl₃ | 33 |
| 1,5′:5,1′-Dianhydro-di-D-ribofuranose | 229—230 | + 78°* | H₂O | 35 |
| | 231—232 | + 8·6° | H₂O | 36, 37 |
| | 230—232 | + 9·5° | H₂O | 38 |
| tetra-O-acetate | 169 | + 51° | CHCl₃ | 35—37 |
| | 171—172 | + 53·5° | CHCl₃ | 38 |
| tetra-O-methyl ether | 130 | | | 36 |
| di-2,3-O-benzylidene derivative | 197—198 | — 36·3° | CHCl₃ | 38 |
| Diheterosorbosan *I* | 249—250 (dec.) | — 11·5° | H₂O | 39 |
| hexa-O-acetate | 168—169 | + 3·7° | CHCl₃ | 39 |
| Diheterosorbosan *II* | 188—189 | 0° | H₂O | 39 |
| hexa-O-acetate | 177—179 | — 19° | CHCl₃ | 39 |
| Diheterolaevulosan *I* | 266—267 | — 43·6° | H₂O | 40, 41 |
| | 263 | — 45·8° | H₂O | 43 |
| | 270—272 | | | 45 |

\* The value +78°, as reported later, [37] is given by mistake instead of +7·8°.

*Table LXIV — continued*

| Anhydro Oligosaccharide | Melting Point °C | $[\alpha]_D$ | Solvent | References |
|---|---|---|---|---|
| hexa-*O*-acetate | 171—173 | — 59·1° | $CHCl_3$ | 41 |
| | | — 41·7° | $C_6H_6$ | 41 |
| hexa-*O*-methyl derivative | 143 —145 | — 46·5° | $CHCl_3$ | 41 |
| Diheterolaevulosan *II* | 257—259 | — 39° | $H_2O$ | 44 |
| | 258—261 | — 35·4° | $H_2O$ | 45 |
| Diheterolaevulosan *III* | 255—258 (dec.) | —179° | $H_2O$ | 45 |
| Di-D-fructose dianhydride *I* | 164 | + 26·9° | $H_2O$ | 46, 47, 51, 54, 63 |
| | 164—165 | + 27·5° | $H_2O$ | 57 |
| hexa-*O*-acetate | 137 | + 0·54° | $CHCl_3$ | 47, 54 |
| hexa-*O*-methyl ether | syrup | + 19·1° | — | 49, 63 |
| | | + 50·4° | $H_2O$ | 49, 63 |
| | | + 23·7° | $CHCl_3$ | 49, 63 |
| 6,6'-di-*O*-trityl ether | 195 | + 20·3° | $CHCl_3$ | 49 |
| 3,4,3',4'-tetra-*O*-acetate | 194 | + 21·1° | $CHCl_3$ | 49 |
| 3,4,3',4'-tetra-*O*-acetate | 173 | — 9·9° | $CHCl_3$ | 49 |
| 6,6'-di-*O*-methyl derivative | 127—128 | + 10·8° | $CHCl_3$ | 49 |
| Di-D-fructose dianhydride *II* | 198 | + 14° | $H_2O$ | 48, 49, 67 |
| | 205 —208 | + 15·1° | $H_2O$ | 45 |
| hexa-*O*-methyl ether | 73 | — 41·9° | — | 49 |
| | | + 6·0° | $H_2O$ | 49 |
| | | — 28·2° | $CHCl_3$ | 49 |
| Di-D-fructose dianhydride *III* | 162 | +135·6° | $H_2O$ | 48, 49 |
| hexa-*O*-methyl ether | syrup | +155·7° | — | 49 |
| | | +164·5° | $H_2O$ | 49 |
| | | +157·9° | $CHCl_2$ | 49 |
| tri-*O*-trityl ether | 127 | + 64·2° | $CHCl_3$ | 49 |

*References see p. 370*

## REFERENCES

1. S. M. Strepkov, Zhur. Obshcheĭ Khim. *28*, 3143 (1958); Chem. Abstr. *53*, 10053 (1959).
2. C. Araki, J. Chem. Soc. Japan *65*, 533 (1944); Chem. Abstr. *42*, 1210 (1948).
3. C. Araki, J. Chem. Soc. Japan *65*, 627 (1944); Chem. Abstr. *45*, 6162 (1951).
4. C. Araki, Mem. Fac. Ind. Arts, Kyoto Techn. Univ., Sci. and Tech., Vol. 2 (B), 43 (1953); Chem. Abstr. *49*, 6138 (1955).
5. S. Hirase and C. Araki, Bull. Chem. Soc. Japan *27*, 105 (1954); Chem. Abstr. *49*, 9517 (1955).
6. C. Araki and S. Hirase, Bull. Chem. Soc. Japan *27*, 109 (1954); Chem. Abstr. *49*, 9517 (1955).
7. C. Araki and K. Arai, Bull. Chem. Soc. Japan *30*, 287 (1957).
8. S. Hirase, C. Araki, and T. Ito, Bull. Chem. Soc. Japan *31*, 428 (1958).
9. A. L. Clingman, J. R. Nunn, and A. M. Stephen, J. Chem. Soc. *1957*, 197.
10. K. Arai, J. Chem. Soc. Japan *82*, 1416 (1961); Chem. Abstr. *57*, 15211 (1962).
11. C. Araki and K. Arai, Bull. Chem. Soc. Japan *29*, 339 (1956).
12. N. A. O'Neill, J. Am. Chem. Soc. *77*, 6324 (1955).
13. T. J. Painter, Can. J. Chem. *38*, 112 (1960).
14. T. J. Painter, Chem. & Ind. (London) *1959*, 1488.
15. A. L. Clingman and J. R. Nunn, J. Chem. Soc. *1959*, 493.
16. A. Pictet, Helv. Chim. Acta *1*, 227 (1918).
17. H. Pringsheim and K. Schmalz, Ber. *55*, 3001 (1922).
18. J. C. Irvine and J. W. H. Oldham, J. Chem. Soc. *127*, 2903 (1925).
19. J. da Silva Carvalho, W. Prins, and C. Schuerch, J. Am. Chem. Soc. *81*, 4054 (1959).
20. I. J. Goldstein and B. Lindberg, Acta Chem. Scand. *16*, 387 (1962).
21. M. L. Wolfrom, A. Thompson, R. B. Ward, D. Horton, and R. H. Moore, J. Org. Chem. *26*, 4617 (1961).
22. W. T. Haskins, R. M. Hann, and C. S. Hudson, J. Am. Chem. Soc. *63*, 1724 (1941).
23. W. T. Haskins, R. M. Hann, and C. S. Hudson, J. Am. Chem. Soc. *64*, 1852 (1942).
24. H. Masamune and S. Kamiyama, Tôhoku J. Exptl. Med. *66*, 43 (1957); Chem. Abstr. *52*, 8974 (1958).
25. E. M. Montgomery, N. K. Richtmyer, and C. S. Hudson, J. Am. Chem. Soc. *65*, 1848 (1943).
26. P. Karrer and J. C. Harloff, Helv. Chim. Acta *16*, 962 (1953).
27. F. Micheel, A. Klemer, and G. Baum, Chem. Ber. *88*, 475 (1955).
28. L. Asp and B. Lindberg, Acta Chem. Scand. *6*, 941 (1952).
29. F. H. Newth, S. D. Nicholas, F. Smith, and L. F. Wiggins, J. Chem. Soc. *1949*, 2550.
30. U. S. Patent 2,365,776.
31. R. C. Hockett and M. Zief, J. Am. Chem. Soc. *72*, 1839 (1950).
32. P. D. Bragg and J. K. N. Jones, Can. J. Chem. *37*, 575 (1959).
33. R. U. Lemieux and J. B. Barrette, J. Am. Chem. Soc. *80*, 2243 (1958).
34. R. U. Lemieux and J. B. Barrette, Can. J. Chem. *37*, 1964 (1959).
35. H. Bredereck, M. Köthning, and E. Berger, Ber. 73, 956 (1940).
36. G. R. Barker and M. V. Lock, J. Chem. Soc. *1950*, 23.
37. R. W. Jeanloz, G. R. Barker, and M. V. Lock, Nature *167*, 42 (1951).
38. H. B. Wood, H. W. Diehl, and H. G. Fletcher, J. Am. Chem. Soc. *78*, 4715 (1956).
39. M. L. Wolfrom and H. N. Hilton, J. Am. Chem. Soc. *74*, 5334 (1952).
40. A. Pictet and J. Chavan, Helv. Chim. Acta *9*, 809 (1926).
41. H. H. Schlubach and C. Behre, Ann. *508*, 16 (1933).

42. E. J. McDoland and R. F. Jackson, J. Research Natl. Bur. Standards *35*, 497 (1945).

43. M. L. Wolfrom and G. Blair, J. Am. Chem. Soc. *70*, 2406 (1948).

44. M. L. Wolfrom, W. W. Binkley, W. L. Shilling, and H. W. Hilton, J. Am. Chem. Soc. *73*, 3553 (1951).

45. M. L. Wolfrom, H. W. Hilton, and W. W. Binkley, J. Am. Chem. Soc. *74*, 2867 (1952).

46. R. F. Jackson and S. M. Goergen, J. Research Natl. Bur. Standards *3*, 27 (1929).

47. R. F. Jackson and S. M. Goergen, J. Research Natl. Bur. Standards 5, 733 (1930).

48. R. F. Jackson and E. J. McDonald, J. Research Natl. Bur. Standards 6, 709 (1931).

49. R. F. Jackson and E. J. McDonald, J. Research Natl. Bur. Standards *24*, 181 (1940).

50. K. Täufel and K. J. Steinbach, Nahrung *3*, 852 (1959); Chem. Abstr. *54*, 14132 (1960).

51. J. C. Irvine and J. W. Stevenson, J. Am. Chem. Soc. *51*, 2197 (1929).

52. H. H. Schlubach and H. Knoop, Ann. *504*, 19 (1933).

53. H. H. Schlubach H. Knoop, and M. Y. Liu, Ann. *511*, 151 (1934).

54. E. W. Bodycote, W. N. Haworth, and C. S. Woolvine, J. Chem. Soc. *1932*, 2389.

55. L. A. Boggs and F. Smith, J. Am. Chem. Soc. *78*, 1878 (1956).

56. W. Will and F. Lenze, Ber. *31*, 68 (1898).

57. A. H. Shamgar and J. Leibowitz, J. Org. Chem. *25*, 430 (1960).

58. A. H. Shamgar and J. Leibowitz, J. Org. Chem. *26*, 285 (1961).

59. W. N. Haworth, E. L. Hirst, and F. A. Isherwood, J. Chem. Soc. *1937*, 782.

60. E. J. McDonald and B. K. Goss, Anal. Chem. *24*, 422 (1952).

61. L. Sattler and F. W. Zerban, Sugar *39*, No. 12, 28 (1944); Chem. Abstr. *39*, 635 (1945).

62. L. Sattler and F. W. Zerban, Ind. Eng. Chem. *37*, 1135 (1945).

63. W. N. Haworth and H. R. L. Streight, Helv. Chim. Acta *15*, 693 (1932).

64. E. J. McDonald and R. F. Jackson, J. Research Natl. Bur. Standards *35*, 497 (1945).

65. P. Karrer and L. Kamienski, Helv. Chim. Acta *15*, 739 (1932).

66. B. Lindberg and L. Selleby, Acta Chem. Scand. *14*, 1051 (1962).

67. E. J. McDonald and A. L. Turcotte, J. Research Natl. Bur. Standards *38*, 423 (1947).

68. Ch. Araki and S. Hirase, Bull. Chem. Soc. Japan *29*, 770 (1956); Chem. Abstr. *51*, 8015 (1957).

# XX

# Condensation Products of Oligosaccharides with Oxo Compounds

The products of the condensation of monosaccharides and their derivatives with oxo compounds represent a very comprehensive and important chapter in the chemistry of monosaccharides, mainly because these substances are advantageous initial materials for further syntheses.[1] It seems very probable that hitherto no substance of this type has been prepared by condensation of an unsubstituted oligosaccharide with an aldehyde or ketone because such reactions proceed in acid solution, where they would be accompanied by the hydrolysis of the glycosidic linkage in the oligosaccharide molecule. The action of even such a mild agent as ethyl metaphosphate[2,3] on sucrose and acetone gives rise to a mixture of isopropylidene derivatives of D-glucose and D-fructose.[4]

An older paper[5] describes the formation of syrupy di-O-ethylidene derivatives from sucrose and maltose by the action of acetaldehyde in the presence of sulphuric acid; this report, however, requires re-examination by means of modern methods.

Glycosides of reducing oligosaccharides, however, may be condensed with oxo compounds. It is known that benzyl β-cellobioside and benzyl β-maltoside, on condensation with benzaldehyde in the presence of zinc chloride, give rise to 4′,6′-mono-O-benzylidene derivatives in good yield; such reactions proceed exclusively at the original non-reducing part of the oligosaccharide molecule.[6,7]

Methyl β-cellobioside (I), too, was recently converted by the action of acetaldehyde, even in the presence of sulphuric acid, into the corresponding 4′,6′-O-ethylidene derivative (II) without hydrolysis of any of the glycosidic linkages present.[8]

In a similar way, benzyl β-maltoside was converted into the corresponding 4′,6′-mono-O-benzylidene derivative.[9]

All other substances of this type in the oligosaccharide series have been prepared by syntheses from suitable lower components,[10-30] such as appropriately substituted monosaccharide derivatives with some of their hydroxyl groups blocked by acetalization or ketalization. Hydrolytic elimination of such blocking groups from the molecule of the substituted oligosaccharide is not diffi-

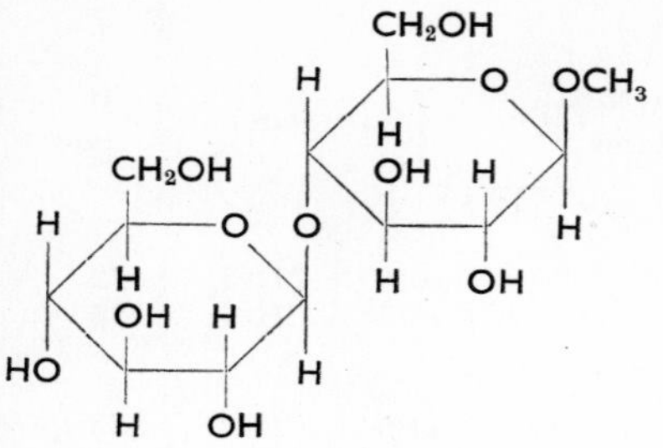

(I)

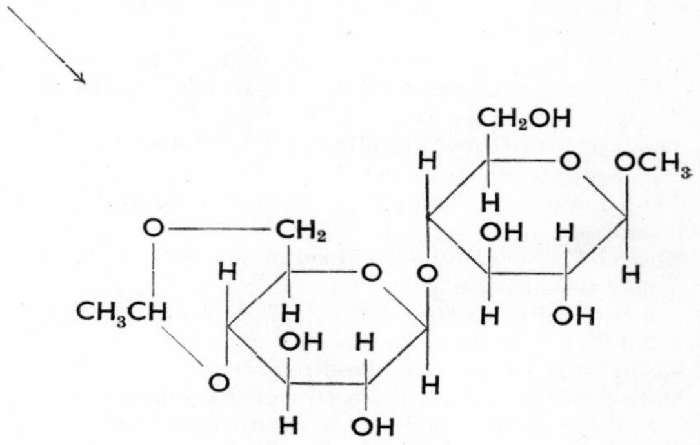

(II)

cult and may be performed in acid solution under such mild conditions[13-17] that the glycosidic linkage of the oligosaccharide itself is not split (see also Chapter VI).

### Table LXVII

Physical Properties of Condensation Products of Oligosaccharides with Oxo Derivatives

| Oligosaccharide Derivative | Melting Point °C | $[\alpha]_D$ | Solvent | References |
|---|---|---|---|---|
| 6-O-β-D-Glucopyranosyl-1,2:3,4-di-O-isopropyli-dene-D-galactopyranose | 84—88 | −67·5° | $H_2O$ | 18 |
| 2,'3',4',6'-tetra-O-acetate | 141 | −52·6° | $C_2H_2Cl_4$ | 18, 29 |
| 3-O-β-(2',3',4',6'-Tetra-O-acetyl-D-glucopyranosyl)-1,2:5,6-di-O-isopropylidene-D-glucofuranose | | | | 15 |
| 3-O-β-D-Glucopyranosyl-1,2-O-isopropylidene-4,6-O-benzylidene-D-glucopyranose | 192 | +39·2° | $C_5H_5N$ | 13 |
| 2',3',4',6'-tetra-O-acetate | 142 | +30·4° | EtOH | 13 |
| 5-O-β-(2',3',4',6'-Tetra-O-acetyl-D-glucopyrano-syl)-1,2-O-isopropylidene-6-deoxy-D-glucofura-nose | 141 | −11·0° | $CHCl_3$ | 19 |
| 3-O-acetate | 128 | −46° | $CHCl_3$ | 19 |
| 6-bromo-6-deoxy-3-O-acetyl derivative | 169 | −59·8° | $C_2H_2Cl_4$ | 20 |
| 1-O-β-D-Glucopyranosyl-2,3:4,5-di-O-isopropyli-dene-D-fructopyranose | 175 | −45·6° | $H_2O$ | 12 |
| 2',3',4',6'-tetra-O-acetate | 163 | −32·9° | $CHCl_3$ | 12, 21 |

*References see p. 374*

*Table LXVII — continued*

| Oligosaccharide Derivative | Melting Point °C | $(\alpha)_D$ | Solvent | References |
|---|---|---|---|---|
| 1-$O$-$\beta$-D-Glucopyranosyl-2,3:4,5-di-$O$-benzylidene-D-fructopyranose | 166—176 | −40·5° | CHCl₃ | 22 |
| 2′,3′,4′,6′-tetra-$O$-acetate | 144 | −41·5° | CHCl₃ | 22 |
| 6-$O$-$\beta$-(2′,3′:5′,6′-di-$O$-isopropylidene-D-galactopyranosyl)-1,2:3,4-di-$O$-isopropylidene-D-galactopyranose | 205—210 | −44·6° | C₂H₂Cl₄ | 23 |
| 2,3:5,6-Di-$O$-isopropylidene-D-mannofuranosyl 2′,3′:5′,6′-di-$O$-isopropylidene-D-mannofuranoside | 181 | +84° | C₂H₂Cl₄ | 23 |
| 6-$O$-$\beta$-(2′,3′,4′,6′-Tetra-$O$-acetyl-D-galactopyranosyl-(1,2:3,4-di-$O$-isopropylidene-D-galactopyranose | 102 | −44·7° | C₂H₂Cl₄ | 23 |
| 6-$O$-$\beta$-(Hepta-$O$-acetylcellobiosyl)-1,2:3,4-di-$O$-isopropylidene-D-galactose | 227 | −47·1° | C₂H₂Cl₄ | 23 |
| 6-$O$-$\beta$-Lactosyl-1,2:3,4-di-$O$-isopropylidene-D-galactose | 117 | −39·8° | H₂O | 23 |
| Methyl 4′,6′-$O$-ethylidene-$\beta$-cellobioside | 281 | | | 8 |
| penta-$O$-acetate | 172 | −45° | CHCl₃ | 8 |
| 6-$O$-trityl-tetra-$O$-acetate | 130 | −23° | CHCl₃ | 8 |
| 2,3,2′,3′-tetra-$O$-acetate | 241 | −56·8° | CHCl₃ | 8 |
| Methyl 4′,6′-$O$-benzylidene-$\beta$-maltoside | | | | 9 |
| Methyl 2-$O$-$\beta$-(2,3,4,6-tetra-$O$-acetyl-D-glucopyranosyl)-4,6-$O$-benzylidene-$\alpha$-D-glucopyranoside | 227 | +42·4° | CHCl₃ | 27, 28 |
| Methyl 2-$O$-$\beta$-(2,3,4,6-tetra-$O$-acetyl-D-glucopyranosyl)-3-$O$-benzyl-4,6-$O$-isopropylidene-D-glucopyranoside | 140—141 | −31·5° | CHCl₃ | 30 |
| Methyl 2-$O$-$\beta$-(2,3,4,6-tetra-$O$-acetyl-D-galactopyranosyl)-4,6-$O$-benzylidene-$\alpha$-D-glucopyranoside | 197—198 | +54·3° | CHCl₃ | 25 |
| Benzyl 4′,6′-$O$-benzylidene-$\beta$-cellobioside | 191 | −47° | MeOH | 6 |
| Benzyl 4′,6′-$O$-benzylidene-$\beta$-maltoside | 116 | +27·3° | MeOH | 6 |
| Benzyl 2-$O$-$\beta$-D-xylopyranosyl-3,4-$O$-isopropylidene-$\beta$-L-arabinopyranoside | 217 | +132° | MeOH | 24 |
| 2′,3′,4′-tri-$O$-acetate | 111 | +71° | CHCl₃ | 24 |

## REFERENCES

1. J. Staněk, M. Černý, J. Kocourek, and J. Pacák, *The Monosaccharides*, Acad. Press, New York 1963.
2. J. Pacák and M. Černý, Chem. listy *51*, 1165 (1957); Chem. Abstr. *51*, 13762 (1957).
3. J. Pacák and M. Černý, Collection Czechoslov. Chem. Communs *23*, 490 (1958).
4. J. Pacák and M. Černý, Collection Czechoslov. Chem. Communs *24*, 3804 (1959).
5. R. Sutra, Bull. soc. chim. France *9*, 794 (1942).
6. K. Hess, H. Hammerstein, and W. Gramberg, Ber. *70*, 1134 (1937).
7. K. Hess and W. Gramberg, Ber. *72*, 1898 (1939).
8. A. Klemer, Chem. Ber. *89*, 2583 (1956).
9. A. Klemer, Angew. Chem. *69*, 638 (1957).
10. K. Freudenberg, W. Dürr, and H. Hochstetter, Ber. *61*, 1735 (1928).
11. R. Kuhn and H. H. Baer, Chem. Ber. *87*, 1560 (1954).
12. B. Helferich and R. Steinpreis, Chem. Ber. *91*, 1794 (1958).

13. M. Gakhokidze, Zhur. Obshcheĭ Khim. *16*, 1923 (1946); Chem. Abstr. *41*, 6210 (1947).

14. S. Haq and W. J. Whelan, J. Chem. Soc. *1958*, 1342.

15. P. Bächli and E. G. V. Percival, J. Chem. Soc. *1952*, 1243.

16. D. H. Ball and J. K. N. Jones, J. Chem. Soc. *1958*, 905.

17. D. H. Ball and J. K. N. Jones, J. Chem. Soc. *1957*, 4871.

18. K. Freudenberg, A. Noë, and E. Knopf, Ber. *60*, 239 (1927).

19. K. Freudenberg, H. Eich, C. Knoevenagel, and W. Westphal, Ber. *73*, 441 (1940).

20. K. Freudenberg, H. Toepffer, and S. H. Zaheer, Ber. *63*, 1966 (1930).

21. E. Pacsu, E. J. Wilson, and L. Graf, J. Am. Chem. Soc. *61*, 2675 (1939).

22. P. Brigl and O. Widmaier, Ber. *69*, 1219 (1936).

23. K. Freudenberg, A. Wolf, E. Knopf, and S. H. Zaheer, Ber. *61*, 1743 (1928).

24. G. O. Aspinall and R. J. Ferrier, J. Chem. Soc. *1958*, 1501.

25. D. Beck and K. Wallenfels, Ann. *655*, 173 (1962).

26. E. J. C. Curtis and J. K. N. Jones, Can. J. Chem. *38*, 1305 (1960).

27. B. Coxon and H. G. Fletcher, J. Org. Chem. *26*, 2892 (1961).

28. K. Freudenberg, H. Toepffer, and C. C. Anderson, Ber. *61*, 1750 (1928).

29. N. K. Kochetkov, A. J. Khorlin, and A. F. Bochkov, Tetrahedron Letters *1964*, 289.

30. P. A. Finan and C. D. Warren, J. Chem. Soc. *1963*, 5229.

# XXI

# Unsaturated Derivatives of Oligosaccharides

## 1. GLYCALS

Acylated halogenoses are readily converted by the action of zinc in acetic acid into unsaturated derivatives, named glycals.[1,2] For monosaccharides, this reaction, described in 1914 by E. Fischer,[3] is of great significance, since it offers the possibility of preparing 2-deoxyaldoses.[4] With regard to the sensitivity of the glycosidic linkage to acid hydrolysis, the glycals are of minor importance in the oligosaccharide series, and in practice it was only Gakhokidze who utilized them for the preparation of the corresponding 2-deoxy derivatives (see Chapter XXII).

Compounds of the glycal type in the oligosaccharide series were described by E. Fischer and his co-workers in 1914,[3,5,6] who first reported on lactal[3,5] and shortly afterwards on cellobial.[6] Hepta-*O*-acetyl-α-lactosyl bromide (I) reacts with zinc in acetic acid to form hexa-*O*-acetyl-lactal (II).[3,5,7-9] The double bond can be reduced with the formation of hexa-*O*-acetyldihydrolactal (III) or can take up two atoms of bromine[5] or chlorine.[10] It is only the halogen atom at C-1 that can be replaced by a hydroxyl group by the action of moist silver oxide or silver carbonate.[10] Deacetylation in alkaline solution converts hexa-*O*-acetyl-lactal (II) into the free lactal (IV); the formerly employed deacetylating agent, barium hydroxide,[5,11] is now being replaced by a solution of ammonia in methanol.[7]

Like tri-*O*-acetyl-D-glucal,[12] hexa-*O*-acetyl-lactal also is converted on heating in aqueous solution, with simultaneous loss of one hydroxyl group and shift of the double bond, and forms penta-*O*-acetyl-ψ-lactal (V); and as in the group of di-*O*-acetyl-ψ-D-glucal, the deacetylation of penta-*O*-acetyl-ψ-lactal[11,13] leads to the so-called isolactal (VI). The solution of the question of whether further substances[13] produced in this reaction are chemical individuals would require the application of more modern methods.

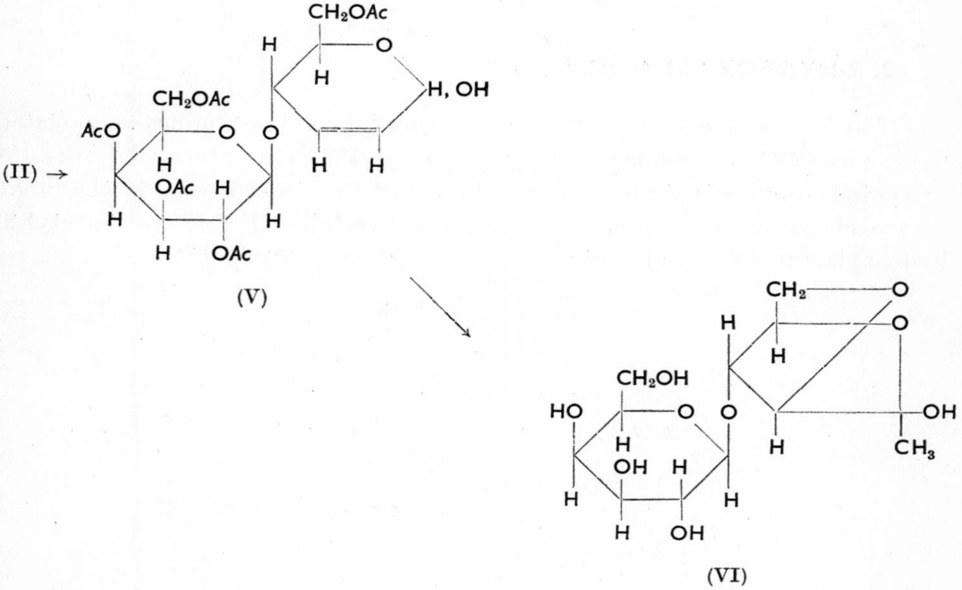

(II) →

(V)

(VI)

*References see p. 379*

Cellobial[6,14–16] has been prepared by a procedure similar to that employed for the synthesis of lactal. In this case, too, the double bond of the hexa-*O*-acetyl derivative takes up two halogen atoms.[17] For cellobial (VII), however, a very interesting possibility of the addition of a water molecule to the double bond has been described, leading to 2-deoxycellobiose (VIII)[17,18] (see also Chapter XXII).

(VII)                                                                     (VIII)

In the maltose series, hexa-*O*-acetylmaltal[11,19,20] and maltal[19,20] were prepared, and the latter substance was converted by the addition of water into 2-deoxymaltose. Gentiobial[21,22] and melibial[23] are also known, as well as the hexa-*O*-acetyl derivatives of these two compounds.

The greatest advantage of glycals in the oligosaccharide series is the possibility of synthesizing new substances, either by hydroxylation of the double bond of the glycals (see Chapter VI) or by oxidative shortening of the carbon chain of the oligosaccharide molecule at the site of the double bond (see Chapter VI).

## 2. 2-HYDROXYGLYCALS

These compounds, formed by the action of secondary amines on acylated halogenoses,[24,25] are comparatively rare even in the monosaccharide series. At present it appears that the only substances of this type known in the oligosaccharide group are hepta-*O*-acetyl-2-hydroxycellobial,[26,27] hepta-*O*-acetyl-2-hydroxylactal (IX)[26] and hepta-*O*-acetyl-2-hydroxygentiobial.[28]

(IX)

## 3. OTHER GLYCOSEENS

Another interesting reaction for introducing a double bond into an oligosaccharide molecule is known from the chemistry of monosaccharides.[29] The action of silver fluoride in pyridine does not convert the per-$O$-acetyl derivative of 6-deoxy-6-iodo-D-glucose into the corresponding 6-deoxy-6-fluoro derivative, but instead splits off a hydrogen iodide molecule to form the tetra-$O$-acetyl derivative of D-gluco-5,6-seen. By treating the hexa-$O$-acetyl derivative of 6,6'-dideoxy-6,6'-di-iodotrehalose, Bredereck[30] obtained a substance with two double bonds, namely 2,3,4,2',3',4'-hexa-$O$-acetyltrehalose-diene.

Similar compounds have been prepared in the series of gentiobiose, namely methyl 2,3,4,2',3'-penta-$O$-acetyl-$\beta$-gentiobioseenide and the free gentiobioseen; similarly, cellobiose has been converted into methyl 2,3,4,2',3'-penta-$O$-acetyl-$\beta$-cellobioseenide.[31]

**Table LXVIII**

Physical Properties of Unsaturated Oligosaccharide Derivatives

| Oligosaccharide Derivative | Melting Point °C | $[\alpha]_D$ | Solvent | References |
|---|---|---|---|---|
| Maltal | 176 | $+ 1 \cdot 16°$ | $H_2O$ | 20 |
|   hexa-$O$-acetate | 131—133 | $+68°$ | $CHCl_3$ | 19, 32 |
| | 134 | $+64 \cdot 4°$ | $C_2H_2Cl_4$ | 33 |
| | 132—136 | $-22 \cdot 5°$ | $CHCl_3$ | 20 |
| Cellobial | 175—176 | $+ 1 \cdot 0°$ | $H_2O$ | 6, 14, 34 |
|   hexa-$O$-acetate | 137 | $-19 \cdot 7°$ | $C_2H_2Cl_4$ | 6, 14—16 |
| Gentiobial | 194 | $- 5 \cdot 8°$ | $H_2O$ | 21, 22 |
|   hexa-$O$-acetate | 126 | $-15 \cdot 1°$ | $C_5H_5N$ | 21, 22 |
| Lactal | 191—192 | $+27 \cdot 5°$ | $H_2O$ | 3, 5, 7, 8, 11 |
|   hexa-$O$-acetate | 113—114 | $-12 \cdot 3°$ | $C_2H_2Cl_4$ | 5, 7—9 |
| Melibial | | | | |
|   hexa-$O$-acetate | 113 | $+87°$ | $CHCl_3$ | 23 |
| 2-Hydroxycellobial | | | | |
|   hepta-$O$-acetate | 125 | $-21 \cdot 5°$ | $CHCl_3$ | 26, 27 |
| 2-Hydroxylactal | | | | |
|   hepta-$O$-acetate | 167 | $-17 \cdot 1°$ | $CHCl_3$ | 26 |
| 2-Hydroxygentiobial | | | | |
|   hepta-$O$-acetate | 126—130 | $-29 \cdot 1°$ | $CHCl_3$ | 28 |

**REFERENCES**

1. J. Staněk, M. Černý, J. Kocourek, and J. Pacák, *The Monosaccharides*, Acad. Press, New York 1963.
2. B. Helferich, Advances in Carbohydrate Chem. *7*, 209 (1952).
3. E. Fischer, Ber. *47*, 196 (1914).
4. Ref. 1, p. 386.

5. E. Fischer and G. O. Curme, Ber. *47*, 2047 (1914).

6. E. Fischer and K. Fodor, Ber. *47*, 2058 (1914).

7. W. N. Haworth, E. L. Hirst, M. T. Plant, and R. J. W. Reynolds, J. Chem. Soc. *1930*, 2644.

8. M. Bergmann, H. Schotte, and E. Rennert, Ann. *434*, 86 (1923).

9. W. T. Haskins, R. M. Hann, and C. S. Hudson, J. Am. Chem. Soc. *64*, 1852 (1942).

10. A. M. Gakhokidze, Zhur. Obshcheĭ Khim. *16*, 1907 (1946); Chem. Abstr. *41*, 6208 (1947).

11. M. Bergmann, Ann. *434*, 79 (1923).

12. Ref. 1, p. 389.

13. M. Bergmann, L. Zervas, and J. Engler, Ann. *508*, 25 (1933).

14. M. Bergmann and H. Schotte, Ber. *54*, 1570 (1921).

15. W. N. Haworth, E. L. Hirst, H. R. Streight, H. A. Thomas, and I. J. Webb, J. Chem. Soc. *1930*, 2636.

16. W. T. Haskins, R. M. Hann, and C. S. Hudson, J. Am. Chem. Soc. *64*, 1289 (1942).

17. A. M. Gakhokidze, Zhur. Obshcheĭ Khim. *16*, 1914 (1946); Chem. Abstr. *41*, 6209 (1947).

18. M. Bergmann and W. Breuers, Ann. *470*, 38 (1929).

19. W. N. Haworth, E. L. Hirst, and R. J. W. Reynolds, J. Chem. Soc. *1934*, 302.

20. A. M. Gakhokidze, Zhur. Obshcheĭ Khim. *18*, 60 (1948); Chem. Abstr. *42*, 4948 (1948).

21. M. Bergmann and W. Freudenberg, Ber. *62*, 2785 (1929).

22. H. J. Dauben and W. L. Evans, J. Am. Chem. Soc. *60*, 886 (1938).

23. P. A. Levene and E. Jorpes, J. Biol. Chem. *86*, 403 (1930).

24. Ref. 1, p. 392.

25. M. G. Blair, Advances in Carbohydrate Chem. *9*, 97 (1954).

26. K. Maurer, Ber. *63*, 25 (1930).

27. G. Zemplén and Z. Bruckner, Ber. *61*, 2484 (1928).

28. K. Maurer and K. Plötner, Ber. *64*, 281 (1931).

29. B. Helferich and E. Himmen, Ber. *61*, 1830 (1928).

30. H. Bredereck, Ber. *63*, 959 (1930).

31. B. Helferich, E. Bohn, and S. Winkler, Ber. *63*, 989 (1930).

32. M. Bergmann and M. Kobel, Ann. *434*, 109 (1923).

33. H. Fischer and F. Kögl, Ann. *436*, 219 (1924).

34. A. M. Gakhokidze, Zhur. Obshcheĭ Khim. *20*, 120 (1950); Chem. Abstr. *44*, 5819 (1950).

# XXII

# Deoxy Sugars

Oligosaccharides containing deoxy derivatives of monosaccharides are not very frequently encountered. At present, only oligosaccharides of one particular type, containing L-fucose, may be isolated from human milk. A larger number of substances is obtainable by hydrolysis of either higher oligosaccharides or polysaccharides, as well as by hydrolysis of heterosides or amino sugars of the oligosaccharide series (see Chapter XXIV). Finally, even some aldobiouronic acids and other substances of this group (see Chapter XXXIV) contain deoxy sugars.

## 1. NATURAL DEOXY SUGARS

### A. PRODUCTS OF DIRECT ISOLATION

While the oligosaccharide content of cow milk is limited to lactose only,[1] a richer source of oligosaccharides is presented by human milk,* from which, besides lactose, *allo*-lactose (6-*O*-β-D-galactopyranosyl-D-glucose)[2-4] has been isolated with certainty, whereas the so-called gynolactose[2,5-7] is a mixture of a larger number of compounds, some of which contain nitrogen (see Chapter XXIV).

The first new substance of this group was isolated in 1954 by Kuhn and associates[8-12] and termed fucosyl-lactose. Its constitution, corresponding to *O*-α-L-fucopyranosyl-(1→2)-*O*-β-D-galactopyranosyl-(1→4)-D-glucose (I) was derived[11] from the results of methylation splitting and fully confirmed by the course of its hydrolysis in weakly alkaline solution[13] (see Chapter VII and p. 147). The trisaccharide A, isolated by Montreuil from human milk,[14] is identical with fucosyl-lactose, while the constitution of another trisaccharide, containing D-glucose, D-galactose and L-fucose,[6,14] is not exactly known. The isolation of fucosyl-lactose was confirmed by other investigators.[15,16]

---

\* For reviews see J. Montreuil, Bull. soc. chim. biol. *39*, 395 (1957); R. Kuhn, Bull. soc. chim. biol. *40*, 297 (1958); J. Montreuil, Bull. soc. chim. biol. *42*, 1399 (1960).

*References see p. 391*

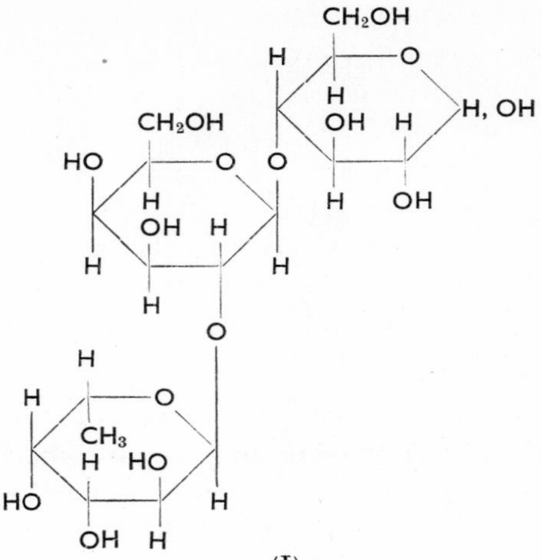

(I)

Montreuil isolated from human milk also a tetrasaccharide[6,17] containing two L-fucose molecules, one D-glucose and one D-galactose molecule, so that this tetrasaccharide may be regarded as difucosyl-lactose. The constitution of this product, which was named lactodifucotetraose, was established by Kuhn[18] from the course of its partial hydrolysis in both acid and alkaline solution and from its degradation by periodic acid. The substance has the structure (II), i e. of the branched tetrasaccharide O-α-L-fucopyranosyl(1→2)-O-β-D-galactopyra-nosyl-(1→4)-O-[α-L-fucopyranosyl-(1→3)]-D-glucopyranose.

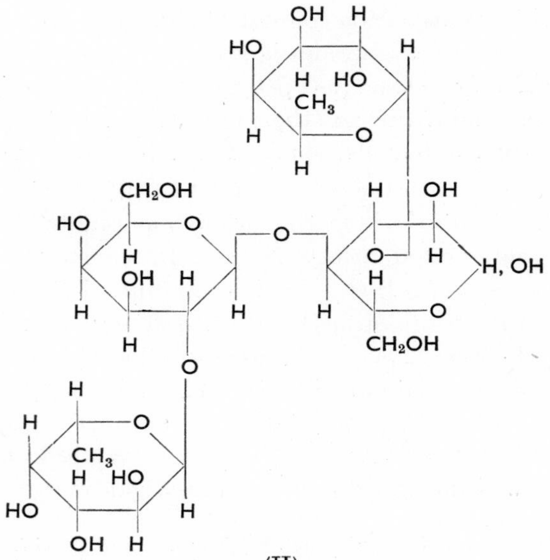

(II)

## B. PRODUCTS OBTAINED BY HYDROLYSIS OF HIGHER OLIGOSACCHARIDES OR POLYSACCHARIDES

Comparatively few cases have been reported in which an oligosaccharide of the deoxy sugar group was obtained by splitting higher oligosaccharides or polysaccharides. These compounds are listed in Table LXIX. Various methods have been employed for preparation purposes (see Chapter X), such as splitting in acid solution[18],[19] and acetolysis.[20] In weakly alkaline solution, 2-O-α-L-fuco-pyranosyl-D-galactose[13] has been obtained from some higher oligosaccharides, 2-O-α-L-fucopyranosyl-D-talose[13] being formed as a by-product (see Chapter VII).

## C. PRODUCTS OBTAINED BY HYDROLYSIS OF HETEROSIDES*

A larger number of deoxy sugars has been obtained by splitting hetero-sides (see Table LXX); some of the oligosaccharides produced in this way have been isolated from different heterosides and are, therefore, the subject of many papers.[21–58] All these oligosaccharides have been prepared by acid hydrolysis or enzymic splitting (see Table LXX), with the exception of solatriose which has been obtained[51] by a special procedure consisting of the hydrolysis of the acety-lated derivative of the alkaloid solanine by hydrogen bromide in acetic acid.

The structures of most disaccharides of this group are known (see Table LXXI). This applies to scillabiose[49],[50],[59] and strophanthobiose;[54] the identity of the latter compound with periplobiose[55] was recently proved.[60] Other com-pounds of known structure are eryperobiose,[32],[36] robinobiose[41] and rutinose. [44–48] Not long ago it was demonstrated[61] that the two latter compounds must be regarded as 6-O-α-L-rhamnopyranosyl derivatives of D-galactose and D-glucose respectively.

It has been known for some time that the hydrolysis of digilanidobiose yields a molecule of D-glucose and a molecule of D-digitoxose.[25] Its structure, how-ever, has been established only quite recently.[36],[62] According to this, digila-nidobiose (III) is 4-O-β-D-glucopyranosyl-D-digitoxose.

(III)

---

* For a review see T. Reichstein and E. Weiss, Advances in Carbohydrate Chem. *17*, 104 (1962).

*References see p. 391*

Less information is available on condurangobiose,[21-23] whose splitting yields a D-glucose molecule and a molecule of the methyl ether of a hexo-methylose. Likewise incomplete are the reports on thevetosylcymarose[63] and a non-reducing (??) disaccharide of the formula $C_{12}H_{22}O_9$, isolated[64] besides D-digitoxose in the hydrolysis of lanadigin.

As far as trisaccharides of this group are concerned, the structures of odorotriose[39] and strophanthotriose[54,57] are well known (see Table LXXI), while information on scillatriose[49] is incomplete. An interesting problem arose in establishing the structure of the branched trisaccharide solatriose[65,66] (also named solanose[67]), which is the sugar component of solanine and other alkaloids. The first structural study,[67,68] undertaken by direct degradation of solanine, led to erroneous results, and it was only Kuhn[51] who established the structure of this branched trisaccharide, which corresponds to the formula (IV), i. e. *O-β-D-glucopyranosyl-(1→3)-O-[α-L-rhamnopyranosyl-(1→2)]-D-galactopyranose*. The structure followed from the finding that partial hydrolysis of solanine gives rise to solabiose, i. e. *3-O-β-D-glucopyranosyl-D-galactose* (V), a substance free of L-rhamnose. It was proved in various ways that L-rhamnose must be linked in position -2- of the galactose part, because solatriose gives no phenylosazone and its oxime cannot be degraded according to Ruff.

(IV)                                   (V)

## 2. SYNTHETIC DEOXY SUGARS

In the monosaccharide series, two methods are currently employed for synthesizing deoxy sugars. These are, on the one hand, the glycal method,[74,75] leading to 2-deoxyaldoses and, on the other hand, the hydrogenolysis of primary tosyl, mesyl and iododeoxy derivatives,[76] leading to methyloses.

The glycal method, consisting of the hydration of the double bond of glycals (see Chapter XXI) by the action of dilute sulphuric acid, has been applied in the oligosaccharide series a few times only.[77–79] Since this reaction is carried out in acid solution, it involves undoubtedly the risk of hydrolysing the glycosidic linkage in the oligosaccharide, nevertheless, it is feasible. Octa-*O*-acetylcellobiose (VI) may be converted via hepta-*O*-acetyl-α-cellobiosyl bromide (VII) and hexa-*O*-acetylcellobial (VIII) into cellobial (IX) which, by the action of dilute sulphuric acid, with simultaneous hydration of the double bond, gives rise to 2-deoxycellobiose (X);[77,78] 2-deoxymaltose has been prepared in a similar way.[79]

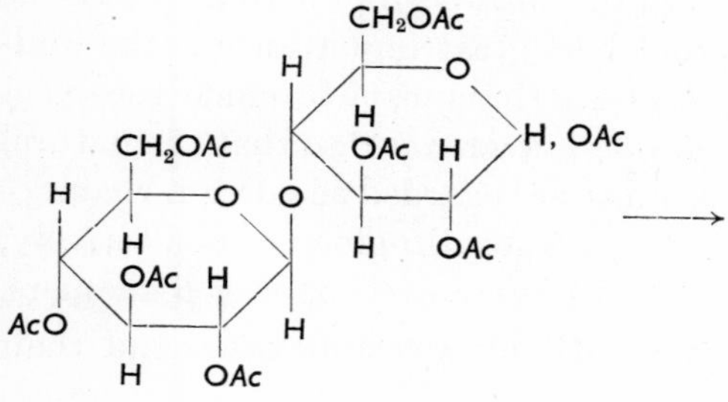

(VI)

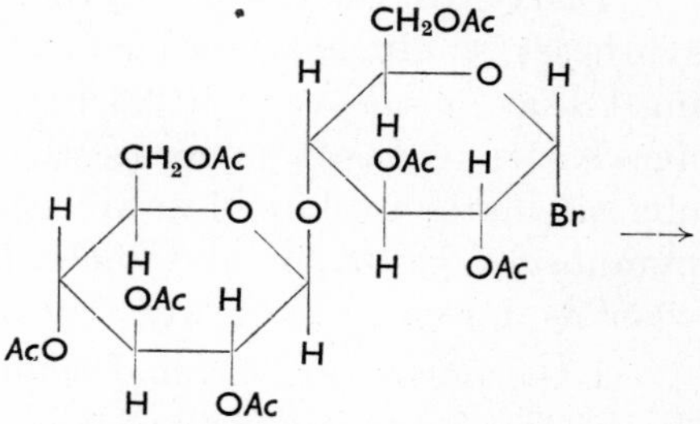

(VII)

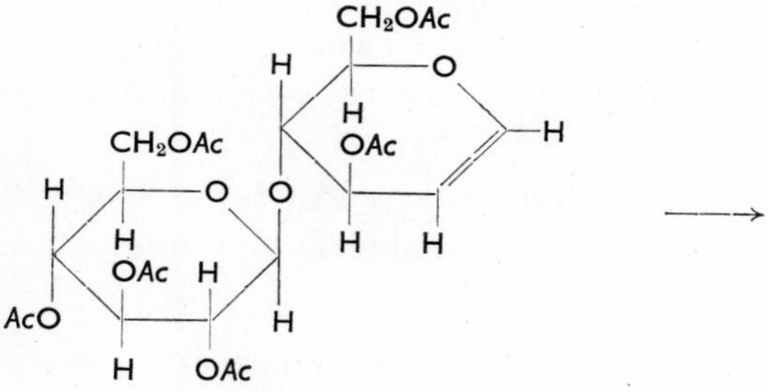

(VIII)

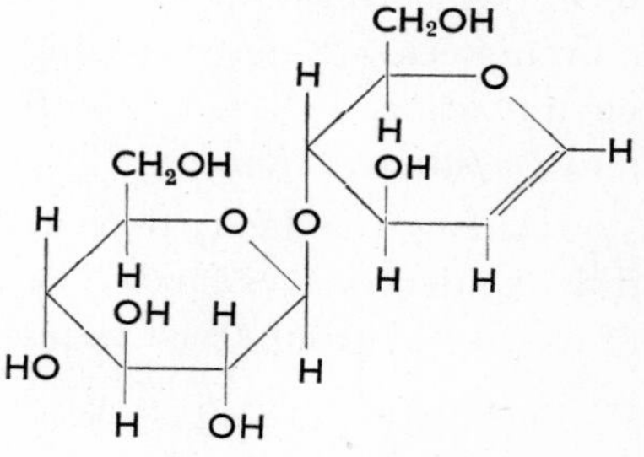

(IX)

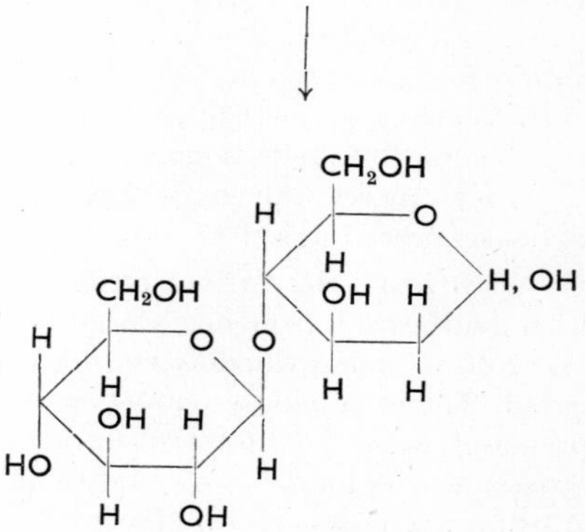

(X)

*References see p. 391*

The hydrogenolytic method has likewise not found much application in the chemistry of oligosaccharides.[80-82] This procedure involves in all cases the removal of the iodine atom from the primary carbon atom and may be effected either with zinc in dilute sulphuric acid,[80,81] in particular with platinum as a catalyst, or, more advantageously, with Raney nickel.[81] Primary tosyl esters may be hydrogenolysed by the action of lithium aluminium hydride;[82] however, the tosyl group at C-1 of the fructofuranose part does not react under such conditions. Consequently, 6,1',6'-tri-O-tosylsucrose is converted by the action of lithium aluminium hydride[82] into the corresponding 6,6'-dideoxy derivative.

Deoxy derivatives of oligosaccharides have also been prepared by various syntheses, as already described in Chapter VI. Of great importance is the finding[83] that in the case of 2,3,4-tri-O-acetyl-α-L-rhamnosyl bromide the Koenigs-Knorr synthesis proceeds without Walden inversion,[83] so that the natural oligosaccharides robinobiose and rutinose must be regarded as 6-O-α-L-rhamnopyranosyl-D-galactose and 6-O-α-L-rhamnopyranosyl-D-glucose respectively, whereas formerly they were considered to be the corresponding β-anomers.

Experiments on thermal condensation of 2-deoxyaldohexoses and their derivatives led to products of polymeric nature.[84,85]

On the other hand, successful attempts were undertaken to synthesize 6-O-β-D-fructofuranosyl-2-deoxy-D-glucose under physiological conditions[86] by administering 2-deoxy-D-glucose to seedlings of corn, wheat, sorghum and cucumber, as well as to the flower buts and leaves of corn, sorghum, tobacco and *Impatiens sultani*.

Among the deoxy derivatives of oligosaccharides may also be included the dideoxy derivatives formed by hydrogenation of the double bond in compounds of the glycal group (see Chapter XXI).

Sulphur-containing oligosaccharides belong among deoxy sugar derivatives. Acetylated halogenoses have been mostly used as starting materials. Thus, from hepta-O-acetyl-α-cellobiosyl bromide the corresponding di-β,β-cellobiosyl disulphide tetradeca-O-acetate has been prepared,[93] and, by its reduction with aluminium amalgam, hepta-O-acetyl-β-cellobiosyl mercaptan, m. p. 197—220°C, $[\alpha]_D$ — 12·8° (CHCl$_3$), has been obtained. A more convenient procedure for the preparation of per-O-acetylated derivatives of the above-type mercaptans is the synthesis from acetylated halogenoses via isothiouronium salts;[94-96] in this way, hepta-O-acetyl derivatives of β-maltosyl mercaptan and β-lactosyl mercaptan have been prepared.[97] Methyl thioglycosides can be obtained by usual procedures.[93-97]

*S*-Benzoyl derivatives of acetylated mercaptans of the oligosaccharide series have been synthesized from acetylated halogenoses by the action of sodium thiobenzoate.[98]

Non-reducing thiodisaccharides (i. e. diglycopyranosyl sulphides) have also been prepared. Thioisotrehalose octa-O-acetate has been reported several times;[99-101] it may be prepared from 2,3,4,6-tetra-O-acetyl-α-D-glucopyranosyl bromide by its reaction with potassium sulphide,[99] with methyl or benzyl xanthate,[100] or by its direct reaction with 2,3,4,6-tetra-O-acetyl-β-D-glucopyranosyl mercaptan.[101] In this way, many thiodisaccharides and their per-O-acetates have been prepared.[97,102,103]

## Table LXIX

Deoxy Sugars Obtained from Higher Oligosaccharides or Polysaccharides

| Oligosaccharide | Natural Substance | Method of Preparation | References |
|---|---|---|---|
| 4-$O$-$\beta$-D-Glucopyranosyl-L-fucose | *Corynebacterium insidiosum* polysaccharide | acid hydrolysis | 19 |
| 4-$O$-$\alpha$-L-Rhamnopyranosyl-D-glucose | reduced polysaccharide from *Acacia senegal* | acetolysis | 90 |
| 2-$O$-$\alpha$-L-Fucopyranosyl-D-galactose | fucosyl-lactose | alkaline hydrolysis | 13 |
| | lacto-$N$-fucopentaose $I$ | alkaline hydrolysis | 13 |
| | lacto-$N$-difucohexaose | alkaline hydrolysis | 13 |
| 2-$O$-$\alpha$-L-Fucopyranosyl-L-fucose | fucoidin | acetolysis | 20 |
| 3-$O$-$\alpha$-L-Fucopyranosyl-L-fucose | fucoidin | acetolysis | 20 |
| 4-$O$-$\alpha$-L-Fucopyranosyl-L-fucose | fucoidin | acetolysis | 20 |
| 2-$O$-$\alpha$-L-Fucopyranosyl-D-xylose | traganthic acid | acetolysis | 91 |
| $O$-$\beta$-D-Glucopyranosyl-$(1\rightarrow4)$-$O$-[$\alpha$-D-galactopyranosyl-$(1\rightarrow3)$]-L-fucose | *Corynebacterium insidiosum* polysaccharide | acid hydrolysis | 19 |
| Fucosyl-lactose | lacto-$N$-difucotetraose | acid hydrolysis | 18 |

The preparation of a reducing trisaccharide Gal-L-Ara-L-Rha (with L-rhamnose as the reducing unit) from *Chlorella pyranoides* polysaccharide has been reported recently, see A. Olaitan and D. H. Northcote, Biochem. **J.** *82*, 509 (1962); the preparation of 3-$O$-$\beta$-D-mannopyranosyl-L-fucose with $[\alpha]_D$ 0° after the acid hydrolysis of *Polyporus giganteus* polysaccharide has been reported by V. P. Bhavanandan, H. O. Bouveng, and B. Lindberg, Acta Chem. Scand. 18, 504 (1964).

## Table LXX

Deoxy Sugars Obtained from Heterosides

| Oligosaccharides | Natural Substance | Method of Preparation | References |
|---|---|---|---|
| Condurangobiose | marsdenin | acid hydrolysis | 21—23 |
| Digilanidobiose | *Digitalis purpurea* glycosides | acid hydrolysis | 24—28 |
| | *Digitalis lanata* glycosides | acid hydrolysis | 29—32 |
| | *Digitalis grandiflora* glycosides | acid hydrolysis | 33 |
| | *Erysimum perofskianum* glycoside (erymoside) | acid hydrolysis | 34—36 |
| | *Strophanthus kombé* glycosides | acid hydrolysis | 37 |
| acetyldigilanidobiose | *Digitalis* spp. glycosides | acid hydrolysis | 28, 32 |
| 2-Deoxycellobiose | *Erysimum canescens* glycoside | acid hydrolysis | 38 |
| D-Glucodigilanidobiose | *Strophanthus kombé* glycosides | acid hydrolysis | 37 |
| Odorotriose | odoroside K | acid hydrolysis | 39 |
| | *Strophanthus intermedius* glycoside | acid hydrolysis | 40 |

*References see p. 391*

25*

*Table LXX — continued*

| Oligosaccharide | Natural Substance | Method of Preparation | References |
|---|---|---|---|
| Robinobiose* | robinin | enzymic hydrolysis | 41 |
| Rutinose | datiscin | enzymic hydrolysis | 44 |
| | nicotiflorin | enzymic hydrolysis | 45 |
| | rutin | enzymic hydrolysis | 46, 47 |
| | | acid hydrolysis | 48 |
| Scillabiose | glucoscilliphäoside | acid hydrolysis | 49 |
| | scillaren A | acid hydrolysis | 50 |
| Scillatriose | glucoscillaren A | acid hydrolysis | 49 |
| Solatriose | solanine | hydrogen bromide in acetic acid | 51 |
| | solasonine | acid hydrolysis | 92 |
| Strophanthobiose periplobiose | strophanthin K | acid hydrolysis | 37, 52–54 |
| | periplocin | acid hydrolysis | 55, 56 |
| Strophanthotriose | echuin | acid hydrolysis | 57 |
| | *Strophanthus* glycosides | acid hydrolysis | 37, 40, 54, 58 |
| 2-O-α-L-Rhamnopyranosyl-D-galactose | solasonine | acid hydrolysis | 92 |

* Robinose was considered[42,43] to be a trisaccharide of the constitution L-Rha-Gal-L-Rha; however, it has been established[41] that the second molecule of L-rhamnose is bound to some other hydroxyl group in the molecule of robinin and that no trisaccharide can be obtained from robinin.

## Table LXXI

Physical Properties of Natural Deoxy Sugars and Their Derivatives

| Deoxy Sugar | Melting Point °C | $[\alpha]_D$ | Solvent | References |
|---|---|---|---|---|
| Condurangobiose | 195—207 (dec.) | +19·5° | $H_2O$ | 21, 22 |
| hexa-O-acetate | 187·5 | —16·5° | $CHCl_3$ | 21 |
| Digilanidobiose | | | | |
| 4-O-β-D-glucopyranosyl-D-digitoxose | 229—230 | +29·5° | $H_2O$ | 36, 62 |
| | 224—230 | +32·6° | $H_2O$ | 33 |
| | 227 | +30° | $H_2O$ | 25 |
| | 211—218 | +29·6° | $H_2O$ | 32 |
| | | +10° | $C_5H_5N$ | 32 |
| acetyldigilanidobiose | 144—165 | +22° | $C_5H_5N$ | 32 |
| | | +49·7° | $H_2O$ | 32 |
| Eryperobiose | | | | |
| 3-O-α-D-digitoxosyl-D-glucose | 227—230 | | | 36 |
| Odorotriose | | | | |
| 4-O-β-gentiobiosyl-D-diginose | | | | |
| O-β-D-glucopyranosyl-(1→6)-O-β-D-glucopyranosyl-(1→4)-D-diginose | | −1·4° ± 1·5° | $H_2O$ | 39 |
| Robinobiose | | | | |
| 6-O-α-L-rhamnopyranosyl-D-galactose | | +5·7° → +1·9° | $H_2O$ | 42 |
| | | +2·7° → 0° | $H_2O$ | 43 |

*Table LXXI — continued*

| Deoxy Sugar | Melting Point °C | $[\alpha]_D$ | Solvent | References |
|---|---|---|---|---|
| hexa-*O*-acetyl-α-robinobio-syl chloride | 166·5—167·5 | +67·6° | CHCl₃ | 69 |
| | 180 (dec.) | — 5·05° | CHCl₃ | 70 |
| Rutinose | | | | |
| 6-*O*-α-L-rhamnopyranosyl-D- | | | | |
| glucose | 189—192 | +3·2° → —0·8° | H₂O | 44,47,71—73 |
| hepta-*O*-acetate | 169 | —29·7° | CHCl₃ | 46, 72 |
| hexa-*O*-acetyl-α-rutinosyl | | | | |
| chloride | 150—151 | +65·9° | CHCl₃ | 46, 72 |
| hexa-*O*-acetyl-α-rutinosyl | | | | |
| bromide | 127—128 | +89·9° | CHCl₃ | 73 |
| Scillabiose | | | | |
| 4-*O*-?-D-glucopyranosyl-L-rham- | | | | |
| nose | | —24·8° | H₂O | 50, 59 |
| hexa-*O*-acetate | 97 | | | 50 |
| Scillatriose | | | | 49 |
| Solatriose, solanose | | | | |
| *O*-β-D-glucopyranosyl-(1→3)-*O*- | | | | |
| [α-L-rhamnopyranosyl(1→2)]- | | | | |
| D-galactose | 160 (dec.) | —7·5° → —4·5° | H₂O | 51 |
| deca-*O*-acetate | 73—77 | | | 51 |
| Strophanthobiose | | | | |
| periplobiose | | | | |
| 4-*O*-β-D-glucopyranosyl-D-cyma- | | | | |
| rose | 208 | +31·1° | H₂O | 54 |
| | 160—170 | +32° | H₂O | 55 |
| | 162—170 | +32·7° | H₂O | 60 |
| penta-*O*-acetate | 184 | +19·5° | CHCl₃ | 55 |
| | 162 | +13·3° | CHCl₃ | 54 |
| | 165—173 | + 9·8° | CHCl₃ | 60 |
| Strophanthotriose | | | | |
| 4-*O*-β-gentiobiosyl-D-cymarose, | | | | |
| *O*-β-D-glucopyranosyl-(1→6)- | | | | |
| *O*-β-D-glucopyranosyl-(1→4)- | | | | |
| D-cymarose | 222 | + 7·75° | H₂O | 54 |
| | 213—214 | +7·6° ± 2° | H₂O | 57 |
| octa-*O*-acetate | 192 | — 5·8° | CHCl₃ | 57 |
| | 192 | — 6·2° | CHCl₃ | 54 |
| 4-*O*-α-L-Rhamnopyranosyl-D-glu-cose | | | | 90 |
| 2-*O*-α-L-Fucopyranosyl-D-galac-tose | amorphous | —56·5° | H₂O | 13 |
| benzylphenylhydrazone | 163 | | | 13 |
| 2-*O*-α-L-Fucopyranosyl-D-talose | amorphous | —120·2° | H₂O | 13 |
| 2-*O*-α-L-Fucopyranosyl-L-fucose | 185—190 | —160° → —169° | H₂O | 20 |
| 3-*O*-α-L-Fucopyranosyl-L-fucose | 198—200 | —200° → —191° | H₂O | 20 |
| 4-*O*-α-L-Fucopyranosyl-L-fucose | amorphous | —170° | H₂O | 20 |
| 2-*O*-α-L-Fucopyranosyl-D-xylose | 185—189 (dec.) | —61° | H₂O | 91 |
| Fucosyl-lactose | | | | |
| *O*-α-L-fucopyranosyl-(1→2)-*O*-β- | | | | |
| D-galactopyranosyl-(1→4)-D- | | | | |
| glucose | 231 (dec.) | —57° | H₂O | 11, 12, 18 |
| *p*-tosylhydrazone | 206 (dec.) | —74° | C₅H₅N/ /H₂O | 11 |

*References see p. 391*

*Table LXXI — continued*

| Deoxy Sugar | Melting Point °C | $[\alpha]_D$ | Solvent | References |
|---|---|---|---|---|
| phenylosazone | 218 (dec.) | $-13\cdot3° \rightarrow -29°$ | $C_5H_5N$ | 11 |
| Lactodifucotetraose $O$-$\alpha$-L-fucopyranosyl-$(1\rightarrow2)$-$O$-$\beta$-D-galactopyranosyl-$(1\rightarrow4)$-$O$-$[\alpha$-L-fucopyranosyl-$(1\rightarrow3)]$-D-glucose | | $-106°$ | $H_2O$ | 18 |
| 4-$O$-$\beta$-D-Glucopyranosyl-L-fucose hepta-$O$-acetate | 228—230 | $-59°$ | $CHCl_3$ | 19 |
| $O$-$\beta$-D-Glucopyranosyl-$(1\rightarrow4)$-$O$-$[\alpha$-D-galactopyranosyl-$(1\rightarrow3)]$-L-fucose | | $+23°$ | $H_2O$ | 19 |
| 2-Deoxycellobiose | 206—214 | $+30\cdot9° \pm 2°$ | $C_5H_5N$ | 38 |

## Table LXXII

Physical Properties of Synthetic Deoxy Sugars and Their Derivatives

| Deoxy Sugar | Melting Point °C | $[\alpha]_D$ | Solvent | References |
|---|---|---|---|---|
| $\alpha$-D-Glucopyranosyl $\beta$-D-rhamnuloside | 188—190 | $+61\cdot5°$ | $H_2O$ | 87, 88 |
| 6-$O$-$\beta$-D-Fructofuranosyl-2-deoxy-D-glucose | 56—85 | $+62° \rightarrow$ | $H_2O$ | 86 |
| | | $\rightarrow +26\cdot8°$ | $H_2O$ | 86 |
| 6-$O$-$\beta$-D-Quinovosyl-D-glucose | | $-6°$ | $H_2O$ | 61 |
| 6-$O$-$\beta$-D-Fucosyl-D-glucose | | $+125°$ | $H_2O$ | 61 |
| 2-$O$-$\alpha$-L-Fucopyranosyl-D-galactose | amorphous | $+56\cdot5°$ | $H_2O$ | 13 |
| 2-$O$-$\alpha$-L-Fucopyranosyl-D-talose | amorphous | $-120\cdot2°$ | $H_2O$ | 13 |
| Fucosyl-lactose $O$-$\alpha$-L-Fucopyranosyl-$(1\rightarrow2)$-$O$-$\beta$-D-galactopyranosyl-$(1\rightarrow4)$-D-glucose | | $-57°$ | $H_2O$ | 11, 18 |
| | 231 (dec.) | $-57°$ | $H_2O$ | 12 |
| 2-Deoxycellobiose | | $+23\cdot2°$ | $H_2O$ | 77 |
| | 215 | $+21\cdot6°$ | $H_2O$ | 78 |
| hexa-$O$-acetate | 196 | $-15°$ | $CHCl_3$ | 77, 89 |
| | 194—198 | $-15\cdot8°\pm2°$ | $CHCl_3$ | 38 |
| hepta-$O$-acetate | 179 | | | 78 |
| phenylhydrazone | 194 | | | 78 |
| 2-Deoxymaltose | 182 | $+30\cdot4°$ | $H_2O$ | 79 |
| hepta-$O$-acetate | 167 | | | 79 |
| phenylhydrazone | 201 | | | 79 |
| Cello-6,6'-bismethylose | 205—206 | $+59° \rightarrow +19°$ | $H_2O$ | 80 |
| hexa-$O$-acetate | 236—237 | $+41\cdot1°$ | $CHCl_3$ | 80 |
| Methyl $\beta$-cello-6,6'-bismethyloside | 199 | $-29\cdot8°$ | $CHCl_3$ | 80 |
| penta-$O$-acetate | 214—215 | $-35\cdot2°$ | $CHCl_3$ | 80 |
| Benzyl $\beta$-6-deoxymaltoside | | $+40°$ | $H_2O$ | 81 |
| hexa-$O$-acetate | 162—163 | $+29\cdot1°$ | $CHCl_3$ | 81 |
| 6,6'-Dideoxy-1'-$O$-tosylsucrose | | $+49\cdot7°$ | | 82 |

## REFERENCES

1. R. E. Trucco, P. Verdier, and A. Rega, Biochim. et Biophys. Acta *15*, 582 (1954).
2. M. Polonovski and A. Lespagnol, Compt. rend. *192*, 1319 (1931).
3. M. Polonovski and A. Lespagnol, Compt. rend. *195*, 465 (1932).
4. M. Polonovski and A. Lespagnol, Bull. soc. chim. biol. *15*, 320 (1933).
5. M. Polonovski and A. Lespagnol, Bull. soc. chim. biol. *12*, 1170 (1930).
6. M. Polonovski and J. Montreuil, Compt. rend. *238*, 2263 (1954).
7. J. Montreuil, Compt. rend. *239*, 510 (1954).
8. A. Gauhe, P. György, J. R. E. Hoover, R. Kuhn, C. S. Rose, H. W. Ruelius, and F. Zilliken, Arch. Biochem. Biophys, *48*, 214 (1954).
9. R. Kuhn, A. Gauhe, and H. H. Baer, Chem. Ber. *86*, 827 (1953).
10. R. Kuhn, A. Gauhe, and H. H. Baer, Chem. Ber. *87*, 289 (1954).
11. R. Kuhn, H. H. Baer, and A. Gauhe, Chem. Ber. *88*, 1135 (1955).
12. R. Kuhn, H. H. Baer, and A. Gauhe, Chem. Ber. *89*, 2513 (1956).
13. R. Kuhn, H. H. Baer, and A. Gauhe, Ann. *611*, 242 (1958).
14. J. Montreuil, Compt. rend. *242*, 192 (1956); Chem. Abstr. *50*, 7260 (1956).
15. F. H. Malpress and F. E. Hytten, Nature *180*, 1201 (1957).
16. F. H. Malpress and F. E. Hytten, Biochem. J. *68*, 708 (1958).
17. J. Montreuil, Compt. rend. *242*, 828 (1956); Chem. Abstr. *50*, 7260 (1956).
18. R. Kuhn and A. Gauhe, Ann. *611*, 249 (1958).
19. P. A. J. Gorin and J. F. T. Spencer, Can. J. Chem. *39*, 2274 (1961).
20. R. H. Côté, J. Chem. Soc. *1959*, 2248.
21. W. Kern and W. Haselbeck, Arch. Pharm. *283*, 102 (1950).
22. T. Baytop, M. Tanker, N. Oener, and S. Tekman, Nature *184*, 1319 (1959).
23. T. Baytop, M. Tanker, S. Tekman, and N. Oener, Folia Pharm. (Istanbul) *4*, 464 (1960); Chem. Abstr. *55*, 8768 (1961).
24. A. Stoll and W. Kreis, Helv. Chim. Acta *16*, 1390 (1933).
25. A. Stoll and W. Kreis, Helv. Chim. Acta *18*, 120 (1935).
26. A. Okano, K. Hoji, T. Miki, and A. Sakashita, Chem. Pharm. Bull. (Tokyo) *7*, 226 (1959).
27. K. Hoji, Chem. Pharm. Bull. (Tokyo) *9*, 291 (1961).
28. K. Hoji, Chem. Pharm. Bull. (Tokyo) *9*, 571 (1961).
29. E. Angliker, F. Barfuss, W. Kussmaul, and J. Renz, Ann. *607*, 131 (1957).
30. A. Wartburg, E. Angliker, F. Barfuss, and J. Renz, Experientia *14*, 439 (1958).
31. E. Angliker, F. Barfuss, and J. Renz, Helv. Chim. Acta *41*, 479 (1958).
32. R. Tschesche, B. Niyomporn, and H. Machleidt, Chem. Ber. *92*, 2258 (1959).
33. R. Repič and Ch. Tamm, Helv. Chim. Acta *40*, 639 (1957).
34. N. K. Abubakirov, V. A. Maslennikova, and M. B. Gorovits, Zhur. Obshcheĭ Khim. *29*, 1235 (1959); Chem. Abstr. *53*, 2280 (1959).
35. V. A. Maslennikova, F. S. Christulas, and N. K. Abubakirov, Doklady Akad. Nauk S.S.S.R. *124*, 822 (1959); Chem. Abstr. *53*, 16204 (1959).
36. Z. Kowalewski, O. Schindler, H. Jäger, and T. Reichstein, Helv. Chim. Acta *43*, 1280 (1960).
37. F. Kaiser, E. Haack, U. Dölberg, and H. Spingler, Ann. *643*, 192 (1961).
38. Š. Bauer, O. Bauerová, L. Masler, and D. Šikl, Experientia *18*, 441 (1962).
39. W. Rittel and T. Reichstein, Helv. Chim. Acta *37*, 1361 (1953).
40. M. I. Turkovic, Bl. Acad. Royal Méd. de Belgique [VI] *19*, 55 (1954).
41. G. Zemplén and R. Bognár, Ber. *74*, 1783 (1941).
42. C. Charaux, Bull. soc. chim. biol. *8*, 915 (1926).

43. G. Zemplén and A. Gerecs, Ber. *68*, 2054 (1935).

44. C. Charaux, Compt. rend. *180*, 1419 (1925); Chem. Abstr. *19*, 2514 (1925).

45. E. Wada, J. Agr. Chem. Soc. Japan *26*, 159 (1952); Chem. Abstr. *48*, 9482 (1954).

46. G. Zemplén and A. Gerecs, Ber. *68*, 1318 (1935).

47. C. Charaux, Compt. rend. *178*, 1312 (1924); Chem. Abstr. *18*, 2348 (1924).

48. G. Zemplén and A. Gerecs, Ber. *71*, 2520 (1938).

49. A. Stoll, W. Kreis, and A. Wartburg, Helv. Chim. Acta *35*, 2495 (1952).

50. A. Stoll, E. Suter, W. Kreis, B. B. Bussemaker, and A. Hofmann, Helv. Chim. Acta *16*, 703 (1933).

51. R. Kuhn, I. Löw, and H. Trischmann, Chem. Ber. *88*, 1492 (1955).

52. W. A. Jacobs and A. Hoffmann, J. Biol. Chem. *67*, 609 (1926); Chem. Abstr. *20*, 1812 (1926).

53. W. A. Jacobs and A. Hoffmann, J. Biol. Chem. *69*, 153 (1926); Chem. Abstr. *20*, 3013 (1926).

54. A. Stoll, J. Renz, and W. Kreis, Helv. Chim. Acta *20*, 1484 (1937).

55. A. Stoll and J. Renz, Helv. Chim. Acta *22*, 1193 (1939).

56. J. Renz, Rev. intern. botan. appl. et agr. trop. *33*, 52 (1953); Chem. Abstr. *48*, 2738 (1954).

57. J. C. Hess, A. Hunger, and T. Reichstein, Helv. Chim. Acta *35*, 2202 (1952).

58. J. Kraus, Naturwissenschaften *25*, 651 (1937).

59. G. Zemplén, Math. naturwiss. Anz. Ungar. Akad. Wiss. *57*, 999 (1938); Chem. Abstr. *33*, 4203 (1939).

60. M. Barbier and O. Schindler, Helv. Chim. Acta *42*, 1065 (1959).

61. P. A. J. Gorin and A. S. Perlin, Can. J. Chem. *37*, 1930 (1959).

62. H. Lichti and A. Wartburg, Helv. Chim. Acta *44*, 238 (1961).

63. E. Abisch, Ch. Tamm, and T. Reichstein, Helv. Chim. Acta *42*, 1014 (1959).

64. C. Mannich, P. Mohs, and W. Mauss, Arch. Pharm. *268*, 453 (1930).

65. W. Arnold, Pharmazie *5*, 490 (1950).

66. K. Schreiber, Chem. Technik *7*, 271 (1955).

67. L. H. Briggs and L. C. Vining, J. Chem. Soc. *1953*, 2809.

68. L. H. Briggs and J. J. Carroll, J. Chem. Soc. *1942*, 17.

69. G. Zemplén, A. Gerecs, and H. Flech, Ber. *71*, 774 (1938).

70. R. T. Major and E. W. Cook, J. Am. Chem. Soc. *58*, 2333 (1936).

71. C. Charaux, Bull. soc. chim. biol. *6*, 631 (1924).

72. G. Zemplén and A. Gerecs, Ber. *67*, 2049 (1934).

73. G. Zemplén and A. Gerecs, Ber. *70*, 1098 (1937).

74. W. G. Overend and M. Stacey, Advances in Carbohydrate Chem. *8*, 45 (1953).

75. J. Staněk, M. Černý, J. Kocourek, and J. Pacák, *The Monosaccharides*, Acad. Press, New York 1963, p. 416.

76. J. Staněk, M. Černý, J. Kocourek, and J. Pacák, *The Monosaccharides*, Acad. Press, New York 1963, p. 415.

77. M. Bergmann and W. Breuers, Ann. *470*, 38 (1929).

78. A. M. Gakhokidze, Zhur. Obshcheĭ Khim. *16*, 1914 (1946); Chem. Abstr. *41*, 6209 (1947).

79. A. M. Gakhokidze, Zhur. Obshcheĭ Khim. *18*, 60 (1948); Chem. Abstr. *42*, 4948 (1948).

80. J. Compton, J. Am. Chem. Soc. *60*, 1203 (1938).

81. B. Helferich and W. Speicher, Ann. *579*, 106 (1953).

82. P. D. Bragg and J. K. N. Jones, Can. J. Chem. *37*, 575 (1959).

83. P. A. J. Gorin and A. S. Perlin, Can. J. Chem. *37*, 1930 (1959).

84. W. G. Overend, F. Shafizadeh, and M. Stacey, J. Chem. Soc. *1951*, 994.

85. P. T. Mora, J. W. Wood, and V. W. McFarland, J. Am. Chem. Soc. *82*, 3418 (1960).
86. G. A. Barber, J. Am. Chem. Soc. *81*, 3722 (1959).
87. R. C. Bean and W. Z. Hassid, J. Am. Chem. Soc. *77*, 5737 (1955).
88. N. J. Palleroni and M. Doudoroff, J. Biol. Chem. *219*, 957 (1956).
89. W. N. Haworth, E. L. Hirst, H. R. L. Streight, H. A. Thomas, and J. I. Webb, J. Chem. Soc. *1930*, 2636.
90. G. O. Aspinall, A. J. Charlson, E. L. Hirst, and R. Young, J. Chem. Soc. *1963*, 1696.
91. G. O. Aspinall and J. Baillie, J. Chem. Soc. *1963*, 1702.
92. L. H. Briggs, R. C. Cambie, and J. L. Hoare, J. Chem. Soc. *1963*, 2848.
93. F. Wrede and O. Hettche, Hoppe-Seyler's Z. physiol. Chem. *172*, 169 (1927).
94. M. Černý, J. Vrkoč, and J. Staněk, Collection Czechoslov. Chem. Communs *24*, 64 (1959).
95. M. Černý and J. Pacák, Collection Czechoslov. Chem. Communs *26*, 2084 (1961).
96. M. Černý, J. Staněk, and J. Pacák, Monatsh. Chem. *94*, 290 (1963).
97. J. Staněk, M. Černý, J. Pacák, M. Šindlerová, and O. Hánová, unpublished results.
98. J. Kocourek, Collection Czechoslov. Chem. Communs *29*, 316 (1964).
99. W. Schneider and F. Wrede, Ber. *50*, 793 (1917).
100. M. Akagi, S. Tejima, M. Haga, and M. Sakata, Chem. and Pharm. Bull. (Tokyo) *11*, 1081 (1963).
101. M. Černý and J. Pacák, Collection Czechoslov. Chem. Communs *24*, 2566 (1959).
102. J. Staněk, M. Černý, and J. Pacák, IUPAC Symposium on the Chemistry of Natural Products, Kyoto, Japan, April 1964.
103. J. Staněk, Internationales Symposium über die Chemie der Kohlenhydrate, Münster, Germany, July 1964.

# XXIII

## Glycosylamines from the Series of Reducing Oligosaccharides

In comparison with the number of glycosylamines derived from mono-saccharides,[1,2] there are relatively few of the analogous compounds in the oligosaccharide group. The only compound of this type that might be regarded as isolated from natural sources is lactosylamine (4-$O$-$\beta$-D-galactopyranosyl-D-glucosylamine), obtained from evaporated milk[3] besides 4-$O$-$\beta$-D-galactopyranosyl-D-fructosamine,[3] which was evidently formed from the first substance by an Amadori re-arrangement.[4]

According to older reports,[5] the reaction of maltose or lactose with methanolic ammonia should give rise to maltosyl- or lactosylamine respectively; however, according to statements in the literature, these substances are unstable, they spontaneously give off ammonia and are reconverted, in particular during recrystallization, into the initial oligosaccharides. Nowadays the reaction of oligosaccharides with methanolic ammonia is carried out in a sealed tube;[6] no mention is made in the respective paper about the instability of the products formed.

Recent papers report the reaction between methanolic ammonia and octa-$O$-acetyl derivatives of cellobiose and lactose, see J. O. Deferrari and R. A. Cadenas, J. Org. Chem. *28*, 1070 (1963); R. A. Cadenas and J. O. Deferrari, J. Org. Chem. *28*, 1072 (1963). $N$-Acetyl-$\alpha$-lactosylamine and hepta-$O$-acetyl-$N$-acetylcellobiosylamine are formed besides compounds of a type not yet described in the oligosaccharide series, i. e. $N,N'$-diacetyl-lactosylidenediamine and $N,N'$-diacetylcellobiosylidenediamine.

According to another paper by R. A. Cadenas and J. O. Deferrari, J. Org. Chem. *28*, 2613 (1963), the reaction of ammonia with maltose $\beta$-octa-$O$-acetate affords $N,N'$-di-acetylmaltosylidendiamine.

More stable products are obtained by the reaction of reducing oligosaccharides with primary aromatic amines. This reaction was originally carried out without a solvent,[7,8] later in aqueous ethanol;[9] however, the opinions about the effect of the water present are very much divided.[10–13a] On the one hand it is recommended that this reaction be carried out in absolutely anhydrous medium,[10,11] since the presence of water leads immediately to undesirable re-arrangements (see later); on the other hand, it is stated[12,13a] that the reaction in aqueous ethanol proceeds quite smoothly in the presence of a small amount of ammonium chloride.

Substituted aromatic amines have also been converted into substituted $N$-glycosylamines, for example, by the reaction with anthranilic acid,[13b] $p$-aminosalicylic acid[14] and its esters,[15] as well as with various derivatives of sulphanilamide.[16-22] In these cases, the preparation of $N$-glycosylamines was obviously undertaken with regard to the possibility of obtaining drugs advantageous from the viewpoint of either solubility or toxicity.

Condensation products of reducing oligosaccharides and primary aliphatic amines are less common; they are formed from the initial components by heating without a solvent.[21]

The reaction of reducing oligosaccharides with secondary amines has not been conducted so far as to permit the isolation of a native product. Maltose and piperidine, on treatment with acetic acid and triethylamine, give rise to 1-piperidyl-1-deoxymaltulose,[22] i. e. a product of the Amadori re-arrangement; the analogous reaction with lactose was a complete failure, leading to $O$-$\beta$-D-galactopyranosylisomaltol.[22]

Unsubstituted glycosylamines derived from reducing oligosaccharides mutarotate in solutions.[23] In acid solution they are subject to hydrolysis,[21,23,24] but the product is probably not identical with the original oligosaccharide[10,11] (see later). Acid hydrolysis of unsubstituted glycosylamines derived from oligosaccharides proceeds more rapidly than that of analogous monosaccharide derivatives.[24] Moreover, lactosylamine is hydrolysed much more readily than maltosylamine.[24]

The Amadori re-arrangement[25,26]* has also been observed in the group of glycosylamines of reducing oligosaccharides. The course of this re-arrangement in the reaction of lactose with $p$-toluidine is said to be enhanced by the presence of water,[10,11] although aqueous ethanol is recommended for the preparation of $N$-arylglycosylamines.[12] By the action of secondary amines, e. g. piperidine, only products arising via the Amadori re-arrangement have been obtained.

The hydrolysis of substituted glycosylamines of reducing oligosaccharides[10,11] yields substances likewise corresponding to the products formed by the Amadori re-arrangement. Thus, $N$-$p$-tolyl-lactosylamine (I) must obviously be first converted into $N$-$p$-tolylisolactosylamine (II) in order that lactulose (4-$O$-$\beta$-D-galactopyranosyl-D-fructose, III) may be isolated from the reaction mixture by hydrolysis.

There is a possibility of mutual exchanges of the aromatic amino components in substituted glycosylamines. In the monosaccharide series, this reaction is well known from the investigations undertaken by Bognár,[27] and it has also been studied in the oligosaccharide group.[28,29] The condensation product of lactose and $p$-aminosalicylic acid, on heating with an ethanolic solution of sulphanilamide in the presence of a trace of hydrogen chloride, yields a condensation product of lactose with sulphanilamide.

---

* For a review see J. E. Hodge, Advances in Carbohydrate Chem. *10*, 169 (1955).

*References see p. 400*

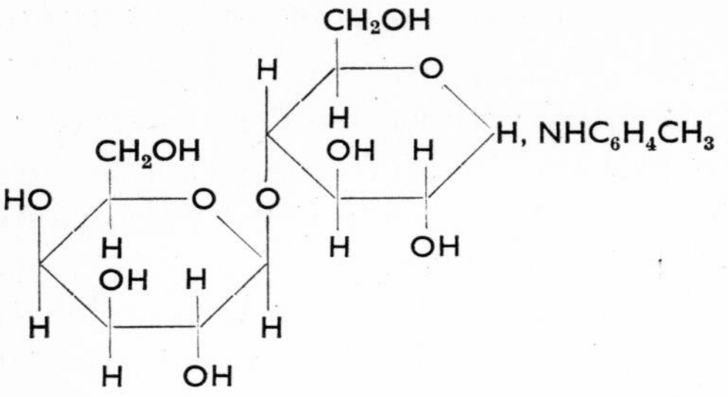

(I)

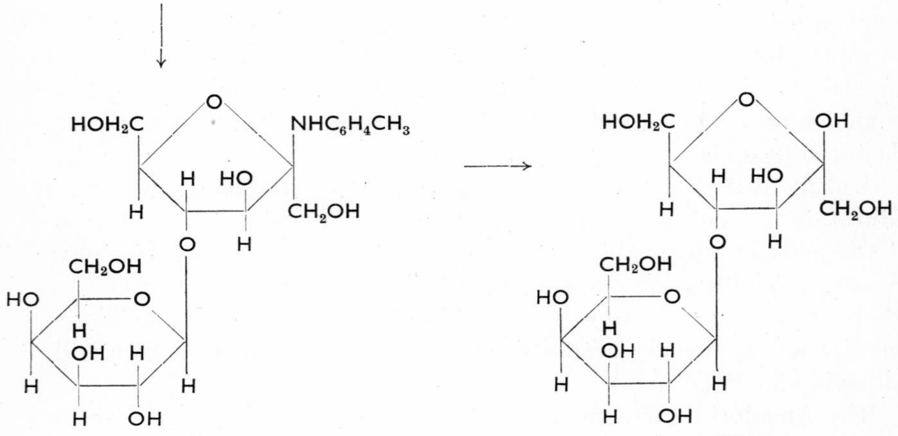

(II)          (III)

Unsubstituted glycosylamines of reducing oligosaccharides react with phenylhydrazine, as do free oligosaccharides, and hence both lactose and lactosylamine give the same phenylosazone.[30] N-Acetyl-lactosylamine, however, does not react with phenylhydrazine.

The primary amino group of lactosylamine may be acetylated selectively by the action of ketene[30] with the formation of an N-acetyl derivative. This acetyl group is bound very firmly, since the per-O-acetates of the N-acetyl derivatives of lactosylamine[30] and cellobiosylamine,[31] on deacetylation according to Zemplén, yield the original N-acetyl derivatives.[30,31] Deacetylation with methanolic ammonia is said to convert hepta-O-acetyl-N-acetylcellobiosylamine into dicellobiosylimine.[6]

Acylated, in particular acetylated, derivatives of glycosylamines and substituted glycosylamines of reducing oligosaccharides are obtainable also by the action of liquid ammonia, which, for example, with octa-O-acetylcellobiose (IV) involves[31] deacetylation and replacement of the hemiacetal hydroxyl group by an acetamido group, so that the final product is N-acetylcellobiosylamine (V).

The reactions of octa-*O*-acetylcellobiose and octa-*O*-acetyllactose with methanolic ammonia have been mentioned on p. 394.

Acylated halogenoses of oligosaccharides, too, may be advantageous initial substances in syntheses of glycosylamines of oligosaccharides. Thus, hepta-*O*-acetyl-α-cellobiosyl bromide is converted by the action of liquid ammonia into acetylated derivatives of cellobiosylamine and dicellobiosyl-imine.[6]

The reaction of dimethylamine with hepta-*O*-acetyl-α-cellobiosyl bromide (VI) gives rise to hepta-*O*-acetyl-β-cellobiosyldimethylamine (VII),[32] and hepta-*O*-acetyl-β-lactosyldimethylamine is formed in a similar way. Another investigator reports[33] that under similar conditions, i. e. with the use of diethyl-amine, a molecule of hydrogen bromide is split off from the molecule of hepta-*O*-acetyl-α-cellobiosyl bromide (VI) with the formation of penta-*O*-acetylcellobioseen (VIII). According to the last paper on this subject,[34] it seems that the reaction of hepta-O-acetyl-α-cellobiosyl bromide with diethylamine leads only to the unsaturated derivative (VIII); hepta-O-acetyl-β-cellobiosyldiethylamine is only formed when hepta-O-acetyl-α-cellobiosyl bromide reacts with diethylsodamide.[34] On the other hand, piperidine is said to react with hepta-O-acetyl-α-cellobiosyl bromide to form hepta-O-acetyl-β-cellobiosylpiperidine.[6,33]

The reaction of tertiary aliphatic amines with acylated halogenoses of oligosaccharides at first gave rise to erroneous conjectures.[35] Shortly afterwards, however, it was found that in the reaction of hepta-O-acetyl-α-cellobiosyl bromide with trimethylamine, a methyl bromide molecule is split off with the formation of hepta-O-acetyl-β-cellobiosyldimethylamine (VII), i.e. the same product as formed by the action of dimethylamine on this acylated halogenose.[33]

Another method for preparing acylated derivatives of maltosyl- and cellobiosylamine is the catalytic hydrogenation[36] of acylated maltosyl or cellobiosyl azides respectively, which are formed from the corresponding acylated halogenoses by the action of silver azide (see Chapter XXVII).

Per-O-acetylated derivatives of reducing oligosaccharides are also converted into per-O-acetylated derivatives of N-arylglycosylamines by heating in ethanolic solution in the presence of an aromatic amine and a small amount of acetic acid.[37,38] This reaction is well known from the chemistry of monosaccharides and consists of a simultaneous removal of the acetoxy group from C-1 and its replacement by the arylamine residue.

The primary aromatic amine may be split off from N-arylsubstituted derivatives of N-glycosylamines by heating with benzaldehyde,[13a] whereby the initial reducing oligosaccharide is regenerated.

* * *

Nucleosides which belong to the group of glycosylamines, too, have so far not been found among natural products; however, several substances of this type, such as 9-β-lactosyl-adenine, 9-β-maltosyladenine, 9-β-cellobiosyladenine and 2,6-diaminolactosylpurine have been synthesized, see M. L. Wolfrom, P. McWain, and F. Shafizadeh, J. Am. Chem. Soc. *81*, 6080 (1959); M. L. Wolfrom, P. McWain, and A. Thompson, J. Am. Chem. Soc. *82*, 4353 (1960).

## Table LXXIII

Physical Properties of Oligosaccharide Glycosyl Amines

| Oligosaccharide Glycosyl Amine | Melting Point °C | $[\alpha]_D$ | Solvent | References |
|---|---|---|---|---|
| Lactosylamine | | $+39\cdot5°$ | $H_2O$ | 5 |
| | | $+38\cdot5°$ | $H_2O$ | 6 |
| N-acetyl derivative,α- | 162—163 | $+71\cdot5°$ | $H_2O$ | 41 |
| hepta-O-acetate | 181—183 | $+66\cdot6°$ | $CHCl_3$ | 41 |
| N-acetyl derivative,β- | 246—248 | $+ 1\cdot5°$ | $H_2O$ | 30 |
| hepta-O-acetate | 142—146 | $+ 2\cdot7°$ | $CHCl_3$ | 30 |
| | | $+ 7\cdot4°$ | MeOH | 30 |
| N,N-dimethyl derivative | | | | |
| hepta-O-acetate | 154 | $-21\cdot4°$ | $CHCl_3$ | 32 |
| N-phenyl derivative | | | | 7, 8 |
| α-anomer | 159 | $-13\cdot5°$ | $C_5H_5N$ | 39 |
| hepta-O-acetate | 197 | | | 37, 38 |
| β-anomer | 199—201 | $-82\cdot1°$ | $C_5H_5N$ | 39 |
| hepta-O-acetate | 152 | | | 37, 38 |
| N-p-ethoxyphenyl derivative | 139 | $-26°$ | $H_2O$ | 12 |
| N-p-tolyl derivative | 133 | | | 10, 11 |
| hepta-O-acetate | 202 | | | 37, 38 |
| N-p-xenyl derivative | 144—148 | | | 21 |
| N-3-hydroxy-4-carbophenoxyphe-nyl derivative | 208—212 | $-69°$ | $C_5H_5N$ | 15 |
| N-3-hydroxy-4-carboxyphenyl derivative | | | | |
| Na salt | | $-89°$ | $H_2O$ | 14 |
| N-p-sulphanilyl derivative | 210—212 | $-69°$ | $C_5H_5N$ | 20 |
| | 208 | $-66°$ | $C_5H_5N$ | 28, 29 |
| | 190 | | | 17, 19 |
| Maltosylamine | 165 (dec.) | $+118°$ | $H_2O$ | 5 |
| hepta-O-acetate | 191·5 | $+73\cdot7°$ | $CHCl_3$ | 36 |
| N-dodecyl derivative | 48—84 | | | 21 |
| N-octadecyl derivative | 80—115 | | | 21 |
| N-phenyl derivative | | | | |
| hepta-O-acetate,β- | 205 | | | 37, 38 |
| N-p-tolyl derivative | | | | |
| hepta-O-acetate,β- | 182 | | | 37, 38 |
| N-o-carboxyphenyl derivative | 153—155 | $+48\cdot9° \rightarrow +68°$ | MeOH | 13 |
| N-3-hydroxy-4-carbophenoxyphe-nyl derivative | 235—240 | $+35\cdot7°$ | $C_5H_5N$ | 14 |
| N-3-hydroxy-4-carboxyphenyl deri-vative | 135—145 | $-42\cdot4°$ | $C_5H_5N$ | 14 |
| N-sulphanilyl derivative | 212—214 | $-59°$ | $C_5H_5N$ | 20 |
| | 236 | | | 17 |
| | | $+80°$ | $C_5H_5N$ | 16 |
| | | $-14°$ | $C_5H_5N$ | 18 |
| Di-N-maltosylbenzidine | 175 | $+13°$ | | 9 |
| Cellobiosylamine | 180—182 | $+20°$ | $H_2O$ | 6 |
| hepta-O-acetate | 200 | $+73\cdot7°$ | $CHCl_3$ | 36 |
| N-acetyl derivative ,α- | | | | |
| hepta-O-acetate | 242—243 | $+54\cdot9°$ | $CHCl_3$ | 42 |
| N-acetyl derivative,β- | 246 | | | 31 |
| hepta-O-acetate | 196 | $- 8\cdot4°$ | $CHCl_3$ | 31 |
| | 188 | $- 7\cdot5°$ | $CHCl_3$ | 6 |
| N,N-diacetyl derivative | | $-20°$ | | 31 |
| hepta-O-acetate | 196 | $- 3\cdot3°$ | $CHCl_3$ | 31 |
| N-ethyl derivative | 110—112 | $- 7\cdot8°$ | | 6 |

*References see p. 400*

*Table LXXIII — continued*

| Oligosaccharide Glycosyl Amine | Melting Point °C | $[\alpha]_D$ | Solvent | References |
|---|---|---|---|---|
| *N,N*-dimethyl derivative | | | | |
| hepta-*O*-acetate | 206 | — 10·7° | $CHCl_3$ | 32 |
| | 205—206 | — 11·5° | $CHCl_3$ | 35 |
| | 203 | — 10·5° | $CHCl_3$ | 33 |
| *N*-phenyl derivative | 133—135 | — 62·3° | | 6 |
| | (dec.) | | | |
| hepta-*O*-acetate,β- | 218 | | | 37 |
| *N*-*p*-tolyl derivative | 122—123 | — 65·8° | | 6 |
| | (dec.) | | | |
| hepta-*O*-acetate,β- | 215 | | | 37 |
| *N*-*p*-sulphanilyl derivative | 215—216 | — 81° | $C_5H_5N$ | 20 |
| | | — 88° | $H_2O$ | 20 |
| Di-*N*-cellobiosylimine | 209—210 | + 4·5° | | 6 |
| Cellobiosylpiperidine | 158—160 | + 3·2° | | 6 |
| hepta-*O*-acetate | 215—220 | — 15·3° | | 33 |
| 3-*O*-β-D-Galactopyranosyl-D-arabinosylamine | | | | |
| *N*-phenyl derivative | 170—171 | +34·7° | $C_5H_5N$ | 13a, 40 |
| | | — 16° → — 42° | $H_2O$ | 13a |
| | | +2·6° → — 44·3° | $H_2O$ | 40 |
| *N*-*p*-tolyl derivative | 162—164 | +11·4° → 0° | $H_2O$ | 13a |
| *N*-α-naphthyl derivative | 196—198 | +84·2° | dimethyl-formamide | 13a |
| | (dec.) | | | |
| *N*-β-naphthyl derivative | 167—169 | +21·5° → +6·5° | dimethyl-formamide | 13a |
| | (dec.) | | | |
| *N*-benzyl derivative | 126 | — 20° → — 29° | $C_5H_5N$ | 13a |

## REFERENCES

1. G. P. Ellis and J. Honeyman, Advances in Carbohydrate Chem. *10*, 95 (1955).
2. J. Staněk, M. Černý, J. Kocourek, and J. Pacák, *The Monosaccharides*, Acad. Press, New York 1963.
3. S. Adachi, Nippon-Nôgei Kagaku Kaishi *30*, 454 (1956); Chem. Abstr. *52*, 5687 (1958).
4. S. Adachi, Nippon-Nôgei Kagaku Kaishi *30*, 459 (1956); Chem. Abstr. *52*, 5687 (1958).
5. C. A. Lobry de Bruyn and F. H. van Leent, Rec. trav. chim. *14*, 134 (1895).
6. F. Micheel, R. Frier, E. Platz, and A. Hiller, Chem. Ber. *85*, 1092 (1952).
7. R. Sachsse, Ber. *4*, 835 (1871).
8. B. Sorokin, J. prakt. Chem. (2) *37*, 305 (1888).
9. O. Adler, Ber. *42*, 1742 (1909).
10. S. Adachi, Chem. & Ind. (London) *1957*, 956; Chem. Abstr. *51*, 17787 (1957).
11. S. Adachi, J. Agr. Chem. Soc. Japan 31, 97 (1957); Chem. Abstr. *52*, 12259 (1958).
12. R. Kuhn and L. Birkofer, Ber. *71*, 621 (1938).
13a. R. Kuhn and W. Kirschenlohr, Ann. *600*, 135 (1956).
13b. J. C. Irvine and A. Hynd, J. Chem. Soc. *99*, 161 (1911).
14. G. Haberland, Arzneimittel-Forsch. *1*, 298 (1951); Chem. Abstr. *36*, 7077 (1942).
15. W. O. Godtfredsen, E. J. Nielsen, R. Reiter, E. Schönfeldt, and I. Steensgaard, Acta Chem. Scand. *7*, 781 (1953).

16. U.S. Patent 2,167,719; Chem. Abstr. *33*, 8924 (1939).
17. French Patent 842,726; Chem. Abstr. *34*, 5857 (1940).
18. Brit. Patent 526,747; Chem. Abstr. *35*, 6978 (1941).
19. G. Cavallini and A. Saccarello, Chim. e Ind. (Milan) *24*, 425 (1942); Chem. Abstr. *38*, 4257 (1944).
20. R. Bognár and P. Nánasi, J. Chem. Soc. *1953*, 1703.
21. W. W. Pigman, E. A. Cleveland, D. H. Couch, and J. H. Cleveland, J. Am. Chem. Soc. *73*, 1876 (1951).
22. E. J. Hodge and E. C. Nelson, Cereal Chem. *38*, 207 (1961).
23. H. Masamune and S. Tsuiki, Tôhoku J. Exptl. Med. *67*, 195 (1958).
24. K. Hanaoka, J. Biochem. (Japan) *31*, 95 (1940); Chem. Abstr. *34*, 4057 (1940).
25. J. E. Hodge, Advances in Carbohydrate Chem. *10*, 169 (1955).
26. Ref. 2, p. 456.
27. Ref. 2, p. 455.
28. R. Bognár, P. Nánási, and É. Nemes-Nánási, J. Chem. Soc. *1955*, 193.
29. R. Bognár, P. Nánási, and É. Nemes-Nánási, Magyar Kém. Folyóirat *62*, 271 (1956).
30. R. Kuhn and G. Krüger, Chem. Ber. *87*, 1544 (1954).
31. L. Zechmeister and G. Tóth, Ann. *525*, 14 (1936).
32. P. Karrer and J. C. Harloff, Helv. Chim. Acta *16*, 962 (1933).
33. G. Zemplén and Z. Bruckner, Ber. *61*, 2481 (1928).
34. W. M. Corbett, J. Kidd, and A. M. Liddle, J. Chem. Soc. *1960*, 616.
35. G. Zemplén, Z. Csürös, and Z. Bruckner, Ber. *61*, 927 (1928).
36. A. Bertho, Ann. *562*, 229 (1949).
37. M. Frèrejacque, Compt. rend. *202*, 1190 (1936); Chem. Abstr. *30*, 4152 (1936).
38. M. Frèrejacque, Compt. rend. *204*, 1480 (1937); Chem. Abstr. *31*, 5769 (1937).
39. S. Tsuiki, Tôhoku J. Exptl. Med. *61*, 267 (1955); Chem. Abstr. *50*, 4043 (1956).
40. R. L. Whistler and K. Yagi, J. Org. Chem. *26*, 1050 (1961).
41. R. A. Cadenas and J. O. Deferrari, J. Org. Chem. *28*, 1072 (1963).
42. J. O. Deferrari and R. A. Cadenas, J. Org. Chem. *28*, 1070 (1963).

# XXIV

# Amino Sugars*

The chemistry of amino sugars of the oligosaccharide series has been extensively developed in recent years; a number of substances of this group belong to physiologically very important compounds. Among them are products obtained by the hydrolysis of various natural nitrogen-containing polysaccharides, such as the hydrolytic products of chitin, chondroitin sulphate and of some bacterial polysaccharides, further splitting products of certain antibiotics, oligosaccharides isolated from human milk, blood, meconium and other natural sources. Some substances of this type contain the amino sugar linked to a uronic acid; these compounds are dealt with in Chapter XXXIV, 4.

## 1. SUBSTANCES OBTAINED BY HYDROLYSIS OF NITROGEN-CONTAINING POLYSACCHARIDES

### A. HYDROLYTIC PRODUCTS OF CHITIN

The polysaccharide chitin, the principal skeletal substance of Crustacea and insects, yields on acid hydrolysis D-glucosamine (2-amino-2-deoxy-D-glucose). According to a recent paper,[1] chitin contains no amino sugar other than D-glucosamine.

By acid hydrolysis it was also possible to obtain the disaccharide chitobiose (I).[2,3] A more advantageous procedure is the degradation of chitin to chitobiose by acetolysis, which leads to N,N'-diacetyl-hexa-O-acetylchitobiose (II),[4-8] whose deacetylation in alkaline solution yields N,N'-diacetylchitobiose (III).[4,5,8,9] From the chemical behaviour of chitobiose it follows that its configuration corresponds to that of cellobiose; the micro-organism Aspergillus oryzae produces the enzyme β-N-acetylglucosaminidase, which splits N,N'-diacetylchitobiose to form 2 molecules of N-acetyl-D-glucosamine.[10]

---

* For reviews see A. B. Foster and M. Stacey, Advances in Carbohydrate Chem. 7, 247 (1952); K. Heyns, Stärke 9, 85 (1957); A. Klemer, Chem. Technik 9, 584 (1957); R. Kuhn, Angew. Chem. 69, 23 (1957); H. H. Baer, Fortschritte chem. Forsch. 3, 822 (1958); A. B. Foster and D. Horton, Advances in Carbohydrate Chem. 14, 213 (1959); G. Baschang, Fortschritte Chem. org. Naturstoffe 20, 200 (1962); J. Montreuil, Bull. soc. chim. biol. 42, 1399 (1960).

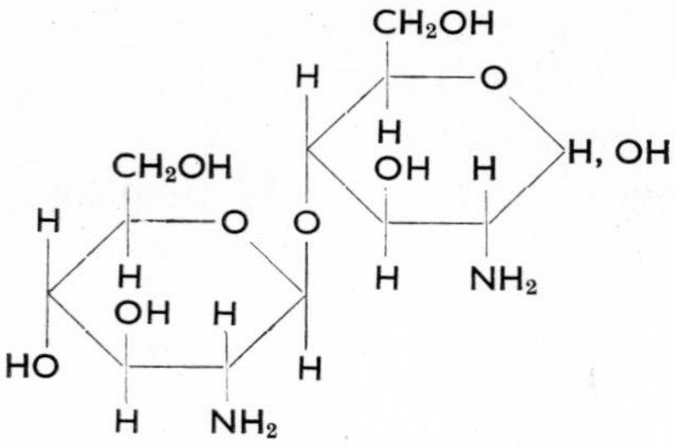

CH₂OH / H—O / H OH H / H, OH / H NH₂
CH₂OH / H—O O / H OH H / HO / H NH₂

(I)

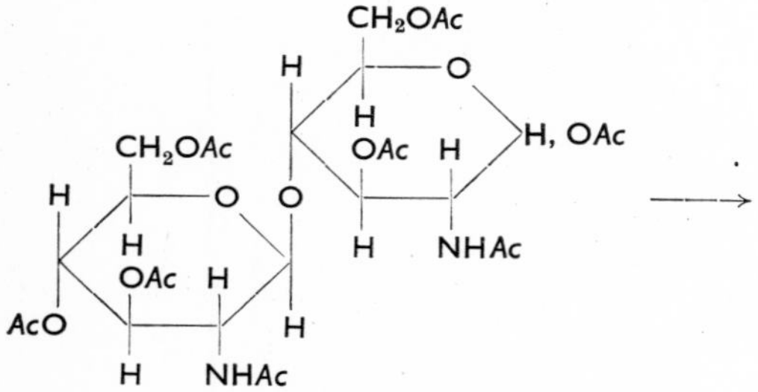

CH₂OAc / H—O / H OAc H / H, OAc / H NHAc
CH₂OAc / H—O O / H OAc H / AcO / H NHAc

(II)

$\longrightarrow$

CH₂OH / H—O / H OH H / H, OH / H NHAc
CH₂OH / H—O O / H OH H / HO / H NHAc

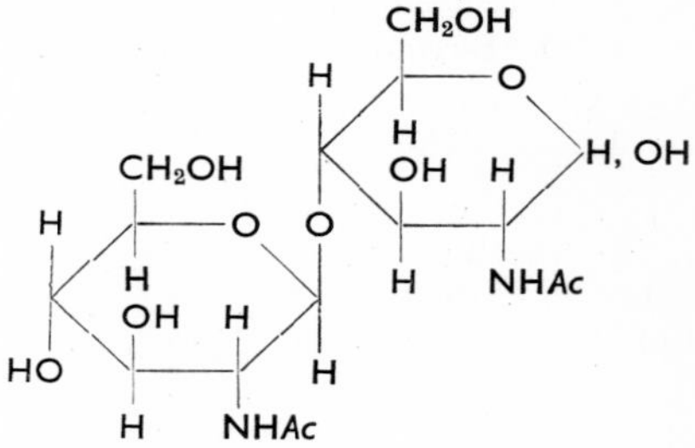

(III)

As far as higher oligosaccharides of this type are concerned, earlier papers[2–4,6] mention only a hendeca-acetyl derivative of chitotriose, which was likewise prepared by the acetolysis of chitin. Other authors[11] reported later that acid hydrolysis of chitosan (obtained by alkaline deacetylation of chitin) leads to a series of oligosaccharides which may be fractionated on ion exchangers. Only the octa-acetyl derivative of chitobiose could be obtained[11] in an established form; other substances were merely proved by paper chromatography.

Graded acid hydrolysis of chitosan followed by selective N-acetylation of the fragments yields a mixture of oligosaccharides[12,13] whose basic constituent is chitobiose. Among the established substances obtained were derivatives of the series from chitobiose to chitopentaose.[13]

Supplementary information in this respect is incorporated in a new paper[14] which records the hydrolysis of chitosan in acid solution and subsequent separation of the hydrolytic products on Dowex 50; in this way it was possible to isolate chitobiose, chitotriose, chitotetraose and chitopentaose.[14]

## B. SUBSTANCES OBTAINED FROM CHONDROITIN AND SIMILAR SUBSTRATES

The oligosaccharides chondrosin (a cleavage product of chondroitin) and heparosin (a cleavage product of heparin) as well as cleavage products of hyaluronic acid also contain amino sugars, which in these cases, however, are

*References see p. 424*

bound to uronic acids. Consequently, these substances belong to nitrogen-containing derivatives of uronic acids (see Chapter XXXIV). Reduction of chondroitin with sodium borohydride, hydrolysis of the reaction product and following acetylation give rise to 3-$O$-$\beta$-D-glucopyranosyl-2-acetamido-2-deoxy-D-galactose, which may be isolated.[15] Similarly, heparin may be desulphated, acetylated, reduced by the action of sodium borohydride, hydrolysed and de-$O$-acetylated to form 4-$O$-$\alpha$-D-glucopyranosyl-2-acetamido-2-deoxy-D-glucose.[16]

The constitution of 4-$O$-$\alpha$-D-glucopyranosyl-2-acetamido-2-deoxy-D-glucose from carboxyl-reduced heparin has been undoubtedly proved by M. L. Wolfrom, J. R. Vercellotti, and D. Horton, J. Org. Chem. *28*, 278 (1963). A second disaccharide has been reported from the same material and provisionally established as 4-$O$-$\alpha$-D-glucosaminyl-D-glucose, see M. L. Wolfrom, J. R. Vercellotti, and D. Horton, J. Org. Chem. *28*, 279 (1963).

Both these mentioned disaccharides have been dealt with in detail by M. L. Wolfrom, J. R. Vercellotti, H. Tomimatsu, and D. Horton, Biochem. et Biophys. Research Communs *12*, 8 (1963); Chem. Abstr. *59*, 11636 (1963) and by M. L. Wolfrom, J. R. Vercellotti, and D. Horton, J. Org. Chem. *29*, 540 (1964).


## C. SUBSTANCES OBTAINED FROM MICRO-ORGANISMS*

This group consists of nitrogen-containing oligosaccharides, isolated after the hydrolysis of polysaccharides from some micro-organisms. Thus, partial hydrolysis of a polysaccharide from the micro-organism *Pseudomonas fluorescens* yielded a tetrasaccharide[17] containing one molecule of D-glucose, one molecule of D-glucosamine and two molecules of L-fucose. The hydrolysis of a polysacccharide from *Pneumococcus* type XIV was found to give rise[18] to four oligosaccharides, two of them in such amounts that their structure could be deduced from various reactions (periodate titration, etc.). The original assumption[18] that these products are 4-$O$-$\beta$-D-glucopyranosyl-2-acetamido-2-deoxy-D-glucose and 3-$O$-$\beta$-(2-acetamido-2-deoxy-D-glucopyranosyl)-D-galactose was fully confirmed in a later paper.[19] Moreover, five oligosaccharides were obtained and the structure of one of them was established as that of $O$-$\beta$-D-galactopyranosyl-(1→4)-$O$-$\beta$-D-glucopyranosyl-(1→4)-2-acetamido-2-deoxy-D-glucose.[19]

A polysaccharide isolated from *Micrococcus lysodeikticus* is split by lysozyme to form a disaccharide containing $N$-acetyl-D-glucosamine and $N$-acetylmuramic acid (i. e. 3-$O$-$\alpha$-carboxyethyl-D-glucosamine).[20,21] The structure of this disaccharide was later determined[22,23] as that of 6-$O$-$\beta$-($N$-acetyl-D-glucosaminyl)-$N$-acetylmuramic acid; the enzymolysis of a native polysaccharide[23] has yielded an analogously built oligosaccharide, namely $O$-$\beta$-$N$-acetyl-

---

* For reviews see D. A. L. Davies, Advances in Carbohydrate Chem. *15*, 271 (1960); M. Stacey and S. A. Barker, *Polysaccharides of Micro-Organisms*, Oxford Univ. Press 1960.

D-glucosaminyl-(1→6)-*O-β-N*-acetylmuramyl-(1→4)-*O-β-N*-acetyl-D-glucosaminyl-(1→6)-*N*-acetylmuramic acid. Other papers[21],[24] are concerned with the linkage of these oligosaccharides to peptides in the above-mentioned *Micrococcus lysodeikticus*.

The isolation of the same tetrasaccharide from *Micrococcus lysodeikticus* has been reported by M. R. J. Salton and J. M. Ghuysen, Biochim. et Biophys. Acta *36*, 552 (1959), too.

O. Hoshino, Chem. Pharm. Bull. (Tokyo) *8*, 405, 411 (1960), reported the isolation of 4-*O-β-N*-acetylmuramyl-*N*-acetyl-D-glucosamine from the digested "mucocomplex" of *Micrococcus lysodeikticus*; however, neither this structure, nor that given by Perkins[22] or Salton and Ghuysen[23] is correct. According to a recent communication by R. W. Jeanloz, N. Sharon, and H. M. Flowers, Biochem. et Biophys. Research Commus *13*, 20 (1963), muramic acid has been identified as the reducing moiety and, consequently, the only structure for this natural disaccharide is 4-*O-β-N*-acetyl-D-glucosaminyl-*N*-acetylmuramic acid (IV).

(IV)

## 2. SUBSTANCES OBTAINED FROM ANTIBIOTICS

A number of antibiotics yield amino sugars as cleavage products;[25],[26] moreover, in some cases it was possible to isolate a further sugar,[26] usually from the group of branched-chain monosaccharides,[27] less frequently D-ribose.[26] An aminodeoxy derivative from the inositol group has also often been isolated.[26]

To the antibiotics of the above-mentioned type belong trehalosamine (containing D-glucosamine and D-glucose),[28] streptomycin (containing *N*-methyl-L-glucosamine, the branched-chain streptose and streptidine),[29-37] erythromycin (containing desoamine and the branched-chain monosaccharide cladinose).[38-41] The branched-chain monosaccharide mycarose has been isolated together with the amino sugar mycaminose from the antibiotic magnamycin;[42-45] the antibiotic spiramycin contains besides mycarose and mycaminose a further amino sugar.[46-48]

The cleavage products of other antibiotics contain besides D-ribose and amino sugars also aminodeoxy derivatives of inositols. To this group belong the neosamines B and C,[49-57] paromomycin[58-60] and zygomycin.[61]

*References see p. 424*

The structure of the oligosaccharidic parts of many of these antibiotics is known, although direct isolation of the oligosaccharide is not always possible; this applies, for instance, to streptobiosamine, a constituent of streptomycin.[37]

An antibiotic whose structure was established with certainty and whose individual constituents were isolated is paromomycin.[58-60] It is split by methanolysis into two components, namely paromamine (V) and the methyl glycosides of „paromobiosamine" (VI).[59] The hydrolysis of paromobiosamine yields D-ribose and a 2,6-diamino-2,6-dideoxyaldohexose, which was termed

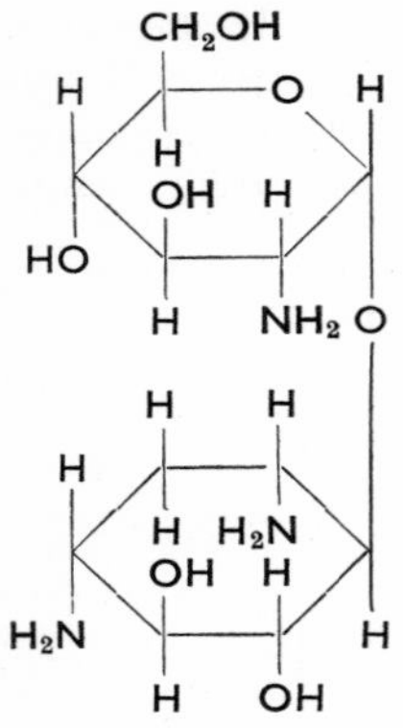

(V)

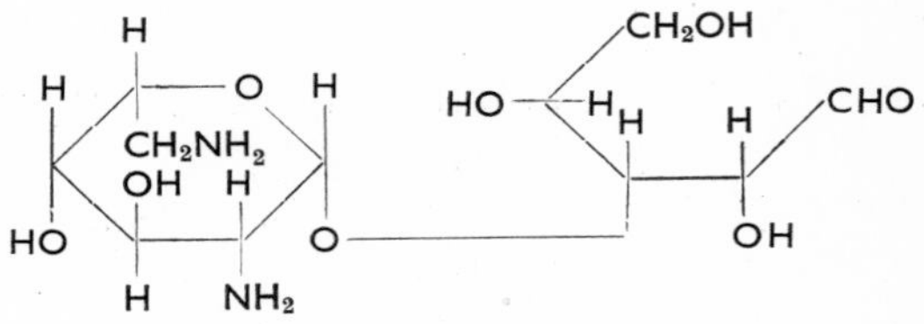

(VI)

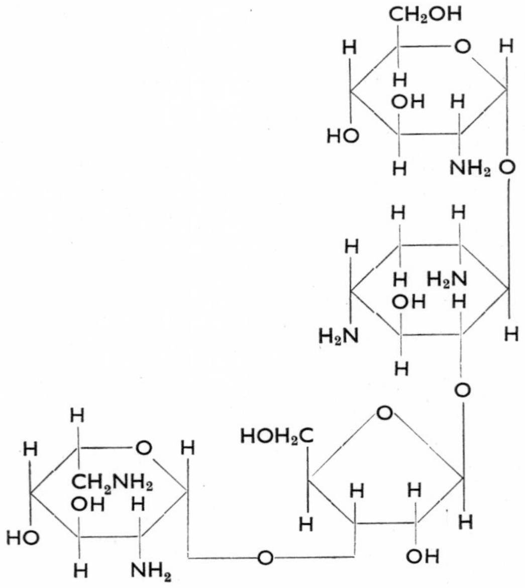

(VII)

paromose.[59]* The structure (VI) was derived for paromobiosamine from the course of various reactions, and the structure (VII) of paromomycin was established after further investigations.[60] Neomycin C[55,57] and zygomycin[61] are antibiotics of very similar types (see also Chapter XXXV).

## 3. SUBSTANCES OBTAINED FROM MUCOPOLYSACCHARIDES

### A. BLOOD-GROUP POLYSACCHARIDES

Polysaccharides combined with proteins are the principal constituents of blood-group polysaccharides; in particular those of the group A have recently become the subject of intense research for their serological properties. A monograph[62] of 1957 presents no detailed information, except the finding that these mucopolysaccharides contain L-fucose, D-galactose, D-glucosamine and D-galactosamine.

All knowledge about oligosaccharides as splitting products of blood-group polysaccharides has been gained in later years,[63–68] mainly thanks to the work of English investigators.[63–66] The first paper in this respect[63] reports that, after hydrolysis in acid solution, 5 disaccharides could be isolated, namely 3-O-β-D-galactopyranosyl-N-acetyl-D-glucosamine (called lacto-N-biose I), 4-O-β-D-galactopyranosyl-N-acetyl-D-glucosamine, 3-O-β-N-acetyl-D-glucosaminyl-D-galactose (termed lacto-N-biose II), 3-O-α-N-acetyl-D-galactosaminyl-D-galactose, and 6-O-α-L-fucopyranosyl-N-acetyl-D-glucosamine. In another paper,[66] this number is increased by 3-O-β-D-galactopyranosyl-N-acetyl-D-galactosamine; two further papers[67,68] report that some of the above disaccharides have also been obtained by hydrazinolysis.[68] Two trisaccharides have also been isolated in these investigations, namely O-α-N-acetyl-D-galactosaminyl-(1→3)-O-β-D-galactopyranosyl-(1→4)-N-acetyl-D-glucosamine[65] and O-α-N-acetyl-D-galactosaminyl-(1→3)-O-β-D-galactopyranosyl-(1→3)-N-acetyl-D-glucosamine.[65,67]

4-O-β-D-Galactopyranosyl-D-glucosamine and its N-acetyl derivative were reported again as hydrolysis products of human plasma glycoproteins (like fetuin and orosomucoid), see R. G. Spiro, J. Biol. Chem. 237, 646 (1962); E. H. Eylar and R. W. Jeanloz, J. Biol. Chem. 237, 622 (1962). According to the last authors, orosomucoid yields on mild hydrolysis an octasaccharide containing two molecules of D-galactose, two molecules of D-mannose and four molecules of N-acetyl-D-glucosamine; the structure of this branched octasaccharide has not been completely elucidated (see E. H. Eylar and R. W. Jeanloz).

The report on the isolation of 6-O-α-D-galactopyranosyl-N-acetyl-D-glucosamine, see E. A. Kabat and S. Leskowitz, J. Am. Chem. Soc. 77, 5159 (1955), has been corrected by T. J. Painter, W. M. Watkins, and W. T. J. Morgan, Nature 193, 1042 (1962). The sub-

---

\* According to recent communications by T. H. Haskell and S. Hanessian, J. Org. Chem. 28, 2598 (1963), and by W. Meyer zu Reckendorf, Angew. Chem. 75, 572 (1963), paromose has been found identical with the synthetically prepared 2,6-diamino-2,6-dideoxy-L-idose.

References see p. 424

stance isolated from human blood group B substance is in fact 3-*O*-α-D-galactopyranosyl D-galactose.

3-*O*-α-D-Galactopyranosyl-*N*-acetyl-D-galactosamine has been mentioned briefly as one of hydrolysis products of blood substances, see W. T. J. Morgan, Naturwissenschaften *46*, 187 (1959); W. T. J. Morgan, Proc. Roy. Soc. (London) *151*, 320 (1960).

The number of trisaccharides isolated from human blood-groups A, B, H, and Leᵃ substance has been increased in a paper by V. P. Rege, T. J. Painter, W. M. Watkins, and W. T. J. Morgan, Nature *20*, 532 (1963). Three trisaccharides have been obtained: *O*-β-*N*-acetyl-D-glucosaminyl-(1→3)-*O*-β-D-galactopyranosyl-(1→3)-*N*-acetyl-D-galacto-samine, *O*-β-D-galactopyranosyl-(1→3)-*O*-β-*N*-acetyl-D-glucosaminyl-(1→3)-D-galactose and *O*-β-D-galactopyranosyl-(1→4)-*O*-β-*N*-acetyl-D-glucosaminyl-(1→3)-D-galactose. 3-*O*-β-*N*-Acetyl-D-glucosaminyl-D-galactose has been obtained by the action of acids in all cases; the other hydrolysis components have been identified as 3-*O*-β-D-galactopyranosyl-*N*-acetyl-D-glucosamine, 3-*O*-β-D-galactopyranosyl-*N*-acetyl-D-galactosamine and 4-*O*-β-D-galactopyranosyl-*N*-acetyl-D-glucosamine, respectively.

Among the products obtained from mucopolysaccharides by hydrolysis in the presence of polystyrenesulphonic acid and following dialysis it was possible to prove the presence of 13 oligosaccharides,[64] two of which are identical with some of the five disaccharides mentioned in the first paper on this subject.[63]

## B. HOG GASTRIC MUCINS

Acid hydrolysis of mucins isolated from the alimentary tract of the hog[69,70] yields 4-*O*-β-D-galactopyranosyl-D-glucosamine,[70] while, according to another paper,[71] acetolysis gives rise to 4-*O*-α-*N*-acetyl-D-galactosaminyl-D-galactose. Further oligosaccharides obtained from this source by acetolysis,[72,73] have so far been designated as gastro-trisaccharide and gastro-*N*-trisaccharide.

## 4. NITROGEN-CONTAINING OLIGOSACCHARIDES FROM HUMAN MILK

Research from recent years[74–76] has shown that human milk is the source of a highly populated group of oligosaccharides; these could be divided into three classes, namely nitrogen-free oligosaccharides containing L-fucose throughout (see Chapter XXII), further nitrogen-containing oligosaccharides, and finally substances containing lactose glycosidically linked to nonulosaminic acids.

Human milk contains a number of interesting nitrogenous oligosaccharides, and some others have been obtained by partial hydrolysis of these native oligosaccharides. An especially rich source of these oligosaccharides is the colostrum (the secretion of the mammary glands first produced after childbirth); these nitrogen-containing oligosaccharides are also found in the meconium (the excretion of the new-born child).

In comparison with human milk, cow milk contains a quite negligible amount of nitrogenous oligosaccharides, certainly less than a hundredth.[74] At present, there is only one concrete report[77] available, stating that from evaporated cow milk a substance has been obtained belonging to the group of amino sugars, namely 4-*O*-β-D-galactopyranosyl-D-fructosamine, linked by a primary amino group to amino acids. This substance is probably formed by an Amadori re-arrangement from 4-*O*-β-D-galactopyranosyl-D-glucosylamine, likewise linked to amino acids and also found in the same source.[77]

A new nitrogen-containing oligosaccharide, termed "gynolactose", was isolated from human milk in 1933.[78] This substance could not be prepared in a crystalline state, undoubtedly for the reason that it was a mixture of a larger number of compounds which, by the methods of that time, could not be separated. Later, when after the year 1952 great advances were achieved in the chemistry of nitrogen-containing oligosaccharides of human milk, it was found by chromatographic investigation of the original "gynolactose" that it is in fact a mixture of a larger number of substances, some of which contain nitrogen.[79,80]

These discoveries were well supported by attempts to find the so-called bifidus factor. It had been known since about 1926[81] that the excretions of babies fed with human milk react more acid than those of babies nourished artificially. At the same time it was also found that the excretions of babies fed with human milk contain the micro-organism *Lactobacillus bifidus*, which splits lactose with the formation of lactic and acetic acids. The acid reaction produced in this way is unfavourable to the development of various other micro-organisms, and the resistance of babies to, for example, typhoid contagion is evidently connected with this phenomenon.[74] Further reports[82,83] that human milk on its own is a good substrate for the growth of *Lactobacillus bifidus* led to a systematic investigation of the oligosaccharides contained in human milk; besides nitrogen-free oligosaccharides (see Chapter XXII), so far 6 nitrogen-containing oligosaccharides have been found, and 4 lower compounds have been obtained by their cleavage.[26,74,75]

New research work in this field was started by Kuhn and his associates in 1952[84] and the advances achieved are due to his school.[26,74,75] It was found that one litre of human milk contains besides 70 g of lactose about 3·0 to 3·3 g of nitrogen-containing oligosaccharides (the colostrum even up to 4 g). This amount corresponds to approximately 0·7 g of *N*-acetyl-D-glucosamine (plus negligible quantities of *N*-acetyl-D-galactosamine). The mixture of these oligosaccharides, free from lactose, yields on complete hydrolysis D-glucose, D-galactose, L-fucose and D-glucosamine.[85]

The first established nitrogen-containing oligosaccharide isolated in the native state was lacto-*N*-tetraose,[85-89] which was obtained in crystalline form in 1953.[87] Its constitution (VIII), corresponding to that of *O*-β-D-galactopyranosyl-(1→3)-*O*-β-2-acetamido-2-deoxy-D-glucopyranosyl-(1 → 3)-*O*-β-D-galactopyranosyl-(1→4)-D-glucopyranose, was derived from a number of observations.

*References see p. 424*

From analysis it followed that the substance in question was a tetrasaccharide containing D-galactose, D-glucose and D-glucosamine in the ratio 2 : 1 : 1. The amino group was acetylated, and the tetrasaccharide was found to yield a phenylosazone containing 5 nitrogen atoms.[88]

The reducing unit of this tetrasaccharide is D-glucose; for if lacto-$N$-tetraose is oxidized to the corresponding lacto-$N$-tetraonic acid, no D-glucose can be found among the products of the hydrolysis of this acid. Some reactions seemed to indicate that D-glucosamine might be the reducing terminal unit; it was in particular the positive Morgan-Elson reaction (violet-red coloration with $p$-dimethylaminobenzaldehyde in alkaline solution) which is characteristic of 2-amino-2-deoxyaldoses. The positive result of this reaction is explained by the lability of the tetrasaccharide in alkaline solution, where the D-glucosamine molecule is uncovered by various splittings of the glycosidic linkages.

The structure of lacto-$N$-tetraose (VIII) followed from an investigation of the course of the hydrolysis in acid solution,[88] where the formation of 3 disaccha-

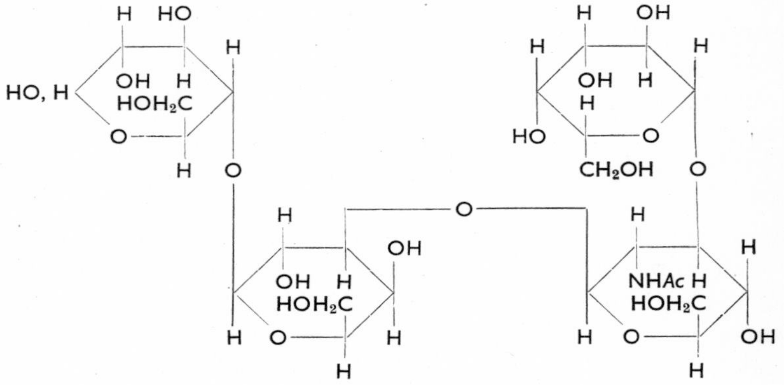

(VIII)

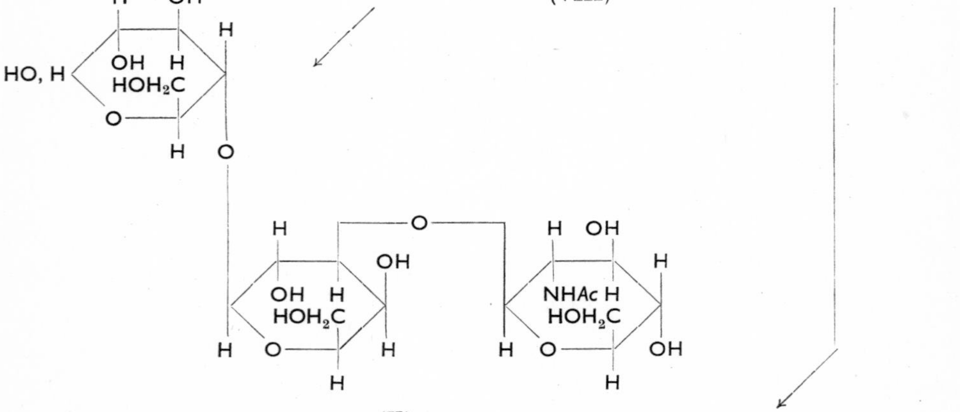

(X)

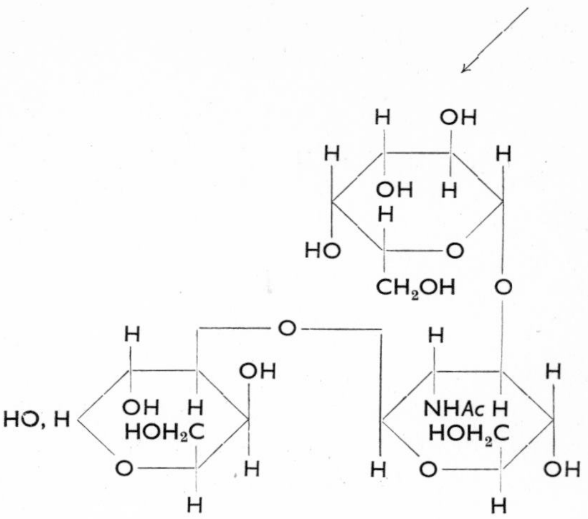

(IX)

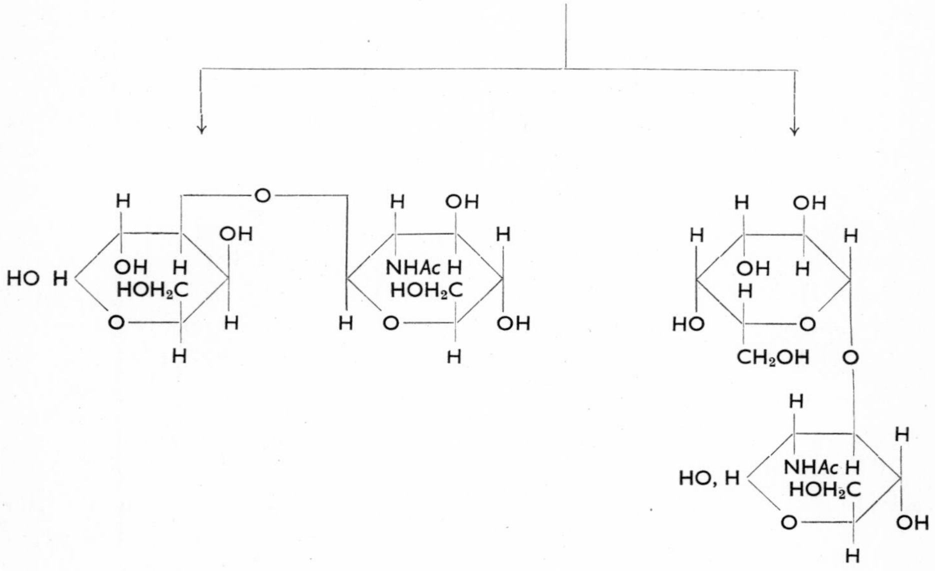

(XII) (XI)

rides (one of them lactose) and 2 trisaccharides may be expected. All these five substances were found by chromatography on activated carbon and Celite, and four of them were obtained in crystalline form.[88]

Lacto-*N*-triose *I* is formed by elimination of the reducing D-glucose molecule; it yields a phenylosazone and is split by $\beta$-galactosidases into D-galactose and lacto-*N*-biose *II* (see later). All findings in this respect[88–90] suggest the

*Re erences see p. 424*

structure (IX), i. e. $O$-$\beta$-D-galactopyranosyl-(1→3)-$O$-$\beta$-2-acetamido-2-deoxy-D-glucopyranosyl-(1→3)-D-galactose.[90]

Lacto-$N$-triose $II$ is composed of one molecule each of D-glucose, D-galactose and $N$-acetyl-D-glucosamine and is produced, therefore, by the elimination of one D-galactose molecule from lacto-$N$-tetraose.[88–90] It is split by $\beta$-$N$-acetylglucosaminidase from the micro-organism *Aspergillus oryzae* to form $N$-acetyl-D-glucosamine and lactose, which is in agreement with the structure (X), i. e. $O$-$\beta$-2-acetamido-2-deoxy-D-glucopyranosyl-(1→3)-$O$-$\beta$-D-galactopyranosyl-(1→4)-D-glucopyranose.[90]

Lacto-$N$-biose $I$ consists of a D-galactose and an $N$-acetyl-D-glucosamine molecule. Its structure (XI) follows from the fact that it yields a phenylosazone which is neither identical with that of lactose nor with that of *allo*-lactose, but is identical with the phenylosazone of the synthetic disaccharides 3-$O$-$\beta$-D-galactopyranosyl-D-glucose and 3-$O$-$\beta$-D-galactopyranosyl-D-fructose.[88,91] Accordingly, lacto-$N$-biose $I$ must be regarded as 3-$O$-$\beta$-D-galactopyranosyl-2-acetamido-2-deoxy-D-glucopyranose.[91]

Lacto-$N$-biose $II$ is formed in the hydrolysis of lacto-$N$-tetraose in a very small amount and has not been obtained in a crystalline state. Its structure (XII), i. e. 3-$O$-$\beta$-2-acetamido-2-deoxy-D-glucopyranosyl-D-galactose, follows from a combination of all the results obtained.[89]

The structure of lacto-$N$-tetraose may be derived unambiguously from all these splitting products. Moreover, it was confirmed by the reduction of lacto-$N$-tetraose to the corresponding lacto-$N$-tetraitol, which was permethylated, whereupon the permethyl ether obtained was hydrolysed into 1,2,3,5,6-penta-$O$-methyl-D-glucitol, 2,4,6-tri-$O$-methyl-D-galactose, 2,3,4,6-tetra-$O$-methyl-D-galactose and 4,6-di-$O$-methyl-D-glucosamine.[89] The identification of all these splitting products confirms the structure (VIII) derived for lacto-$N$-tetraose.

Another tetrasaccharide of this type has recently been obtained, namely lacto-$N$-*neo*-tetraose.[92] It is likewise composed of one D-glucose molecule, one $N$-acetyl-D-glucosamine molecule and two D-galactose molecules; however, the linkage differs in one place. Lacto-$N$-*neo*-tetraose (XIII) is $O$-$\beta$-D-galactopyranosyl-(1→4)-$O$-$\beta$-2-acetamido-2-deoxy-D-glucopyranosyl-(1→3)-$O$-$\beta$-D-galactopyranosyl-(1→4)-D-glucopyranose.

Partial acid hydrolysis of this tetrasaccharide yields such lower oligosaccharides as lactose, lacto-$N$-biose $II$ (XII), lacto-$N$-triose $II$ (X), and, because the different linkage between the terminal D-galactose and $N$-acetyl-D-glucosamine must give rise to additional splitting products, lacto-$N$-*neo*-triose $I$ (XIV), i. e. $O$-$\beta$-D-galactopyranosyl-(1→4)-$O$-$\beta$-2-acetamido-2-deoxy-D-glucopyranosyl-(1→3)-D-galactopyranose, and $N$-acetyl-lactosamine, i. e. 4-$O$-$\beta$-D-galactopyranosyl-2-acetamido-2-deoxy-D-glucose (XV).[92]

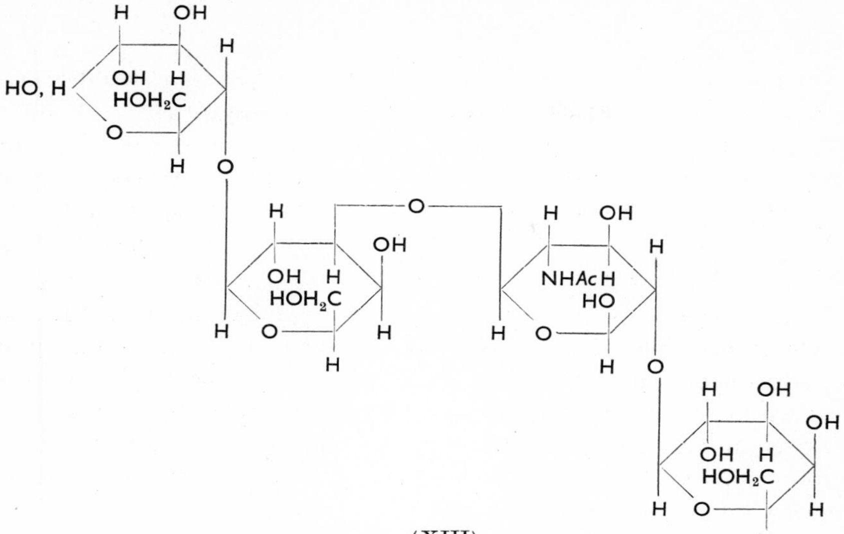

(XIII)

(X)

(XII)

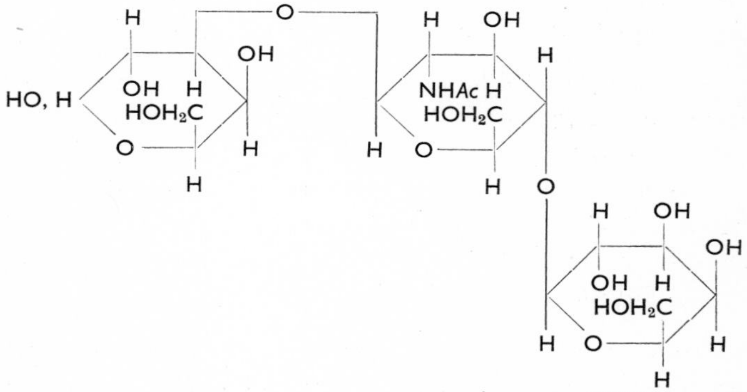

(XIV)

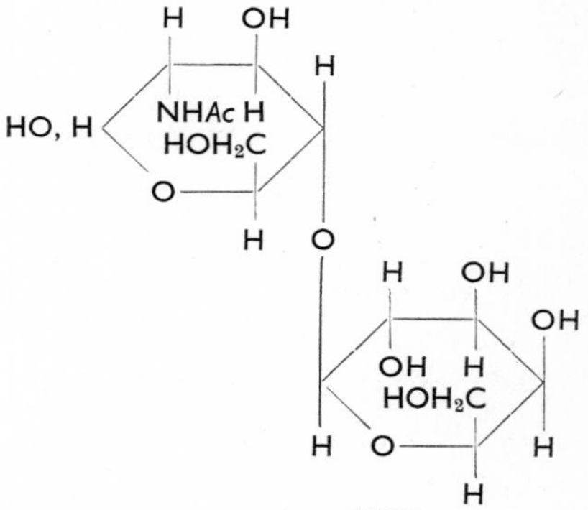

(XV)

Further, four higher oligosaccharides, namely two pentasaccharides and two hexasaccharides, have been isolated from human milk. Lacto-*N*-fucopentaose *I*[93] is based directly on the structure of lacto-*N*-tetraose, which may also be obtained from it by hydrolytic elimination of an L-fucose molecule.[93] The structure (XVI) was derived by methylation analysis of its reduction product, lacto-*N*-pentaitol, in a similar way as in the case of lacto-*N*-tetraose. L-Fucose is attached to the last D-galactose unit by an α-linkage in position -2-. In alkaline solution, lacto-*N*-fucopentaose *I* is split into smaller fragments, besides other products, down to *O*-α-L-fucopyranosyl-D-galactose and *O*-α-L-fucopyranosyl-D-talose (which is obviously formed by epimerization of a D-galactose unit in the molecule of the above-mentioned compound). The structure of lacto-*N*-fucopentaose *I*, expressed in detail, is *O*-α-L-fucopyranosyl-(1→2)-*O*-β-D-galactopyranosyl-(1→3)-*O*-β-2-acetamido-2-deoxy-D-glucopyranosyl-(1→3)-*O*-β-D-galactopyranosyl-(1→4)-D-glucopyranose.

(XVI)

Lacto-*N*-fucopentaose *II* is an isomer of the foregoing compound.[95] Acid hydrolysis splits off also a molecule of L-fucose with the formation of lacto-*N*-tetraose, but in this case the L-fucose is bound to C-4 of the D-glucosamine part of the molecule. Consequently, lacto-*N*-fucopentaose *II* is a branched pentasaccharide of the structure (XVII), which was proved by methylation analysis of its reduction product, lacto-*N*-pentaitol.

Lacto-*N*-difucohexaose *I* is the di-L-fucopyranosyl derivative of lacto-*N*-tetraose, in which both L-fucose molecules are linked in the same way as

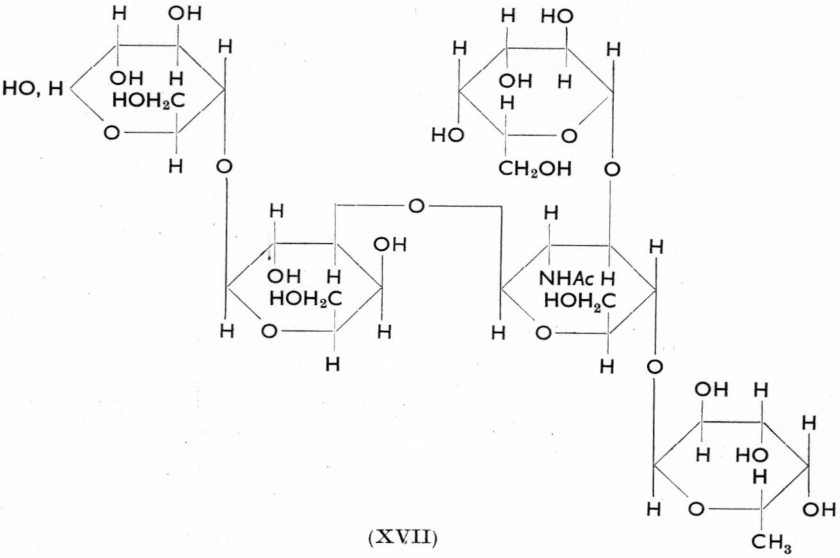

(XVII)

in the molecules of both lacto-$N$-fucopentaose $I$ and lacto-$N$-fucopentaose $II$. The structure of lacto-$N$-difucohexaose $I$ is therefore given by the formula (XVIII).[93,94]

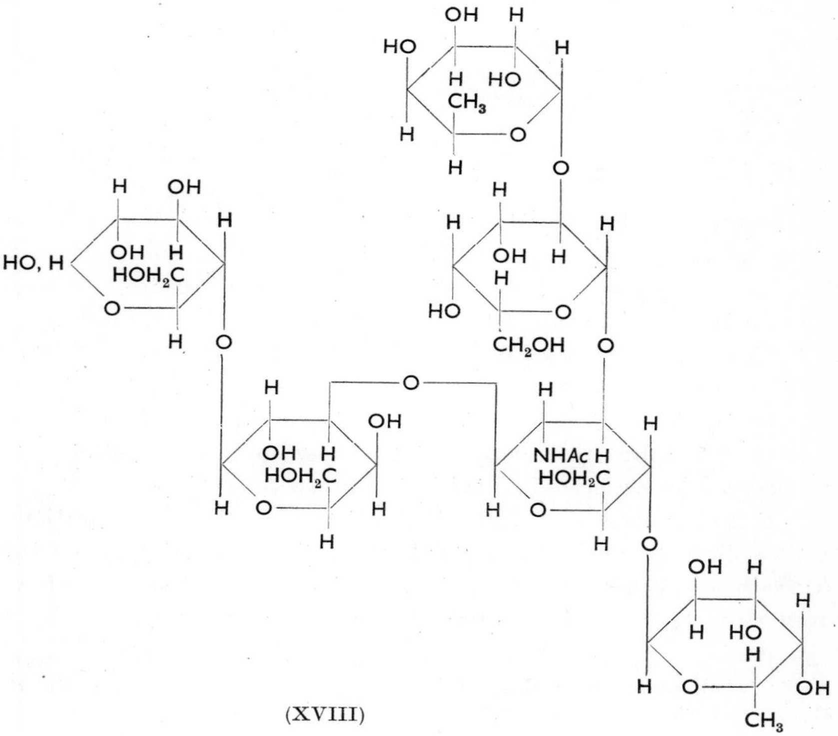

(XVIII)

Lacto-*N*-difucohexaose *II*, recently isolated,[96] is split into lacto-*N*-tetraose and lacto-*N*-biose *II* and corresponds to the formula (XIX).

(XIX)

Another group of authors[97] has found lacto-*N*-tetraose in human milk besides higher oligosaccharides of this type, later established[98] as di-(lacto-*N*-tetraose), monofuco-di-(lacto-*N*-tetraose), difuco-di-(lacto-*N*-tetraose), as well as monofuco and difuco derivatives of tri-(lacto-*N*-tetraose). Kuhn's lacto-*N*-difucohexaose *II* is probably identical with the polyoside 10, isolated by another investigator.[80]

Of the blood-group substances contained in meconium, there has as yet been isolated by hydrolysis 4-*O*-$\beta$-D-galactopyranosyl-2-acetamido-2-deoxy-D-glucose (also named *N*-acetyl-lactosamine, XV).[99]

It is obvious at first sight that establishing the configurations of various amino-oligosaccharides by conventional methods is not easy; for this reason, a procedure has been worked out, using the infra-red spectra of *N*-acetylated amino sugars,[100] and this is recommended.

Heterosaccharides of human colostrum, containing amino-oligosaccharides chemically bound to amino acids, are dealt with in a paper by R. Got, J. Font, and R. Bourrillon, Biochim. et Biophys. Acta *78*, 367 (1963).

## 5. BOUND FORM OF LACTAMINIC ACID*

Lactaminic acid (neuraminic, sialic, generally nonulosaminic acid), whose constitution and importance have been established,[26,74,75,101–106] is, in the organism, bound to lactose.[107–111] In this form it is contained not only in milk [108,109,111] but also in other organic materials.[107,110] This bound form of lactaminic acid, however, is extraordinarily labile, it is split in both acid and alkaline media, and even in aqueous solution by its own acidity. The isolation of this substance in the pure form was therefore difficult;[109] nevertheless, a reliable isolating procedure is now known.[112]

The structure of the bound form of lactaminic acid has been established with certainty.[113–115] This was considerably facilitated by the finding[116] that splitting in acid solution gives rise to lactaminic acid and lactose; however, the constitution itself was elucidated by methylation analysis.[115,116] The per-O-methyl derivative, prepared by methylation with methyl iodide in the presence of silver oxide and barium oxide in dimethylformamide, yielded on hydrolysis a mixture of methyl ethers. Although only 2,3,6-tri-O-methyl-D-glucose and 2,4,6-tri-O-methyl-D-galactose could be isolated from this mixture,[113,114] this finding is sufficient for it to be stated that lactaminic acid must be linked to

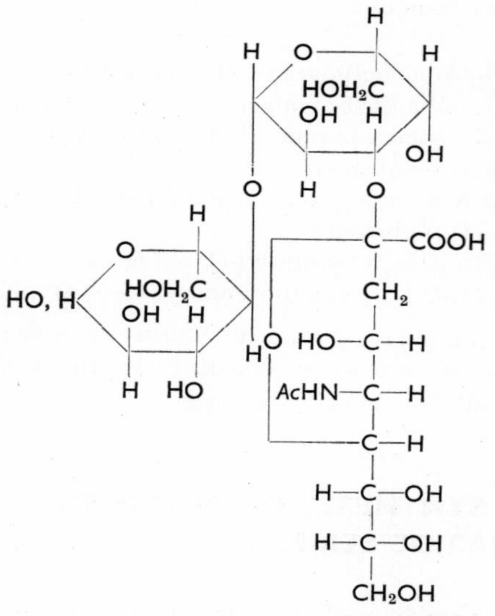

(XX)

---

* For reviews see: R. Kuhn, Angew. Chem. 69, 23 (1957); H. H. Baer, Fortschritte chem. Forsch. 3, 822 (1958); W. J. Whelan, Ann. Reports 54, 319 (1958); F. Zilliken and M. W. White house, Advances in Carbohydrate Chem. 13, 237 (1958); A. Gottschalk, Bull. soc. chim. biol. 42, 1387 (1960); J. Montreuil, Bull. soc. chim. biol. 42, 1399 (1960); G. Baschang, Fortschritte Chem. org. Naturstoffe 20, 200 (1962); A. Gottschalk, Rev. Pure Appl. Chem. (Australia) 12, 46 (1962).

References see p. 424

C-3 of the galactose part of lactose according to the formula (XX)[114] which, without further proof, is also given by another writer.[115]

Chemically, this substance must be designated as 3-$O$-$\beta$-lactaminyl-lactose with the remark that the anomeric arrangement at C-2 in the lactaminic acid unit has not yet been established.

A new product isolated from the mammary glands of rats is 3-$O$-lactaminyl-lactose 6′-phosphate,[117] and mention is also made of the isolation from natural material of both 6-$O$-lactaminyl-lactose[118] and di-$O$-lactaminyl-lactose.[119] A recent paper[120] describes the isolation from human milk of higher oligosaccharides containing one molecule each of lactaminic acid, D-glucose and $N$-acetyl-D-glucosamine and two molecules of D-galactose. Of these three substances, two contain lactaminic acid linked to lacto-$N$-tetraose, while in the third compound the lactaminic acid is attached to lacto-$N$-$neo$-tetraose.[120]

The problem of nitrogen-containing oligosaccharides from human brain, mentioned shortly by R. Kuhn and H. Wiegandt, Angew. Chem. *73*, 580 (1961), has been followed thoroughly by the same authors in Chem. Ber. *96*, 866 (1963). Five gangliosides were obtained containing one common tetrasaccharide (ganglio-$N$-tetraose); the gangliosides mentioned above are more complicated substances containing $N$-acetylneuraminic acid.

The structure of ganglio-$N$-tetraose was elucidated from its cleavage products obtained by partial acid hydrolysis or by acetolysis. Two trisaccharides (ganglio-$N$-triose $I$ and ganglio-$N$-triose $II$) as well as three disaccharides (ganglio-$N$-biose $I$, ganglio-$N$-biose $II$ and lactose) have been obtained. The structures of these five nitrogen-containing oligosaccharides are:

Ganglio-$N$-biose   $I$: 3-$O$-$\beta$-D-galactopyranosyl-$N$-acetyl-D-galactosamine

Ganglio-$N$-biose   $II$: 4-$O$-$\beta$-$N$-acetyl-D-galactosaminyl-D-galactose

Ganglio-$N$-triose   $I$: $O$-$\beta$-D-galactopyranosyl-$(1\rightarrow3)$-$O$-$\beta$-$N$-acetyl-D-galactosaminyl-$(1\rightarrow4)$-D-galactose

Ganglio-$N$-triose   $II$: $O$-$\beta$-$N$-acetyl-D-galactosaminyl-$(1\rightarrow4)$-$O$-$\beta$-D-galactopyranosyl-$(1\rightarrow4)$-D-glucose

Ganglio-$N$-tetraose: $O$-$\beta$-D-galactopyranosyl-$(1\rightarrow3)$-$O$-$\beta$-$N$-acetyl-D-galactosaminyl-$(1\rightarrow4)$-$O$-$\beta$-D-galactopyranosyl-$(1\rightarrow4)$-D-glucose

The isolation of 3-$O$-$\beta$-D-galactopyranosyl-$N$-acetyl-D-galactosamine has been reported by another group of authors, too, see E. Klenk, U. W. Hendriks, and W. Gielen, Hoppe-Seyler's Z. physiol. Chem. *330*, 140 (1962).

## 6. CHEMICAL SYNTHESES OF AMINO SUGARS FROM THE OLIGOSACCHARIDE SERIES

The first reliably confirmed synthesis in the group of nitrogen-containing oligosaccharides is that of 4-$O$-$\beta$-D-galactopyranosyl-D-glucosamine (i. e. lactosamine), which is produced besides isolactosamine (i. e. 1-amino-1-deoxylactulose) by the hydrogenation of phenyl-lactosazone.[121] Lactosamine was several times obtained from natural material and probably even synthesized, but in impure form, in 1956.[122] The synthesis started from 3-$O$-$\beta$-D-galactopyranosyl-

D-arabinose, analogously to Fischer's synthesis of D-glucosamine,[123] but the yield was negligible. A more advantageous procedure is the conversion of 3-$O$-$\beta$-D-galactopyranosyl-D-arabinose into the corresponding phenylglycosyl-amine; subsequent addition of hydrogen cyanide gives rise to a product which on hydrogenation yields lactosamine,[124] and this was obtained in the form of the $N$-acetyl derivative.

Maltosamine, i. e. 4-$O$-$\alpha$-D-glucopyranosyl-2-amino-2-deoxy-D-glucose, has been prepared similarly by the hydrogenation of phenylmaltosazone, see M. L. Wolfrom, H. El Khadem, and J. R. Vercellotti, Chem. & Ind. (London) *1964*, 545.

The $N$-acetyl-hepta-$O$-acetyl derivative of lactosamine is formed in small yield by the condensation of 2,3,4,6-tetra-$O$-acetyl-$\alpha$-D-galactopyranosyl bromide with $N$-acetyl-1,3,6-tri-$O$-acetyl-D-glucosamine.[125]

The Koenigs-Knorr synthesis has been applied several times in the group of nitrogen-containing oligosaccharides with 1→6 linkages. Thus, 2,3,4,6-tetra-$O$-acetyl-$\alpha$-D-galactopyranosyl bromide reacts with $N$-acetyl-1,3,4-tri-$O$-acetyl-D-glucosamine to form the $N$-acetyl-hepta-$O$-acetyl derivative of 6-$O$-$\beta$-D-galactopyranosyl-D-glucosamine (i. e. *allo*-lactosamine).[126,127]

These reactions have also been carried out with halogenoses derived from acylated derivatives of amino sugars. So, the reaction of $N$-acetyl-3,4,6-tri-$O$-acetyl-$\alpha$-D-glucosaminyl bromide with 1,2,3,4-tetra-$O$-acetyl-D-glucopyranose yields the hepta-$O$-acetyl derivative of 6-$O$-$\beta$-($N$-acetyl-D-glucosaminyl)-D-glucose,[128] and the analogous derivative of D-galactose, i. e. 6-$O$-$\beta$-($N$-acetyl-D-glucosaminyl)-D-galactose, has been prepared in a similar way.[128] The same principle has been utilized for preparing derivatives of 6-$O$-($N$-acetyl-D-glucosaminyl)-$N$-acetyl-D-glucosamine, the so-called isochitobiose.[129]

Attempts have also been undertaken to prepare oligosaccharides with $\alpha$-linkages in the place of the glycosidic union, i. e. to conduct the Koenigs-Knorr synthesis without Walden inversion. This has been carried out using 1,2:3,4-di-$O$-isopropylidene-D-galactopyranose and 3,4,6-tri-$O$-acetyl-2-(2,4-dinitrophenylamino)-2-deoxy-$\alpha$-D-glucopyranosyl bromide.[130] The voluminous substituent at C-2 evidently influences the course of the reaction from the stereochemical viewpoint, so that the condensations of both components in chloroform, in the presence of pyridine, yield 30% of the $\alpha$-derivative and 15% of the $\beta$-derivative, whereas in the presence of silver carbonate only the $\beta$-derivative is formed.[130]

Of oligosaccharides produced by the reaction of acylated halogenoses with a secondary hydroxyl group, one further substance[131] has been prepared in addition to the above-mentioned lactosamine.[125] The reaction of 2,3,4,6-tetra-$O$-acetyl-$\alpha$-D-glucopyranosyl bromide with methyl $N$-acetyl-4,6-$O$-benzylidene-$\alpha$-D-glucosaminide gives rise to the expected derivative of 3-$O$-$\beta$-D-glucopyranosyl-$N$-acetyl-D-glucosamine.[131]

*References see p. 424*

Starting with benzyl 2-acetamido-2-deoxy-4,6-*O*-benzylidene-α-D-glucopyranoside and 2,3,4,6-tetra-*O*-acetyl-α-D-galactopyranosyl bromide and using mercuric cyanide in a mixture of benzene and nitromethane, the synthesis of 3-*O*-β-D-galactopyranosyl-2-acetamido-2-deoxy-D-glucose derivatives was achieved, see H. M. Flowers and R. W. Jeanloz, J. Org. Chem. *28*, 1377 (1963).

Another synthesis of a disaccharide containing D-glucosamine and muramic acid has been reported by H. M. Flowers and R. W. Jeanloz, J. Org. Chem. *28*, 1564 (1963); from 3,4,6-tri-*O*-acetyl-2-acetamido-2-deoxy-α-D-glucosaminyl bromide and a suitable derivative of muramic acid, the synthesis of methyl 6-*O*-(2-acetamido-2-deoxy-3,4,6-tri-*O*-acetyl-β-D-glucopyranosyl)-2-acetamido-2-deoxy-4-*O*-acetyl-3-*O*-[D-1-(methyl carboxylate)ethyl]-α-D-glucopyranoside has been prepared.

For another synthesis of the same disaccharide see R. W. Jeanloz, N. Sharon, and H. M. Flowers, Biochim. et Biophys. Research Communs *13*, 20 (1963).

Micheel utilized his synthesis of glycosides of D-glucosamine in the oligosaccharide series also.[132,133] The reaction of 2-phenyl-4,5-(3,4,6-tri-*O*-acetyl-D-glucopyranoso)-$\Delta^2$-oxazoline (XXI) with 1,2,3,4-tetra-*O*-acetyl-β-D-glucopyranose (XXII) gives rise to the hepta-*O*-acetyl derivative of 6-*O*-β-(*N*-benzoyl-D-glucosaminyl)-D-glucose (XXIII). The reaction of the mentioned oxazoline derivative with methyl 2,3,4-tri-*O*-acetyl-α-D-glucopyranoside proceeds analogously.

A recent report deals with a further possibility of synthesis, which, however, has so far been realized only on a micro-scale on paper. D-Glucosamine hydrochloride and D-mannose, when their spots on paper are warmed, yield only *N*-D-mannopyranosyl-D-glucosamine.[134] More drastic conditions give also rise to 6-*O*-D-mannopyranosyl-D-glucosamine.[135]

The Amadori re-arrangement is also of importance in syntheses of nitrogen-containing derivatives of oligosaccharides.[136,137] Thus, *N*-*p*-tolyl-lactosylamine (XXIV) yields very readily, already in its preparation in a moist solvent, *N*-*p*-tolylisolactosamine (XXV). This substance can be very easily separated from the reaction mixture by its reaction with diazotized *p*-toluidine (see p. 105). Maltose reacts with piperidine in acetic acid, in the presence of triethylamine, to form 1-piperidinyl-1-deoxymaltulose, a product of the Amadori re-arrangement.[138]

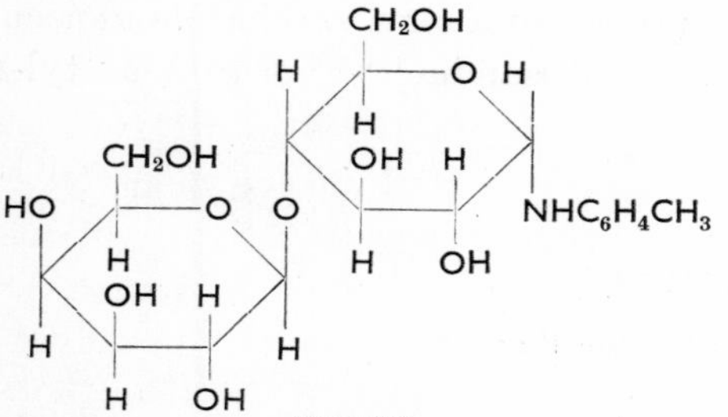

(XXIV)

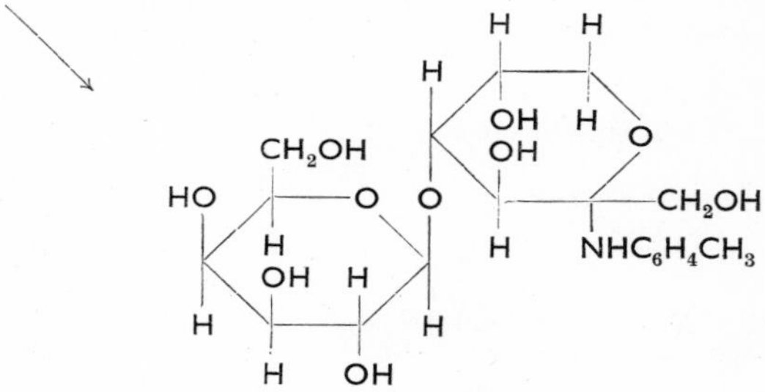

(XXV)

Some *N*-acetyl derivatives of nitrogen-containing oligosaccharides are subject to epimerization in the presence of ammonia. For example, *N*-acetyllactosamine (i. e. 4-*O*-β-D-galactopyranosyl-*N*-acetyl-D-glucosamine) yields under such conditions 4-*O*-β-D-galactopyranosyl-*N*-acetyl-D-mannosamine.[139]

The Schiff bases, which are often used in the synthesis and separation of nitrogen-containing oligosaccharides, can be converted back to the parent amino-oligosaccharides by hydrogenation on palladium, as described, for example, in the case of lactosamine.[140]

## 7. ENZYMIC SYNTHESES OF AMINO SUGARS OF THE OLIGOSACCHARIDE SERIES

The action of enzymes from the micro-organism *Escherichia coli* upon a mixture of *N*-acetyl-D-glucosamine and phenyl β-D-galactopyranoside produces 6-*O*-β-D-galactopyranosyl-*N*-acetyl-D-glucosamine.[126] The same initial substances are converted by the enzymes from *Bacterium bifidum* var. Penn. into a mixture of 6-*O*-β- and 4-*O*-β-D-galactopyranosyl-*N*-acetyl-D-glucosami- ne.[141,142] The action of enzymic preparations from various organs of the rat upon the same initial substances gives, besides the two last-mentioned disaccha- rides, also 3-*O*-β-D-galactopyranosyl-*N*-acetyl-D-glucosamine (lacto-*N*-biose *I*).[143]

Galactosyl derivatives of *N*-acetyl-D-glucosamine, not specified in detail, are produced from lactose and *N*-acetyl-D-glucosamine by the action of enzy- mes from the micro-organism *Escherichia coli*.[144] Nitrogen-containing oligo- saccharides are also formed[145,146] by the transfer of a monosaccharide molecule from sucrose[145] or raffinose[146] to *N*-acetyl-D-glucosamine[145,146] or to *N*-acetyl-D- galactosamine.[146]

### Table LXXIV

Physical Properties of Amino Sugars*

| Amino Sugar | Melting Point °C | $[\alpha]_D$ | Solvent | References |
|---|---|---|---|---|
| *N*,*N*'-Diacetylchitobiose | 185 (dec.) | | | 4, 5, 9 |
| | 245—247 (dec.) | $+39 \cdot 5° \rightarrow +18 \cdot 5°$ | $H_2O$ | 8 |
| hexa-*O*-acetate | 291 | $+55 \cdot 3°$ | AcOH | 4, 8 |
| | 289 | $+50 \cdot 3°$ | AcOH | 5 |
| | 302 | $+55°$ | AcOH | 7 |
| | 285 | $+58 \cdot 7°$ | AcOH | 3 |
| *N*,*N*',*N*''-Triacetylchitotriose | 309—311 (dec.) | $+ 2 \cdot 5°$ | $H_2O$ | 13 |
| octa-*O*-acetate | 304—305 (dec.) | $+30°$ | AcOH | 13 |
| | 310 | $+31 \cdot 2°$ | AcOH | 3 |
| | 315 | $+33°$ | AcOH | 2, 4 |
| Tetra-*N*-acetylchitotetraose | 290—300 (dec.) | $- 4 \cdot 1°$ | $H_2O$ | 13 |
| Penta-*N*-acetylchitopentaose | 285—295 (dec.) | $- 9 \cdot 1°$ | $H_2O$ | 13 |
| Hexa-*N*-acetylchitohexaose | | $-11 \cdot 4°$ | $H_2O$ | 13 |
| Hepta-*N*-acetylchitoheptaose | | $-12 \cdot 6°$ | $H_2O$ | 13 |
| Lacto-*N*-biose *I* | 166—167 | $+32° \rightarrow +14°$ | $H_2O$ | 88, 91 |
| Lacto-*N*-triose *I* | 185 (dec.) | $+21 \cdot 5° \rightarrow +19 \cdot 3°$ | $H_2O$ | 75, 90 |
| Lacto-*N*-triose *II* | 202 (dec.) | $+40 \cdot 7°$ | $H_2O$ | 75, 90 |
| Lacto-*N*-tetraose | 205 | $+25 \cdot 5°$ | $H_2O$ | 75, 93 |
| | | $+36° \rightarrow +24°$ | $H_2O$ | 95 |
| Lacto-*N*-*neo*-tetraose | 214—218 (dec.) | | | 120 |
| | | $+33° \rightarrow +27°$ | $H_2O$ | 92 |
| Lacto-*N*-fucopentaose *I* | | $-11 \cdot 6° \rightarrow -16°$ | $H_2O$ | 75, 93 |
| Lacto-*N*-fucopentaose *II* | | $-28°$ | $H_2O$ | 75 |
| | | $-30 \cdot 4°$ | $H_2O$ | 95 |
| Lacto-*N*-difucohexaose *I* | | $-66°$ | $H_2O$ | 75 |
| Lacto-*N*-difucohexaose *II* | 218—220 (dec.) | $-68 \cdot 8°$ | $H_2O$ | 96 |
| Ganglio-*N*-biose *I* | | $+24°$ | $H_2O$ | 148 |
| Ganglio-*N*-biose *II* | | | | 148 |
| Ganglio-*N*-triose *I* | | $+12°$ | $H_2O$ | 148 |
| Ganglio-*N*-triose *II* | | $+17°$ | $H_2O$ | 148 |
| Ganglio-*N*-tetraose | | $+13 \cdot 9°$ | $H_2O$ | 148 |

\* For a review see Y. Ito, Yakugaku Kenkyu *34*, 1—35, 74—99 (1962); Chem. Abstr. *57*, 12629 (1962).

*Table LXXIV — continued*

| Amino Sugar | Melting Point °C | $[\alpha]_D$ | Solvent | References |
|---|---|---|---|---|
| Trehalosamine* | | | | |
| 2-amino-2-deoxy-α-D-glucopyranosyl α-D-glucopyranoside | | | | |
| hydrochloride | | +176° | $H_2O$ | 28, 147 |
| *N*-acetyl derivative | | | | |
| hepta-*O*-acetate | 100—102 | | | 28, 147 |
| Lactosamine | | | | |
| 4-*O*-β-D-galactopyranosyl-*N*-acetyl-D-glucosamine | 169—171 | +51·5° → +28·5° | $H_2O$ | 99, 121, 124, 127 |
| | 170 | +30·9° | $H_2O$ | 139 |
| | 164 | +31·5° | $H_2O$ | 70 |
| hepta-*O*-acetate | 220 | +61·6° | $CHCl_3$ | 70 |
| | 224—225 | +57·7° | $CHCl_3$ | 125, 141, 142 |
| 4-*O*-β-D-Galactopyranosyl-*N*-acetyl-D-mannosamine | 237 (dec.) | +30·9° | | 139 |
| 4-*O*-α-D-Glucopyranosyl-D-glucosamine | | | | |
| hydrochloride | 180 | +100° → +81° | $H_2O$ | 16 |
| *N*-acetyl derivative | 144—146 | + 85° → +39° | $H_2O$ | 16 |
| Isolactosamine | | | | |
| 4-*O*-β-D-galactopyranosyl-D-fructosamine | | | | 77 |
| *N*-*p*-tolyl derivative | 168 | | | 137 |
| 3-*O*-β-D-Glucopyranosyl-D-galactosamine | | | | |
| *N*-acetyl derivative, dihydrate | 155—157 | +47° → +19° | | 15 |
| 3-*O*-α-*N*-Acetyl-D-galactosaminyl-D-galactose | | +150° | | 63 |
| 6-*O*-β-D-Glucosaminyl-D-glucose | | | | |
| *N*-acetyl derivative | | + 3·7° | $H_2O$ | 128 |
| hepta-*O*-acetate | 218—219 | — 9·5° | $CHCl_3$ | 128 |
| *N*-benzoyl derivative | | — 6·2° | $H_2O$ | 132 |
| hepta-*O*-acetate | 251—253 | — 2·3° | $CHCl_3$ | 132 |
| 6-*O*-β-D-Galactopyranosyl-D-glucosamine | | | | |
| *N*-acetyl derivative | | +30·9° | $H_2O$ | 126 |
| 6-*O*-β-D-Glucosaminyl-D-galactose | | | | |
| *N*-acetyl derivative | | + 9·2° | $H_2O$ | 128 |
| hepta-*O*-acetate | 197—198 | + 6·3° | $CHCl_3$ | 128 |
| 6-*O*-β-D-Glucosaminyl-D-glucosamine | | | | |
| *N*,*N'*-diacetyl derivative | | + 4·4° | $CHCl_3$ | 129 |
| hexa-*O*-acetate | 236—238 | +12° | $CHCl_3$ | 129 |
| Methyl (6-*O*-β-D-glucosaminyl)-α-D-glucopyranoside | | | | |
| *N*-benzoyl derivative | 265 (dec.) | +35·1° | $H_2O$ | 132 |
| hexa-*O*-acetate | 214—216 | +68·7° | $CHCl_3$ | 132 |

* The structure of trehalosamine has been established as 2-amino-2-deoxy-α-D-glucopyranosyl α-D-glucopyranoside, see F. Arcamone, L. Valentini, and M. Reggiani, Gazz. Chim. Ital. *87*, 1499 (1957); Chem. Abstr. *52*, 13424 (1958).

*References see p. 424*

## REFERENCES

1. N. E. Dweltz and N. Anand, Biochim. et Biophys. Acta *50*, 357 (1961).
2. L. Zechmeister and G. Tóth, Ber. *65*, 151 (1932).
3. L. Zechmeister and G. Tóth, Hoppe-Seyler's Z. physiol. Chem. *223*, 53 (1934).
4. L. Zechmeister and G. Tóth, Ber. *64*, 2028 (1934).
5. M. Bergmann, L. Zervas, and E. Silberkweit, Ber. *64*, 2436 (1931).
6. L. Zechmeister and G. Tóth, Ber. *65*, 161 (1932).
7. L. Zechmeister and I. Pinczési, Hoppe-Seyler's Z. physiol. Chem. *242*, 97 (1936).
8. F. Zilliken, G. A. Braun, C. S. Rose, and P. György, J. Am. Chem. Soc. *77*, 1296 (1955).
9. M. Bergmann and E. Silberkweit, Naturwissenschaften *19*, 20 (1931).
10. R. Kuhn and H. Tiedemann, Chem. Ber. *87*, 1141 (1954).
11. S. T. Horowitz, S. Roseman, and H. J. Blumenthal, J. Am. Chem. Soc. *79*, 5046 (1957).
12. S. A. Barker, A. B. Foster, M. Stacey, and J. M. Webber, Chem. & Ind. (London) *1957*, 208.
13. S. A. Barker, A. B. Foster, M. Stacey, and J. M. Webber, J. Chem. Soc. *1958*, 2218.
14. H. P. Lenk, M. Wenzel, and E. Schütte, Naturwissenschaften *47*, 516 (1960).
15. M. L. Wolfrom and B. O. Juliano, J. Am. Chem. Soc. *82*, 1673 (1960).
16. M. L. Wolfrom, J. R. Vercellotti, and D. Horton, J. Org. Chem. *27*, 705 (1962).
17. R. G. Eagon and R. Dedonder, Compt. rend. *241*, 579 (1955).
18. S. A. Barker, M. Heidelberger, M. Stacey, and D. J. Tipper, J. Chem. Soc. *1958*, 3468.
19. S. A. Barker, M. C. Keith, and M. Stacey, Nature *189*, 746 (1961).
20. R. E. Strange and L. H. Kent, Biochem. J. *71*, 333 (1959).
21. J. M. Ghuysen and M. R. J. Salton, Biochim. et Biophys. Acta *40*, 462 (1960).
22. H. R. Perkins, Biochem. J. *74*, 182 (1960).
23. M. R. J. Salton and J. M. Ghuysen, Biochim. et Biophys. Acta *45*, 355 (1960).
24. J. M. Ghuysen, Biochim. et Biophys. Acta *47*, 561 (1961).
25. J. Staněk, M. Černý, J. Kocourek, and J. Pacák, *The Monosaccharides*, Acad. Press, New York 1963.
26. G. Baschang, Fortschr. Chem. org. Naturstoffe *20*, 219 (1962).
27. Ref. 25, p. 83.
28. F. Arcamone and F. Bizioli, Gazz. chim. ital. *87*, 896 (1957); Chem. Abstr. *52*, 4503 (1958).
29. F. A. Kuehl, E. H. Flynn, F. W. Holly, R. Mozingo, and K. Folkers, J. Am. Chem. Soc. *68*, 536 (1946).
30. F. A. Kuehl, E. H. Flynn, N. G. Brink, and K. Folkers, J. Am. Chem. Soc. *68*, 2096 (1946).
31. N. G. Brink, F. A. Kuehl, H. E. Flynn, and K. Folkers, J. Am. Chem. Soc. *68*, 2405 (1946).
32. F. A. Kuehl, E. H. Flynn, N. G. Brink, and K. Folkers, J. Am. Chem. Soc. *68*, 2679 (1946).
33. J. Fried, D. E. Walz, and O. W. Wintersteiner, J. Am. Chem. Soc. *68*, 2746 (1946).
34. F. A. Kuehl, E. H. Flynn, F. W. Holly, R. Mozingo, and K. Folkers, J. Am. Chem. Soc. *69*, 3032 (1947).
35. F. A. Kuehl, M. N. Bishop, E. H. Flynn, and K. Folkers, J. Am. Chem. Soc. *70*, 2613 (1948).
36. M. L. Wolfrom and C. S. DeWalt, J. Am. Chem. Soc. *70*, 3148 (1948).

37. R. U. Lemieux and M. L. Wolfrom, Advances in Carbohydrate Chem. *3*, 327 (1948).

38. E. H. Flynn, M. V. Sigal, P. F. Wiley, and K. Gerzon, J. Am. Chem. Soc. *76*, 3121 (1954).

39. P. F. Wiley and O. Weaver, J. Am. Chem. Soc. *77*, 3422 (1955).

40. M. V. Sigal, P. F. Wiley, K. Gerzon, E. H. Flynn, U. C. Quarck, and O. Weaver, J. Am. Chem. Soc. *78*, 388 (1956).

41. P. F. Wiley and O. Weaver, J. Am. Chem. Soc. *78*, 808 (1956).

42. P. P. Regna, F. A. Hochstein, R. L. Wagner, and R. B. Woodward, J. Am. Chem. Soc. *75*, 4625 (1953).

43. R. L. Wagner, F. A. Hochstein, K. Murai, K. Messina, and P. P. Regna, J. Am. Chem. Soc. *75*, 4684 (1953).

44. F. A. Hochstein and K. Murai, J. Am. Chem. Soc. *76*, 5080 (1954).

45. F. A. Hochstein and P. P. Regna, J. Am. Chem. Soc. *77*, 3353 (1955).

46. R. Paul and S. Tchelitcheff, Bull. soc. chim. France *1957*, 443.

47. R. Paul and S. Tchelitcheff, Bull. soc. chim. France *1957*, 734.

48. R. Paul and S. Tchelitcheff, Bull. soc. chim. France *1957*, 1059.

49. J. D. Dutcher and M. N. Donin, J. Am. Chem. Soc. *74*, 3420 (1952).

50. F. A. Kuehl, M. N. Bishop, and K. Folkers, J. Am. Chem. Soc. *73*, 881 (1951).

51. K. L. Rinehart, P. W. K. Woo, A. D. Argoudelis, and A. M. Giesbrecht, J. Am. Chem. Soc. *79*, 4567 (1957).

52. K. L. Rinehart, P. W. K. Woo, and A. D. Argoudelis, J. Am. Chem. Soc. *79*, 4568 (1957).

53. K. L. Rinehart, P. W. K. Woo, and A. D. Argoudelis, J. Am. Chem. Soc. *80*, 6461 (1958).

54. K. L. Rinehart, A. D. Argoudelis, W. A. Goss, A. Sohler, and C. P. Schaffner, J. Am. Chem. Soc. *82*, 3938 (1960).

55. K. L. Rinehart, A. D. Argoudelis, T. P. Culbertson, W. Scott Chilton, and K. Streigler, J. Am. Chem. Soc. *82*, 2970 (1960).

56. H. E. Carter, J. R. Dyer, P. D. Shaw, K. L. Rinehart, and M. Hichens, J. Am. Chem. Soc. *83*, 3723 (1961).

57. K. L. Rinehart, M. Hichens, A. D. Argoudelis, W. Scott Chilton, H. E. Carter, M. P. Georgiadis, C. P. Schaffner, and R. T. Schillings, J. Am. Chem. Soc. *84*, 3218 (1962).

58. T. H. Haskell, J. C. French, and Q. R. Bartz, J. Am. Chem. Soc. *81*, 3480 (1959).

59. T. H. Haskell, J. C. French, and Q. R. Bartz, J. Am. Chem. Soc. *81*, 3481 (1959).

60. T. H. Haskell, J. C. French, and Q. R. Bartz, J. Am. Chem. Soc. *81*, 3482 (1959).

61. H. Hitomi, S. Horii, T. Yamaguchi, and A. Miyake, Chem. Pharm. Bull. (Tokyo) *9*, 541 (1961).

62. W. Pigman, *The Carbohydrates*, Acad. Press, New York 1957, p. 721.

63. R. H. Côté and W. T. J. Morgan, Nature *178*, 1171 (1956).

64. T. J. Painter and W. T. J. Morgan, Nature *191*, 39 (1961).

65. I. A. F. Lister Cheese and W. T. J. Morgan, Nature *191*, 149 (1961).

66. T. J. Painter, I. A. F. Lister Cheese, and W. T. J. Morgan, Chem. & Ind. (London) *1962*, 1535.

67. G. Schiffman, E. A. Kabat, and S. Leskowitz, J. Am. Chem. Soc. *84*, 73 (1962).

68. Z. Yosizawa, J. Biochem. (Japan) *51*, 1 (1962).

69. R. M. Tomarelli, J. B. Hassinen, E. R. Eckhardt, R. H. Clark, and F. W. Bernhart, Arch. Biochem. Biophys. *48*, 225 (1954).

70. F. Zilliken, P. N. Smith, R. M. Tomarelli, and P. György, Arch. Biochem. Biophys. *54*, 398 (1955).

71. H. Sinohara, Tôhoku J. Exptl. Med. *67*, 141 (1958); Chem. Abstr. *52*, 17335 (1958).

72. H. Masamune and H. Sinohara, Tôhoku J. Exptl. Med. *69*, 59 (1958).

73. H. Masamune and H. Sinohara, Tôhoku J. Exptl. Med. *69*, 65 (1958).

74. R. Kuhn, Angew. Chem. *69*, 23 (1957).

75. H. H. Baer, Fortschr. chem. Forsch. *3*, 822 (1958).

76. Ref. 26, p. 221.

77. A. Adachi, Nippon Nôgei-kagaku Kaishi *30*, 454 (1956); Chem. Abstr. *52*, 5687 (1958).

78. M. Polonovski and A. Lespagnol, Bull. soc. chim. biol. *15*, 320 (1933).

79. M. Polonovski and J. Montreuil, Compt. rend. *238*, 2263 (1954).

80. J. Montreuil, Bull. soc. chim. biol. *39*, 395 (1957).

81. H. Schönfeld, Jahrbuch Kinderheilkunde *113*, 19 (1926).

82. R. F. Norris, T. Flanders, R. M. Tomarelli, and P. György, J. Bacteriol. *60*, 681 (1950).

83. P. György, R. F. Norris, and C. S. Rose, Arch. Biochem. Biophys. *48*, 193 (1954).

84. R. Kuhn, Angew. Chem. *64*, 493 (1952).

85. A. Gauhe, P. György, J. R. E. Hoover, R. Kuhn, C. S. Rose, H. W. Ruelius, and F. Zilliken, Biochim. et Biopyhs. Acta *48*, 214 (1954).

86. R. Kuhn, H. H. Baer, and A. Gauhe, Chem. Ber. *88*, 1135 (1955).

87. R. Kuhn, A. Gauhe, and H. H. Baer, Chem. Ber. *86*, 827 (1953).

88. R. Kuhn, A. Gauhe, and H. H. Baer, Chem. Ber. *87*, 289 (1954).

89. R. Kuhn, H. H. Baer, and A. Gauhe, Chem. Ber. *89*, 504 (1956).

90. R. Kuhn, A. Gauhe, and H. H. Baer, Chem. Ber. *89*, 1027 (1956).

91. R. Kuhn, H. H. Baer, and A. Gauhe, Chem. Ber. *87*, 1553 (1954).

92. R. Kuhn and A. Gauhe, Chem. Ber. *95*, 518 (1962).

93. R. Kuhn, H. H. Baer, and A. Gauhe, Chem. Ber. *89*, 2514 (1956).

94. R. Kuhn, H. H. Baer, and A. Gauhe, Ann. *611*, 242 (1958).

95. R. Kuhn, H. H. Baer, and A. Gauhe, Chem. Ber. *91*, 364 (1958).

96. R. Kuhn and A. Gauhe, Chem. Ber. *93*, 647 (1960).

97. F. H. Malpress and F. E. Hytten, Nature *180*, 1201 (1957).

98. F. H. Malpress and F. E. Hytten, Biochem. J. *68*, 708 (1958).

99. R. Kuhn and W. Kirschenlohr, Chem. Ber. *87*, 560 (1954).

100. W. Otting, Ann. *612*, 68 (1958).

101. J. Staněk, M. Černý, J. Kocourek, and J. Pacák, *The Monosaccharides*, Acad. Press, New York 1963.

102. W. J. Whelan, Ann. Reports *54*, 319 (1958).

103. A. Gottschalk, Bull. soc. chim. biol. *42*, 1387 (1960).

104. F. Zilliken and M. W. Whitehouse, Advances in Carbohydrate Chem. *13*, 237 (1958).

105. J. Montreuil, Bull. soc. chim. biol. *42*, 1399 (1960).

106. A. Gottschalk, Rev. Pure Appl. Chem. (Australia) *12*, 46 (1962).

107. R. E. Trucco and R. Caputto, J. Biol. Chem. *206*, 901 (1954).

108. R. Kuhn and R. Brossmer, Angew. Chem. *66*, 211 (1954).

109. R. Kuhn and R. Brossmer, Chem. Ber. *89*, 2013 (1956).

110. R. Heyworth and J. S. D. Bacon, Biochem. J. *66*, 41 (1957).

111. R. Heimer and K. Meyer, Biochim. et Biophys. Acta *27*, 490 (1958).

112. Biochem. Preparations *9*, 1 (1962).

113. R. Kuhn and R. Brossmer, Angew. Chem. *70*, 25 (1958).

114. R. Kuhn and R. Brossmer, Chem. Ber. *92*, 1667 (1959).

115. A. Gottschalk, Biochim. et Biophys. Acta *23*, 645 (1957).

116. R. Kuhn, Bull. soc. chim. biol. *40*, 297 (1958).

117. R. Carubelli, L. C. Ryan, R. E. Trucco, and R. Caputto, J. Biol. Chem. *236*, 2381 (1961).

118. R. Kuhn, Naturwissenschaften *46*, 43 (1959).

119. Ref. 26, p. 224.

120. R. Kuhn and A. Gauhe, Chem. Ber. *95*, 513 (1962).

121. R. Kuhn and W. Kirschenlohr, Chem. Ber. *87*, 1547 (1954).

122. Z. Yoshizawa, Tôhoku J. Exptl. Med. *68*, 313 (1958); Chem. Abstr. *54*, 6562 (1960).

123. E. Fischer and H. Leuchs, Ber. *36*, 24 (1903).

124. R. Kuhn and W. Kirschenlohr, Ann. *600*, 135 (1956).

125. T. Okuyama, Tôhoku J. Exptl. Med. *68*, 313 (1958); Chem. Abstr. *54*, 6562 (1960).

126. R. Kuhn, H. H. Baer, and A. Gauhe, Chem. Ber. *88*, 1713 (1955).

127. T. Okuyama, Tôhoku J. Exptl. Med. *68*, 319 (1958); Chem. Abstr. *54*, 6562 (1960).

128. R. Kuhn and W. Kirschenlohr, Chem. Ber. *87*, 384 (1954).

129. Wang Yu and Tai Hsiung-I, Acta Chim. Sinica *25*, 54 (1959).

130. P. F. Lloyd and G. P. Roberts, Proc. Chem. Soc. *1960*, 250.

131. R. W. Jeanloz and H. M. Flowers, J. Am. Chem. Soc. *84*, 3030 (1962).

132. F. Micheel and E. Drescher, Chem. Ber. *91*, 670 (1958).

133. F. Micheel and E. Drescher, Chem. Ber. *95*, 1020 (1962).

134. S. A. Barker, K. Murray, and M. Stacey, Nature *191*, 142 (1961).

135. S. A. Barker, K. Murray, M. Stacey, and D. B. E. Stroud, Nature *191*, 143 (1961).

136. S. Adachi, Chem. & Ind. (London) *1957*, 956; Chem. Abstr. *51*, 17787 (1957).

137. S. Adachi, J. Agr. Chem. Soc. Japan *31*, 97 (1957). Chem. Abstr. *52*, 12259 (1958).

138. E. J. Hodge and E. C. Nelson, Cereal Chem. *38*, 207 (1961).

139. R. Kuhn and A. Gauhe, Chem. Ber. *94*, 842 (1961).

140. R. Kuhn, H. J. Haas, ans A. Seeliger, Chem. Ber. *94*, 1259 (1961).

141. F. Zilliken, P. N. Smith, C. S. Rose, and P. György, J. Biol. Chem. *208*, 299 (1954).

142. F. Zilliken, P. N. Smith, C. S. Rose, and P. György, J. Biol. Chem. *217*, 79 (1955).

143. A. Alessandrini, E. Schmidt, F. Zilliken, and P. György, J. Biol. Chem. *220*, 71 (1956).

144. K. Wallenfels, Angew. Chem. *65*, 137 (1953).

145. S. Srinivasan and J. H. Quastel, Science *127*, 143 (1958); Chem. Abstr. *52*, 11139 (1958).

146. W. M. Watkins, Nature *181*, 117 (1958).

147. F. Arcamone, L. Valentini, and M. Reggiani, Gazz. chim. ital. *87*, 1488 (1957); Chem. Abstr. *52*, 13424 (1958).

148. R. Kuhn and H. Wiegandt, Chem. Ber. *96*, 866 (1963).

# XXV

# Oximes of Reducing Oligosaccharides

Reducing oligosaccharides, in particular those with an aldehydic group, should react with hydroxylamine to form the corresponding oximes. Such reactions were actually carried out with a number of reducing oligosaccharides, for example, with cellobiose,[1,2] lactose,[3,4] melibiose,[5] maltose,[6] sophorose (2-O-$\beta$-D-glucopyranosyl-D-glucose),[7] and 3-O-$\beta$-D-glucopyranosyl-D-glucose.[8] The reaction definitely took place in all these cases; however, only the oximes of melibiose,[5] cellobiose[2] and later also of lactose[4] could be obtained in established crystalline forms. Otherwise it was necessary to convert the oxime by acetylation and simultaneous dehydration[1,3,5-8] into the corresponding aldonic acid nitrile (see Chapter XXXII).

Cellobiose oxime is converted by acetylation with acetic anhydride with an addition of pyridine in the cold[9] into the hepta-O-acetyl derivative. The latter is likely to have an acyclic structure because with nitrous acid it yields the hepta-O-acetyl derivative of the aldehydo form of cellobiose, which in turn is reconverted into the initial acetylated oxime on treatment with hydroxylamine.

A by-product obtained in the dehydration and acetylation of cellobiose oxime was a substance[1] which was regarded as an octa-O-acetyl derivative of "cellobiose antioxime". Other writers claim[9] that this substance is identical with the product obtained by the reaction of hepta-O-acetylcellobiose with hydroxylamine and subsequent acetylation. The analysis suggests, however, that this substance is not the octa-O-acetyl but rather the nona-O-acetyl derivative of cellobiose oxime.

### Table LXXV

Physical Properties of Reducing Oligosaccharide Oximes

| Oligosaccharide Oxime | Melting Point °C | $[\alpha]_D$ | Solvent | References |
|---|---|---|---|---|
| Cellobiose oxime | 123 | $-26\cdot1°$ | $H_2O$ | 2 |
| hepta-$O$-acetate |  | $+35°$ | $CHCl_3$ | 2 |
| octa-$O$-acetate | 165 | $-7\cdot9°$ | $CHCl_3$ | 1 |
| nona-$O$-acetate | 195 | $-8\cdot5°$ | $CHCl_3$ | 9 |
| Maltose oxime |  | $+85\cdot6°$ | $H_2O$ | 6 |
| Lactose oxime | 183—185 | $+38\cdot3° \rightarrow +15\cdot5°$ | $H_2O$ | 4 |
| $N$-acetyl-derivative | 232 (dec.) | $+14\cdot1° \rightarrow +16°$ | $H_2O$ | 4 |
| Melibiose oxime | 184—186 | $+95°$ | $H_2O$ | 5 |

### REFERENCES

1. G. Zemplén, Ber. *59*, 1254 (1926).
2. P. A. Levene and M. L. Wolfrom, J. Biol. Chem. *77*, 671 (1928); Chem. Abstr. *22*, 2925 (1928).
3. G. Zemplén, Ber. *59*, 2402 (1926).
4. R. Kuhn and W. Kirschenlohr, Ann. *600*, 135 (1956).
5. G. Zemplén, Ber. *60*, 923 (1927).
6. G. Zemplén, Ber. *60*, 1309 (1927).
7. M. Gakhokidze, Zhur. Obshcheǐ Khim. *11*, 117 (1941); Chem. Abstr. *35*, 5467 (1941).
8. M. Gakhokidze, Zhur. Obshcheǐ Khim. *16*, 1923 (1946); Chem. Abstr. *41*, 6210 (1947).
9. M. L. Wolfrom and S. Soltzberg, J. Am. Chem. Soc. *58*, 1783 (1936).

# XXVI

# Phenylhydrazones and Phenylosazones of Reducing Oligosaccharides and Their Derivatives

Reducing oligosaccharides usually react with phenylhydrazine with direct formation of phenylosazones. In a few cases it was possible to isolate the intermediate product of this reaction, which must obviously be the corresponding phenylhydrazone. Until quite recently, only one report had been available concerning this.[1] It stated that the reaction of phenylhydrazine with an aqueous solution of melibiose in the cold gave rise to the corresponding phenylhydrazone. This finding was later supplemented by another paper[2] on the formation of phenylhydrazones of reducing oligosaccharides.

Such phenylhydrazine derivatives, which in the monosaccharide series always yield exclusively products of the hydrazone type,[3] give analogously in the oligosaccharide group only substituted hydrazones and never osazones. $p$-Toluenesulphohydrazine has also been recommended[4] for characterizing reducing oligosaccharides in the form of substituted hydrazones.

The formation of phenylosazones is not to be expected, of course, in cases where this formation is evidently excluded by the molecular constitution. Hence, it is only possible to prepare phenylhydrazones of 2-deoxy derivatives of reducing oligosaccharides, such as 2-deoxycellobiose[5] and 2-deoxymaltose.[6] Neither may the formation of phenylosazones be expected in the case of reducing oligosaccharides with 1→2 linkages, such as 2-$O$-α-L-fucopyranosyl-D-galactose.[7] On the other hand, glycosylamines, for example, lactosylamine (i. e. 1-amino-1-deoxylactose), are readily converted by the action of phenylhydrazine into the corresponding phenylosazones;[8] this reaction is not feasible, however, with the $N$-acetyl derivatives of glycosylamines.

The preparation of phenylosazones is generally not difficult. It is recommended[9] that the reducing oligosaccharide be first converted into the corresponding $N$-$p$-phenetidide and the reaction mixture then heated in acetic acid with added phenylhydrazine.

Two quite remarkable features have been observed in the group of oligosaccharides and their hydrazones. Contrary to expectations, the branched trisaccharide solatriose (solanose, I) does not react at all with phenylhydrazine.[10] Moreover, the action of phenylhydrazine upon the branched oligosaccharide 2-$O$-$\alpha$-D-glucopyranosyl-lactose[11] splits off the part bound by a 2-$O$-$\alpha$-linkage because it leads to the phenylosazones of both D-glucose and lactose.

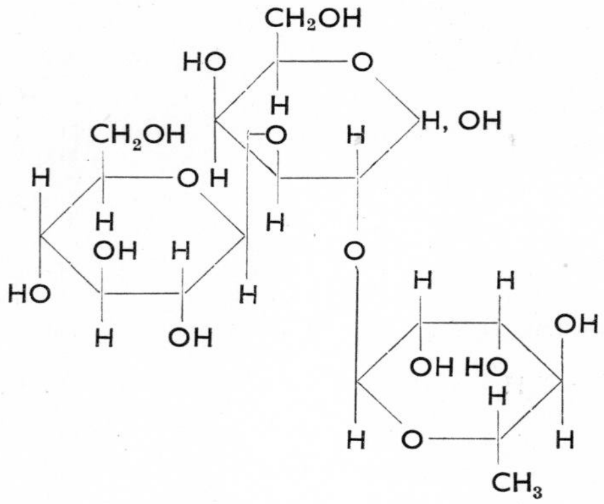

(I)

Analogously to monosaccharides, in the group of reducing oligosaccharides two epimeric aldoses and the ketose corresponding to them always give the same osazone. This applies, for instance, to the phenylosazone prepared from nigerose (i. e. 3-$O$-$\alpha$-D-glucopyranosyl-D-glucose, II)[12] and to that prepared from turanose (3-$O$-$\alpha$-D-glucopyranosyl-D-fructose, III).[12-14]

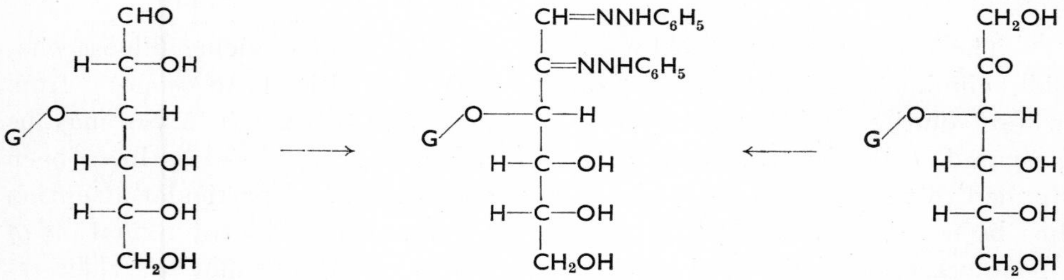

(II)                    (III)

Identical phenylosazones have been obtained in the same way from 3-$O$-$\beta$-D-galactopyranosyl-D-glucose and from 3-$O$-$\beta$-D-galactopyranosyl-D-fructose.[15]

Oligosaccharide phenylosazones are not very suitable for exact identification on the basis of their melting points and values of specific rotation. Otting[16] reports that the infra-red spectra are better criteria in this respect. Nothing particular has been observed in the oxidation of oligosaccharide phenylosazones with periodic acid.[17]

*References see p. 438*

The hydrogenation of phenylosazones of reducing oligosaccharides gives rise to both the expected substances; thus, lactose phenylosazone (IV) yields lactosamine (2-amino-2-deoxylactose, V) and isolactosamine (1-amino-1-deoxy-lactulose, VI).[18]

The action of nitrous acid upon phenylosazones of reducing oligosaccharides eliminates both nitrogen-containing residues and leads to osones,[19] from whose solutions substituted osone hydrazones and other substances may be prepared. Only few reactions of monosaccharide phenylosazones have been applied to analogous compounds of oligosaccharides, and particular attention has been paid only to the formation of phenylosotriazoles (by oxidation of phenylosazones) and of anhydro derivatives of phenylosazones (by their reaction in acid solution).

## 1. PHENYLOSOTRIAZOLES OF REDUCING OLIGOSACCHARIDES

These compounds are formed, as in the corresponding monosaccharide derivatives, by the oxidation of phenylosazones of reducing oligosaccharides with copper sulphate. This reaction has been carried out successfully with the phenylosazones of cellobiose,[20] gentiobiose,[21] nigerose,[14] turanose,[13] lactose,[20] and melibiose.[22]

## 2. ANHYDRO DERIVATIVES OF PHENYLOSAZONES OF REDUCING OLIGOSACCHARIDES

Phenyl-lactosazone in acid solution, as has been known for a long time, splits off a water molecule.[23] However, the reaction proceeds more readily in alcoholic solution, in the presence of a small amount of sulphuric acid,[24] and the same product is also obtained by the deacetylation of the hepta-$O$-acetyl derivative of phenyl-lactosazone.[25] Of much interest also is the finding[26,27] that phenyl-lactosazone is converted into the anhydro derivative even in its crystallization from ethanol in the presence of activated carbon.

The structure (VII)[25] originally given for the anhydro derivative of phenyl-lactosazone is not in agreement with two later findings.[27] The anhydro derivative of phenyl-lactosazone is converted by the action of benzaldehyde into the anhydro-osone derivative, which is remarkably stable in acid solution (in contrast to lactosone, which is readily hydrolysed to D-glucose and D-galactose). Moreover, it was found that the anhydro derivative of phenyl-lactosazone may be converted by oxidation with copper sulphate into the corresponding anhydrophenylosotriazole, and this excludes the existence of a nitrogenous heterocycle according to the formula (VII). Another writer reports[28] that the phenylosotriazole of anhydrolactose is split in acid solution with the formation of D-galactose and 3,6-anhydro-D-allose osotriazole, so that the structure of anhydrolactose phenylosazone must correspond to the phenylosazone of 4-$O$-$\beta$-D-galactopyranosyl-3,6-anhydro-D-allose (VIII).[27]

```
        CH=NNHC₆H₅                      CH=NNHC₆H₅
           |                                |
           C———NH                           C=NNHC₆H₅
           |                                |
        HO—C—H                          H—C————
           |                                |
   O    H—C———————O                  H—C————————O
           |         \Gal                |          \Gal
        H—C———N                       H—C—OH  O       Gal
           |     |                       |
         ——CH₂   C₆H₅                  ——CH₂——
          (VII)                           (VIII)
```

Another, later, work[19] is likewise concerned with the formation of the anhydro derivative in the deacetylation of mixed lactose osazones. The writer arrives at the same conclusions, stating that the opposite configuration at C-3 in the original nitrogenous part of the molecule cannot be excluded.

Cellobiose phenylosazone yields the analogous anhydro derivative in acid solution[29] or by the deacetylation of the hepta-$O$-acetyl derivative.[30] For this anhydro derivative, too, a structural formula with a nitrogenous heterocycle has been suggested,[30] but, in agreement with the proofs of the structure of

*References see p. 438*

anhydrolactosazone it is assumed[27] that the actual structure of this substance corresponds to that of the phenylosazone of 4-*O*-β-D-glucopyranosyl-3,6-anhydro-D-allose. In another paper,[19] dealing with the course of the formation of anhydro derivatives in the deacetylation of mixed cellobiose osazones, the same formula is given, but it is stated that the configuration at C-3 has so far not been established.

The problem of two isomeric anhydro derivatives of maltose phenylosazones[24,25] has likewise not been solved. According to a later report,[19] both anhydro derivatives differ in their configuration at C-3.

## Table LXXVI

Physical Properties of Oligosaccharide Phenylhydrazones

| Oligosaccharide Phenylhydrazone | Melting Point °C | $[\alpha]_D$ | Solvent | References |
|---|---|---|---|---|
| Maltose $\beta$-naphthylhydrazone | 176 | $+10\cdot6°$ | MeOH | 31 |
| Lactose  allylphenylhydrazone | 132 | $-14\cdot6°$ | MeOH | 31 |
| benzylphenylhydrazone | 128 | $-25\cdot7°$ | | 32 |
| Melibiose  phenylhydrazone | 145 | | | 1 |
| $\beta$-naphthylhydrazone | 135 | $+15\cdot9°$ | | 31 |
| allylphenylhydrazone | 197 | $+21\cdot2°$ | | 31 |
| Mannobiose phenylhydrazone | 198—199 | | | 2 |
| 2-Deoxymaltose phenylhydrazone | 201 | | | 6 |
| 2-Deoxycellobiose phenylhydrazone | 194 | | | 5 |
| 5-O-$\beta$-D-Glucopyranosyl-D-glucose $p$-toluenesulphohydrazone | 180 (dec.) | $-22°$ | $C_5H_5N/H_2O$ (4 : 1) | 4 |
| 6-O-$\alpha$-D-Galactopyranosyl-D-mannose phenylhydrazone | 168—169 | | | 2 |
| 4-O-$\alpha$-L-Arabinopyranosyl-D-glucose azobenzenesulphohydrazone | 170—172 | | | 33 |
| 2-O-$\alpha$-L-Fucopyranosyl-D-galactose benzylphenylhydrazone | 163·5 | | | 7 |
| Fucosyl-lactose tosylhydrazone | 206 (dec.) | $-74°$ | $C_5H_5N$ | 34 |

## Table LXXVII

Physical Properties of Oligosaccharide Phenylosazones

| Oligosaccharide Phenylosazone | Melting Point °C | $[\alpha]_D$ | Solvent | References |
|---|---|---|---|---|
| Phenylosazone of agarobiose | 218—219 | | | 35 |
| | 219—220 | $-136\cdot8° \rightarrow -107\cdot3°$ | $C_5H_5N/EtOH$ | 36 |
| | 220—221 | $-136\cdot8° \rightarrow -108\cdot8°$ | $C_5H_5N/EtOH$ | 37, 38 |
| | 222—224 | $-115°$ | $C_5H_5N/EtOH$ | 39 |
| $neo$-agarobiose | 199—200 | $+59\cdot8° \rightarrow +56\cdot1°$ | $C_5H_5N/EtOH$ | 79 |
| carrabiose | | $+46\cdot0°$ | | 125 |
| cellobiose | 198—200 | $-6\cdot5°$ | $C_5H_5N/EtOH$ | 40—42 |
| | 208—210 | | | 43 |
| gentiobiose | 170—173 | $-74° \rightarrow -44\cdot4°$ | $C_5H_5N/EtOH$ | 44—46 |
| | 184—186 | $-66° \rightarrow -58°$ | MeCellos. | 47 |
| | 179—181 | | | 48, 49 |
| | 166—172 | | | 50 |
| isomaltose, isomaltulose, palatinose | 150—208* | | | 51—60 |
| | 177—179 | $+32\cdot6° \rightarrow +46°$ | MeCellos. | 47 |
| | 201—202 | | | 61 |
| | 174—176 | $+40°$ | | 62, 63 |
| | 171—173 | | | 64 |

* The melting points and specific rotations given by several authors[51-60] refer to substances which were not sufficiently pure.

*References see p. 438*

*Table LXXVII — continued*

| Oligosaccharide Phenylosazone | Melting Point °C | $[\alpha]_D$ | Solvent | References |
|---|---|---|---|---|
| lactose | 193—195 | | | 11 |
| | 203—205 | | | 14 |
| | 210 (dec.) | | | 19 |
| | 206—207 | $-13\cdot5° \to -10°$ | MeOH | 27, 65 |
| | 210—212 | $-25\cdot4° \to - 7\cdot9°$ | MeOH | 66—69 |
| | | $-31°$ | | 70 |
| *allo*-lactose | 176 | $-69\cdot6°$ | $C_5H_5N$ | 71, 72 |
| | 185 | $-69\cdot6°$ | $C_5H_5N$ | 73 |
| | 188—189 | $-74\cdot5° \to -51\cdot6°$ | | 74, 75 |
| | 186—188 | | | 76 |
| *neo*-lactose | 195 | | | 77, 78 |
| laminaribiose | 199—201 | $-76°$ | EtOH | 80 |
| | | $-71\cdot5°$ | | 81, 82 |
| | | $-79\cdot6°$ | | 83 |
| leucrose | 186—188 | | | 64 |
| | 186 | | | 84 |
| lycobiose | 205—210 (dec.) | | | 9 |
| lycotriose | 222 (dec.) | $-16°$ | $C_5H_5N$ | 9 |
| maltose, maltulose | 202—204 | | | 64 |
| | 201—203 | | | 62 |
| | 206 | $+82\cdot6°$ | $C_5H_5N$/EtOH | 66, 67, 85, 86 |
| | 204—206 | $+81°$ | $C_5H_5N$/EtOH | 87—91 |
| melibiose | 176—178 | $+43\cdot2°$ | $C_5H_5N$ | 73 |
| primeverose | 220 | $-109\cdot7°$ | | 92 |
| rhodymenabiose | 194—196 | $+47°$ | $C_5H_5N$ | 93 |
| solabiose | 225 | | | 10, 126 |
| turanose, nigerose | 202—204 | | | 64 |
| | 204—206 | | | 12, 14 |
| | 202—204 | $+33°$ | $C_5H_5N$/EtOH | 84, 87 |
| | 200—205 (dec.) | $+24\cdot5° \to +33°$ | $C_5H_5N$/EtOH | 13 |
| xylobiose | 204—206 | | | 94, 127 |
| | 210—213 | | | 95 |
| | 207 | $-6° \to -50°$ | $C_5H_5N$/EtOH | 96 |
| 6-*O*-β-D-glucopyranosyl-D-galactose | 200 | | | 97, 98 |
| 3-*O*-α-D-glucopyranosyl-L-arabinose | | | | 99 |
| 3-*O*-α-D-glucopyranosyl-D-arabinose | 195—200 | | | 6, 100 |
| 3-*O*-α-D-glucopyranosyl-D-xylose | 213—215 | | | 101 |
| 3-*O*-β-D-glucopyranosyl-D-xylose | 205—206 | | | 102 |
| 5-*O*-β-D-glucopyranosyl-D-xylose | 211—213 (dec.) | | | 129 |
| 4-*O*-α-D-mannopyranosyl-D-mannose | 200—201 | | | 103 |
| 4-*O*-β-D-mannopyranosyl-D-glucose | 149—152 | | | 103 |
| 6-*O*-β(?)-D-mannopyranosyl-D-mannose | 122—128 | | | 104 |

*Table LXXVII — continued*

| Oligosaccharide Phenylosazone | Melting Point °C | $[\alpha]_D$ | Solvent | References |
|---|---|---|---|---|
| 3-O-α-D-galactopyranosyl-D-galactose | 237—239 | +115° | $C_5H_5N$ | 105 |
| 6-O-β-D-galactopyranosyl-D-galactose | 188—190 | | | 76 |
| | 203—204 | | | 106 |
| | 206 | | | 107 |
| 3-O-β-D-galactopyranosyl-D-glucose | 185 | +15·2° → —5° | $C_5H_5N$ | 15 |
| | 176 | | | 76 |
| 3-O-β-D-galactopyranosyl-D-fructose | 185 | +13·0° → —4° | $C_5H_5N$ | 15 |
| 3-O-β-D-galactopyranosyl-D-arabinose | 242 | | | 108, 109 |
| | 236—238 | | | 110 |
| | 236 | | | 100 |
| 3-O-α-L-arabinofuranosyl-L-arabinose | 200 | | | 106, 111 |
| 3-O-β-L-arabinopyranosyl-L-arabinose | 234 | | | 112, 113 |
| | 233 | | | 114 |
| | 235 | | | 115 |
| 5-O-α-L-arabinofuranosyl-L-arabinose | 184—186 | | | 106 |
| | 177 | —72° ± 3° | | 111 |
| 3-O-α-D-xylopyranosyl-L-arabinose | 226 | | | 115 |
| 5-O-β-D-xylopyranosyl-L-arabinose | 216 | | | 106, 114 |
| manninotriose | 122—124 | | | 116—118 |
| fucosyl-lactose | 218 (dec.) | —18° → —29° | $C_5H_5N$ | 34 |
| 6-O-β-cellobiosyl-D-glucose | 224 (dec.) | +61·5° | $C_5H_5N$ | 119 |
| 6-O-β-cellobiosyl-D-galactose | 207 (dec.) | | | 98 |
| 6-O-β-lactosyl-D-galactose | 223 (dec.) | —50·5° | $C_5H_5N$ | 119 |
| | 211 | | | 98 |
| O-β-D-galactopyranosyl-(1→6)-O-β-D-galactopyranosyl-(1→4)-D-glucose | 229—231 | | | 48 |
| O-α-4-O-methyl-D-glucopyranosyl-(1→2)-O-β-D-xylopyranosyl-(1→4)-D-xylose | 240—241 | | | 128 |

## Table LXXVIII

Physical Properties of Substituted Phenylosazones of Oligosaccharides

| Oligosaccharide Phenylosazone | | Melting Point °C | $[\alpha]_D$ | Solvent | References |
|---|---|---|---|---|---|
| Maltose | p-bromophenylosazone | 198 | | | 120, 121 |
| | p-iodophenylosazone | 208 | +82·9° → +66·1° | $C_5H_5N$ | 122 |
| | p-nitrophenylosazone | 261 | | | 123 |
| Lactose | p-nitrophenylosazone | 258 | | | 123 |
| | substituted phenylosazones | | | | 19 |
| Melibiose | p-bromophenylosazone | 182 | | | 120, 124 |

*References see p. 438*

### Table LXXIX

Physical Properties of Oligosaccharide Phenylosotriazoles

| Oligosaccharide Phenylosotriazole | Melting Point °C | $[\alpha]_D$ | Solvent | References |
|---|---|---|---|---|
| Phenylosotriazole of | | | | |
| cellobiose | 164—165 | −50·8° | $H_2O$ | 20 |
| gentiobiose | 91—93 | −34·3° | $H_2O$ | 21 |
| hepta-*O*-acetate | 144—146 | −28·1° | $CHCl_3$ | 21 |
| hepta-*O*-benzoate | 122—123 | + 1·5° | $CHCl_3$ | 21 |
| isomaltose | 179—180 | | | 61 |
| | 168—178 | +42·5° | $H_2O$ | 47 |
| lactose | 180—181 | −43·6° | $H_2O$ | 20 |
| melibiose | 153—154 | +61·2° | $H_2O$ | 22 |
| nigerose, turanose | 193—194 | +74·5° | $H_2O$ | 14 |
| 3-*O*-α-D-glucopyranosyl-L-arabinose | | +80° | $H_2O$ | 99 |
| 4-*O*-β-D-glucopyranosyl-3,6-anhydro-D-allose | 174—176 | −77·7° | $H_2O$ | 27 |
| 4-*O*-β-D-galactopyranosyl-3,6-anhydro-D-allose | 160 | −67·8° | $H_2O$ | 27 |

## REFERENCES

1. C. Scheibler and H. Mittelmeier, Ber. *23*, 1438 (1890).
2. A. K. Mukherjee, D. Choudhury, and P. Bagchi, Can. J. Chem. *39*, 1408 (1961).
3. J. Staněk, M. Černý, J. Kocourek, and J. Pacák, *The Monosaccharides,* Acad. Press, New York 1963.
4. J. C. Sowden and A. S. Spriggs, J. Am. Chem. Soc. *78*, 2503 (1956).
5. A. M. Gakhokidze, Zhur. Obshcheĭ Khim. *16*, 1914 (1946); Chem. Abstr. *41*, 6209 (1947).
6. A. M. Gakhokidze, Zhur. Obshcheĭ Khim. *18*, 60 (1948); Chem. Abstr. *42*, 4948 (1948).
7. R. Kuhn, H. H. Baer, and A. Gauhe, Ann. *611*, 242 (1958).
8. R. Kuhn and G. Krüger, Chem. Ber. *87*, 1544 (1954).
9. R. Kuhn and I. Löw, Chem. Ber. *86*, 1027 (1953).
10. R. Kuhn, I. Löw, and H. Trischmann, Chem. Ber. *88*, 1492 (1955).
11. R. W. Bailey, S. A. Barker, E. J. Bourne, and M. Stacey, Nature *176*, 1164 (1955).
12. J. H. Pazur and T. Budovich, J. Am. Chem. Soc. *78*, 1885 (1936).
13. C. S. Hudson, J. Org. Chem. *9*, 470 (1944).
14. S. A. Barker, E. J. Bourne, and M. Stacey, J. Chem. Soc. *1953*, 3084.
15. R. Kuhn and H. H. Baer, Chem. Ber. *87*, 1560 (1954).
16. W. Otting, Ann. *640*, 44 (1961).
17. J. E. Courtois, A. Wickström, and P. Le Dizet, Bull. soc. chim. France *1952*, 1006.
18. R. Kuhn and W. Kirschenlohr, Chem. Ber. *87*, 1547 (1954).
19. G. Henseke and E. Brose, Chem. Ber. *91*, 2273 (1958).
20. W. T. Haskins, R. M. Hann, and C. S. Hudson, J. Am. Chem. Soc. *67*, 939 (1945).
21. W. T. Haskins, R. M. Hann, and C. S. Hudson, J. Am. Chem. Soc. *70*, 2288 (1948).
22. W. T. Haskins, R. M. Hann, and C. S. Hudson, J. Am. Chem. Soc. *69*, 1461 (1947).
23. E. Fischer, Ber. *20*, 821 (1887).
24. O. Diels and R. Meyer, Ann. *519*, 157 (1935).
25. E. E. Percival and E. G. V. Percival, J. Chem. Soc. *1937*, 1320.
26. S. Bayne, Biochem. J. *50*, XXVII (1952).

122. E. Fischer and K. Freudenberg, Ber. *46*, 1116 (1913).

123. E. Hyde, Ber. *32*, 1816 (1899).

124. E. O. Lippmann, Ber. *53*, 2069 (1920).

125. Ch. Araki and S. Hirase, Bull. Chem. Soc. Japan *29*, 770 (1956); Chem. Abstr. *51*, 8015 (1957).

126. L. H. Briggs, R. C. Cambie, and J. L. Hoare, J. Chem. Soc. *1963*, 2848.

127. G. O. Aspinall, I. M. Cairncross, and K. M. Ross, J. Chem. Soc. *1963*, 1721.

128. S. C. McKee and E. E. Dickey, J. Org. Chem. *28*, 1561 (1963).

129. J. K. N. Jones and P. E. Reid, Can. J. Chem. *41*, 2382 (1963).

# XXVII

## Azido Sugars of the Oligosaccharide Series and Condensation Products of Oligosaccharides and Substances of the Urea Group

Acylated halogenoses react with sodium azide or, more advantageously, with silver azide to form acylated glycosyl azides; in the monosaccharide series, this reaction was described several times by Bertho,[1] while in the oligosaccharide group it was mentioned only once.[2] Hepta-*O*-acetyl-α-cellobiosyl bromide, or hepta-*O*-acetyl-α-maltosyl bromide, is converted by the action of silver azide in ether into the corresponding acylated cellobiosyl or maltosyl azide respectively, which may be hydrogenated to the acylated cellobiosyl- or maltosylamine.[2]

Free reducing oligosaccharides react readily with substances of the urea group. Such reactions have been carried out with lactose and urea,[3-7] semicarbazide[8] and aminoguanidine,[9] also with cellobiose and semicarbazide[8] and thiosemicarbazide.[10] The hydrazones of oligosaccharide osones are likewise converted by the action of thiosemicarbazide into the corresponding thiosemicarbazones.[11]

Substances of this type may also be obtained by the reaction of hepta-*O*-acetyl-α-cellobiosyl bromide with potassium thiocyanate.[12] The hepta-*O*-acetyl-β-cellobiosyl isothiocyanate produced in this way reacts with alcohols to form the corresponding alkyl thiourethans.

## Table LXXX

Physical Properties of Some Other Nitrogenous Oligosaccharide Derivatives

| Oligosaccharide Derivative | Melting Point °C | $[\alpha]_D$ | Solvent | References |
|---|---|---|---|---|
| β-Maltosyl azide hepta-O-acetate | 91 | +53° | CHCl$_3$ | 2 |
| β-Cellobiosyl azide hepta-O-acetate | 181—182·5 | —30·9° | CHCl$_3$ | 2 |
| Lactosylurea | 230—240 | + 2·1° | H$_2$O | 4 |
| | 234 (dec.) | | | 6, 7 |
| Lactosyl semicarbazide | 185 | +10·6° | H$_2$O | 8 |
| Cellobiosyl semicarbazide | 183—185 | — 7·8° | H$_2$O | 8 |
| Cellobiosyl thiosemicarbazide | 170 (dec.) | | | 10 |
| Lactosyl aminoguanidine | | | | 9 |
| Lactosone α-methyl-p-bromophenylhydrazone 2-thiosemicarbazone | 156—157 | | | 11 |
| Cellobiosyl isothiocyanate hepta-O-acetate | 205 | — 8·6° | CHCl$_3$ | 12 |

## REFERENCES

1. J. Staněk, M. Černý, J. Kocourek, and J. Pacák, *The Monosaccharides*, Acad. Press, New York 1963.
2. A. Bertho, Ann. *562*, 229 (1949).
3. N. Schoorl, Rec. trav. chim. *22*, 1 (1903).
4. N. Schoorl, Rec. trav. chim. *22*, 72 (1903).
5. A. Hynd and M. G. Macfarlane, Biochem. J. *20*, 1264 (1926).
6. S. Adachi, Nippon Nôgei-kagaku Kaishi *30*, 372 (1956); Chem. Abstr. *52*, 5687 (1958).
7. S. Adachi, Nippon Nôgei-kagaku Kaishi *30*, 709 (1956); Chem. Abstr. *52*, 5688 (1958).
8. L. Maquenne and W. Goodwin, Bull. soc. chim. France [3] *31*, 1078 (1904).
9. H. Wolff, Ber. *28*, 2613 (1895).
10. K. Freudenberg, K. Friedrich, and I. Bumann, Ann. *494*, 41 (1932).
11. G. Henseke and E. Brose, Chem. Ber. *91*, 2273 (1958).
12. A. Wilhelms, Magyar Biol. Lutató Intézet Munkái *13*, 525 (1941); Chem. Abstr. *36*, 411 (1942).

# XXVIII

## Osones of Oligosaccharides and Their Derivatives except Osazones*

Phenylosazones of monosaccharides may be converted, by the action of hydrochloric acid with simultaneous removal of the nitrogenous residues, into dicarbonyl compounds, which are termed osones.[1] This reaction was also applied to phenylosazones of reducing disaccharides and carried out with lactose phenylosazone,[2] however, it was not possible to isolate an established lactosone from the reaction mixture. Since the action of phenylhydrazine upon the reaction mixture containing the assumed lactosone again yielded lactose phenylosazone, it was believed that no noticeable hydrolysis of the glycosidic linkage of the oligosaccharide had occurred in the decomposition of the original lactose phenylosazone in the strongly acid solution.

With regard to the possibility of the cleavage of the glycosidic linkage in acid solution and to the possibility of the formation of anhydro derivatives from phenylosazones in acid solution,[3] the preparation of oligosaccharide osones was usually carried out by decomposing the phenylosazones with benzaldehyde. This method was employed for preparing cellobiosone,[4] maltosone,[5-10] lactosone,[5,9-11] and melibiosone.[5,8] This decomposition proceeded, as was observed in the preparation of maltosone, especially readily in the presence of about one part in ten of benzoic acid.[6] The existence of osones, or their solutions, prepared by other methods,[12] is doubtful because the initial substances were obviously not sufficiently pure.[13,14]

Anyhow, the prepared disaccharide osones are not established chemical compounds, and the proof of their existence is in any case based on the findings that the reaction with substituted hydrazines gives rise to osazones[5,6,15,16] and that their enzymic cleavage yields a monosaccharide molecule and a molecule of a monosaccharide osone.[4,5] Such a cleavage is also effected by warming with hydrochloric acid.[2,7,9]

A more advantageous procedure for preparing oligosaccharide osones, or their solutions, consists of the decomposition of the appropriate phenylosazones by the action of nitrous acid.[15] From the fact that the action of phenylhydra-

---

* For a review see S. Bayne and J. A. Fewster, Advances in Carbohydrate Chem. *11*, 44 (1956).

zine on the solution of the osone obtained in this way regenerates the phenyl-osazone in a yield of 62%, it may be concluded that the decomposition of the original phenylosazone to the osone proceeds with a satisfactory yield.

Oxidative methods setting out from free reducing disaccharides are unsuccessful. It has been reported that maltose[7] reacts with Fehling solution to form maltosone; hydrogen peroxide in the presence of ferrous salts (Fenton reagent) does not oxidize reducing oligosaccharides to the corresponding osones.[17]

The proofs of the existence of oligosaccharide osones are also based on further reactions. Thus, maltosone is oxidized by bromine water to 2-oxomaltobionic acid,[8] which could be isolated only in the form of its brucine salt. A reliable proof of the existence of the osone is given by the conversion of the lactosone (I) into the corresponding quinoxaline derivative (II), i. e. 2-(2-$O$-$\beta$-D-galacto-pyranosyl-D-*arabino*-tetrahydroxybutyl)quinoxaline,[15] by heating aqueous lact-osone solutions with $o$-phenylenediamine hydrochloride in the presence of sodium acetate on the water bath.

In the treatment of lactosone with substituted phenylhydrazine derivatives, such as $\alpha$-methyl-$p$-bromophenylhydrazine or $\alpha$-benzylphenylhydrazine, it is only the aldehydic group of the osone molecule that reacts to form a substituted osone phenylhydrazone.[15]

There is still another reaction characteristic of oligosaccharide osones;[18] the hepta-$O$-acetyl derivative of 2-hydroxycellobial (III) adds chlorine to its double bond to form a crystalline dichloride and a mixture of non-crystallizing dichlorides. The crystalline substance is converted by the action of silver acetate in acetic acid into the nona-$O$-acetyl derivative (IV), while the non-crystalliz-ing components react with silver carbonate to form the hepta-$O$-acetyl derivative (V). Both substances, (IV) and (V), on heating with a mixture of pyridine and acetic anhydride, yield a crystalline hepta-$O$-acetyl derivative of cellobiosone (VI).

*References see p. 446*

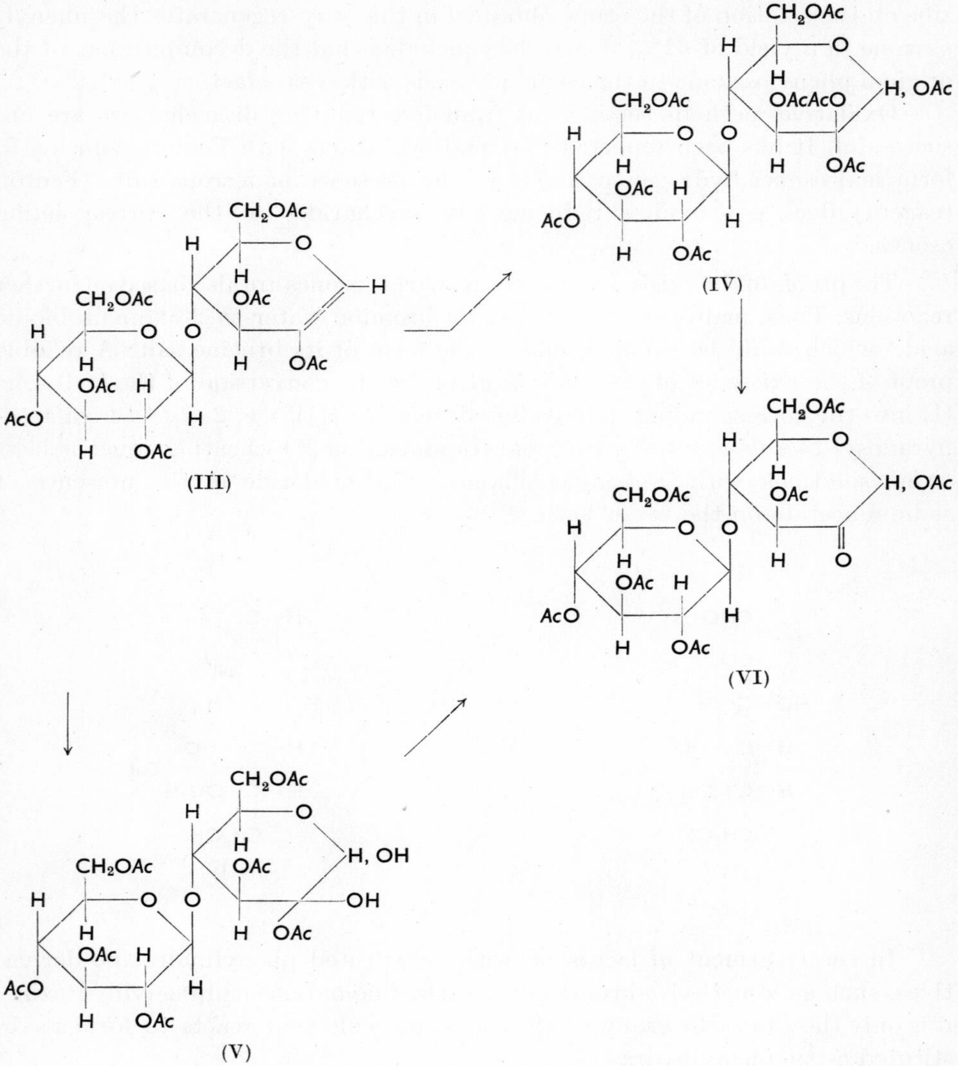

(III)

(IV)

(VI)

(V)

## REFERENCES

1. S. Bayne and J. A. Fewster, Advances in Carbohydrate Chem. *11*, 44 (1956).
2. E. Fischer, Ber. *21*, 2621 (1888).
3. E. Fischer, Ber. *20*, 821 (1887).
4. E. Fischer and G. Zemplén, Ann. *365*, 1 (1909).
5. E. Fischer and E. F. Armstrong, Ber. *35*, 3141 (1902).
6. E. Fischer, Ber. *44*, 1898 (1911).
7. W. L. Lewis, Am. Chem. J. *42*, 301 (1909).

8. T. Kitasato, Biochem. Z. *207*, 217 (1929).

9. A. Hynd, Proc. Roy. Soc. (London) B *101*, 244 (1927).

10. D. K. Baird, W. N. Haworth, R. Herbert, E. L. Hirst, F. Smith, and M. Stacey, J. Chem. Soc. *1934*, 62.

11. S. Bayne, Biochem. J. *50*, XXVII (1956).

12. E. Fischer, Ber. *23*, 3690 (1890).

13. H. Berlin, J. Am. Chem. Soc. *48*, 1107 (1936).

14. H. H. Schlubach and W. Rauchenberger, Ber. *59*, 2102 (1926).

15. G. Henseke and E. Brose, Chem. Ber. *91*, 2273 (1958).

16. E. Fischer and K. Freudenberg, Ber. *46*, 1116 (1913).

17. R. S. Morrell and A. E. Bellars, J. Chem. Soc. *87*, 280 (1905).

18. K. Maurer and K. Plötner, Ber. *64*, 281 (1931).

# XXIX

# Oligosaccharide Derivatives with an Acyclic Reducing Part of the Molecule

## 1. OLIGOSACCHARIDE THIOACETALS

Monosaccharide thioacetals are commonly obtainable substances, and their preparation is among the easiest of operations in the chemistry of monosaccharides.[1] The preparation of analogous compounds derived from reducing oligosaccharides will probably be more difficult with regard to the possible hydrolysis of the glycosidic linkage. The first papers on this subject, published by Japanese writers,[2-4] describe the reactions of butanethiol,[2] propane-1-thiol[3] and propane-2-thiol[4] with lactose,[2] maltose[2-4] and sucrose (!!).[2-4] The first important work in this respect seems to be the preparation of maltose diethyl dithioacetal,[5] although the substance could be obtained only in the form of the crystalline octa-O-acetyl derivative. The paper in question[5] emphasizes the necessity for carrying out the reaction at the lowest possible temperature and for rapid neutralization of the hydrochloric acid.

The preparation of lactose dibenzyl dithioacetal, reported later,[6,7] is probably doubtful, because in another paper[8] it is stated that the reactions of maltose and lactose with benzyl mercaptan (and with other mercaptans, too) lead to substances with a higher sulphur content; the author[8] of this paper points out that, besides the formation of the thioacetal, two hydroxyl groups are replaced by –SR groups.

Using a very interesting method, Japanese investigators[9] succeeded, in preparing agarobiose diethyl dithioacetal (i. e. 4-O-β-D-galactopyranosyl-3,6-anhydro-L-galactose diethyl dithioacetal, see Chapter XIX). By treating the polysaccharide agarose with ethanethiol and hydrochloric acid, they obtained from the reaction mixture agarobiose diethyl dithioacetal in syrupy form. This substance was converted into the crystalline hexa-O-acetyl derivative, which on treatment with alcoholic ammonia yielded pure free agarobiose diethyl dithioacetal, which in turn was converted into the corresponding hexa-O-methyl derivative.

In a similar way, other investigators[10] obtained 4-O-β-D-galactopyranosyl-3,6-anhydro-D-galactose diethyl dithioacetal in the mercaptolysis of the polysaccharide $\varkappa$-carrageenin. The same product is formed by the mercaptolysis of the polysaccharides of the red alga *Furcillaria fastigiata*.[11,12]

### Table LXXXI

Physical Properties of Oligosaccharide Thioacetals and Their Derivatives

| Oligosaccharide Thioacetal | Melting Point °C | $[\alpha]_D$ | Solvent | References |
|---|---|---|---|---|
| Diethyl dithioacetal of | | | | |
| maltose | | | | |
|   octa-$O$-acetate | 122 | $+88\cdot3°$ | $CHCl_3$ | 5 |
|   agarobiose | 172 | $-20\cdot9°$ | MeOH | 9 |
| | | $-8\cdot47°$ | $H_2O$ | 9 |
| | | $-51\cdot7°$ | $C_5H_5N$ | 9 |
|   hexa-$O$-acetate | $103\cdot5$ | $-11\cdot8°$ | $CHCl_3$ | 9 |
| | | $-22\cdot1°$ | $C_5H_5N$ | 9 |
| | | $-16\cdot7°$ | EtOH | 9 |
|   hexa-$O$-methyl ether | syrup | $-17\cdot5°$ | $CHCl_3$ | 9 |
| | | $-12\cdot5°$ | EtOH | 9 |
| 4-$O$-$\beta$-D-galactopyranosyl-3,6-anhydro-D-galactose | 116—117 | $+14°$ | $CHCl_3$ | 11, 12 |
|   hexa-$O$-acetate | 121 | $+12°$ | $CHCl_3$ | 12 |
| Di-$n$-propyl dithioacetal of | | | | |
| maltose | 146 | $+25°$ | | 3 |
| sucrose (???) | | | | 3 |
| Di-$n$-butyl dithioacetal of | | | | |
| maltose | 126 | $+12°$ | | 2 |
| lactose | 106 | $+23\cdot6°$ | | 2 |
| sucrose (???) | | | | 2 |
| Di-isobutyl dithioacetal of | | | | |
| maltose | 140 | $+13\cdot2°$ | | 4 |
| sucrose (???) | | | | 4 |
| Di-$n$-hexyl dithioacetal of | | | | |
| lactose | | | | |
|   bisthiohexyl ether | 129 | $-7\cdot31°$ | $C_5H_5N$ | 8 |
|    HgCl$_2$ compound | 173 (dec.) | | | 8 |
| maltose | | | | |
|   bisthiohexyl ether | 109 | $-\ 8\cdot5°$ | $C_5H_5N$ | 8 |
| Dibenzyl dithioacetal of | | | | |
| lactose | 128 | $-38\cdot2°$ | EtOH | 6, 7 |
|   octa-$O$-acetate | 145 | $+26\cdot2°$ | EtOH | 6, 7 |
|   octa-$O$-methyl ether | 49 | $-50°$ | EtOH | 6, 7 |
|   bisthiobenzyl ether | 128 | $-\ 4\cdot5°$ | $C_5H_5N$ | 8 |
|    HgCl$_2$ compound | 171 (dec.) | | | 8 |
| maltose | | | | |
|   bisthiobenzyl ether | 140 | $-101\cdot9°$ | $C_5H_5N$ | 8 |
|    HgCl$_2$ compound | 173(dec.) | | | 8 |
| Di-$\beta$-phenylethyl dithioacetal of | | | | |
| lactose | | | | |
|   bisthio-$\beta$-phenylethyl ether | 137 | $+\ 4\cdot5°$ | $C_5H_5N$ | 8 |
|    HgCl$_2$ compound | 229(dec.) | | | 8 |
| maltose | | | | |
|   bisthio-$\beta$-phenylethyl ether | 148 | $+10\cdot5°$ | $C_5H_5N$ | 8 |
|    HgCl$_2$ compound | 235 (dec.) | | | 8 |

*References see p. 451*

## 2. ACYLATED AND ALKYLATED DERIVATIVES OF THE OXO FORMS OF OLIGOSACCHARIDES AND THEIR ACETALS

A generally known method for preparing acylated derivatives of the oxo forms of monosaccharides consists of the removal of the mercapto groups from the acylated derivatives of monosaccharide thioacetals by the action of a mercuric chloride solution. For analogous oligosaccharide derivatives, this procedure has as yet been applied only once,[9] namely for the preparation of hexa-O-methyl-*aldehydo*-agarobiose from hexa-O-methylagarobiose diethyl dithioacetal.

The same investigators[13] have prepared other derivatives of this type in a very unusual way, i.e. methanolysis of agarose. Thus they prepared agarobiose dimethyl acetal and its hexa-O-acetyl derivative, which is identical with the substance formed from hexa-O-acetyl agarobiose diethyl dithioacetal by the action of mercuric chloride in methanol. A similar method was employed for obtaining agarobiose dimethyl acetal by methanolysis of the mucilage of the red alga *Gloiopeltis fuscata*[14] or the methanolysis of the polysaccharide of *Gracilaria confervoides*.[15]

Agarobiose dimethyl acetal may be obtained also in the methanolysis of *Ahnfeltia plicata* agar-agar;[16] dimethyl acetal of the corresponding tetrasaccharide, *neo*-agarotetraose, has been obtained from the same agar-agar, too.[16]

The native form of agarobiose contains pyruvic acid, chemically bound.[17–19] Methanolysis of agar-agar yielded also the corresponding derivative of agarobiose, i. e. dimethyl acetal of 4-O-4′,6′-O-1″-carboxyethylidene-β-D-galactopyranosyl-3,6-anhydro-L-galactose (I).[18,19]

(I)

*Chondrus ocellatus* mucilage afforded 4-O-β-D-galactopyranosyl-3,6-anhydro-D-galactose (carrabiose) on methanolysis.[20] The polysaccharide from the alga *Hypnea specifera* contains obviously the same disaccharide in its sugar-unit chain, as after methanolysis, subsequent hydrolysis and reduction with sodium borohydride, 4-O-β-D-galactopyranosyl-3,6-anhydro-D-galactitol was obtained.[21]

## Table LXXXII

Physical Properties of Reducing Oligosaccharide Acyclic Derivatives

| Acyclic Derivative | Melting Point °C | $[\alpha]_D$ | Solvent | References |
|---|---|---|---|---|
| aldehydo-Agarobiose hexa-O-methyl ether | 92—93 | — 9·3° | $H_2O$ | 9 |
| | | —53·7° | $CHCl_3$ | 9 |
| Agarobiose dimethyl acetal | 164 | —37·4° | MeOH | 13—16 |
| | 166 | —29·3° | $H_2O$ | 14 |
| hexa-O-acetate | 87—88 | — 5·76° | $CHCl_3$ | 13 |
| | | —12·5° | $C_6H_6$ | 13 |
| | 136—137 | — 5·8° | $CHCl_3$ | 14 |
| | | —12·5° | $C_6H_6$ | 14 |
| | 138·5 | —13·5° | $C_6H_6$ | 15 |
| neo-Agarotetraose dimethyl acetal | | + 3·2° | $H_2O$ | 16 |
| deca-O-acetate | 116—117 | — 6·7° | $CHCl_3$ | 16 |
| Carrabiose dimethyl acetal hexa-O-acetate | 147—149 | —16·0° | $CHCl_3$ | 20 |

## REFERENCES

1. J. Staněk, M. Černý, J. Kocourek, and J. Pacák, *The Monosaccharides,* Acad. Press, New York 1963.
2. Y. Uyeda and J. Kamon, Bull. Chem. Soc. Japan *1*, 179 (1926); Chem. Abstr. *21*, 64 (1927).
3. Y. Maeda and Y. Uyeda, Bull. Chem. Soc. Japan *1*, 181 (1926); Chem. Abstr. *21*, 64 (1927).
4. Y. Uyeda, Bull. Chem. Soc. Japan *4*, 264 (1929); Chem. Abstr. *24*, 11352 (1930).
5. M. L. Wolfrom and M. R. Newlin, J. Am. Chem. Soc. *53*, 4379 (1931).
6. J. Staněk and J. Šáda, Chem. listy *43*, 160 (1949).
7. J. Staněk and J. Šáda, Collection Czechoslov. Chem. Communs *14*, 540 (1949).
8. Zaki el Heweihi, Chem. Ber. *86*, 862 (1953).
9. S. Hirase and Ch. Araki, Bull. Chem. Soc. Japan *27*, 105 (1954); Chem. Abstr. *49*, 9517 (1955).
10. N. A. O'Neill, J. Am. Chem. Soc. *77*, 6324 (1955).
11. T. J. Painter, Chem. & Ind. (London) *1959*, 1488.
12. T. J. Painter, Can. J. Chem. *38*, 112 (1960).
13. Ch. Araki and S. Hirase, Bull. Chem. Soc. Japan *27*, 109 (1954); Chem. Abstr. *49*, 9518 (1955).
14. S. Hirase, Ch. Araki, and T. Ito, Bull. Chem. Soc. Japan *31*, 428 (1958).
15. A. L. Clingman, J. R. Nunn, and A. M. Stephen, J. Chem. Soc. *1957*, 177.
16. K. Arai, J. Chem. Soc. Japan (Nippon Kagaku Zasshi) *82*, 1416 (1961); Chem. Abstr. *57*, 15211 (1962).
17. S. Hirase, Bull. Chem. Soc. Japan *30*, 70 (1957); Chem. Abstr. *52*, 9480 (1958).
18. S. Hirase, Bull. Chem. Soc. Japan *30*, 75 (1957); Chem. Abstr. *52*, 9481 (1958).
19. S. Hirase, Mem. Fac. Ind. Arts Kyoto Tech. Univ., Sci. Technol. *1957*, 17; Chem. Abstr. *52*, 16221 (1958).
20. Ch. Araki and S. Hirase, Bull. Chem. Soc. Japan *29*, 770 (1956); Chem. Abstr. *51*, 8015 (1957).
21. A. L. Clingman and J. R. Nunn, J. Chem. Soc. *1959*, 493.

# XXX

# Reduction Products of Reducing Oligosaccharides

The reduction products of reducing oligosaccharides, i. e. sugar alcohols of the oligosaccharide series (also designated as glycosyl derivatives of polyhydric alcohols) are known in many cases as natural substances either directly isolated from plant material or obtained by the hydrolysis of other, more complicated substances.

Thus, mono-$O$-$\beta$- and di-$O$-$\beta$-D-glucosides of D-mannitol have been isolated from the seaweed *Fucus vesiculosus*.[1] A later paper reports the isolation of the D-galactosyl derivative of D-mannitol from the lichen *Peltigera horizontalis*.[2]* Some papers[3–5] are concerned with the isolation of umbilicin, i. e. 3-$O$-$\beta$-D-galactofuranosyl-D-arabitol, from the lichen *Umbilicaria pustulata*; the same substance has been found in other lichens, such as *U. rigida, Cladonia rangifera, Haematomma ventosum, Cetraria islandica*, and *Lecanora atra*.[4] Umbilicin was first regarded erroneously as 3-$O$-$\beta$-D-galactopyranosyl-D-arabitol,[3] and this assumption was corrected[5] also on the basis of the finding that umbilicin is not identical with the product of the reduction of 3-$O$-$\beta$-D-galactopyranosyl-D-arabinose by sodium borohydride.

Another frequently occurring substance is 2-$O$-$\alpha$-D-galactopyranosyl-glycerol contained in some algae,[6–8] for example, in the red alga *Rhodymenia palmata*,[6,7] further in *Irideaea laminarioides*,[9] *Gelidium pristoides*,[10] *Gracilaria confervoides*,[10] and *Furcillaria fastigiata*.[11] Sometimes this substance is also mentioned under the name floridoside.[6,7,9,11] 1-$O$-$\alpha$-D-Galactopyranosyl-D-glycerol has been isolated from the red alga *Porphyra perforata*, where also the presence of the non-isolated 2-$O$-$\alpha$-D-galactopyranosylglycerol has been proved.[12]

Another substance isolated from *Furcillaria fastigiata* is the 3-$O$-$\alpha$-D-mannopyranosyl derivative of floridoside.[11]

---

* The constitution of this compound has been proved by B. Lindberg, B. G. Silvander, and C. A. Wachtmeister, Acta Chem. Scand. *18*, 213 (1964); it is 3-$O$-$\beta$-D-galactopyranosyl-D-mannitol. The same paper reports the isolation of 3-$O$-$\beta$-D-glucopyranosyl-D-mannitol in eight *Peltigera* spp. The last compound has been obtained from *Peltigera aphthosa*, see B. Lindberg, B. G. Silvander, and C. A. Wachtmeister, Acta Chem. Scand. *17*, 1348 (1963), and synthesized from 4-$O$-$\beta$-D-glucopyranosyl-D-mannose by its reduction with sodium borohydride.

From the red algae *Polysiphonia fastigiata* and *Corallina officinalis* has been obtained $O$-α-D-galactopyranosyl-(1→6)-$O$-β-D-galactopyranosyl-(1→1)-D-glycerol,[13] which is hydrolysed by α-galactosidase with the formation of 1-$O$-β-D-galactopyranosyl-D-glycerol. The configuration was fully confirmed by syntheses [14] of the 1-$O$-β-D-galactopyranosyl derivatives of D- and L-glycerol.

It is interesting to note that both 1-$O$-β-D-galactopyranosyl-D-glycerol and $O$-α-D-galactopyranosyl-(1→6)-$O$-β-D-galactopyranosyl-(1→1)-D-glycerol have also been obtained by deacylation of wheat flour lipids.[15] Both these substances and the ester of the first one with sulphuric acid have been isolated from de-acylated leaf and chloroplast lipids.[16]

New types of compounds of this group have been obtained from deacylated sulpholipids. After a preliminary communication[17] that sulpholipids are likely to contain sulphodeoxy derivatives of glycosylglycerol, and a further report[18] stating that the sugar component is 6-sulpho-D-quinovose (6-sulpho-6-deoxy-D-glucose), it was reliably established[19-21] that the substance isolated from deacylated sulpholipids is 1-$O$-α-(6-sulpho-D-quinovosyl)-glycerol (I). The constitution of this product was confirmed by synthesis.[21]

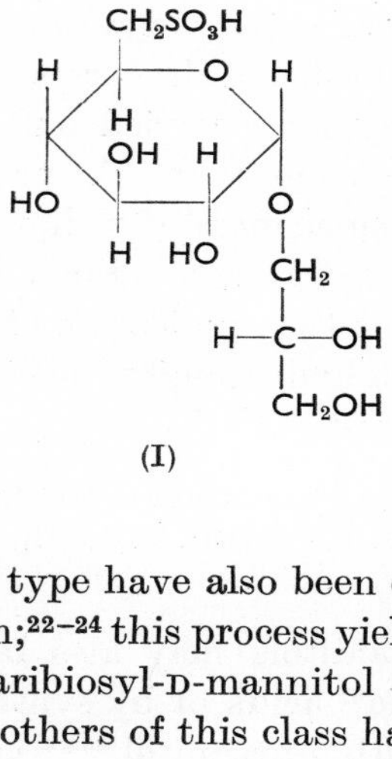

(I)

Substances of a similar type have also been obtained by the hydrolysis of the polysaccharide laminarin;[22-24] this process yields 1-$O$-β-D-glucopyranosyl-D-mannitol and 1-$O$-β-laminaribiosyl-D-mannitol along with other products. Both these compounds and others of this class have been prepared by synthesis[25] (see later).

Some xylans are likewise converted by periodic acid oxidation and subsequent hydrolysis and reduction into glycosylalditols; for example, 2-$O$-β-D-xylopyranosylglycerol has been isolated in this way.[26]

Rye-flour arabinoxylan yields after oxidation with periodic acid, reduction and hydrolysis 2-$O$-β-D-xylopyranosylglycerol and the corresponding higher members of the series 2-$O$-β-xylobiosylglycerol and 2-$O$-β-xylotriosylglycerol, see G. O. Aspinall and K. M. Ross, J. Chem. Soc. *1963*, 1681.

*References see p. 460*

Interesting sources of glycosyl derivatives of alditols recently described are various polymeric esters of phosphoric acids, present in the walls and cell contents of a number of bacteria and designated in general as teichoic acids. Their composition will obviously differ according to their individual sources; however, their common feature is that they contain ribitol, a hexose — usually D-glucose or N-acetyl-D-glucosamine — phosphoric acid and D-alanine. The sugar residue has in many cases been obtained by degradation reactions, and thus it has been found that the teichoic acid from *Bacillus subtilis*[27-31] contains 4-O-β-D-glucopyranosyl-D-ribitol, which has also been synthesized;[31] in the teichoic acid from *Staphylococcus aureus*[28,32*] the D-glucose is replaced by N-acetyl-D-glucosamine, which is linked to ribitol by both α- and β-bonds.[32] The teichoic acid from *Lactobacillus arabinosus*[28,33,34] contains 3-O-α-D-glucopyranosyl-D-ribitol, 4-O-α-D-glucopyranosyl-D-ribitol and 3,4-di-O-α-D-glucopyranosyl-D-ribitol,[33] of which 4-O-α-D-glucopyranosyl-D-ribitol has been prepared synthetically.[34]

* * *

The majority of glycosyl derivatives of alditols have been prepared synthetically, most frequently by reduction of the corresponding reducing oligosaccharides. This reduction was originally carried out with sodium[35] or calcium[36] amalgam in a carbon dioxide atmosphere. At present, preference is given to sodium borohydride as reducing agent;[5,22,37-55] however, this procedure, though simple, necessitates the removal of the inorganic cations on ion exchangers.[40,42,46] For this reason, apart from the application of sodium borohydride, the reduction is mainly effected with hydrogen,[56-65] using platinum,[61-63] palladium[64] or Raney nickel[55-59,65] as catalyst.

Sodium borohydride has been recommended for the reduction of laminaritriose to laminaritriitol, see T. E. Nelson, J. V. Scaletti, F. Smith, and S. Kirkwood, Can. J. Chem. *41*, 1671 (1963).

Glycosyl derivatives of alditols may also be obtained by reduction of aldobionic[66] and aldobiouronic[67] acids or by synthesis. Besides acid-catalysed condensation of D-galactose with D-mannitol,[68**] a number of substances of this

---

* 2-O-β-Gentiobiosylglycerol has been recently found after chemical degradation of intracellular teichoic acid from *Staphylococcus aureus*, see U. L. Rajbhandary and J. Baddiley, Biochem. J. *87*, 429 (1963).

** Acid catalysed condensation of aldoses with polyols has been investigated by V. I. Sharkov, R. I. Ul'yanovskaya, and A. K. Bolotova, Sb. Tr., Gos. Nauchn. Issled. Inst. Gidroliz. i Sul'fitno-Spirt. Prom. *9*, 138 (1961); Chem. Abstr. *60*, 15973 (1964); heating of aldoses with polyols on a water bath at 30—700 mm with sulphuric acid as a catalyst has been recommended for the preparation of D-xylopyranosyl derivatives of D-glucitol etc. The substances obtained may be used as glycerol substitutes.

group have been prepared by modifications of the conventional Koenigs-Knorr synthesis.[14,31,69,92] For example, the condensation of 2,3,4,6-tetra-$O$-acetyl-$\alpha$-D-glucopyranosyl bromide with 1,3-$O$-benzylideneglycerol proceeds according to expectations,[69] and the same initial halogenose (II) reacts with 5-$O$-benzyl-2,3-$O$-isopropylidene-1-$O$-triphenylmethyl-D-ribitol (III) to form the product (IV) which, after removal of the blocking groups, yields 4-$O$-$\beta$-D-glucopyranosyl-D-ribitol (V),[31] which is identical with the degradation product of the ribitol teichoic acid from the walls of *Bacillus subtilis*.

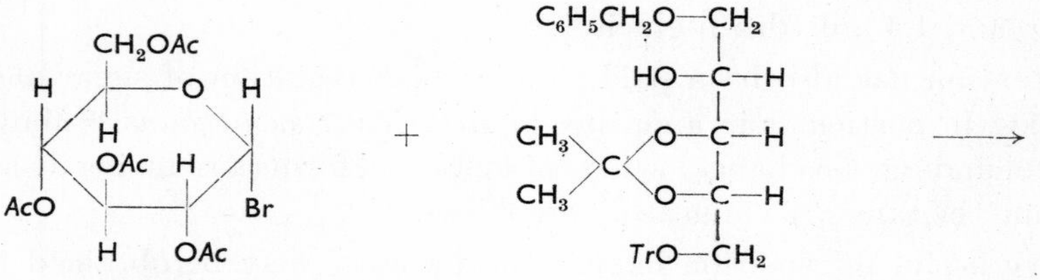

(II)           (III)

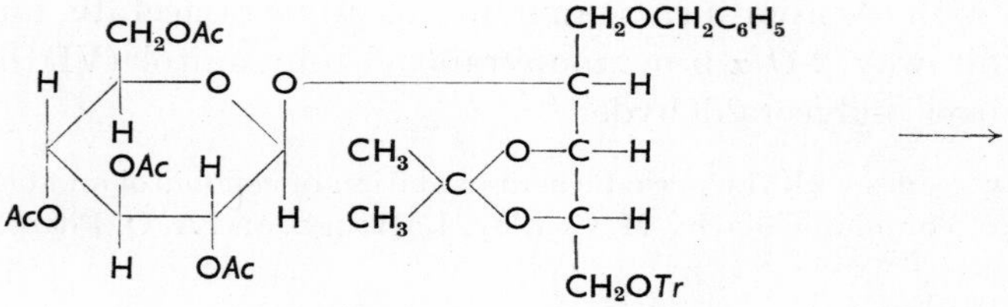

(IV)

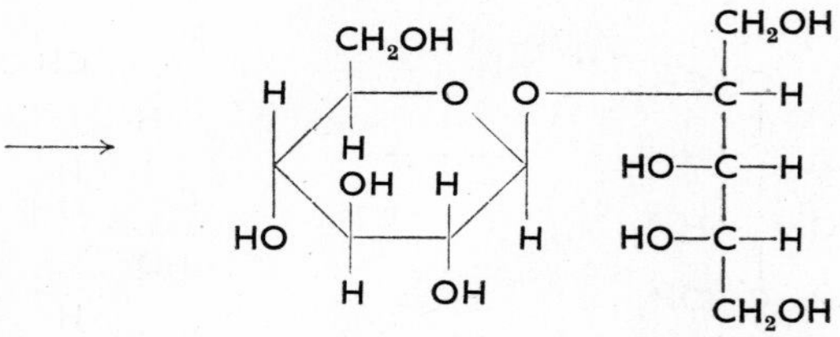

(V)

Recently, 2,3,4-tri-$O$-acetyl-$\alpha$-D-xylopyranosyl bromide and 1,3-$O$-benzylideneglycerol yielded derivatives of 2-$O$-$\beta$-D-xylopyranosylglycerol, see G. O. Aspinall and K. M. Ross, J. Chem. Soc. *1963*, 1681.

Similarly, the Brigl anhydride, i. e. 3,4,6-tri-$O$-acetyl-1,2-anhydro-$\alpha$-D-glucopyranose, can be utilized for preparing derivatives of 4-$O$-$\alpha$-D-glucopyranosyl-D-ribitol.[34]

It may be expected that usual preparative methods will lead to various substituted derivatives of sugar alcohols in the series of reducing oligosaccharides, such as per-$O$-acetylated, per-$O$-methylated and other derivatives. The number of other reactions carried out in this field is relatively small. Subjects of special investigation have been the kinetics of the acid hydrolysis of isomaltotriitol[65] and the decomposition of cellobiitol, lactitol and maltitol in alkaline solution at elevated pressure and temperature.[39] The alcohol unit of the molecule is always converted into the corresponding 1,4-anhydro derivative of an alditol of the monosaccharide series, while the other part of the molecule gives rise to the corresponding 1,6-anhydrohexose, so that cellobiitol yields laevoglucosan and 1,4-anhydro-D-glucitol.

Attention has also been paid to microbial oxidation of sugar alcohols of this series, in particular in a culture of *Acetobacter suboxydans*.[68] Maltitol and melibiitol undergo no change, while *epi*-melibiitol forms a reducing disaccharide exhibiting the same $R_F$ value as planteobiose.

Very useful information in structural studies may be obtained from the course of the oxidation of glycosyl derivatives of alditols with periodic acid.[65, 70,71] In some cases[40,41] it is possible to prepare a lower reducing oligosaccharide by oxidation with the appropriate amount of lead tetra-acetate, for instance, to convert in this way 2-$O$-α-D-mannopyranosyl-D-mannitol (VI) into 2-$O$-α-D-mannopyranosyl-D-glyceraldehyde.

Some new results with the periodic acid oxidation of cellobiitol and other substances of this group are communicated by M. Cantley, L. Hough, and A. O. Pittet, J. Chem. Soc. *1963*, 2527.

(VI)                    (VII)

## Table LXXXIII

Physical Properties of Oligosaccharide Alditols

| Oligosaccharide Alditol | Melting Point °C | $[\alpha]_D$ | Solvent | References |
|---|---|---|---|---|
| 2-O-α-D-Glucopyranosylglycerol | syrup | +121° | $H_2O$ | 41, 42, 92 |
| hexa-O-benzoate | 137—138 | + 96° | $CHCl_3$ | 41, 92 |
| 2-O-β-D-Glucopyranosylglycerol | 165 | — 30·2° | $H_2O$ | 40, 69 |
| 1,3-O-benzylidene derivative | 138 | — 18·5 | EtOH | 69 |
| 1′,2′,3′,4′-tetra-O-acetate | 137 | — 34·2° | $CHCl_3$ | 69 |
| 1′,2′,3′,4′-tetra-O-acetate | 103 | + 3·3° | $CHCl_3$ | 69 |
| hexa-O-acetate | 128 | | | 69 |
| hexa-O-benzoate | 145—146 | — 4° | $CHCl_3$ | 41 |
| 2-O-α-D-Glucopyranosyl-D-erythritol | 148 | +130° | $H_2O$ | 40 |
| hepta-O-acetate | 97—98 | +105° | $CHCl_3$ | 40 |
| 2-O-β-D-Glucopyranosyl-D-erythritol | 187 | — 17° | $H_2O$ | 40, 88 |
|  | 191—194 | — 15·2° | $H_2O$ | 49 |
| hepta-O-acetate | 116 | — 1·4° | $CHCl_3$ | 40 |
| 4-O-α-D-Glucopyranosyl-D-ribitol | 122—124 | | | 34, 92 |
| 4-O-β-D-Glucopyranosyl-D-ribitol | 134—137 | — 22° | $H_2O$ | 31, 92 |
| octa-O-acetate | 100 | — 14·1° | $CHCl_3$ | 31 |
| 3-O-α-D-Glucopyranosyl-D-arabitol | hygroscop. | +113° | $H_2O$ | 50 |
| Maltitol | | | | |
| 4-O-α-D-glucopyranosyl-D-glucitol | | + 90° | $H_2O$ | 59 |
| nona-O-acetate | | + 86° | $CHCl_3$ | 59 |
| Cellobiitol | | | | |
| 4-O-β-D-glucopyranosyl-D-glucitol | 133 | — 8·7° | $H_2O$ | 58, 59 |
|  | syrup | — 7·9° | $H_2O$ | 54 |
|  | 143 | — 7·8° | $H_2O$ | 76 |
| nona-O-acetate | 105—107 | + 18·8° | $CHCl_3$ | 34 |
| Isomaltitol | | | | |
| 6-O-α-D-glucopyranosyl-D-glucitol | not given | not given | | 77 |
| Gentiobiitol | | | | |
| 6-O-β-D-glucopyranosyl-D-glucitol | not given | not given | | 48 |
| Kojibiitol | | | | |
| 2-O-α-D-glucopyranosyl-D-glucitol | | + 81° | $H_2O$ | 67 |
| Sophoritol | | | | |
| 2-O-β-D-glucopyranosyl-D-glucitol | | — 18·6° | $H_2O$ | 82 |
| nona-O-acetate | 151—152 | — 21° | $CHCl_3$ | 82 |
| 1-O-β-D-Glucopyranosyl-D-mannitol | 141 | — 18° | $H_2O$ | 1 |
|  | | — 20·7° | $H_2O$ | 23 |
|  | | — 19·8° | $H_2O$ | 25 |
| nona-O-benzoate | 88—92 | + 39·7° | $CHCl_3$ | 22, 23 |
| 3-O-β-D-Glucopyranosyl-D-mannitol | 97—100 | — 6° | $H_2O$ | 86, 87 |
| 1,6-Di-O-β-D-glucopyranosyl-D-mannitol | | — 23·5° | $H_2O$ | 25 |
|  | | — 14° | $H_2O$ | 1 |
| dodeca-O-acetate | 136—138 | — 7·7° | $CHCl_3$ | 25 |
| 4-O-β-D-Glucopyranosyl-D-galactitol | 204 | — 13° | $H_2O$ | 52 |
| 6-O-β-D-Glucopyranosyl-D-galactitol | 160—162 | — 17° | $H_2O$ | 52 |
| nona-O-acetate | 149—150 | | | 52 |
| 2-O-α-D-Mannopyranosylglycerol | syrup | + 51° | $H_2O$ | 41 |
| hexa-O-p-nitrobenzoate | 101—103 | — 62° | $CHCl_3$ | 41 |
| 2-O-β-D-Mannopyranosylglycerol | syrup | — 43° | $H_2O$ | 41 |
| hexa-O-p-nitrobenzoate | 114 | —113° | $CHCl_3$ | 41 |
| 2-O-β-D-Mannopyranosyl-D-erythritol | syrup | — 35° | $H_2O$ | 41 |
| hepta-O-p-nitrobenzoate | 118 | —106° | $CHCl_3$ | 41 |

*References see p. 460*

*Table LXXXIII — continued*

| Oligosaccharide Alditol | Melting Point °C | $[\alpha]_D$ | Solvent | References |
|---|---|---|---|---|
| 2-O-α-D-Mannopyranosyl-D-mannitol | 137 | + 45° | $H_2O$ | 46 |
| 1-O-β-D-Galactopyranosylglycerol | 140 | + 3·8° | $H_2O$ | 15 |
| Isofloridoside | | | | |
| 1-O-α-D-galactopyranosylglycerol | | | | 78 |
| Floridoside | | | | |
| 2-O-α-D-galactopyranosylglycerol | 128 | +165° | $H_2O$ | 9, 11 |
| | 127·5 | +172° | $H_2O$ | 10 |
| hexa-O-acetate | 101 | +114° | acetone | 9 |
| hexa-O-benzoate | 157 | +120° | lutidine | 11 |
| hexa-O-methyl ether | | +156° | $H_2O$ | 9 |
| 2-O-β-D-Galactopyranosylglycerol | 127 | − 2° | $H_2O$ | 41 |
| hexa-O-benzoate | 63 | + 36° | lutidine | 42 |
| | | + 25° | lutidine | 42 |
| 2-O-β-D-Galactopyranosyl-D-erythritol | 184 | + 7° | $H_2O$ | 41 |
| 2-O-α-D-Galactopyranosyl-L-erythritol | 158 | +145° | $H_2O$ | 42 |
| 4-O-α-D-Galactopyranosyl-D-erythritol | 133 | +134° | $H_2O$ | 40 |
| Umbilicin | | | | |
| 3-O-β-D-galactofuranosyl-D-arabitol | 138—139 | − 81° | $H_2O$ | 3 |
| octa-O-acetate | 84—85 | − 20° | $CHCl_3$ | 3 |
| 3-O-β-D-Galactopyranosyl-D-arabitol | not given | not given | | 5 |
| 4-O-β-D-Galactopyranosyl-D-arabitol | 179 | − 7° | $H_2O$ | 42 |
| Lactitol, lactitobiotit, lactoside | | | | |
| 4-O-β-D-galactopyranosyl-D-glucitol | 146 | + 14° | $H_2O$ | 59, 60 |
| | 140 | + 16·4° | $H_2O$ | 66 |
| dihydrate* | 78 | + 12·2° | $H_2O$ | 57, 72 |
| tri-O-trityl, hexa-O-acetyl derivative | 250 | − 40·7° | $CHCl_3$ | 60 |
| Melibiitol | 176 | +114° | $H_2O$ | 73, 74, 83 |
| nona-O-acetate | 98 | + 66° | $CHCl_3$ | 73, 74 |
| *epi*-Melibiitol | 157 | | | 73 |
| nona-O-acetate | 122 | +104° | $CHCl_3$ | 73 |
| Xylobiitol | | − 36·4° | $H_2O$ | 89 |
| 3-O-β-D-Galactopyranosyl-D-mannitol | 162 | − 55·5° | $H_2O$ | 2 |
| | 161—163 | − 64° | $H_2O$ | 87 |
| 5-O-β-D-Galactofuranosyl-D-galactitol | 151 | − 65° | $H_2O$ | 47 |
| 6-O-β-D-Fructofuranosyl-D-glucitol | | − 23·7° | $H_2O$ | 37 |
| 2-O-α-L-Arabinopyranosylglycerol | syrup | − 5° | $H_2O$ | 42 |
| 1,3-O-benzylidene derivative | 121—122 | + 4° | EtOH | 42 |
| tri-O-benzoate | 170—172 | +114° | lutidine | 42 |
| penta-O-benzoate | 53—57 | + 93° | $CHCl_3$ | 42 |
| 2-O-β-L-Arabinopyranosylglycerol | 154—155 | +204° | $H_2O$ | 42 |
| penta-O-benzoate | 48—50 | +164° | $CHCl_3$ | 42 |
| 2-O-α-L-Arabinofuranosylglycerol | syrup | −129° | $H_2O$ | 47 |
| 2-O-β-L-Arabinopyranosyl-L-erythritol | syrup | +135° | $H_2O$ | 42 |
| hexa-O-benzoate | 131—134 | +114° | $CHCl_3$ | 42 |
| 2-O-α-D-Xylopyranosylglycerol | syrup | + 95° | $H_2O$ | 42 |
| penta-O-benzoate | 51—55 | + 51° | $CHCl_3$ | 42 |
| 2-O-β-D-Xylopyranosylglycerol | syrup | − 37° | $H_2O$ | 42, 84 |
| | | − 33° | $H_2O$ | 26 |
| penta-O-benzoate | 51—53 | − 36° | $CHCl_3$ | 42 |
| 2-O-α-D-Xylopyranosyl-L-erythritol | | + 91° | $H_2O$ | 42 |
| hexa-O-benzoate | 64—67 | + 98° | $CHCl_3$ | 42 |

* The compound was previously considered to be a monohydrate.[57] This has been corrected.[72] In addition to this, the compound softens at 80°C, melts at 130—140°C and decomposes at 190—200°C.[66]

*Table LXXXIII — continued*

| Oligosaccharide Alditol | Melting Point °C | $[\alpha]_D$ | Solvent | References |
|---|---|---|---|---|
| 2-$O$-$\beta$-D-Xylopyranosyl-L-arabitol | 185—187 | — 33° | $H_2O$ | 42 |
| Cellotriitol | 160 | — 5·5° | $H_2O$ | 76 |
| Isomaltotriitol | not given | not given | | 77 |
| Isopanitol | | | | |
| dodeca-$O$-acetate | 69—72 | + 88° | $CHCl_3$ | 85 |
| Laminaritriitol | not given | not given | | 48 |
| Lycotriitol | 142 | — 27° | $H_2O$ | 64 |
| dodeca-$O$-methyl ether | | | | 64 |
| Manninotriitol | 190 | +147° | $H_2O$ | 75 |
| Mannotriitol | 112 | —20° ± 5° | $H_2O$ | 55 |
| dodeca-$O$-acetate | 114 | — 21° | $CHCl_3$ | 61 |
| Panitol | | | | |
| dodeca-$O$-acetate | 148 | +119° | $CHCl_3$ | 79, 80, 85 |
| Xylotriitol | | — 53·9° | $H_2O$ | 89 |
| 2-$O$-$\beta$-Cellobiosylglycerol | 138—141 | — 15·6° | $H_2O$ | 49 |
| 2-$O$-$\beta$-Cellobiosyl-D-erythritol | 209—211 | — 8·3° | $H_2O$ | 49 |
| 2-$O$-$\beta$-Laminaribiosyl-D-erythritol | 164—166 | — 23·8° | $H_2O$ | 49 |
| 1-$O$-$\beta$-Laminaribiosyl-D-mannitol | | — 24·8° | $H_2O$ | 22, 23, 25 |
| dodeca-$O$-acetate | 145 | — 18·6° | $CHCl_3$ | 22, 23, 25 |
| $O$-$\alpha$-D-Galactopyranosyl-(1→6)-$O$-$\beta$-D-galacto-pyranosyl-1-$O$-glycerol | 182—184 | + 86·4° | $H_2O$ | 15 |
| 3-$O$-$\alpha$-D-Mannopyranosylfloridoside nona-$O$-acetate | 153—154 | +103° | $CHCl_3$ | 11 |
| $O$-$\beta$-D-Galactopyranosyl-(1→4)-$O$-[$\alpha$-D-glucopyra-nosyl-(1→2)]-D-glucitol | | + 89° | $H_2O$ | 45 |
| $O$-$\beta$-D-Galactopyranosyl-(1→4)-$O$-$\beta$-D-galacto-pyranosyl-(1→2)-D-erythritol | 180—183 | + 13° | $H_2O$ | 90 |
| $O$-$\beta$-D-Glucopyranosyl-(1→2)-$O$-$\beta$-D-xylopyranosyl-(1→4)-D-xylitol deca-$O$-methyl ether | | + 35·6° | | 81 |
| 4,6-Di-$O$-$\alpha$-D-glucopyranosyl-D-glucitol | | +110° | $H_2O$ | 91 |
| Maltotetraitol | | +149·9° | | 62 |
| pentadeca-$O$-acetate | 113·5 | + 52·6° | $CHCl_3$ | 62 |
| 2-$O$-$\beta$-Cellotriosylglycerol | 234—237 | — 12·4° | $H_2O$ | 49 |
| 1-$O$-$\beta$-Laminaritriosyl-D-mannitol | | — 26° | $H_2O$ | 25 |
| pentadeca-$O$-acetate | | — 24° | $CHCl_3$ | 25 |
| Xylotetraitol | | — 64·2° | $H_2O$ | 89 |
| Cellopentaitol | 284·5 | — 4·6° | $H_2O$ | 54 |
| Maltopentaitol | | +158° | $H_2O$ | 63 |
| Xylopentaitol | | — 67·4° | $H_2O$ | 89 |
| octadeca-$O$-acetate | 197·5 | +132·7° | $CHCl_3$ | 63 |
| 1-$O$-$\beta$-Laminaritetraosyl-D-mannitol | | — 28·1° | $H_2O$ | 25 |
| octadeca-$O$-acetate | | — 34·1° | $CHCl_3$ | 25 |
| 6-$O$-$\alpha$-Isomaltohexaosyl-D-glucitol | not given | not given | | 53 |
| 6-$O$-$\alpha$-Isomaltoheptaosyl-D-glucitol | not given | not given | | 53 |

*References see p. 460*

## REFERENCES

1. B. Lindberg, Acta Chem. Scand. *7*, 1119 (1953).
2. G. Pueyo, Compt. rend. *248*, 2788 (1959).
3. B. Lindberg, C. A. Wachtmeister, and B. Wickberg, Acta Chem. Scand. *6*, 1052 (1952).
4. B. Lindberg, A. Misiorny, and C. A. Wachtmeister, Acta Chem. Scand. *7*, 591 (1953).
5. B. Lindberg and B. Wickberg, Acta Chem. Scand. *8*, 821 (1954).
6. H. Colin and E. Guéguen, Compt. rend. *191*, 163 (1930).
7. H. Colin and J. Augier, Compt. rend. *195*, 1042 (1933).
8. H. Colin, Bull. soc. chim. France [5] *4*, 277 (1937).
9. E. W. Putman and W. Z. Hassid, J. Am. Chem. Soc. *76*, 2221 (1954).
10. J. R. Nunn and M. M. Holdt, J. Am. Chem. Soc. *77*, 2551 (1955).
11. B. Lindberg, Acta Chem. Scand. *8*, 869 (1954).
12. Choug-Ching Su and W. Z. Hassid, Biochemistry *1*, 468 (1962); Chem. Abstr. *57*, 2589 (1962).
13. B. Wickberg, Acta Chem. Scand. *12*, 1183 (1958).
14. B Wickberg, Acta Chem. Scand. *12*, 1187 (1958).
15. H. E. Carter, R. H. McCluer, and E. D. Slifer, J. Am. Chem. Soc. *78*, 3735 (1956).
16. J. F. G. M. Wintermans, Biochim. et Biophys. Acta *44*, 49 (1962).
17. A. A. Benson, H. Daniel, and R. Wiser, Proc. Natl. Acad. Sci. *45*, 1582 (1959).
18. H. Daniel, M. Miyano, R. O. Mumme, T. Yagi, M. Lepage, I. Shibuya, and A. A. Benson, J. Am. Chem. Soc. *83*, 1765 (1961).
19. M. Lepage, H. Daniel, and A. A. Benson, J. Am. Chem. Soc. *73*, 157 (1962).
20. M. Miyano and A. A. Benson, J. Am. Chem. Soc. *84*, 57 (1962).
21. M. Miyano and A. A. Benson, J. Am. Chem. Soc. *84*, 59 (1962).
22. S. Peat, W. J. Whelan, H. G. Lawley, and J. M. Evans, Biochem. J. *61*, X (1955).
23. S. Peat, W. J. Whelan, and H. G. Lawley, J. Chem. Soc. *1958*, 729.
24. I. J. Goldstein, F. Smith, and A. M. Unrau, Chem. & Ind. (London) *1959*, 124.
25. S. Peat, W. J. Whelan, and J. M. Evans, J. Chem. Soc. *1960*, 175.
26. G. G. S. Dutton and A. M. Unrau, Can. J. Chem. *40*, 348 (1962).
27. J. J. Armstrong, J. Baddiley, and J. G. Buchanan, Nature *181*, 1692 (1958).
28. J. J. Armstrong, J. Baddiley, J. G. Buchanan, B. Carss, and G. R. Greenberg, J. Chem. Soc. *1958*, 4344.
29. J. J. Armstrong, J. Baddiley, and J. G. Buchanan, Biochem. J. *76*, 610 (1960).
30. J. J. Armstrong, J. Baddiley, and J. G. Buchanan, Biochem. J. *80*, 254 (1961).
31. J. Baddiley, J. G. Buchanan, and F. E. Hardy, J. Chem. Soc. *1961*, 2180.
32. J. Baddiley, J. G. Buchanan, U. L. Raj Bhandary, and A. R. Sanderson, Biochem. J. *82*, 439 (1962).
33. A. R. Archibald, J. Baddiley, and J. G. Buchanan, Biochem. J. *81*, 124 (1961).
34. L. J. Sargent, J. G. Buchanan, and J. Baddiley, J. Chem. Soc. *1962*, 2184.
35. G. Bouchardat, Bull. soc. chim. France *16*, 38 (1871).
36. C. Neuberg and F. Marx, Biochem. Z. *3*, 543 (1907).
37. W. J. Whelan and D. M. Jones, Biochem. J. *54*, XXXIV (1953).
38. A. L. Clingman, J. R. Nunn, and A. M. Stephen, J. Chem. Soc. *1957*, 197.
39. E. Dryselius, B. Lindberg, and O. Theander, Acta Chem. Scand. *11*, 663 (1957).
40. A. J. Charlson and A. S. Perlin, Can. J. Chem. *34*, 1200 (1956).
41. A. J. Charlson, P. A. J. Gorin, and A. S. Perlin, Can. J. Chem. *34*, 1811 (1956).
42. A. J. Charlson, P. A. J. Gorin, and A. S. Perlin, Can. J. Chem. *35*, 365 (1957).
43. L. Hough, B. M. Woods, and M. B. Perry, Chem. & Ind. (London) *1957*, 1100.
44. T. J. Painter, Can. J. Chem. *38*, 112 (1960).

45. R. W. Bailey, S. A. Barker, E. J. Bourne, P. M. Grant, and M. Stacey, J. Chem. Soc. *1958*, 1895.
46. P. A. J. Gorin and A. S. Perlin, Can. J. Chem. *34*, 1796 (1956).
47. P. A. J. Gorin and J. F. T. Spencer, Can. J. Chem. *37*, 499 (1959).
48. J. R. Turvey and J. M. Evans, J. Chem. Soc. *1960*, 2366.
49. F. W. Parrish, A. S. Perlin, and E. T. Reese, Can. J. Chem. *38*, 2094 (1960).
50. J. L. Bose, A. B. Foster, N. Salim, M. Stacey, and J. M. Webber, Tetrahedron *14*, 201 (1961).
51. S. A. Barker, M. C. Keith, and M. Stacey, Nature *189*, 746 (1961).
52. P. A. J. Gorin and J. F. T. Spencer, Can. J. Chem. *39*, 2282 (1961).
53. R. W. Bailey, D. H. Hutson, and H. Weigel, Biochem. J. *80*, 514 (1961).
54. E. Beélik and J. K. Hamilton, J. Org. Chem. *26*, 5074 (1961).
55. J. K. N. Jones and T. J. Painter, J. Chem. Soc. *1957*, 669.
56. V. Ipatieff, Ber. *45*, 3218 (1912).
57. J. B. Senderens, Compt. rend. *170*, 47 (1920).
58. P. A. Levene and M. Kuna, Science *85*, 550 (1937); Chem. Abstr. *31*, 5324 (1937).
59. P. Karrer and J. Büchi, Helv. Chim. Acta *20*, 88 (1937).
60. M. L. Wolfrom, W. J. Burke, K. R. Brown, and R. S. Rose, J. Am. Chem. Soc. *60*, 571 (1938).
61. R. L. Whistler and Ch. Smith, J. Am. Chem. Soc. *74*, 3795 (1952).
62. R. L. Whistler and J. L. Hickson, J. Am. Chem. Soc. *76*, 1671 (1954).
63. R. L. Whistler and J. H. Duffy, J. Am. Chem. Soc. *77*, 1017 (1955).
64. R. Kuhn, I. Löw, and H. Trischmann, Chem. Ber. *90*, 203 (1957).
65. R. W. Jones, D. J. Dimler, and C. E. Rist, J. Am. Chem. Soc. *77*, 1659 (1955).
66. J. W. E. Glattfeld and G. W. Schimpff, J. Am. Chem. Soc. *57*, 2204 (1935).
67. S. A. Barker, A. Gómez-Sánchez, and M. Stacey, J. Chem. Soc. *1959*, 3264.
68. D. French, R. J. Suhadolnik, and L. A. Underkofler, Science *117*, 100 (1953).
69. N. M. Carter, Ber. *63*, 1684 (1930).
70. M. Cantley, L. Hough, and A. O. Pittet, Chem. & Ind. (London) *1959*, 1253.
71. M. J. Clancy and W. J. Whelan, Chem. & Ind. (London) *1959*, 673.
72. M. L. Wolfrom, R. M. Hann, and C. S. Hudson, J. Am. Chem. Soc. *74*, 1105 (1952).
73. D. French, G. M. Wild, B. Young, and W. J. James, J. Am. Chem. Soc. *75*, 709 (1953).
74. M. L. Wolfrom and I. S. Gardner, J. Am. Chem. Soc. *62*, 2553 (1940).
75. D. French, G. M. Wild, and W. J. James, J. Am. Chem. Soc. *75*, 3664 (1953).
76. J. K. N. Jones and M. B. Perry, J. Am. Chem. Soc. *79*, 2787 (1957).
77. E. J. Bourne, D. H. Hutson, and H. Weigel, Biochem. J. *79*, 549 (1961).
78. J. R. Turvey, Colloq. Intern, Centre Nat. Rech. Sci. (Paris) No. 103, 29 (1960); Chem. Abstr. *57*, 7620 (1962).
79. S. Peat, J. R. Turvey, and J. M. Evans, Nature *179*, 261 (1957).
80. A. Sato, Y. Ito, and H. Ono, Chem. & Ind. (London) *1962*, 301.
81. H. C. Srivastava, C. T. Bishop, and G. A. Adams, J. Org. Chem. *26*, 3958 (1961).
82. M. J. Clancy, J. Chem. Soc. *1960*, 4213.
83. A. Assarson and O. Theander, Acta Chem. Scand. *12*, 1319 (1958).
84. G. O. Aspinall and K. M. Ross, J. Chem. Soc. *1963*, 1681.
85. H. O. Bouveng, H. Kiessling, B. Lindberg, and J. McKay, Acta Chem. Scand. *17*, 797 (1963).
86. B. Lindberg, B. G. Silvander, and C. A. Wachtmeister, Acta Chem. Scand. *17*, 1348 (1963).
87. B. Lindberg, B. G. Silvander, and C. A. Wachtmeister, Acta Chem. Scand, *18*, 213 (1964).

88. J. H. Sloneker, D. G. Orentas, and A. Jeannes, Can. J. Chem. *42*, 1261 (1964).

89. R. H. Marchessault and T. E. Timell, J. Polymer. Sci. Pt. C. No 2, 49 (1963); Chem. Abstr. *59*, 8847 (1963).

90. P. A. J. Gorin, J. F. T. Spencer, and H. J. Phaff, Can J. Chem. *42*, 1341 (1964).

91. R. de Souza and I. J. Goldstein, Tetrahedron Letters *1964*, 1215.

92. P. W. Austin, F. E. Hardy, J. G. Buchanan, and J. Baddiley, J. Chem. Soc. *1964*, 2128.

## 1. ANHYDRO DERIVATIVES OF GLYCOSYLALDITOLS

Some substances belonging to this relatively broad group may be obtained from natural products. Thus, 4-*O*-β-D-galactopyranosyl-3,6-anhydro-D-galactose (I) may be converted by reduction with sodium borohydride into 4-*O*-β-D-galactopyranosyl-3,6-anhydro-D-galactitol (II);[1,2] the same initial substance (I) may be converted into the substituted thioacetal (III),[3] which on desulphurization with Raney nickel then yields 4-$O$-$\beta$-D-galactopyranosyl-1-deoxy-3,6-anhydro-D-galactitol (IV).[3] The reduction of 4-$O$-$\beta$-D-galactopyranosyl-3,6-anhydro-L-galactose has been effected in a similar way.[4]

Most easily accessible purely synthetic substances of this type are the 1,5-anhydro derivatives of glycosylalditols. They are obtainable, on the one hand, by hydrogenation of glycoseens derived from reducing oligosaccharides[5] (see Chapter XXI), and on the other hand, by desulphurization of thioglycosides of reducing oligosaccharides with Raney nickel[6,7] (see Chapter XVI).

The first procedure led originally to erroneous conclusions.[5] The hydrogenation of hepta-$O$-acetyl-2-hydroxycellobial (V), on the assumption of the creation of a new asymmetric centre at C-2, may give rise to a derivative of either the mannose series (VI) or the glucose series (VII). By analogy it was first

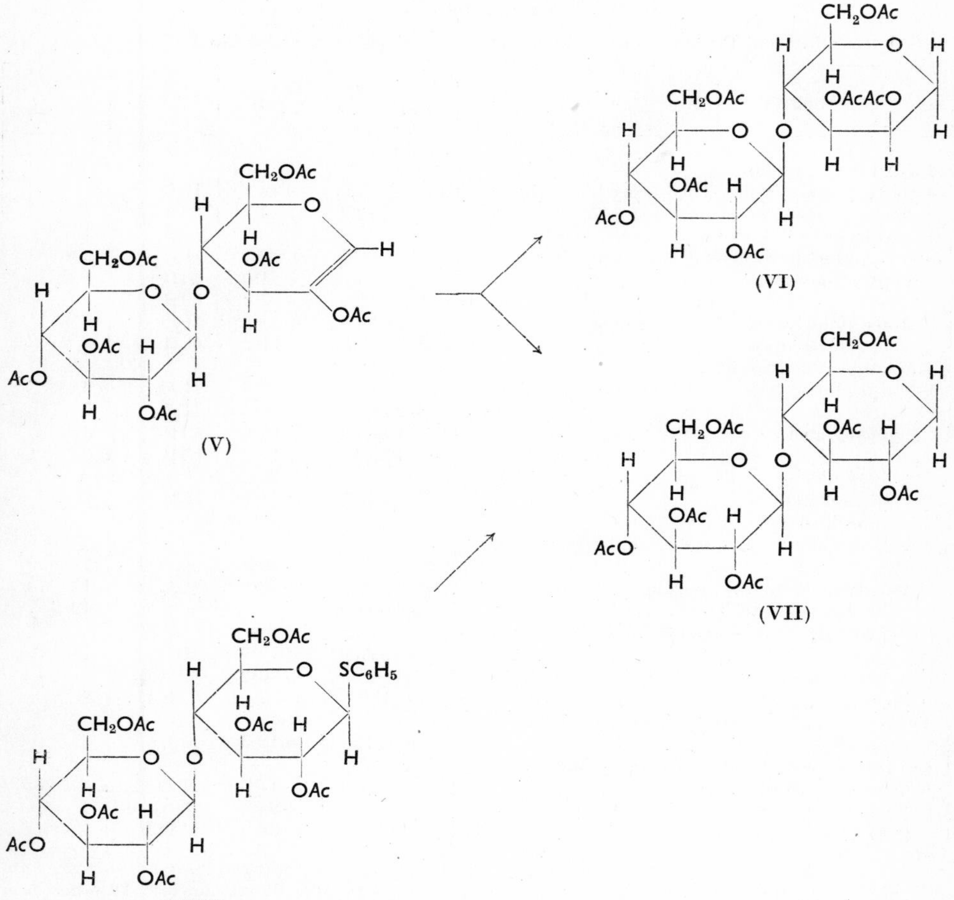

(V)

(VI)

(VII)

(VIII)

believed that a substance with mannose configuration was formed, namely a derivative of 4-O-β-D-glucopyranosylstyracitol (VI), and the course of the hydrogenation of hepta-O-acetyl-2-hydroxygentiobial was considered similar.[5]

Other investigators obtained by desulphurization of phenyl hepta-O-acetyl-β-thiocellobioside (VIII) and deacetylation the same product[6] as formed by hydrogenation of hepta-O-acetyl-2-hydroxycellobial (V) and subsequent deacetylation. Consequently, the substance produced in this way cannot have the structure of 4-O-β-D-glucopyranosylstyracitol (VI), but must correspond to 4-O-β-D-glucopyranosyl-1,5-anhydro-D-glucitol (VII). Derivatives of 1,5-anhydrolactitol and 1,5-anhydromaltitol were prepared analogously.[7]

Included among the anhydro derivatives of reduction products of reducing oligosaccharides are the dihydro derivatives of glycals derived from reducing oligosaccharides (see Chapter XXI).

### Table LXXXIV

Physical Properties of Anhydro Derivatives of Oligosaccharide Alditols

| Oligosaccharide Derivative | Melting Point °C | $[\alpha]_D$ | Solvent | References |
|---|---|---|---|---|
| 1,5-Anhydromaltitol | | | | |
| 4-O-α-D-glucopyranosyl-1,5-anhydro-D-glucitol | amorphous | +132° | $H_2O$ | 7 |
| hepta-O-acetate | 133—134 | +82° | $CHCl_3$ | 7 |
| 1,5-Anhydrocellobiitol | | | | |
| 4-O-β-D-glucopyranosyl-1,5-anhydro-D-glucitol* | 172 | +29·3° | $H_2O$ | 5, 6 |
| hepta-O-acetate | 195 | + 4·0° | $CHCl_3$ | 6 |
| | 187 | + 7·0° | $CHCl_3$ | 5 |
| 2-deoxyderivative, hydrocellobial | 222 | + 4·2° | $H_2O$ | 8, 9 |
| hexa-O-acetate | 133—134 | +11·2° | $C_2H_2Cl_4$ | 8, 9 |
| 1,5-Anhydrogentiobiitol | | | | |
| 6-O-β-D-glucopyranosyl-1,5-anhydro-D-glucitol | 240 | + 3·6° | $H_2O$ | 6 |
| | 223 | + 2·4° | $H_2O$ | 5 |
| hepta-O-acetate | 153 | +13·0° | $CHCl_3$ | 6 |
| | 152 | +17·2° | $CHCl_3$ | 6 |
| 2-deoxyderivative, hydrogentiobial | | | | |
| hexa-O-acetate | 132—133 | +11·1° | $C_5H_5N$ | 10, 11 |
| 1,5-Anhydrolactitol | | | | |
| 4-O-β-D-galactopyranosyl-1,5-anhydro-D-glucitol | 233—237 | +49·4° | $H_2O$ | 7 |
| 2-deoxyderivative, hydrolactal | 204—205 | +26·6° | $H_2O$ | 12—14 |
| hexa-O-acetate | amorphous | | | 12 |
| 4-O-β-D-Galactopyranosyl-3,6-anhydro-D-galactitol | 173·5 | +12·7° | $H_2O$ | 1 |
| hepta-O-acetate | 146 | − 6·2° | $CHCl_3$ | 1 |
| | 145 | − 7·6° | $CHCl_3$ | 2 |
| 4-O-β-D-Galactopyranosyl-1-deoxy-3,6-anhydro-D-galactitol | 135—136 | +12·5° | $H_2O$ | 3 |
| 4-O-β-D-Galactopyranosyl-1-deoxy-3,6-anhydro-L-galactitol | 174 | −15° | $H_2O$ | 4 |
| penta-O-benzoate | | +64° | $CHCl_3$ | 4 |
| penta-O-methyl ether | | −36° | MeOH | 4 |

* The compound was previously considered to be a derivative of styracitol.[5] This has been corrected.[6]

## REFERENCES

1. T. J. Painter, Can. J. Chem. *38*, 112 (1960).
2. A. L. Clingman and J. R. Nunn, J. Chem. Soc. *1959*, 493.
3. N. A. O'Neill, J. Am. Chem. Soc. *77*, 6324 (1955).
4. A. L. Clingman, J. R. Nunn, and A. M. Stephen, J. Chem. Soc. *1957*, 197.
5. K. Maurer and K. Plötner, Ber. *64*, 281 (1931).
6. H. G. Fletcher and C. S. Hudson, J. Am. Chem. Soc. *70*, 309 (1948).
7. H. G. Fletcher, L. H. Koehler, and C. S. Hudson, J. Am. Chem. Soc. *71*, 3679 (1949).
8. E. Fischer and K. Fodor, Ber. *47*, 2058 (1914).
9. M. Bergmann and H. Schotte, Ber. *54*, 1570 (1921).
10. M. Bergmann and W. Freudenberg, Ber. *62*, 2785 (1929).
11. H. J. Dauben and W. L. Evans, J. Am. Chem. Soc. *60*, 886 (1938).
12. E. Fischer and G. O. Curme, Ber. *47*, 2047 (1914).
13. W. N. Haworth, E. L. Hirst, M. T. Plant, and R. J. W. Reynolds, J. Chem. Soc. *1930*, 2644.
14. M. Bergmann, H. Schotte, and E. Rennert, Ann. *434*, 86 (1923).

# 2. AMINODEOXY DERIVATIVES OF GLYCOSYLALDITOLS

Some natural reducing aminodeoxy oligosaccharides have been converted into the corresponding aminodeoxy derivatives of glycosylalditols by reduction [1-3] either with sodium borohydride[1,3] or catalytically on palladium.[2] In this way di-$N$-acetylchitobiitol and tri-$N$-acetylchitotriitol,[1] as well as lacto-$N$-fucopentaitol $I$[2] and lacto-$N$-fucopentaitol $II$[3] have been obtained.

Several new compounds have been obtained by reduction of disaccharides produced by graded acid hydrolysis of carboxyl reduced heparin; 4-$O$-α-D-glucopyranosyl-2-acetamido-2-deoxy-D-glucitol, $[\alpha]_D + 75°$ ($H_2O$) and 3-$O$-α-2-acetamido-2-deoxy-D-glucopyranosyl-L-gulitol, $[\alpha]_D + 55°$ have been described by M. L. Wolfrom, J. R. Vercellotti, and D. Horton, J. Org. Chem. *29*, 540 (1964).

4-$O$-β-D-Glucosaminyl-D-ribitol has been obtained among degradation products of *Staphylococcus aureus* teichoic acid.[4] Both 4-$O$-α-D-glucosaminyl-D-ribitol and 4-$O$-β-D-glucosaminyl-D-ribitol have been synthesized by a Koenigs-Knorr procedure from convenient starting compounds.[5]

$N$-Methylmaltamine, i. e. 4-$O$-α-1-deoxy-1-methylamino-D-glucopyranosyl-D-glucitol, has been prepared by E. Ulsperger and G. Eugler, J. prakt. Chem. *21*, 173 (1963); Chem. Abstr. *60*, 4229 (1964) by the reduction of maltose in the presence of methylamine and Raney nickel.

*References see p. 466*

## Table LXXXV

Physical Properties of Aminodeoxy Derivatives of Oligosaccharide Alditols

| Oligosaccharide Derivative | Melting Point °C | $[\alpha]_D$ | Solvent | References |
|---|---|---|---|---|
| Chitobiitol<br>$N,N'$-diacetyl derivative | 102—105 | | | 1 |
| Chitotriitol<br>$N,N',N''$-triacetyl derivative | 195—200 | | | 1 |
| Lacto-$N$-fucopentaitol $I$ | | −30° | $H_2O$ | 2 |
| Lacto-$N$-fucopentaitol $II$<br>hendeca-$O$-methyl ether | 205—210<br>119—120 | −46°<br>−58° | $H_2O$<br>$CHCl_3$ | 3<br>3 |

## REFERENCES

1. S. A. Barker, A. B. Foster, M. Stacey, and J. M. Webber, J. Chem. Soc. *1958*, 2218.
2. R. Kuhn, H. H. Baer, and A. Gauhe, Chem. Ber. *89*, 2514 (1956).
3. R. Kuhn, H. H. Baer, and A. Gauhe, Chem. Ber. *91*, 364 (1958).
4. A. R. Sanderson, J. L. Strominger, and S. G. Nathenson, J. Biol. Chem. *237*, 3603 (1962).
5. F. E. Hardy, J. G. Buchanan, and J. Baddiley, J. Chem. Soc. *1963*, 3360.

# XXXI

## Aldonic Acids from the Series of Reducing Oligosaccharides

Aldobionic, aldotrionic and also higher acids are without exception prepared synthetically by various procedures, the easiest of them being oxidation of the reducing oligosaccharide; for example, gentiobiose (I) is oxidized to the corresponding aldonic acid, i. e. gentiobionic acid, which is usually obtained in the form of its lactone (II).

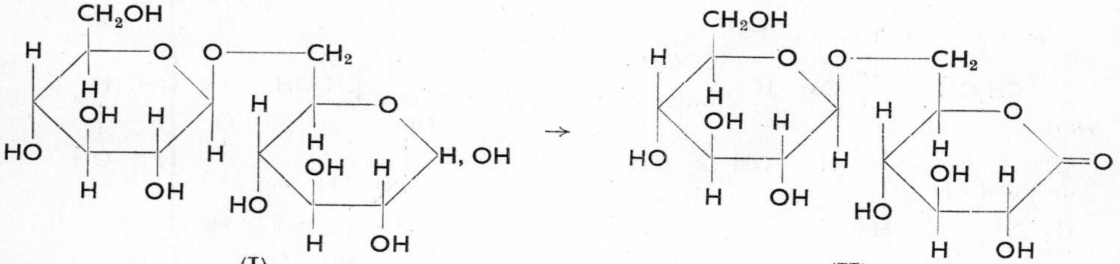

(I)    (II)

Less common methods for preparing aldonic acids from the oligosaccharide series are either degradation of reducing oligosaccharides or their derivatives, or syntheses of higher aldonic acids by addition of hydrogen cyanide.

The oxidation of reducing oligosaccharides is usually effected by means of bromine in the presence of calcium carbonate or another calcium salt, such as calcium benzoate. This method has been employed for oxidizing maltose,[1-4] lactose,[5-12a] cellobiose,[12b] melibiose,[13-16] gentiobiose,[17] isomaltose,[17] vicianose,[18, 19] primeverose,[20,21] 4-O-α-D-glucopyranosyl-D-xylose,[22] 2-O-β-D-glucopyranosyl-D-galactose,[23] 6-O-α-D-galactopyranosyl-D-galactose,[24] 2-O-β-D-mannopyranosyl-D-mannose,[25] 2-O-α-D-glucopyranosyl-D-erythrose,[26] 2-O-β-D-glucopyranosyl-D-erythrose,[27] 2-O-β-D-galactopyranosyl-D-erythrose,[28] 2-O-β-D-glucopyranosyl-D-arabinose,[29] and manninotriose.[30-33]

According to more recent investigations,[12] there exists a certain difference between the rates of oxidation of the anomeric forms of individual oligosaccharides. For example, β-lactose is oxidized by bromine twice as rapidly as the corresponding α-anomer.

According to some papers, it is more advantageous to oxidize lactose and maltose electrolytically in the presence of bromine and calcium carbonate.[4,34,35]

*References see p. 471*

30*

Less common oxidants are hypochlorites,[36] hypobromites[37] and hypoiodites.[38,39]
The oxidation of a reducing oligosaccharide may also be brought about by
means of mercuric oxide,[39] although this possibility was originally denied.[40] One
report only deals with the possibility of microbial oxidation of lactose to lactobionic acid by the action of the micro-organism *Pseudomonas graveolens*.[41]

Aldonic acids, however prepared, have been obtained in the majority of
cases in the form of their calcium salts, frequently as double salts with calcium
chloride[42] or calcium bromide.[43] In some cases, the free aldobionic acid could
be produced by the reaction of its calcium salt with carbon dioxide and precipitation of calcium carbonate.[35] As far as it is sterically possible, aldobionic acids,
too, form lactones. Lactobionic acid (III) can form only the δ-lactone (IV),[35,44]
and the same applies to cellobionic acid,[45] although in this case the possibility of
lactone formation has been disputed.[39] 3-O-α-D-Glucopyranosyl-D-arabonic
acid (V) can form both the γ-lactone (VI) and the δ-lactone (VII).[45]

The shortening of the carbon chain of reducing oligosaccharides, which is usually carried out with glycals as initial substances, leads generally to aldonic acids (see Chapter XXX). The double bond in the glycal molecule may be split oxidatively by the action of potassium permanganate. For example, maltal (VIII) is converted in this way into 3-$O$-α-D-glucopyranosyl-D-arabonic acid (IX),[26] and a similar degradation has been carried out with a number of other compounds.[27,28,46]

(VIII) → (IX)

According to a later paper, maltose, cellobiose and lactose were degraded by oxygen in alkaline solution to 3-$O$-glycosyl derivatives of D-arabonic acid.[47]

The lengthening of the molecule of a reducing oligosaccharide by the cyanohydrin synthesis has been known for a long time;[48,49] however, the first experiments, undertaken with lactose, did not lead to crystalline products, which were obtained only much later.[50] Neither did the first experiments with maltose lead to defined substances;[49] these were obtained later[51] from both maltose and cellobiose. It is interesting to note that the carboxylic acids produced from lactose and cellobiose form lactones, while the corresponding acid prepared from maltose gives no lactone.[51] These substances have also been investigated from the viewpoint of Hudson's Isorotation Rules.[52]

The cyanohydrin synthesis for preparing aldonic acids of the oligosaccharide series is most frequently utilized for the preparation of labelled oligosaccharides,[4,53] such as [1—14C]-lactose[53] and [1—14C]-maltose[4] (see also Chapter VI).

Aldobionic acids may be converted by reduction with sodium amalgam into the corresponding reducing oligosaccharides, for example maltobionic acid into maltose.[4,54] These acids are of greatest importance, however, in many structural studies, because by hydrolysis of an aldobionic acid it is possible to determine which of two mutually linked aldoses is the reducing unit in the oligosaccharide.[22] Of special value in this respect has been the hydrolysis of the aldobionic acid per-$O$-methyl ethers.[32,55] Periodic acid oxidation of aldobionic acids, too, offers a better insight into the structure of the molecule.[33,56]

Moreover, aldobionic acids have been used in some cases as initial substances in several procedures for shortening the carbon chain of oligosaccharides (see Chapter VI).

*References see p. 471*

Lactobionic acid and maltobionic acid are oxidized enzymically by the action of *Alcaligenes faecalis* to the corresponding 3-keto derivatives.[57,58]

Octa-$O$-acetylcellobionic acid, m. p. 138°C, $[\alpha]_D + 8\cdot9°$ (CHCl$_3$), its chloride, m. p. 115°C, $[\alpha]_D + 2\cdot1°$ (CHCl$_3$) and azide, m. p. 112°C, $[\alpha]_D + 12\cdot9°$ (CHCl$_3$) have been prepared by R. Bognár, I. Farkas, I. F. Szabó, and G. D. Szabó, Chem. Ber. *96*, 689 (1963).

## Table LXXXVI

Physical Properties of Oligosaccharide Aldonic Acids

| Oligosaccharide Aldonic Acid | Melting Point °C | $[\alpha]_D(H_2O)$ | References |
|---|---|---|---|
| Maltobionic acid | | $+ 98\cdot3°$ | 1, 2, 33 |
| labelled | | $+104\cdot1°$ | 4 |
| brucine salt | 153 | $+ 38\cdot1°$ | 2 |
| methyl ester octa-$O$-methyl ether | | $+120\cdot8°$ | 55 |
| $\delta$-lactone | 192—195 | $+123°$ | 4 |
| Cellobiobionic acid | | $- 3\cdot6° \rightarrow +1°$ | 39 |
| Sophoronic acid | | | |
| Ba salt | | $-4\cdot2° \rightarrow -5\cdot1°$ | 59 |
| Lactobionic acid | syrup | $+166° \rightarrow +2°$ | 3—11 |
| Na salt | | $+22\cdot3°$ | 41 |
| $\delta$-lactone | 195—196 | $+54° \rightarrow + 22\cdot3°$ | 35, 44 |
| Melibionic acid | | $+106° \rightarrow +113\cdot8°$ | 13—16, 33 |
| methyl ester octa-$O$-methyl ether | | $+106\cdot4°$ | 15 |
| Vicianobionic acid | | | 18, 19 |
| Primeverobionic acid | | | 20, 21 |
| Manninotrionic acid | | $+157\cdot5° \rightarrow +138\cdot7°$ | 30—32 |
| | | $+131\cdot4°$ | 33 |
| 4-$O$-$\alpha$-D-Glucopyranosyl-D-xylonic acid | | | 22 |
| 2-$O$-$\beta$-D-Glucopyranosyl-D-galactonic acid | | | 23 |
| 2-$O$-$\alpha$-D-Glucopyranosyl-D-erythronic acid | | | 26 |
| 2-$O$-$\beta$-D-Glucopyranosyl-D-erythronic acid | | | 27 |
| 3-$O$-$\alpha$-D-Glucopyranosyl-D-arabonic acid | | | 26, 46 |
| brucine salt | 152—154 | $+50°$ | 47 |
| 3-$O$-$\beta$-D-Glucopyranosyl-D-arabonic acid | | | 27 |
| brucine salt | 149—150 (dec.) | $- 6\cdot2°$ | 47 |
| 2-$O$-$\beta$-D-Galactopyranosyl-D-erythronic acid | | | 28 |
| 3-$O$-$\beta$-D-Galactopyranosyl-D-arabonic acid | | | 28 |
| brucine salt | 144—145 | $- 3\cdot4°$ | 47 |
| 2-$O$-$\beta$-D-Mannopyranosyl-D-mannonic acid | | | 25 |
| 5-$O$-$\beta$-D-Galactopyranosyl-D-*glycero*-D-*gulo*-heptonic acid | | | |
| 5-$O$-$\beta$-D-galactopyranosyl-$\alpha$-D-glucoheptonic acid | 186 (dec.) | $+11\cdot2°$ | 50 |
| | | $+12\cdot8°$ | 51, 52 |
| brucine salt | 173 (dec.) | $- 7\cdot6°$ | 50 |
| quinine salt | 170 (dec.) | $-71\cdot9°$ | 50 |
| 5-$O$-$\alpha$-D-Glucopyranosyl-D-*glycero*-D-*gulo*-heptonic acid | | | |
| 5-$O$-$\alpha$-D-glucopyranosyl-$\alpha$-D-glucoheptonic acid | | $+34\cdot8°$ | 51, 52 |
| 5-$O$-$\beta$-D-Glucopyranosyl-D-*glycero*-D-*gulo*-heptonic acid | | | |
| 5-$O$-$\beta$-D-glucopyranosyl-$\alpha$-D-glucoheptonic acid | | $+ 6\cdot5°$ | 51, 52 |

## REFERENCES

1. E. Fischer and J. Meyer, Ber. *22*, 1941 (1889).
2. J. K. E. Glattfeld and M. T. Hauke, J. Am. Chem. Soc. *40*, 973 (1918).
3. R. L. Whistler and K. Yagi, J. Org. Chem. *26*, 1050 (1961).
4. H. S. Isbell and R. Schaffer, J. Am. Chem. Soc. *78*, 1887 (1956).
5. E. Fischer and J. Meyer, Ber. *22*, 361 (1889).
6. O. Ruff and G. Ollendorf, Ber. *33*, 1806 (1900).
7. P. A. Levene and H. Sobotka, J. Biol. Chem. *71*, 471 (1927).
8. W. F. Goebel, J. Biol. Chem. *72*, 809 (1927).
9. G. Zemplén, Ber. *60*, 1310 (1927).
10. W. N. Haworth and C. W. Long, J. Chem. Soc. *1927*, 544.
11. C. S. Hudson and H. S. Isbell, J. Am. Chem. Soc. *51*, 2225 (1929).
12a. G. Malyoth and H. W. Stein, Klin. Wochschr. *30*, 14 (1952); Chem. Abstr. *46*, 10109 (1952).
12b. L. Maquenne and W. Goodwin, Bull. soc. chim. France [3] *31*, 857 (1904).
13. C. Neuberg, L. Scott, and S. Lachmann, Biochem. Z. *24*, 162 (1910).
14. P. A. Levene and O. Wintersteiner, J. Biol. Chem. *75*, 321 (1927).
15. W. N. Haworth, J. V. Loach, and C. W. Long, J. Chem. Soc. *1927*, 3146.
16. P. A. Levene and E. Jorpes, J. Biol. Chem. *86*, 403 (1930).
17. M. L. Wolfrom, A. Thompson, and A. M. Brownstein, J. Am. Chem. Soc. *80*, 2015 (1958).
18. G. Bertrand and G. Weisweiller, Compt. rend. *151*, 885 (1910).
19. G. Bertrand and G. Weisweiller, Bull. soc. chim. France [4] *9*, 147 (1911).
20. A. Goris and Ch. Vischniac, Compt. rend. *169*, 976 (1919).
21. A. Goris and Ch. Vischniac, Bull. soc. chim. France [4] *27*, 263 (1920).
22. E. W. Putman, C. F. Litt, and W. Z. Hassid, J. Am. Chem. Soc. *77*, 4351 (1955).
23. A. M. Gakhokidze and M. Kutidze, Zhur. Obshcheĭ Khim. *22*, 139 (1952); Chem. Abstr. *46*, 11116 (1952).
24. C. N. Turton, A. Bebbington, S. Dixon, and E. Pacsu, J. Am. Chem. Soc. *77*, 2565 (1955).
25. A. M. Gakhokidze and M. Kutidze, Zhur. Obshcheĭ Khim. *22*, 247 (1952); Chem. Abstr. *46*, 11117 (1952).
26. A. M. Gakhokidze, Zhur. Obshcheĭ Khim. *20*, 116 (1950); Chem. Abstr. *44*, 5819 (1950).
27. A. M. Gakhokidze, Zhur. Obshcheĭ Khim. *20*, 289 (1950); Chem. Abstr. *44*, 6822 (1950).
28. A. M. Gakhokidze, Zhur. Obshcheĭ Khim. *20*, 120 (1950); Chem. Abstr. *44*, 5819 (1950).
29. A. M. Gakhokidze, Zhur. Obshcheĭ Khim. *19*, 2082 (1949); Chem. Abstr. *44*, 3914 (1950).
30. C. Tanret, Compt. rend. *134*, 1589 (1902).
31. C. Tanret, Bull. soc. chim. France [3] *27*, 958 (1902).
22. M. Onuki, J. Agr. Chem. Soc. Japan *8*, 445 (1932); Chem. Abstr. *26*, 4308 (1932).
33. J. E. Courtois, A. Wickström, and P. Le Dizet, Bull. soc. chim. biol. *35*, 1117 (1953).
34. H. S. Isbell and H. L. Frush, J. Research Natl. Bur. Standards *6*, 1145 (1931); Chem. Abstr. *25*, 4850 (1931).
35. H. S. Isbell, J. Research Natl. Bur. Standards *11*, 713 (1933); Chem. Abstr. *28*, 1667 (1934).
36. Ger. Patent 461, 370; Chem. Zentr. *1928*, II, 1382.
37. M. Hönig and W. Ruzicka, Biochem. Z. *218*, 397 (1930).

38. W. F. Goebel, J. Biol. Chem. *72*, 809 (1927).

39. K. Freudenberg, K. Friedrich, and I. Bumann, Ann. *494*, 41 (1932).

40. H. Pringsheim and A. M. Meerkatz, Hoppe-Seyler's Z. physiol. Chem. *105*, 173 (1915).

41. G. E. N. Nelson and F. H. Stodola, J. Am. Chem. Soc. *75*, 1748 (1953).

42. U. S. Patent 1,980,996; Chem. Abstr. *29*, 478 (1935).

43. H. S. Isbell, J. Research Natl. Bur. Standards *17*, 331 (1936).

44. J. W. E. Glattfeld and G. W. Schimpff, J. Am. Chem. Soc. *57*, 2204 (1935).

45. P. A. Levene and M. L. Wolfrom, J. Biol. Chem. *77*, 671 (1928); Chem. Abstr. *22*, 2925 (1928).

46. A. M. Gakhokidze, Zhur. Obshcheĭ Khim. *19*, 2100 (1949); Chem. Abstr. *44*, 3913 (1950).

47. E. Hardegger, K. Kreis, and H. El Khadem, Helv. Chim. Acta *35*, 618 (1952).

48. E. Fischer, Ber. *23*, 932 (1890).

49. O. Reinbrecht, Ann. *272*, 197 (1892).

50. R. M. Hann and C. S. Hudson, J. Am. Chem. Soc. *56*, 1390 (1934).

51. M. Uenaka, Scientific Papers Osaka Univ. *1951*, No. 23.

52. M. Uenaka, Scientific Papers Osaka Univ. *1951*, No. 24.

53. H. L. Frush and H. S. Isbell, J. Research Natl. Bur. Standards *50*, 133 (1953).

54. U. S. Patent 2,606,918.

55. W. N. Haworth and S. Peat, J. Chem. Soc. *1926*, 3094.

56. M. J. Clancy and W. J. Whelan, Chem. & Ind. (London) *1959*, 673.

57. M. J. Bernaerts and J. DeLey, Biochim. et Biophys. Acta *30*, 661 (1958).

58. M. J. Bernaerts, J. Furnelle, and J. DeLey, Biochim. et Biophys. Acta *69*, 322 (1963).

59. M. J. Clancy, J. Chem. Soc. *1960*, 4213.

# XXXII

# Acylated Derivatives of Aldobionic Acid Nitriles

Oximes of reducing oligosaccharides with a reducing aldehyde group may usually be converted by acetylation with simultaneous dehydration into acetylated nitriles of aldobionic acids. This was carried out with the use of the oximes of cellobiose,[1] lactose,[2,3] melibiose,[4] and maltose;[5] however, only in the case of cellobiose[1] and later of lactose[3] was it possible to obtain in this way a crystalline acetylated aldobionic acid nitrile. Cellobiose oxime (I) on the assumption of an acyclic structure of the reducing part of the molecule thus reacts with acetic anhydride to form octa-O-acetylcellobionic acid nitrile (II).[1]

(I)                                                 (II)

## Table LXXXVII

Physical Properties of Acylated Derivatives of Aldobionic Acid Nitriles

| Acylated Aldobionic Acid Nitrile | Melting Point °C | $[\alpha]_D$ | Solvent | References |
|---|---|---|---|---|
| Octa-O-acetyl- | | | | |
| cellobionic acid nitrile | 132 | $+34 \cdot 8°$ | $CHCl_3$ | 1 |
| lactobionic acid nitrile | 90—93 | $+35 \cdot 5°$ | MeOH | 2, 3 |
| melibionic acid nitrile | | | | 4 |
| maltobionic acid nitrile | | $+92 \cdot 8°$ | $CHCl_3$ | 5 |

*References see p. 474*

## REFERENCES

1. G. Zemplén, Ber. *59*, 1254 (1926).
2. G. Zemplén, Ber. *59*, 2402 (1926).
3. R. Kuhn and W. Kirschenlohr, Ann. *600*, 135 (1956).
4. G. Zemplén, Ber. *60*, 923 (1927).
5. G. Zemplén, Ber. *60*, 1555 (1927).

# XXXIII

# Saccharinic Acids of the Oligosaccharide Series

The so-called saccharinic acids are not unusual substances in the mono-saccharide series. Analogous reactions of reducing oligosaccharides in alkaline solution (see Chapter VII) involve in most cases a cleavage of the glycosidic linkage of the oligosaccharide, so that the reaction product is a saccharinic acid of common type. So far in two cases only has it been possible to obtain a saccharinic acid of the oligosaccharide series by an isolation procedure;[1,2] it has been established with certainty that the alkaline decomposition of guaran yields 5-*O*-α-D-galactopyranosyl-β-D-isosaccharinic acid besides D-mannosyl-β-D-isosaccharinic acid, whose structure has not yet been precisely established. In connection with this finding, 5-*O*-α-D-galactopyranosyl-α-D-isosaccharinic acid has also been synthesized[1] (see Chapter VI).

A recent paper[2] describes another saccharinic acid of the oligosaccharide series. The branched trisaccharide 3,6-di-*O*-β-D-glucopyranosyl-D-glucose yields in alkaline solution 6-*O*-β-D-glucopyranosyl derivatives of both D-gluco-metasaccharinic acids.

### REFERENCES

1. R. L. Whistler and J. N. BeMiller, J. Org. Chem. *26*, 2886 (1961).
2. A. Klemer and K. Homberg, Chem. Ber. *96*, 631 (1963).

# XXXIV

## Oligouronic Acids

To the class of oligouronic acids there at present belong four types of natural products derived from reducing oligosaccharides. The first, most comprehensive group is formed by oligouronic acids proper, in the simplest case composed of a monosaccharide molecule and a molecule of an uronic acid with a glycosidic linkage. This uronic acid is consequently the non-reducing part of the molecule. Substances of this type, of the general formula (I), are characterized by a considerable resistance of the glycosidic linkage toward acid hydrolysis. Much less common acids of the second possible type are also known, i. e. those of the general formula (II), where the uronic acid is the reducing part of the molecule. These substances, termed pseudoaldobiouronic acids, are hydrolysed in acid solution even more slowly than the foregoing compounds.

(I)                                    (II)

A further type, of the general formula (III), comprises polyuronic acids, which are obtained by hydrolysis of miscellaneous natural materials and, in the simplest cases, are paired uronic acids. Finally, among the group of oligouronic acids must be included various nitrogen-containing substances, which are characterized by a glycosidic linkage of the uronic acid to the amino sugar molecule according to the general formula (IV). They are often encountered as cleavage products of natural materials.

(III)                                                                    (IV)

## 1. OLIGOURONIC ACIDS PROPER

Oligouronic acids of the formula (I) may be obtained comparatively easily from natural materials (polysaccharides of miscellaneous types, such as hemicelluloses, xylans, gums, mucilages, and even microbial polysaccharides). The common procedure is acid hydrolysis, however, under more drastic conditions than those of the hydrolysis of the glycosidic linkage proper. This is due to the fact that, in comparison with the glycosidic linkage of the oligosaccharide, the bond of the glycosidically attached uronic acid is considerably more stable, so that the hydrolysis must be carried out by boiling with appropriately diluted sulphuric acid for several hours. This procedure usually leads to aldobiouronic acids (see for example Refs 1—23), although higher acids of this type may be isolated also (see later). Enzymic hydrolysis produces as a rule higher oligouronic acids (see for example Refs 24 and 25).

It has also been reported that an oligouronic acid may be obtained from a polysaccharide by catalytic oxidation of the latter on platinum[26-28] and following hydrolysis of the oxidation product.

The constitution of aldobiouronic acids has been derived in all cases by identification of the hydrolysis products, in particular of those formed by the hydrolysis of per-O-methylated derivatives of aldobiouronic acids.[8,29-41] These per-O-methylated derivatives of aldobiouronic acids have in some cases also been obtained by the hydrolysis of the fully methylated native material.[7,41-44] Conclusions about the constitution of aldobiouronic acids may often be drawn by identification of the reduction product or products of the permethylated derivatives.[45-47]

The glycosidic linkages in the molecules of aldobiouronic acids may be $\alpha$ as well as $\beta$. The first type is no rarity. The configuration of glycosidic linkages is best established[48] by oxidative degradation of the reducing part of the molecule with lead tetra-acetate to a three-carbon residue, whereupon the rotations

*References see p. 489*

of the 2-uronosyl derivatives of glycerol obtained in this way can be compared.[48] The uronic acid most frequently encountered in the study of the composition of oligouronic acids is D-glucuronic acid; less often appear D-galacturonic acid and L-arabinuric acid, the latter being formed secondarily from artificially prepared oxidation products of polysaccharides. These acids are in the majority of cases linked to D-xylose, less frequently to D-glucose, D-galactose, D-mannose, L-arabinose or L-rhamnose.

A frequent component of oligouronic acids is 4-O-methyl-D-glucuronic acid. Reports stating that here 3-O-methyl-D-glucuronic acid is concerned,[49,50] as derived on the basis of periodic acid oxidation, were shortly afterwards corrected in favour of the structure given first.[51]

According to D. I. Vincent, Chem. & Ind. (London) *1960*, 1109, *Laminaria digitata* alginic acids contain D-mannuronic acid and L-guluronic acid. This statement has been verified by E. L. Hirst, E. Percival, and J. K. Wold, Chem. & Ind. (London) *1963*, 257, who identified D-mannosyl-L-gulose among partial acid hydrolysis products of reduced alginic acids.

In one case,[10,52] 2-O-(4-O-methyl-α-D-glucopyranosyluronic acid)-D-lyxose also was isolated from a number of aldobiouronic acids formed in the hydrolysis of hemicelluloses from *Pinus pinaster*. The authors point out correctly, however, that this compound is a secondary product and presents no proof of the existence of D-lyxose among natural substances. This aldobiouronic acid is readily formed by the subsequent epimerization (by the action of a barium carbonate suspension in the heat) to the corresponding uronosyl derivative of D-xylose.

Very little attention has so far been paid to the specific reactions of aldobiouronic acids and to the preparation of their derivatives. 6-O-(β-D-Glucopyranosyluronic acid)-D-galactose, on treatment[53] with methanolic hydrogen chloride at 110°C, yields the corresponding methyl α-glycoside, $[\alpha]_D$ +22.8°, while the reaction at a temperature of 25°C leads to the methyl β-glycoside, $[\alpha]_D$ —66.4°. The paper in question[53] also mentions that this acid can be oxidized with barium bromate to 2-O-(β-D-glucopyranosyluronic acid)-D-galactonic acid.

The stability of 2-O-(4-O-methyl-α-D-glucopyranosyl uronic acid)-D-xylose in alkali solutions has been studied by R. Aurell, N. Hartler, and G. Persson, Acta Chem. Scand. *17*, 545 (1963).

Interesting substances have been obtained in the reduction of aldobiouronic acids by the action of potassium borohydride;[47] the carboxyl group is not reduced under these conditions, so that uronosyl derivatives of alditols are formed, which then may be converted by further reduction with lithium aluminium hydride into glycosyl derivatives of alditols.[47] If the aldobiouronic acid is first converted into the methyl ester by the action of diazomethane, both reducible groups are as a rule reduced simultaneously, so that the glycosyl derivative of the alditol is formed directly.[47]

In some cases, aldobiouronic acids have also been obtained by purely chemical syntheses. The condensation of an ester of 2,3,4-tri-O-acetyl-1-bromo-1-deoxy-α-D-glucuronic acid (I) with 1,2-O-isopropylidene-5-O-trityl-D-xylofuranose (II) under the conditions of the Koenigs-Knorr reaction leads to the expected product (III).[54] The action of hydrogen halides in a non-aqueous medium eliminates the trityl group, following hydrolysis by sulphuric acid in ethanol splits off the blocking isopropylidene group with simultaneous hydrolysis of the ester, whereupon the acetyl groups are removed by a barium hydroxide solution, so that 3-O-(β-D-glucopyranosyluronic acid)-D-xylose (IV) is formed.

Gentiobiouronic acid,[55,56] 6-$O$-($\beta$-D-glucopyranosyluronic acid)-D-galacto-se[55,57] and 2-$O$-($\beta$-D-glucopyranosyluronic acid)-D-xylose[58] have also been synthesized under the conditions of the Koenigs-Knorr reaction.

Cellobiouronic acid [i. e. 4-$O$-($\beta$-D-glucopyranosyluronic acid)-D-glucose] has been synthesized by another procedure, which seems to be thus the more interesting in view of the fact that cellobiouronic acid is produced in the hydrolysis of some *Pneumococcus* polysaccharides.[45,55,59-62] The first synthesis[63] sets out from benzyl $\beta$-cellobioside (V); it is noteworthy that by the action of oxygen on platinum only the primary alcoholic group of the non-reducing part of the molecule is oxidized with the formation of benzyl $\beta$-cellobiouronide (VI). Hydrogenation of this compound gives rise to cellobiouronic acid (VII).

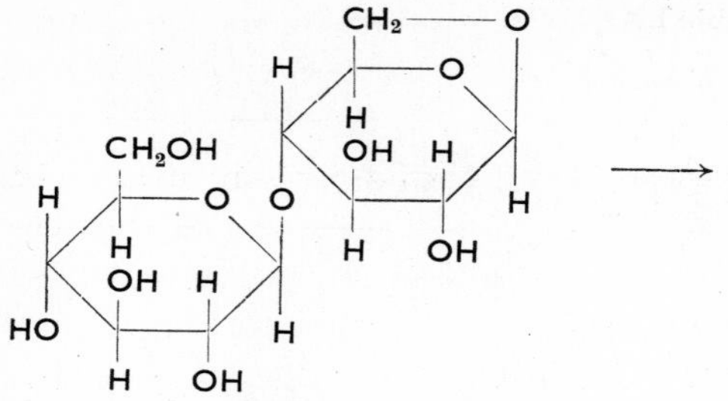

(VIII) 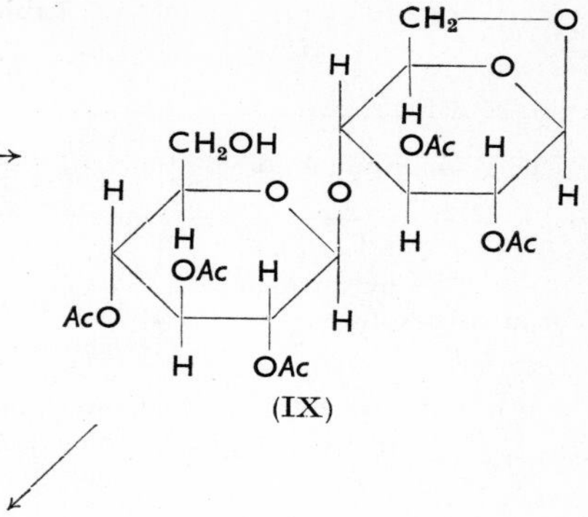 → (IX) 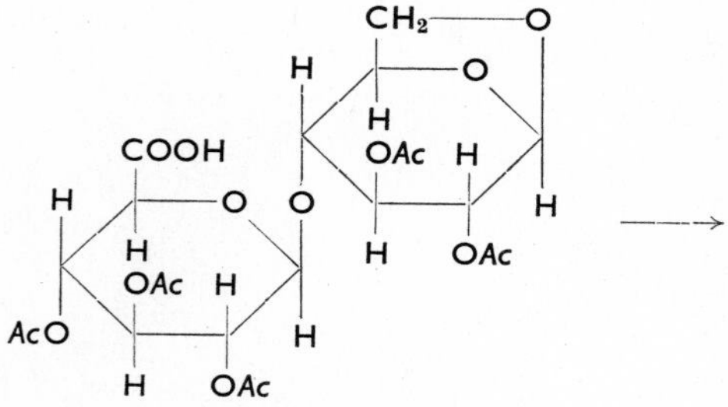 → (X) → (VII)

Cellobiouronic acid may also be synthesized from 1,6-anhydrocellobiose (VIII).[64] Tritylation, acetylation and detritylation lead to 2,3,2′,3′,4′-penta-*O*-acetyl-1,6-anhydrocellobiose (IX), in which the free primary alcoholic group may be oxidized with powdered potassium permanganate in acetic acid with the formation of the corresponding penta-*O*-acetyl derivative of 1,6-anhydro-cellobiouronic acid (X). Hydrolytic elimination of the acetyl groups by an aqueous potassium hydroxide solution and opening of the 1,6-anhydro ring by the action of sulphuric acid likewise gives rise to cellobiouronic acid (VII).

Maltobiouronic acid has been obtained by chemical synthesis independently in two laboratories. Y. Hirasaka, I. Matsunaga, K. Umemoto, and M. Sukegawa, J. Pharm. Soc. Japan (Yakugaku Zasshi) *83*, 971 (1963); Chem. Abstr. *60*, 4233 (1964), obtained this compound using hepta-*O*-acetylmaltose as starting material. Its oxidation with potassium permanganate yielded 4-*O*-(α-D-glucopyranosyl uronic acid)-D-glucose hepta-*O*-acetate. Catalytic oxidation of benzyl maltoside has been reported by Y. Hirasaka, J. Pharm. Soc. Japan (Yakugaku Zasshi) *83*, 960 (1963); Chem. Abstr. *60*, 4232 (1964), and by G. G. S. Dutton and K. N. Slessor, Can. J. Chem. *42*, 1110 (1964).

A survey of the aldobiouronic acids so far described, their sources, and some of their properties is presented in Table LXXXVIII, which also contains data on aldobiouronic acids whose structure has not been quite reliably established.

\* \* \*

*References see p. 489*

### Table LXXXVIII

Oligobiouronic Acids

| Oligobiouronic Acid | Source | Melting Point °C | $[\alpha]_D$ | Solvent | References |
|---|---|---|---|---|---|
| 2-O-(α-D-Glucopyranosyluronic acid)-D-xylose | wheat straw xylan | | +101° | | 79 |
| | chagual gum (*Puya chilensis*) | | +95° | $H_2O$ | 29 |
| | hemicelluloses of | | | | |
| | wheat bran | | | | 80 |
| | oat hulls | | | | 72 |
| | corn cobs | | | | 81—84 |
| | corn hulls | | | | 41, 85 |
| | *Pinus pinaster* wood | | +37° | $H_2O$ | 5, 10, 52 |
| | | | | | 86 |
| | | | +89° | $H_2O$ | 87 |
| per-O-methyl derivative | | | +146° | | 82 |
| 2-O-(Methyl-2,3,4-tri-O-methyl-α-D-glucopyranosyluronate)-D-xylose | | 168 | +85° | $H_2O$ | 41 |
| 2-O-(β-D-Glucopyranosyluronic acid)-D-xylose | synthetic compound | | + 5·7° | | 58 |
| 3-O-(α-D-Glucopyranosyluronic acid)-D-xylose | wheat straw xylan | | +18·5° | $H_2O$ | 54, 88, 89 |
| | pear wall xylan | | | | 90 |
| per-O-methyl derivative | | | +12·4° | $CHCl_3$ | 54 |
| 3-O-(β-D-Glucopyranosyluronic acid)-D-xylose | synthetic compound | | — 3·97° | $H_2O$ | 54 |
| per-O-methyl derivative | | | — 4·79° | $CHCl_3$ | 54 |
| 4-O-(α-D-Glucopyranosyluronic acid)-D-xylose | corn cobs xylan | | | | 46, 83 |
| Cellobiuronic acid | | | | | |
| 4-O-(β-D-glucopyranosyluronic acid)-D-glucose | polysaccharide of *Pneumococcus*, Type III | | | | 55, 59, 60, 62 |
| | *Pneumococcus*, Type VIII | | + 7° | $H_2O$ | 45, 61 |
| | synthetic compound | 190 (dec.) | +14·7° | $H_2O$ | 63 |
| hepta-O-acetate | | 239 (dec.) | +52·9° | $CHCl_3$ | 63 |
| methyl ester | | 254 | +45·3° | $CHCl_3$ | 63 |
| | | 251—252 | +44° | $CHCl_3$ | 64 |
| | | 251 | +42° | $CHCl_3$ | 45 |
| methyl glycoside | | | | | |
| methyl ester | | | | | |
| hexa-O-methyl derivative | | 114 | — 32° | $CHCl_3$ | 63 |
| benzyl glycoside | | 190 | — 53·3° | MeOH | 63 |
| methyl ester | | 200 | — 42·4° | MeOH | 63 |
| hexa-O-acetate | | 196 | — 48·8° | $CHCl_3$ | 63 |
| 6-O-(α-D-Glucopyranosyluronic acid)-D-glucose | | | | | |
| methyl ester | | | | | |
| hepta-O-acetate | synthetic compound | 202 | +48·4° | $CHCl_3$ | 55, 56 |

*Table LXXXVIII — continued*

| Oligobiouronic Acid | Source | Melting Point °C | $[\alpha]_D$ | Solvent | References |
|---|---|---|---|---|---|
| 6-O-($\beta$-D-Glucopyranosyluronic acid)-D-glucose methyl ester hepta-O-acetate | synthetic compound | 199 | — 11° | CHCl₃ | 55, 56 |
| 2-O-($\beta$-D-Glucopyranosyluronic acid)-D-mannose | plant gums | | — 32° | H₂O | 2, 17, 18, 31, 91 to 94 |
| | polysaccharide of *Aerobacter aerogenes* | | | | 19 |
| | *Xanthomonas campestris* | | — 30·6° | H₂O | 95 |
| | *Xanthomonas hyacinthi* | | | | 166 |
| | *Xanthomonas oryzae* | | — 28·0° | H₂O | 96 |
| | *Asparagus fulcinus* | | | | 97 |
| methyl glycoside methyl ester hexa-O-methyl ether | | 142—143 | | | 96 |
| amide hexa-O-methyl ether | | 186 | — 64·4° | H₂O | 96 |
| 4-O-($\beta$-D-Glucopyranosyluronic acid)-L-rhamnose | polysaccharide of *Acrosiphonia centralis* | | — 6° | H₂O | 3 |
| | *Enteromorpha compressa* | | — 12° | H₂O | 3, 98 |
| | *Ulva lactuca* | | — 22° | H₂O | 99 |
| 4-O-($\alpha$-D-Glucopyranosyluronic acid)-D-galactose | lemon gum | | | | 100 |
| | *Acacia karroo* | | | | 101 |
| 6-O-($\beta$-D-Glucopyranosyluronic acid)-D-galactose | gum arabic | 116 (dec.) | — 8·3° | H₂O | 53, 102 to 108 |
| | gum of *Acacia karroo* | | | | 101 |
| | *A. pycnantha* | | | | 16, 109 |
| | *A. mollissima* | | | | 110 |
| | *A. cyanophylla* | | | | 111 |
| | *A. sundra* | | | | 30, 164 |
| | *A. catechu* | | | | 32, 112 |
| | *A. senegal* | | | | 102 |
| | *Anogeissus latifolia* (gum ghatti) | | | | 2, 31 |
| | *Anogeissus shimperi* | | | | 17 |
| | *Virgilia oroboides* | | — 3° | H₂O | 93 |
| | mucilage of | | | | 14 |
| | *Afraegla paniculata* | | | | 14 |
| | hemicelluloses of *Pinus pinaster* | | | | 5, 10, 52, 86 |
| | polysaccharide of *Gibberella fujikuroi* (*Fusarium moniliforme*) | | | | 9 |
| | synthetic compound | 120 (dec.) | +9·4° → → — 7·3° | H₂O | 61 |
| methyl ester | | 119 (dec.) | — 2·9° | H₂O | 55, 56 |

*References see p. 489*

31*

*Table LXXXVIII — continued*

| Oligobiouronic Acid | Source | Melting Point °C | $[\alpha]_D$ | Solvent | References |
|---|---|---|---|---|---|
| hepta-O-acetate methyl glycoside, α- β- | | 203 | $-17\cdot3°$ $+22\cdot80°$ $-66\cdot4°$ | $CHCl_3$ | 55, 56 53 53 |
| 3-O-(?-D-Mannopyranosyluronic acid)-D-glucose hexa-O-methyl ether | polysaccharide of *Serratia marcenses* | | | | 44 |
| 4-O-(α-D-Galactopyranosyluronic acid)-D-xylose | mucilage of *Plantago arenaria* hemicelluloses of *Pinus pinaster* | | $+67°$ | $H_2O$ | 113–115 5, 10, 52, 86 |
| 3-O-(β-D-Galactopyranosyluronic acid)-D-galactose | *Odina wodier* | | | | 167 |
| 6-O-(β-D-Galactopyranosyluronic acid)-D-galactose | oxid. ε-galactan from *Larix decidua* *Salmalia malabarica* gum synthetic compound | | | | 27 165 26 |
| 2-O-(α-D-Galactopyranosyluronic acid)-L-rhamnose | plant mucilages *Plantago ovata* *Plantago arenaria* *Medicago sativa* *Salvia aegyptica* *Abelmoschus esculentus* *Opuntia fulgida* *Cochlospermum gossypium* *Ulmus fulva* *Fagus silvatica* *Pinus pinaster* | | | | 116, 117 118–120 115 15 33 34 121, 122 12 123–126 127 5, 10, 52, 86 |
| methyl glycoside penta-O-methyl ether | | 67— 69 | $+92°$ | $CHCl_3$ | 12, 15 |
| 6-O-(β-L-Arabinofuranosyluronic acid)-D-galactose | oxid. ε-galactan from *Larix decidua* synthetic compound | | | | 26, 27 26, 27 |
| 3-O-(?-L-Arabinofuranosyluronic acid)-D-xylose | oxid. arabinoxylan | | | | 28 |
| 2-O-(4-O-Methyl-α-D-glucopyranosyluronic acid)-D-xylose | hemicelluloses of *Picea sitchensis* *Picea nigra* *Picea excelsa* *Picea glauca* *Pinus silvestris* *Pinus taeda* *Pinus radiata* *Pinus elliottii* *Pinus pinaster* | | | | 35, 128 129 130 65 129 6, 131 66, 73 132 5, 10, 52, 86 |

*Table LXXXVIII — continued*

| Oligobiuronic Acid | Source | Melting Point °C | $[\alpha]_D$ | Solvent | References |
|---|---|---|---|---|---|
| | *Larix decidua* | | | $H_2O$ | 133 |
| | *Larix laricina* | | +98° | | 20 |
| | *Tsuga heterophylla* | | | | 36 |
| | *Thuja plicata* | | | | 134 |
| | *Populus tremula* | | | | 135, 136 |
| | *Populus tremuloides* | | | | 67, 137 |
| | *Populus tacamahacca* | | | | 48, 138 |
| | *Betula verrucosa* | | | | 139 |
| | *Betula papyrifera* | | | | 8, 40 |
| | *Betula lutea* | | | | 140 |
| | *Quercus* spp. | | | | 1 |
| | *Fagus grandifolia* | | | | 141 |
| | *Fagus silvatica* | | | | 142 |
| | *Acer saccharum* | | | | 42 |
| | *Ulmus americana* | | +110° | $H_2O$ | 38 |
| | *Wikstroemia sikhiana* | | | | 23 |
| | *Hibiscus cannabinus* | | +105° | $H_2O$ | 21, 168 |
| | *Hibiscus sabdariffa* | | +105° | $H_2O$ | 22 |
| | *Ceiba pentandra* | | | | 42 |
| | *Osmunda cinnamomea* | | | | 143 |
| | *Corchorus capsularis* | | +84·7° | $H_2O$ | 4, 68, 144 |
| | *Eucalyptus regnans* | | | | 145 |
| | *Conium* spp. | | | | 69, 146 |
| | *Linum usitatissimum* | | | | 37 |
| | *Asclepias syriaca* | | | | 74, 75 |
| | *Triticum sativum* | | | | 79, 147 |
| | wheat bran | | | | 79, 80 |
| | oat hulls | | | | 72 |
| | maize cobs | | | | 148 |
| methyl glycoside tetra-*O*-acetate | | 201 | +99·6° | $CHCl_3$ | 21 |
| methyl ester tetra-*O*-acetate | | 201 | +100° | $CHCl_3$ | 11, 149 |
| 2,3,4,3′-tetra-*O*-methyl ether | | 168 | +80° | $H_2O$ | 20, 40, 150 |
| 2,3,3′-tri-*O*-methyl ether | | | | | 42, 43, 128 |
| 2-*O*-(4-*O*-Methyl-α-D-gluco-pyranosyluronic acid)-D-ly-xose | | | +60·5° | $H_2O$ | 52 |
| | | | +37° | $H_2O$ | 10 |
| 3-*O*-(4-*O*-Methyl-α-D-glucopy-ranosyluronic acid)-D-xylose | hemicelluloses of *Pinus radiata* | | | | 73 |
| 3-*O*-(4-*O*-Methyl-α-D-glucopy-ranosyluronic acid)-L-arabi-nose | plant gums | | | | 151 |
| 4-*O*-(4-*O*-Methyl-α-D-glucopy-ranosyluronic acid)-L-arabi-nose | plant gums | | | | 39 |

*References see p. 489*

*Table LXXXVIII — continued*

| Oligobiouronic Acid | Source | Melting Point °C | $[\alpha]_D$ | Solvent | References |
|---|---|---|---|---|---|
| 4-O-(4-O-Methyl-α-D-glucopy-ranosyluronic acid)-D-galactose | gum myrrh gum of Khaya spp. Prosopis juliflora Albizzia zygia Fagara xanthoxyloides | | | | 153, 154 48, 155 18  13 |
| 6-O-(4-O-Methyl-α-D-glucopy-ranosyluronic acid)-D-galactose | gum of Prosopis juliflora | | | | 156–158 |
| 6-O-(4-O-Methyl-β-D-glucopy-ranosyluronic acid)-D-galactose | gum of Lannea grandis plant gums Fagus silvatica galactan | | | | 159, 160 151  127  161 |
| GA-Xyl | cotton seed hemicelluloses | | | | 161 162 |
| GalA-L-Ara | cotton seed hemicelluloses | | | | |
| GA-Xyl | Corchorus capsularis | | | | 152 |

Aldotriouronic acids have also been isolated in some cases from natural materials. Most attention has been paid to an acid whose type corresponds to 2-O-(4-O-methyl-α-D-glucopyranosyluronic acid)-D-xylose; it is O-(4-O-methyl-α-D-glucopyranosyluronic acid)-(1→2)-β-D-xylopyranosyl-(1→4)-D-xylose (XI).

This substance may be regarded as D-glucuronic acid glycosidically linked to xylobiose, an oligosaccharide relatively frequently encountered as hydrolysis product (see Chapter X).

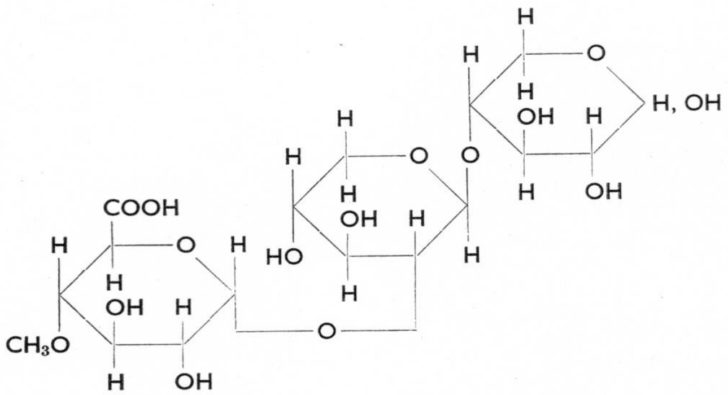

(XI)

This aldotriouronic acid has several time been obtained with certainty [47,65–71] in the hydrolysis of natural products; in some other cases,[72–76] it is very probable that the same acid is concerned. Its structure has been established from the course of the cleavage of the per-O-methyl derivative.[65]

Other aldotriouronic acids encountered as hydrolysis products are O-(α-D-glucopyranosyluronic acid)-(1→4)-O-β-D-xylopyranosyl-(1→4)-D-xylose[77] and O-(β-D-glucopyranosyluronic acid)-(1→4)-O-β-D-glucopyranosyl-(1→4)-D-glucose.[45]

The properties of these aldotriouronic acids together with those of other compounds of not fully established constitution are listed in Table LXXXIX.

\* \* \*

Exactly established higher oligouronic acids are: two aldotetraouronic acids, namely O-(4-O-methyl-α-D-glucopyranosyluronic acid)-(1→2)-O-β-D-glucopyranosyl-(1→4)-O-β-D-xylopyranosyl-(1→4)-D-xylose[78] and O-(β-D-glucopyranosyluronic acid)-(1→4)-O-β-D-glucopyranosyl-(1→4)-O-α-D-glucopyranosyl-(1→4)-D-galactose;[45] the pentaouronic acid O-(4-O-methyl-α-D-glucopyranosyluronic acid)-(1→2)-O-β-D-xylopyronosyl-(1→4)-O-β-D-xylopyranosyl-(1→4)-O-β-D-xylopyranosyl-(1→4)-D-xylose;[24] the next higher member of this series, namely the hexaouronic acid O-(4-O-methyl-α-D-glucopyranosyluronic acid)-(1→2)-O-β-D-xylopyranosyl-(1→4)-O-β-D-xylopyranosyl-(1→4)-O-β-D-xylopyranosyl-(-1→4)-D-xylose.[25]

The properties of these oligouronic acids are summarized in Table LXXXIX.

### Table LXXXIX

Oligotrio-, Oligotetrao- and Higher Uronic Acids

| Oligouronic acid | Source | Melting Point °C | [α]D | Solvent | References |
|---|---|---|---|---|---|
| O-(β-D-Glucopyranosyluronic acid)-(1→4)-O-β-D-glucopyranosyl-(1→4)-D-glucose | *Pneumococcus*, Type VIII | | +12° | H₂O | 45 |
| O-(β-D-Glucopyranosyluronic acid)-(1→4)-O-β-D-glucopyranosyl-(1→4)-O-α-D-glucopyranosyl-(1→4)-D-galactose | *Pneumococcus*, Type VIII | | +65° | H₂O | 45 |
| O-(α-D-Glucopyranosyluronic acid)-(1→4)-O-β-D-xylopyranosyl)-(1→4)-D-xylose | corn cobs | | | | 77 |
| O-(4-O-Methyl-α-D-glucopyranosyluronic acid)-(1→2)-O-β-D-xylopyranosyl-(1→4)-D-xylose | hemicelluloses of | | | | |

*References see p. 489*

*Table LXXXIX — continued*

| Oligouronic Acid | Source | Melting Point °C | $[\alpha]_D$ | Solvent | References |
|---|---|---|---|---|---|
| | *Picea glauca* | | +59° | $H_2O$ | 65 |
| | *Pinus radiata* | | | | 66, 73 |
| | *Pinus pinaster* | | +49·3° | $H_2O$ | 10 |
| | *Tsuga heterophylla* | | +57° | $H_2O$ | 69 |
| | *Thuja plicata* | | | | 71 |
| | *Populus tremuloides* | | | | 67 |
| | *Corchorus olitorius* | 183 | +58° | $H_2O$ | 47, 68 |
| | *Conium* spp. | | | | 69 |
| | *Prosopis juliflora* | | | | 70 |
| | *Asclepias syriaca* | | | | 74, 75 |
| | *Ceiba pentandra* | | | | 76 |
| | oat hulls | | | | 72 |
| O-(4-O-Methyl-α-D-glucopyranosyl-uronic acid)-(1→2)-O-β-D-xylopyranosyl-(1→4)-O-β-D-xylopyranosyl-(1→4)-D-xylose | *Betula papyrifera* xylan* | | +23° | $H_2O$ | 78 |
| O-(4-O-Methyl-α-D-glucopyranosyl-uronic acid)-(1→2)-O-β-D-xylopyranosyl-(1→4)-O-β-D-xylopyranosyl-(1→4)-O-β-D-xylopyranosyl-(1→4)-D-xylose | *Betula papyrifera* xylan* | | +0·63° | $H_2O$ | 24 |
| O-(4-O-Methyl-α-D-glucopyranosyl-uronic acid)-(1→2)-O-β-D-xylopyranosyl-(1→4)-O-β-D-xylopyranosyl-(1→4)-O-β-D-xylopyranosyl-(1→4)-O-β-D-xylopyranosyl-(1→4)-D-xylose | *Betula papyrifera* xylan* | | −11·8° | $H_2O$ | 25 |
| O-(β-D-Glucopyranosyluronic acid)-(1→6)-O-β-D-galactopyranosyl-(1→6)-D-galactose | hemicelluloses of *Pinus pinaster* | | | | 10 |
| | gum of *Moringa pterygosperma* | | +28° | $H_2O$ | 163 |
| O-(?-D-Mannopyranosyluronic acid)-(1→3)-D-glucopyranosyl-(1→3)-D-glucose nona-O-methyl ether | polysaccharide of *Serratia marcescens* | | | | 44 |
| O-(β-D-Glucopyranosyluronic acid)-(1→2)-D-mannopyranosyl-D-glucose | polysaccharide of *Xanthomonas campestris* | | | | 95 |
| GA-Man-Gal | polysaccharide from *Gibberella fujikuroi* (*Fusarium moniliforme*) | | | | 9 |
| ManA-Gal-Man | polysaccharide from *Gibberella fujikuroi* (*Fusarium moniliforme*) | | | | 9 |
| GA-Xyl-Gal | oat hulls | | | | 72 |
| GalA-L-Rha-Gal | plant mucilages | | | | 34 |
| Gal-GalA-L-Rha | plant mucilages | | | | 34 |
| Higher oligouronic acid (GluA-L-Rha) | *Acrosiphonia centralis* | | | | 3 |

\* A recent paper by R. H. Marchessault and T. E. Timell, J. Polymer. Sci. Pt. C. No 2, 49 (1963); Chem. Abstr. *59*, 8847 (1963), reports the isolation of a homologous series of *Betula papyrifera* uronic acids of the type $O$-(4-$O$-methyl-$\alpha$-D-glucopyranosyl uronic acid)-(1→2)-$O$-$\beta$-D-xylopyranosyl-(1→4)-$O$-$\beta$-D-xylopyranosyl-(1→4)-D-xylose. Besides the known tetraouronic,[78] pentaouronic[24] and hexaouronic acids,[25] some other members of this series have been obtained: heptaouronic acid $[\alpha]_D - 20\cdot8°$ ($H_2O$) and octaouronic acid $[\alpha]_D - 25\cdot7°$ ($H_2O$).

## REFERENCES

1. M. H. O'Dwyer, Biochem. J. *28*, 2116 (1934).
2. D. Hanna and E. H. Shaw, Proc. S. Dakota Acad. Sci. *21*, 78 (1941).
3. J. J. O'Donnell and E. Percival, J. Chem. Soc. *1959*, 2168.
4. G. O. Aspinall and P. C. Das Gupta, J. Chem. Soc. *1958*, 3627.
5. A. Roudier and L. Eberhard, Compt. rend. *240*, 2012 (1955).
6. J. K. N. Jones and T. J. Painter, J. Chem. Soc. *1957*, 669.
7. J. K. N. Jones and T. J. Painter, J. Chem. Soc. *1959*, 573.
8. C. P. J. Glaudemans and T. E. Timell, J. Am. Chem. Soc. *80*, 941 (1958).
9. I. R. Siddiqui and G. A. Adams, Can. J. Chem. *39*, 1683 (1961).
10. A. Roudier and L. Eberhard, Bull. soc. chim. France *1960*, 2074.
11. P. J. Garegg and B. Lindberg, Acta Chem. Scand. *14*, 871 (1960).
12. G. O. Aspinall, E. L. Hirst, and M. J. Johnston, J. Chem. Soc. *1962*, 2785.
13. F. G. Torto, J. Chem. Soc. *1961*, 3166.
14. F. G. Torto, J. Chem. Soc. *1961*, 5234.
15. G. O. Aspinall and R. S. Fanshawe, J. Chem. Soc. *1961*, 4215.
16. G. O. Aspinall, E. L. Hirst, and A. Nicholson, J. Chem. Soc. *1959*, 1697.
17. G. O. Aspinall and T. B. Christensen, J. Chem. Soc. *1961*, 3461.
18. D. W. Drummond and E. Percival, J. Chem. Soc. *1961*, 3908.
19. S. A. Barker, A. B. Foster, S. J. Pirt, I. R. Siddiqui, and M. Stacey, Nature *181*, 999 (1958).
20. G. A. Adams, Can. J. Chem. *38*, 2402 (1960).
21. S. K. Sen and P. C. Das Gupta, Can. J. Chem. *40*, 572 (1962).
22. P. C. Das Gupta, J. Chem. Soc. *1961*, 5262.
23. S. Machida and S. Nishihori, Bull. Chem. Soc. Japan *34*, 916 (1961).
24. T. E. Timell, Acta Chem. Scand. *16*, 1027 (1962).
25. T. E. Timell, J. Org. Chem. *27*, 1804 (1962).
26. G. O. Aspinall, I. M. Cairncross, and A. Nicholson, Proc. Chem. Soc. *1959*, 270.
27. G. O. Aspinall and A. Nicholson, J. Chem. Soc. *1960*, 2503.
28. G. O. Aspinall and I. M. Cairncross, J. Chem. Soc. *1960*, 3998.
29. J. K. Hamilton, D. R. Spriesterbach, and F. Smith, J. Am. Chem. Soc. *79*, 443 (1957).
30. S. Mukherjee and A. N. Srivastava, J. Am. Chem. Soc. *80*, 2536 (1958).
31. G. O. Aspinall, E. L. Hirst, and A. Wickström, J. Chem. Soc. *1955*, 1160.
32. R. K. Hulyarkar, T. R. Ingle, and B. V. Bhide, J. Indian Chem. Soc. *36*, 31 (1959).
33. A. K. Chatterjee and S. Mukherjee, J. Am. Chem. Soc. *80*, 2538 (1958).
34. R. L. Whistler and H. E. Conrad, J. Am. Chem. Soc. *76*, 3544 (1954).
35. G. G. S. Dutton and K. Hunt, J. Am. Chem. Soc. *80*, 4420 (1958).
36. G. G. S. Dutton and F. Smith, J. Am. Chem. Soc. *78*, 2505 (1956).
37. J. D. Geerdes and F. Smith, J. Am. Chem. Soc. *77*, 3569 (1955).
38. J. K. Gilham and T. E. Timell, Can. J. Chem. *36*, 410 (1958).
39. P. Andrews and J. K. N. Jones, J. Chem. Soc. *1954*, 1724.
40. C. P. J. Glaudemans and T. E. Timell, J. Am. Chem. Soc. *80*, 1209 (1958).
41. R. Montgomery, F. Smith, and H. C. Srivastava, J. Am. Chem. Soc. *79*, 698 (1957).

42. A. L. Currie and T. E. Timell, Can. J. Chem. *37*, 922 (1959).

43. T. E. Timell, Can. J. Chem. *37*, 893 (1959).

44. H. C. Srivastava and G. A. Adams, Can. J. Chem. *40*, 1415 (1962).

45. J. K. N. Jones and M. B. Perry, J. Am. Chem. Soc. *79*, 2787 (1957).

46. R. L. Whistler and G. E. Lauterbach, J. Am. Chem. Soc. *80*, 1987 (1958).

47. H. C. Srivastava, C. T. Bishop, and G. A. Adams, J. Org. Chem. *26*, 3958 (1961).

48. P. A. J. Gorin and A. S. Perlin, Can. J. Chem. *36*, 999 (1958).

49. P. C. Das Gupta and B. P. Sarkar, Textile J. Research *24*, 705 (1954); Chem. Abstr. 3533 (1955).

50. P. C. Das Gupta and B. P. Sarkar, Textile J. Research *24*, 1071 (1954); Chem. Abstr. *49*, 3534 (1955).

51. H. C. Srivastava and G. A. Adams, Chem. & Ind. (London) *1958*, 920.

52. A. Roudier and L. Eberhard, Compt. rend. *247*, 1505 (1958).

53. M. Heidelberger and F. E. Kendall, J. Biol. Chem. *84*, 639 (1929); Chem. Abstr. *24*, 1625 (1930).

54. C. T. Bishop, Can. J. Chem. *31*, 134 (1953).

55. R. D. Hotchkiss and W. F. Goebel, J. Biol. Chem. *115*, 285 (1936).

56. R. D. Hotchkiss and W. F. Goebel, Science *83*, 353 (1936); Chem. Abstr. *30*, 3782 (1936).

57. R. D. Hotchkiss and W. F. Goebel, J. Am. Chem. Soc. *58*, 858 (1936).

58. W. D. S. Bowering and T. E. Timell, J. Am. Chem. Soc. *82*, 2827 (1960).

59. M. Heidelberger and W. F. Goebel, J. Biol. Chem. *74*, 613 (1927).

60. M. Heidelberger and W. F. Goebel, J. Biol. Chem. *74*, 619 (1927).

61. W. F. Goebel, J. Biol. Chem. *110*, 391 (1935).

62. R. D. Hotchkiss and W. F. Goebel, J. Biol. Chem. *121*, 195 (1937).

63. G. Jayme and W. Demmig, Chem. Ber. *93*, 356 (1960).

64. B. Lindberg and L. Selleby, Acta Chem. Scand. *14*, 1051 (1960).

65. G. A. Adams, Can. J. Chem. *37*, 29 (1959).

66. D. J. Brasch and L. E. Wise, Tappi *39*, 581 (1956); Chem. Abstr. *50*, 15078 (1956).

67. J. E. Milks and C. B. Purves, J. Am. Chem. Soc. *78*, 3738 (1956).

68. H. C. Srivastava and G. A. Adams, J. Am. Chem. Soc. *81*, 2409 (1959).

69. J. K. Hamilton and N. S. Thompson, J. Am. Chem. Soc. *79*, 6464 (1957).

70. L. Sands and P. Nutter, J. Biol. Chem. *110*, 17 (1935).

71. J. K. Hamilton and N. S. Thompson, Pulp. Paper Mag. Can. *59*, 233 (1958); Chem. Abstr. *53*, 9659 (1959).

72. E. L. Falconer and G. A. Adams, Can. J. Chem. *34*, 338 (1956).

73. D. J. Brasch and L. E. Wise, Tappi *39*, 768 (1956); Chem. Abstr. *51*, 1602 (1957).

74. F. W. Barth and T. E. Timell, Can. J. Chem. *36*, 1321 (1958).

75. F. W. Barth and T. E. Timell, J. Am. Chem. Soc. *80*, 6320 (1958).

76. E. Anderson, R. Kaster, and M. G. Seeley, J. Biol. Chem. *144*, 767 (1942).

77. R. L. Whistler and D. I. McGilvray, J. Am. Chem. Soc. *77*, 2212 (1955).

78. T. E. Timell, Can. J. Chem. *40*, 22 (1962).

79. A. Roudier, Compt. rend. *248*, 1432 (1959); Chem. Abstr. *53*, 15217 (1959).

80. G. A. Adams and C. T. Bishop, J. Am. Chem. Soc. *78*, 2842 (1956).

81. R. Montgomery and F. Smith, J. Agric. and Food Chem. *4*, 716 (1957).

82. R. Montgomery, F. Smith, and H. C. Srivastava, J. Am. Chem. Soc. *78*, 2837 (1956).

83. R. L. Whistler and L. Hough, J. Am. Chem. Soc. *75*, 4918 (1953).

84. R. Montgomery, F. Smith, and H. C. Srivastava, J. Am. Chem. Soc. *78*, 6169 (1956).

85. H. C. Srivastava and F. Smith, J. Am. Chem. Soc. *79*, 982 (1957).

86. A. Roudier and L. Eberhard, Tappi *38*, 156 A (1955); Chem. Abstr. *50*, 2164 (1956).

87. S. A. Barker, A. Gómez-Sánchez, and M. Stacey, J. Chem. Soc. *1959*, 3264.
88. G. O. Aspinall and R. S. Mahomed, J. Chem. Soc. *1954*, 1731.
89. G. A. Adams, Can. J. Chem. *30*, 698 (1952).
90. S. K. Chanda, E. L. Hirst, and E. G. V. Percival, J. Chem. Soc. *1951*, 1240.
91. E. L. Hirst and J. K. N. Jones, J. Chem. Soc. *1938*, 1174.
92. J. K. N. Jones, J. Chem. Soc. *1939*, 558.
93. F. Smith and A. M. Stephen, J. Chem. Soc. *1961*, 4892.
94. A. M. Stephen, J. Chem. Soc. *1956*, 4487.
95. J. H. Sloneker and A. Jeanes, Can. J. Chem. *40*, 2066 (1962).
96. A. Misaki, S. Kirkwood, J. V. Scaletti, and F. Smith, Can. J. Chem. *40*, 2204 (1962).
97. P. S. Rao, O. N. Rozdon, and R. P. Budhiraja, Proc. Indian Acad. Sci. *32 A*, 264 (1950); Chem. Abstr. *46*, 1277 (1952).
98. J. P. McKinnell and E. Percival, J. Chem. Soc. *1962*, 3141.
99. J. P. McKinnell and E. Percival, J. Chem. Soc. *1962*, 2082.
100. J. J. Connell, R. M. Hainsworth, E. L. Hirst, and J. K. N. Jones, J. Chem. Soc. *1950*, 1696.
101. A. J. Charlson, J. R. Nunn, and A. M. Stephen, J. Chem. Soc. *1955*, 1428.
102. C. L. Butler and L. H. Cretcher, J. Am. Chem. Soc. *51*, 1519 (1929).
103. S. W. Challinor, W. N. Haworth, and E. L. Hirst, J. Chem. Soc. *1931*, 258.
104. W. E. Goebel and R. E. Reeves, J. Biol. Chem. *124*, 207 (1938).
105. P. A. Levene and R. S. Tipson, J. Biol. Chem. *125*, 345 (1938).
106. P. A. Levene, G. M. Meyer, and M. Kuna, J. Biol. Chem. *125*, 703 (1938).
107. S. N. Mukherjee and K. B. Ghosh, J. Indian Chem. Soc. *26*, 277 (1949).
108. M. Heidelberger, T. Avery, and W. F. Goebel, J. Exptl. Chem. *49*, 847 (1929); Chem. Abstr. *23*, 3002 (1929).
109. E. L. Hirst and A. S. Perlin, J. Chem. Soc. *1954*, 2622.
110. A. M. Stephen, J. Chem. Soc. *1951*, 646.
111. A. J. Charlson, J. R. Nunn, and A. M. Stephen, J. Chem. Soc. *1955*, 269.
112. R. K. Hulyarkar, T. R. Ingle, and B. V. Bhide, J. Indian Chem. Soc. *33*, 861 (1956).
113. W. A. G. Nelson and E. G. V. Percival, J. Chem. Soc. *1949*, 1600.
114. F. Hostettler and H. Deuel, Helv. Chim. Acta *34*, 2440 (1951).
115. E. L. Hirst, E. G. V. Percival, and C. B. Wylam, J. Chem. Soc. *1954*, 189.
116. E. Anderson and J. A. Crowder, J. Am. Chem. Soc. *52*, 3711 (1930).
117. R. S. Tipson, C. C. Christman, and P. A. Levene, J. Biol. Chem. *123*, 609 (1939).
118. R. A. Laidlaw and E. G. V. Percival, J. Chem. Soc. *1950*, 528.
119. L. Anderson and M. Fireman, J. Biol. Chem. *109*, 437 (1935).
120. R. A. Laidlaw and E. G. V. Percival, J. Chem. Soc. *1949*, 1600.
121. E. Anderson, L. Sands, and N. Sturgis, Amer. J. Pharm. *97*, 589 (1925).
122. L. Sands and R. Klaas, J. Am. Chem. Soc. *51*, 3441 (1929).
123. E. Anderson, J. Biol. Chem. *104*, 163 (1934).
124. R. E. Gill, E. L. Hirst, and J. K. N. Jones, J. Chem. Soc. *1939*, 1469.
125. L. Hough and J. K. N. Jones, Nature *165*, 34 (1950).
126. L. Hough and J. K. N. Jones, J. Chem. Soc. *1951*, 323.
127. H. Meier, Acta Chem. Scand. *16*, 2275 (1962).
128. G. G. S. Dutton and K. Hunt, J. Am. Chem. Soc. *82*, 1682 (1960).
129. A. R. N. Gorrod and J. K. N. Jones, J. Chem. Soc. *1954*, 2522.
130. G. O. Aspinall and M. E. Carter, J. Chem. Soc. *1956*, 3744.
131. D. H. Ball, J. K. N. Jones, W. H. Nicholson, and T. J. Painter, Tappi *39*, 438 (1956); Chem. Abstr. *50*, 12469 (1956).
132. R. L. Whistler and G. N. Richards, J. Am. Chem. Soc. *80*, 4888 (1958).

133. G. O. Aspinall and J. E. McKey, J. Chem. Soc. *1958*, 1059.

134. J. K. Hamilton and E. V. Partlow, J. Am. Chem. Soc. *80*, 4880 (1958).

135. J. K. N. Jones and L. E . Wise, J. Chem. Soc. *1952*, 2750.

136. J. K. N. Jones and L. E. Wise, J. Chem. Soc. *1952*, 3389.

137. J. K. N. Jones, E. Merler, and L. E. Wise, Can. J. Chem. *35*, 634 (1956).

138. P. A. J. Gorin, Can. J. Chem. *35*, 595 (1957).

139. J. Saarnio, K. Wathen, and C. Gustafsson, Acta Chem. Scand. *8*, 825 (1954).

140. T. E. Timell, J. Am. Chem. Soc. *81*, 4989 (1959).

141. G. A. Adams, Can. J. Chem. *25*, 556 (1957).

142. G. O. Aspinall, E. L. Hirst, and R. S. Mahomed, J. Chem. Soc. *1954*, 1734.

143. T. E. Timell, Svensk Papperstidn. *65*, 122 (1962); Chem. Abstr. *57*, 12607 (1962).

144. G. G. S. Dutton and I. H. Rogers, J. Am. Chem. Soc. *81*, 2413 (1959).

145. C. M. Stewart and D. H. Foster, Nature *171*, 792 (1953).

146. G. G. S. Dutton and F. Smith, J. Am. Chem. Soc. *78*, 2505 (1956).

147. A. Roudier, Compt. rend. *237*, 662 (1953).

148. R. L. Whistler, H. E. Conrad, and L. Hough, J. Am. Chem. Soc. *76*, 1668 (1954).

149. T. E. Timell, Can. J. Chem. *37*, 827 (1959).

150. G. G. S. Dutton and F. Smith, J. Am. Chem. Soc. *78*, 3744 (1956).

151. B. O. Lindgren, Acta Chem. Scand. *11*, 1365 (1957).

152. J. K. N. Jones and J. R. Nunn, J. Chem. Soc. *1955*, 3001.

153. G. O. Aspinall, E. L. Hirst, and N. K. Matheson, J. Chem. Soc. *1956*, 989.

154. G. O. Aspinall, M. J. Johnston, and A. M. Stephen, J. Chem. Soc. *1960*, 4918.

155. F. Smith, J. Chem. Soc. *1951*, 2646.

156. E. Anderson and L. Otis, J. Am. Chem. Soc. *52*, 4461 (1930).

157. E. V. White, J. Am. Chem. Soc. *70*, 367 (1948).

158. M. Abdel-Akker, F. Smith, and D. Spriesterbach, J. Chem. Soc. *1952*, 3637.

159. V. M. Parikh, T. R. Ingle, and B. V. Bhide, J. Indian Chem. Soc. *33*, 119 (1956).

160. V. M. Parikh, T. R. Ingle and B. V. Bhide, J. Indian Chem. Soc. *33*, 125 (1956).

161. M. H. O'Dwyer, Biochem. J. *20*, 664 (1926); Chem. Abstr. *21*, 174 (1927).

162. D. B. Das, P. K. R. Choudhury, and J. F. Wareham, Sci. and Culture (Calcutta) *18*, 197 (1952); Chem. Abstr. *47*, 2980 (1953).

163. T. R. Ingle and B. V. Bhide, J. Indian Chem. Soc. *39*, 623 (1962).

164. A. N. Shrivastava, Agra Univ. J. Res. Pt 1, *11*, 237 (1962); Chem. Abstr. *58*, 6911 (1963).

165. S. Bose and A. S. Dutta, J. Indian Chem. Soc. *40*, 257 (1963).

166. P. A. J. Gorin and J. F. T. Spencer, Can. J. Chem. *41*, 2357 (1963).

167. A. K. Bhattacharyya and C. V. N. Rao, Can. J. Chem. *42*, 107 (1964).

168. S. K. Sen, Can. J. Chem. *41*, 2346 (1963).

## 2. PSEUDOALDOBIOURONIC ACIDS

Substances of this type, whose existence has been correctly assumed before they were found in nature,[1] have been described only quite recently. The enzymic action of *Aspergillus niger*[2] converts maltose and D-glucurone into 2-*O*-α-D-glucopyranosyl-D-glucuronic acid (I), whose sodium salt exhibits $[\alpha]_D$ +89.0°. The same procedure was employed for isolating a higher oligosaccharide of similar type,[2] namely *O*-α-D-glucopyranosyl-(1→6)-*O*-α-D-glucopyranosyl-(1→2)-D-glucuronic acid.

Pseudocellobiouronic acid, i. e. 4-$O$-$\beta$-D-glucopyranosyl-D-glucuronic acid, has been synthesized by I. Johansson, B. Lindberg, and O. Theander, Acta Chem. Scand. *17*, 2019 (1963).

One of the most recent papers[3] reports the isolation of 3-$O$-$\beta$-D-xylopyranosyl-D-galacturonic acid from the mixture of hydrolysis products of traganthic acid.

2-$O$-$\alpha$-D-Glucopyranosyl-D-glucuronic acid may be transformed into its methyl glycoside by the action of triethyl orthoformate, and then esterified by the action of diazomethane. Reduction with lithium aluminium hydride yields the corresponding disaccharide (i. e. kojibiose)[2] in the form of its methyl glycoside.

### REFERENCES

1. W. Pigman, *The Carbohydrates*, Acad. Press, New York 1957, p. 319.
2. S. A. Barker, A. Gómez-Sánchez, and M. Stacey, J. Chem. Soc. *1959*, 3264.
3. G. O. Aspinall and J. Baillie, J. Chem. Soc. *1963*, 1702.

## 3. POLYURONIC ACIDS

Of greatest importance among polyuronic acids are at present di-, tri- and higher D-galacturonic acids, which may be obtained by hydrolysis (enzymic or in acid solution) of pectins.[1–16] The fractions corresponding to individual stages of the hydrolysis can be separated on ion exchangers.[3–5] Later isolated in pure form from the fractions containing di- to penta-D-galacturonic acids[3] were di-D-galacturonic acid,[1,2,5–7,10–13] tri-D-galacturonic acid[1,2,5,7,10–13] and tetra-D-galacturonic acid.[1,2,4,5,8] The preparation of an oligo-D-galacturonic acid con-

*References see p. 496*

taining 8 basic units has also been described.[15] Especially suitable for identification are the brucine salts of these acids.[11]

The structure of di-D-galacturonic acid (I) has been reliably established from the course of methylation cleavage.[12,13] The formula (I) given for 4-$O$-($\alpha$-D-galactopyranosyluronic acid)-D-galactopyranosyl uronic acid was further confirmed by the conversion of this substance into the corresponding ethyl glycoside (II) by the action of ethyl orthoformate in the presence of a trace of hydrogen chloride;[14] this glycoside in turn was converted by its reaction with diazomethane into the corresponding dimethyl ester (III), which on reduction with lithium aluminium hydride yielded ethyl 4-$O$-$\alpha$-D-galactopyranosyl-D-galactopyranoside (IV). Hydrolysis of this compound gave rise to 4-$O$-$\alpha$-D-galactopyranosyl-D-galactose (V).

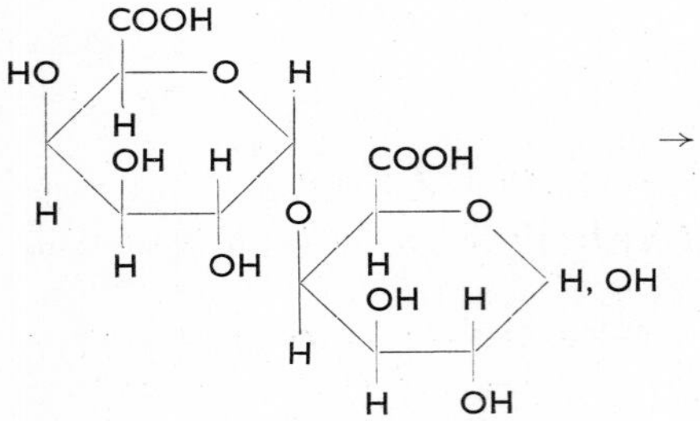

(I) 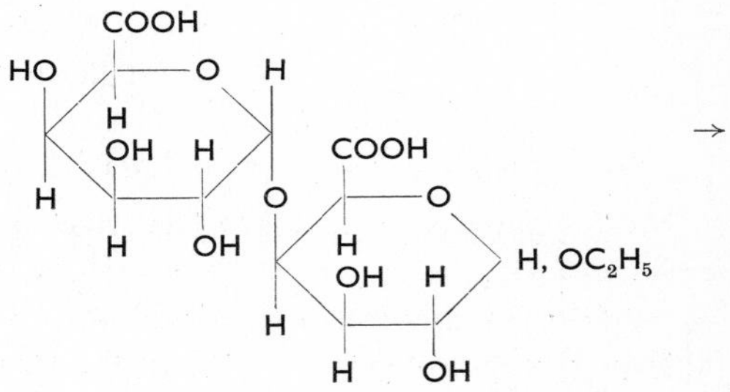                    (II)

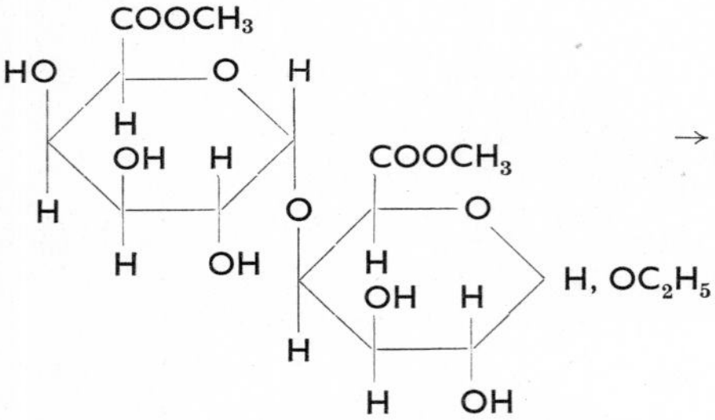

(III) 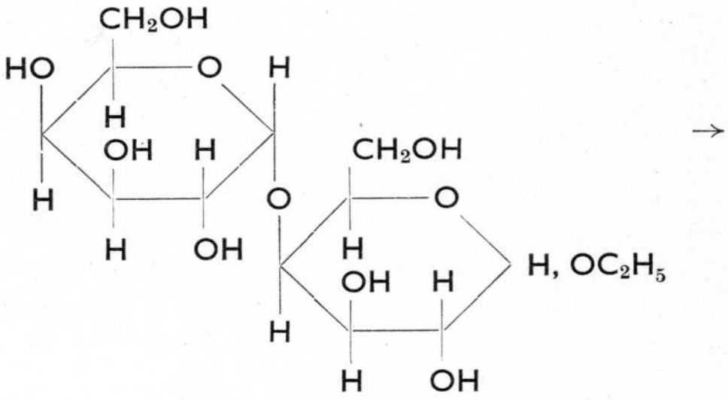                    (IV)

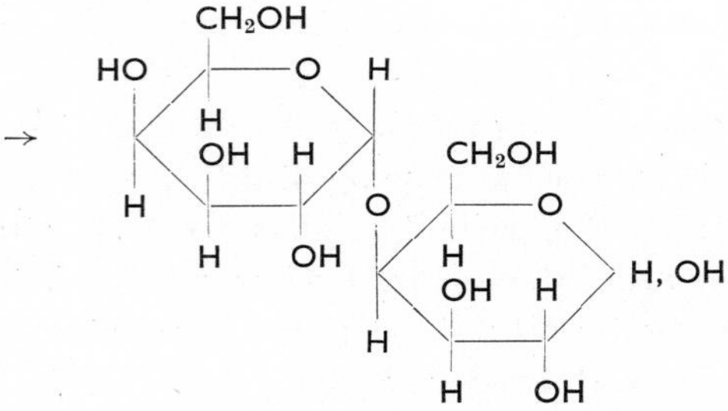

(V)

The dimethyl ester of the methyl glycoside (VI) may be obtained directly by heating the brucine salt of di-D-galacturonic acid with methanolic hydrogen chloride.[17] The cleavage of this substance in alkaline solution proceeds in an interesting way,[18] leading, on the one hand, to D-galacturonic acid methyl ester (VII) and, on the other, to an unsaturated compound, namely methyl[4,5]-$\Delta$-D-galacturonoside methyl ester (VIII).[18]

An unsaturated di-D-galacturonic acid corresponding to the type given above has been described by S. Hasegawa and C. W. Nagel, J. Biol. Chem. *237*, 619 (1962). Pectolytic enzymes of *Bacillus polymyxa* yielded 4-*O*-($\alpha$-D-4,5-dehydro-D-galactopyranosyluronic acid)-D-galactopyranosyluronic acid (IX) from pectic acid. Another unsaturated diuronide containing two units of D-mannuronic acid as fundamental units has been reported by I. Tsujino, Agric. Biol. Chem. (Japan) *27*, 236 (1963).

Genetically connected to di-D-galacturonic acids also is a trisaccharide containing two molecules of D-galacturonic acid and one molecule of L-rhamnose. Japanese investigators have obtained this substance by acid hydrolysis of the mucilage from *Hibiscus manihot* (*Abelmoschus manihot*).[19]

Another source of polyuronic acids, of another type, however, will obviously be alginic acids. They were regarded for some time as poly-D-mannuronic acids with $\beta,1 \rightarrow 4$ linkages;[20-22] however, they are likely to contain uronic acids other than D-mannuronic acid, namely D-glucuronic acid and L-guluronic acid.[23,24] The preparation of a pure di-D-mannuronic acid, i. e. 4-*O*-($\beta$-D-mannopyranosyluronic acid)-D-mannopyranosyluronic acid, by the hydrolysis of alginic acids with oxalic acid has been described in a recent paper.[25]

*References see p. 496*

The isolation of D-mannuronic acid and L-guluronic acid by the enzymic hydrolysis of alginates has been reported by M. Yoshikawa, Hyogo Noka Daigaku Kenkyu Hokoku, Nogei-kagaku Heu 5, 94 (1961); Chem. Abstr. 60, 1915 (1964), too.

4-$O$-($\beta$-D-Glucopyranosyluronic acid)-D-glucopyranosyluronic acid has been synthesized by oxidation of cyclohexyl $\beta$-maltoside 2,3,2′,3′,4′-penta-$O$-acetate.[26]

For another synthesis of this type see Y. Hirasaka, I. Matsunaga, K. Umemoto, and M. Sukegawa, J. Pharm. Soc. Japan (Yakugaku Zasshi) 83, 971 (1963); Chem. Abstr. 60, 4233 (1964). From suitable initial substances, 4-$O$-($\alpha$-D-glucopyranosyl uronic acid)-D-glucopyranosyl uronic acid has been obtained.

### Table XC

Polyuronic Acids

| Polyuronic Acid | Melting Point °C | $[\alpha]_D (H_2O)$ | References |
|---|---|---|---|
| Di-D-galacturonic acid | | | 13, 27 |
| brucine salt | | + 25° | 11 |
| methyl glycoside dimethyl ester | 121 | +126·6° | 17 |
| Tri-D-galacturonic acid | | | 13, 27 |
| brucine salt | | + 35° | 11 |
| Tetra-D-galacturonic acid | 159 — 160 (dec.) | | 8 |
| Di-D-mannuronic acid | 182 | −4·2° → −46·5° | 25 |

### REFERENCES

1. B. S. Luc and H. J. Phaff, Arch. Biochem. Biophys. 33, 212 (1951).
2. H. Altermatt and H. Deuel, Helv. Chim. Acta 35, 1422 (1952).
3. J. Solms, H. Deuel, and L. Anyas-Weisz, Helv. Chim. Acta 35, 2363 (1952).
4. H. Altermatt and H. Deuel, Helv. Chim. Acta 36, 340 (1953).
5. R. Derungs and H. Deuel, Helv. Chim. Acta 37, 657 (1954).
6. H. Altermatt and H. Deuel, Helv. Chim. Acta 37, 770 (1954).
7. A. L. Demain and H. J. Phaff, Arch. Biochem. Biophys. 51, 102 (1954); Chem. Abstr. 48, 11515 (1954).
8. A. L. Demain and H. J. Phaff, Arch. Biochem. Biophys. 51, 114 (1954); Chem. Abstr. 48, 11515 (1954).
9. R. M. McCready and C. G. Seegmiller, Arch. Biochem. Biophys. 50, 440 (1954); Chem. Abstr. 48, 10806 (1954).
10. J. Ashby, J. Brooks, and W. W. Reid, Chem. & Ind. (London) 1955, 360; Chem. Abstr. 50, 1596 (1956).
11. R. M. McCready, E. A. McComb, and D. R. Black, J. Am. Chem. Soc. 76, 3035 (1954).
12. J. K. N. Jones and W. W. Reid, Chem. & Ind. (London) 1953, 303.
13. J. K. N. Jones and W. W. Reid, J. Chem. Soc. 1954, 1361.
14. J. K. N. Jones and W. W. Reid, J. Chem. Soc. 1955, 1890.

15. Y. Mihashi, Yakugaku Zasshi (J. Pharm. Soc. Japan) *81*, 1000 (1961); Chem. Abstr. *56*, 3552 (1962).

16. Y. Mihashi, Yakugaku Zasshi (J. Pharm. Soc. Japan) *81*, 1003 (1961); Chem. Abstr. *56*, 3553 (1962).

17. M. Gee, J. K. N. Jones, and R. M. McCready, J. Org. Chem. *23*, 620 (1958).

18. P. Heim and H. Neukom, Helv. Chim. Acta *45*, 1737 (1962).

19. T. Oshibuchi and H. Kusunose, Nippon Nôgei-kagaku Kaishi (J. Agr. Chem. Soc. Japan) *31*, 481 (1957); Chem. Abstr. *52*, 15940 (1958).

20. W. L. Nelson and L. H. Cretcher, Science *67*, 537 (1928).

21. W. L. Nelson and L. H. Cretcher, J. Am. Chem. Soc. *52*, 2130 (1930).

22. G. Lunde, E. Heen, and E. Öy, Kolloid Z. *83*, 196 (1938).

23. F. G. Fischer and H. Dörfel, Hoppe-Seyler's Z. physiol. Chem. *302*, 186 (1955).

24. D. L. Vincent, Chem. & Ind. (London) *1960*, 1109.

25. G. Jayme and K. Kringstad, Chem. Ber. *93*, 2263 (1960).

26. B. Lythgoe and S. Tripett, J. Chem. Soc. 1950, 1983.

27. G. O. Aspinall and R. S. Fanshawe, J. Chem. Soc. *1961*, 4215.

## 4. NITROGEN-CONTAINING OLIGOURONIC ACIDS*

To the nitrogen-containing oligouronic acids belong some very significant cleavage products of important natural substances.

The polysaccharide chondroitin, occuring in nature in the form of its sulphates,[1] yields on hydrolysis the disaccharide chondrosin.[2] This is composed of a molecule of D-glucuronic acid and a molecule of D-chondrosamine (D-galactosamine, 2-amino-2-deoxy-D-galactose); it was prepared some time ago as the crystalline hydrochlorides of its ethyl ester[3] and its methyl ester.[4] In chondroitin, the primary amino groups of the chondrosamine parts are acetylated. Japanese investigators[5] have deduced from the course of the periodic acid oxidation of chondrosin that the substance in question is 3-O-(D-glucopyranosyluronic acid)-D-chondrosamine; this was fully confirmed by later papers[6-8] with the remark that both components of the molecule are connected by a $\beta$-glycosidic linkage.

The structure of chondrosin (I), which was obtained in crystalline form,[7-9] $[\alpha]_D$ +40°,[7,8] and as the dihydrate, m. p. 155—157°C, $[\alpha]_D$ +47°→+19°, is obvious from the fact that the conversion of chondrosin into its methyl ester, reduction of the latter with sodium borohydride and acetylation of the reaction product lead to the 3-O-$\beta$-D-glucopyranosyl derivative of 2-acetamido-2-deoxy-D-galactitol (II). Acid hydrolysis of this product gives rise to D-glucose, which must be the non-reducing part of the molecule; also since chondrosin is split by emulsin, it must contain a $\beta$-linkage.

Oxidation of chondrosin methyl ester with ninhydrin causes deamination of the reducing part of the molecule with simultaneous formation of a substitut-

---

* For reviews see R. Kuhn, Angew. Chem. *69*, 23 (1957); H. H. Baer, Fortschritte chem. Forsch. *3*, 822 (1958); G. Baschang, Fortschritte Chem. org. Naturstoffe *20*, 232 (1962).

*References see p. 500*

ed D-glucuronosyl derivative of D-lyxose, which has been isolated from the reaction mixture.[10]

(I)                                  (II)

It is assumed that the structural element (I) is the repeating unit in the chondroitin molecule.[7,8,11,12] It has also been reported, however, that in chondroitin B the D-glucuronic acid is replaced by L-iduronic acid.[10] Some chondroitin sulphates could be split by chondroitinase from the micro-organism *Proteus vulgaris* with the formation of $O$-($\Delta^{4,5}$-D-glucopyranosyluronic acid)-$N$-acetyl-D-galactosamine.[13]

Chondrosin derivatives have recently been synthesized.[14] The methyl ester of 2,3,4-tri-$O$-acetyl-1-bromo-1-deoxy-α-D-glucuronic acid reacts under the conditions of the Koenigs-Knorr synthesis with benzyl 2-amino-$N$-benzyloxy-carbonyl-2-deoxy-4,6-$O$-ethylidene-α-D-galactopyranoside to form the expected chondrosin derivative, from which the blocking groups may be split off by conventional procedures. It is interesting to note that the reaction does not take place if instead of the above-mentioned 4,6-$O$-ethylidene derivative the corresponding 4,6-$O$-benzylidene derivative is employed.[14]

A substance of similar type is hyalbiouronic acid, a cleavage product of hyaluronic acid (the oligosaccharide mucosin[15] seems to be identical with hyalbiouronic acid).[16] Hyalbiouronic acid is formed by acid hydrolysis[17,18] of hyaluronic acid (it seems again that the polysaccharide mucoitin[19] may be identical with hyaluronic acid).[16]

Hyalbiouronic acid, isolated as crystalline product, gives on further hydrolysis D-glucuronic acid and D-glucosamine. The structure has been established in a similar way to that described in the case of chondrosin. Degradation of the molecule of hyalbiouronic acid converts the nitrogen-containing part of the molecule into D-arabinose, and, consequently, the structure of hyalbiouronic acid must correspond to the formula (III), i. e. 3-$O$-($\beta$-D-gluco-pyranosyluronic acid)-D-glucosamine.[20,21]

(III)

Enzymic degradation of hyaluronic acid produced in addition to $N$-acetyl-hyalbiouronic acid, which is a native component of the molecule, six further oligosaccharides, among them an established tetrasaccharide,[22] which is a doubled molecule of hyalbiouronic acid. Disputes whether D-glucosamine is glycosidically linked to D-glucuronic acid by 1→3[23] or 1→4[24] bonds or by alternating bonds of these types,[25] were unambigously decided in favour of the 1→4 bonds.[26] This was fully confirmed by recent methylation studies.[27]

In a newer paper,[28] Jeanloz describes a synthesis leading to a derivative of hyalbiouronic acid, namely the reaction of methyl 2-acetamido-2-deoxy-4,6-$O$-benzylidene-$\alpha$-D-glucopyranoside with methyl 2,3,4-tri-$O$-acetyl-1-bromo-1-deoxy-$\alpha$-D-glucuronic acid in nitromethane in the presence of mercuric cyanide; this procedure yields the expected condensation product which, on hydrolytic elimination of the blocking benzylidene group and subsequent acetylation, is converted into the methyl ester of methyl 3-$O$-(2,3,4-tri-$O$-acetyl-$\beta$-D-gluco-pyranosyluronic acid)-2-acetamido-2-deoxy-4,6-di-$O$-acetyl-$\alpha$-D-glucopyrano-side. The same substance is obtained by methanolysis of hyaluronic acid and furter by conversion of the product obtained into the methyl ester and the per-$O$-acetyl derivative.[28]

Methanolysis of hyaluronic acid yielded also 3-$O$-($\beta$-D-glucopyranosyl uronic acid)-D-glucosamine, see R. W. Jeanloz and D. A. Jeanloz, Biochemistry *3*, 121 (1964). The methyl ester hepta-acetate of this compound has been prepared, see H. M. Flowers and R. W. Jeanloz, Biochemisty *3*, 123 (1964), from methyl (2,3,4-tri-$O$-acetyl-$\alpha$-D-glucopyranosylu-ronate) bromide and methyl 2-acetamido-4,6-$O$-benzylidene-2-deoxy-$\alpha$-D-glucopyranosi-de under the conditions of the Koenigs-Knorr reaction. Removal of the benzylidene group, $O$-acetylation and acetolysis yielded the derivative mentioned above.

*References see p. 500*

32*

The last substance of this type hitherto defined is heparosin, a nitrogen-containing disaccharide produced by hydrolysis of heparin (this hydrolysis involves not only the degradation of a polysaccharidic substance to a disaccharide but also hydrolytic elimination of the acetyl groups and the esterically linked sulphuric acid). Heparosin is composed of a molecule of D-glucuronic acid and a molecule of D-glucosamine; the opinions about its structure were formerly different.[29],[30] The last study on this subject[31] has proved that heparosin isolated in the form of its hydrochloride, m. p. $180-185°C$, $[\alpha]_D$ $+100°\rightarrow+81°$ ($H_2O$), has the structure of 4-$O$-($\alpha$-D-glucopyranosyluronic acid)-D-glucosamine (IV).

(IV)

## REFERENCES

1. G. Baschang, Fortschr. Chem. org. Naturstoffe *20*, 232 (1962).
2. H. H. Baer, Fortschr. chem. Forsch. *3*, 882 (1958).
3. J. Hebting, Biochem. Z. *63*, 353 (1914).
4. P. A. Levene, J. Biol. Chem. *140*, 267 (1941).
5. H. Masamune, Z. Yosizawa, and M. Maki, Tôhoku J. Exptl. Med. *55*, 47 (1951); Chem. Abstr. *46*, 10111 (1952).
6. E. A. Davidson and K. Meyer, J. Biol. Chem. *211*, 605 (1954).
7. E. A. Davidson and K. Meyer, J. Am. Chem. Soc. *76*, 5686 (1954).
8. E. A. Davidson and K. Meyer, J. Am. Chem. Soc. *77*, 4796 (1955).
9. M. L. Wolfrom and B. O. Juliano, J. Am. Chem. Soc. *82*, 1673 (1960).
10. M. Satake and H. Masamune, Tôhoku J. Exptl. Med. *68*, 44 (1958); Chem. Abstr. *53*, 9080 (1959).
11. K. H. Meyer and G. Baldin, Helv. Chim. Acta *36*, 597 (1953).
12. M. L. Wolfrom, R. K. Madison, and M. J. Cron, J. Am. Chem. Soc. *74*, 1491 (1952).
13. S. Suzuki, J. Biol. Chem. *235*, 3580 (1960).
14. S. Takanashi, Y. Hirasaka, M. Kawada, and M. Ishidate, J. Am. Chem. Soc. *84*, 3029 (1962).
15. T. Ishikawa, Tôhoku J. Exptl. Med. *53*, 217 (1951).
16. W. Pigman, *The Carbohydrates*, Acad. Press, New York 1957, p. 717.
17. M. M. Rapport, B. Weissmann, A. Linker, and K. Meyer, Nature *168*, 996 (1951).
18. B. Weissmann, M. M. Rapport, A. Linker, and K. Meyer, J. Biol. Chem. *205*, 205 (1953).
19. M. Suzuki, J. Biochem. (Japan) *27*, 479 (1938).
20. B. Weissmann and K. Meyer, J. Am. Chem. Soc. *74*, 4729 (1952).
21. B. Weissmann and K. Meyer, J. Am. Chem. Soc. *76*, 1753 (1954).
22. B. Weissmann, K. Meyer, P. Sampson, and A. Linker, J. Biol. Chem. *208*, 417 (1954).

23. R. W. Jeanloz and E. Firchielli, J. Biol. Chem. *190*, 537 (1951).
24. K. H. Meyer, J. Fellig, and E. H. Fischer, Helv. Chim. Acta *34*, 939 (1951).
25. G. Blix, Acta Chem. Scand. *5*, 981 (1951).
26. A. Linker, K. Meyer, and P. Hoffman, J. Biol. Chem. *219*, 13 (1956).
27. S. Hirano, and P. Hoffman, J. Org. Chem. *27*, 395 (1962).
28. R. W. Jeanloz and H. M. Flowers, J. Am. Chem. Soc. *84*, 3030 (1962).
29. M. L. Wolfrom, R. Montgomery, J. V. Carabinos, and P. Rathgeb, J. Am. Chem. Soc. *72*, 5796 (1950).
30. H. Masamune, T. Ishikawa, and Y. Katabira, Tôhoku J. Exptl. Med. *55*, 29 (1951).
31. M. L. Wolfrom, J. R. Vercellotti, and D. Horton, J. Org. Chem. *27*, 705 (1962).

# XXXV

## Glycosyl Derivatives of Inositols

Galactinol, $O$-$\alpha$-D-galactopyranosyl-(1→1)-D-$myo$-inositol (I), was isolated from sugar beet (*Beta vulgaris*) in 1953;[1] the structure of this product follows from the finding that its hydrolysis leads to D-galactose and $myo$-inositol and has been exactly established by the investigation of the hydrolysis of the per-$O$-methyl derivative.[2] Galactinol forms colourless crystals of m. p. 220—222°C, and a dihydrate, m. p. 113—114°C, $[\alpha]_D$ +135·6° ($H_2O$).

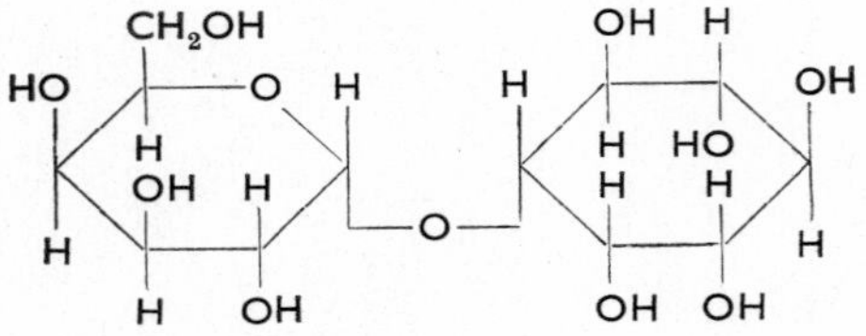

(I)

In several cases it has been found that some antibiotics* contain in their molecule a cyclohexane derivative, an amino sugar and an aldose, usually D-ribose. This applies to the antibiotics paromomycin, neomycin B and C, kanamycin and zygomycin A (see also Chapter XXIV). By partial hydrolysis it was usually possible to isolate glycosyl derivatives of aminodeoxyinositols from the antibiotics mentioned above.

Thus, paromomycin[3] is decomposed by methanolysis into two components, namely paromamine and methyl glycosides of paromobiosaminide[4] (the parent substance of the last compound, paromobiosamine, is identical with neobiosamine B of American authors).[5,6] Paromamine then gives on drastic hydrolysis with hydrogen bromide the optically inactive 1,3-diamino-4,5,6-trihydroxy-cyclohexane (termed deoxystreptamine); under less drastic conditions it is

---

* Chemistry of streptomycin has been a subject of a review by R. U. Lemieux and M. L. Wolfrom, Advances in Carbohydrate Chem. *3*, 337 (1948). The configuration of the glycosidic linkage between $N$-methyl-L-glucosamine and streptose has been shown to be $\alpha$, while that between streptose and streptidine is $\beta$, see M. L. Wolfrom, M. J. Cron, C. W. deWalt, and R. M. Husband, J. Am. Chem. Soc. *76*, 3675 (1954). The absolute configuration of strepti-dine in streptomycin has been dealt recently by J. R. Dyer and A. W. Todd, J. Am. Chem. Soc. *85*, 3896 (1963).

possible to obtain also the other component of paromamine, namely D-glucosamine.[4] All three amino groups of the paromamine molecule are primary, unsubstituted (the substance gives a trihydrochloride and a tri-$N$-acetyl derivative), and the structure of paromamine (II) as well as that of paromomycin (III) was derived from the consumption of periodic acid in the oxidation of these substances.[7]

The absolute configuration of paromomycin has been dealt with by M. Hichens and K. L. Rinehart, J. Am. Chem. Soc. *85*, 1547 (1963).

Paromomycin *II*, mentioned briefly,[6] might contain neobiosamine C instead of neobiosamine B.

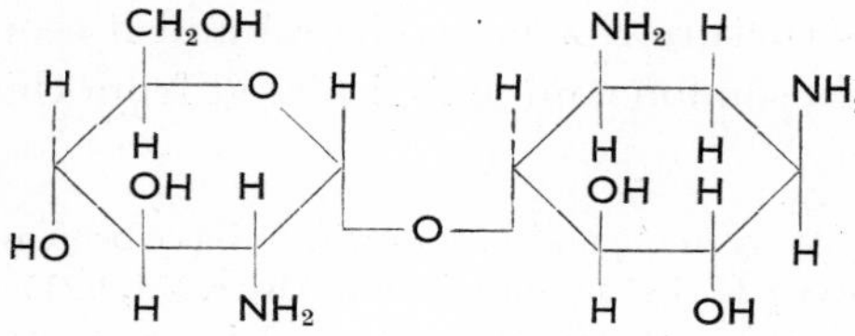

(II)

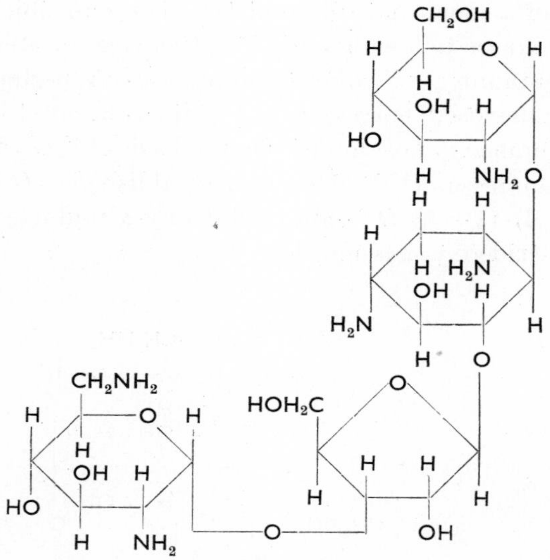

(III)

The structure of neamine, obtained from neomycin B and neomycin C has also been established with certainty.[8] The substance differs from paromamine in that it contains 2,6-diamino-2,6-dideoxy-D-glucose instead of D-glucosamine and consequently has the formula (IV). The structures of both neomycins have recently been given.[5,6]

*References see p. 506*

Even here, the absolute configuration of both neomycins is the subject of a paper by M. Hichens and K. L. Rinehart, J. Am. Chem. Soc. *85*, 1547 (1963).

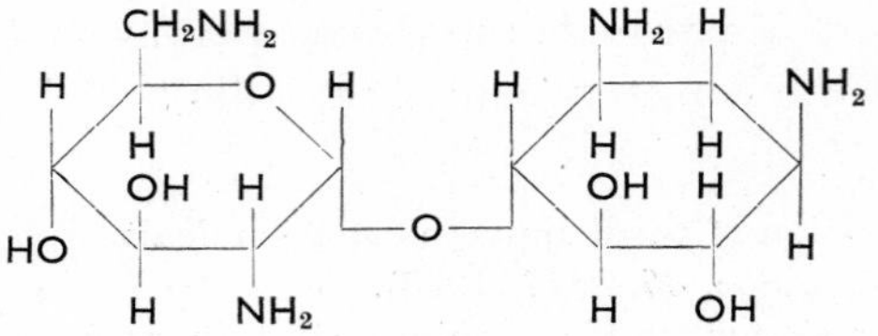

(IV)

Of quite similar structure is zygomycin A,[9] and it seems to be almost certain that the so-called pseudoneamine A, isolated from this antibiotic, is identical with paromamine.

The structures of zygomycin $A_1$ and zygomycin $A_2$ have been recently described by S. Horii, J. Antibiotics (Tokyo) *15*, 187 (1962); Chem. Abstr. *58*, 9217 (1963); later by S. Tatsuoka, S. Horii, T. Yamaguchi, H. Hitomi, and A. Miyake, Antimicrobial Agents Chemotherapy *1962*, 188; Chem. Abstr. *59*, 11641 (1963).

A substance of a somewhat different type is the antibiotic kanamycin (or better kanamycin A, see following note).[10-12] Cleavage products of this antibiotic are deoxystreptamine,[12-14] later 6-amino-6-deoxy-D-glucose,[15,16] and a 3-amino-3-deoxyaldohexose,[17] corresponding in its structure to 3-amino-3-deoxy-D-glucose[18,19] and named kanosamine.[19] On the basis of these and other findings, the structure of kanamycin (V)[20-26] has been established as $O$-(6-amino-6-deoxy-$\alpha$-D-glucopyranosyl)-(1 → 6)-$O$-[3-amino-3-deoxy-$\alpha$-D-glucopyranosyl-(1 → 4)]-1,3-diamino-1,2,3-trideoxy-*myo*-inositol.

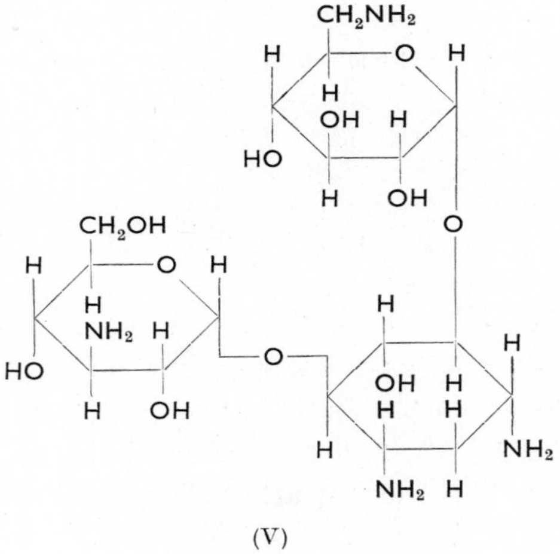

(V)

This structure has been confirmed by S. Umezawa and T. Tsuchiya, J. Antibiotics (Tokyo) *15*, 51 (1962); Chem. Abstr. 58, 2499 (1963). The authors succeeded in isolating a 6-amino-6-deoxy-α-D-glucopyranosyl derivative of deoxystreptamine from kanamycin A.

Some similar antibiotics of the same type have been found in addition to kanamycin A. Kanamycin B, see H. Schmitz, O. B. Fardig, F. A. O'Herron, M. A. Rousche, and I. R. Hooper, J. Am. Chem. Soc. *80*, 2912 (1958), contains a diaminodideoxyhexose, probably 2,6-diamino-2,6-dideoxy-D-glucose instead of 6-amino-6-deoxy-D-glucose. Kanamycin C, see T. Wakazawa and S. Fukatsu, J. Antibiotics (Tokyo) *15*, 223 (1962); M. Murase, J. Antibiotics (Tokyo) *14*, 367 (1961); M. Murase, J. Antibiotics (Tokyo) *14*, 367 (1961); Chem. Abstr. *57*, 9940 (1962), contains D-glucosamine instead of 6-amino-6-deoxy-D-glucose and corresponds to the 3-amino-3-deoxy-D-glucopyranosyl derivative of paromamine.

The absolute configurations of all isomeric kanamycins have been dealt with by M. Hichens and K. L. Rinehart, J. Am. Chem. Soc. *85*, 1547 (1963).

The synthesis of deoxykanamycin has been reported by T. Tsuchiya, S. Iriyama, and S. Umezawa, J. Antibiotics (Tokyo) *16 A*, 173 (1963); Chem. Abstr. *59*, 12902 (1963).

Bluensomycin, see B. Bannister and A. D. Argoudelis, J. Am. Chem. Soc. *85*, 234 (1963), belongs to this class of substances, too.

Hygromycin B, see P. F. Wiley, M. V. Sigal, and P. Weaver, J. Org. Chem. *27*, 2793 (1962), belongs to the aminodeoxy derivatives of the inositol group, too. The substance is a D-talosyl derivative of *N*-methyl-2-deoxystreptamine, named hyosamine.

Glebomycin, see T. Naito, Penishirin Sono Ta Koseibusshitzu *15*, 373 (1962); Chem. Abstr. *60*, 4230 (1964), is a new type in this group. Its hydrolysis yields besides other substances also 3-O-carbamoyl-1-deoxy-1-guanidino-*scyllo*-inositol, called glebidine.

In connection with the chemistry of kanamycin, 4,6-di-O-β-D-glucopyranosyldeoxystreptamine was synthesized as a model.[27] The preparation started from 2,3,4,6-tetra-O-acetyl-α-D-glucopyranosyl bromide and the *N,N'*-dicarbobenzoxy derivative of deoxystreptamine, which were condensed in the presence of mercuric cyanide. Here it is interesting to note that the condensation of the mentioned components proceeds only in nitromethane and not at all in the usual solvents for condensations of this type (see Chapter VI), which are chloroform, benzene, dioxane and dimethylformamide.[27]

Another synthesis of a cyclitol glycoside has been reported by K. A. Caldwell, S. P. Raman, and L. Anderson, Nature *199*, 373 (1963). By the action of 2,3,4,6-tetra-O-acetyl-α-D-glucopyranosyl bromide on 1,2-3,4-di-O-isopropylidene-5-O-methyl-D-inositol [i. e. a derivative of (+)pinitol] under the conditions of the Koenigs-Knorr reaction derivatives and free 6-O-β-D-glucopyranosyl-5-O-methyl-D-inositol have been obtained.

A quite different type of substances of this group has been described by French investigators.[28-31] From a mutant of *Mycobacterium tuberculosis*, resistant to streptomycin, they isolated a substance containing two molecules of D-mannose linked to a molecule of *myo*-inositol, which, moreover, is esterified with phosphoric acid;[28-30] besides this product, others were isolated containing inositol phosphate linked to one D-mannose molecule, and in addition to this, a product containing five D-glucose molecules was found. All these compounds

*References see p. 506*

are obviously linked through phosphoric acid to glycerol, two hydroxyl groups of which are esterified with a higher aliphatic acid.

The structure of the first of these substances, i.e. that containing two D-mannose molecules, has been established for the greater part; the D-mannose molecules are mutually linked in the form of 6-*O*-α-D-mannopyranosyl-D-mannose; the exact linkage of this disaccharide to inositol phosphate has not been determined[31] and the partial structure of the product in question is expressed by formula (VI).[31]

(VI)

The 6-*O*-α-D-mannopyranosyl-D-mannopyranosyl derivative of *myo*-inositol is identical with manninositose.[32] The structure of this compound, as well as of the D-mannopyranosyl derivative of *myo*-inositol, has been fully elucidated by Angyal and Shelton,[33] who synthesized both compounds mentioned.

### REFERENCES

1. R. J. Brown and R. F. Serro, J. Am. Chem. Soc. *75*, 1040 (1953).
2. E. A. Kabat, D. L. MacDonald, C. E. Ballou, and H. O. L. Fischer, J. Am. Chem. Soc. *75*, 4507 (1953).
3. T. H. Haskell, J. C. French, and Q. R. Bartz, J. Am. Chem. Soc. *81*, 3480 (1959).
4. T. H. Haskell, J. C. French, and Q. R. Bartz, J. Am. Chem. Soc. *81*, 3481 (1959).
5. K. L. Rinehart, W. S. Chilton, M. Hichens, and W. von Phillipsborn, J. Am. Chem. Soc. *84*, 3216 (1962).
6. K. L. Rinehart, M. Hichens, A. D. Argoudelis, W. S. Chilton, H. E. Carter, M. P. Georgiadis, C. P. Schaffner, and R. T. Schillings, J. Am. Chem. Soc. *84*, 3218 (1962).
7. T. H. Haskell, J. C. French, and Q. R. Bartz, J. Am. Chem. Soc. *81*, 3482 (1959).
8. H. E. Carter, J. R. Dyer, P. D. Shaw, K. L. Rinehart, and M. Hichens, J. Am. Chem. Soc. *83*, 3723 (1961).
9. H. Hitomi, S. Horii, T. Yamaguchi, and A. Miyake, Chem. Pharm. Bull. (Tokyo) *9*, 541 (1961).

10. H. Umezawa, M. Ueda, K. Maeda, K. Yagishita, S. Kondo, Y. Okami, R. Utahara, Y. Osate, K. Nitta, and T. Takeuchi, J. Antibiotics (Tokyo) *10*, 181 (1957); Chem. Abstr. *53*, 22221 (1959).

11. K. Maeda, M. Ueda, K. Yagishita, S. Kawaji, S. Kondo, M. Murase, T. Takeuchi, Y. Okami, and H. Umezawa, J. Antibiotics (Tokyo) *10*, 228 (1957); Chem. Abstr. *53*, 22222 (1959).

12. M. J. Cron, D. L. Johnson, F. M. Palermiti, Y. Perron, H. D. Taylor, D. F. Whitehead, and I. R. Hooper, J. Am. Chem. Soc. *80*, 752 (1958).

13. K. Maeda, M. Murase, H. Mawatari, and H. Umezawa, J. Antibiotics (Tokyo) *11*, 73 (1958); Chem. Abstr. *53*, 20526 (1959).

14. H. Ogawa and T. Ito, J. Antibiotics (Tokyo) *10*, 267 (1957); Chem. Abstr. *53*, 18877 (1959).

15. M. J. Cron, O. B. Fardig, D. L. Johnson, H. Schmitz, D. F. Whitehead, I. R. Hooper, and R. U. Lemieux, J. Am. Chem. Soc. *80*, 2342 (1958).

16. H. Ogawa, T. Ito, S. Inoue, and S. Kondo, J. Antibiotics (Tokyo) *11*, 70 (1958); Chem. Abstr. *53*, 18877 (1959).

17. H. Ogawa, T. Ito, S. Inoue, and S. Kondo, J. Antibiotics (Tokyo) *11*, 72 (1958); Chem. Abstr. *53*, 18877 (1959).

18. H. Ogawa, T. Ito, S. Inoue, and S. Kondo, J. Antibiotics (Tokyo) *11*, 166 (1958); Chem. Abstr. *53*, 18877 (1959).

19. M. J. Cron, O. B. Fardig, D. L. Johnson, H. Schmitz, D. F. Whitehead, I. R. Hooper, and R. U. Lemieux, J. Am. Chem. Soc. *80*, 4741 (1958).

20. K. Maeda, M. Murase, H. Mawatari, and H. Umezawa, J. Antibiotics (Tokyo) *11*, 163 (1958); Chem. Abstr. *53*, 20527 (1959).

21. S. Umezawa, Y. Ito, and S. Fukatsu, J. Antibiotics (Tokyo) *11*, 162 (1958); Chem. Abstr. *53*, 18875 (1959).

22. H. Umezawa, K. Maeda, M. Murase, and H. Mawatari, J. Antibiotics (Tokyo) *11*, 163 (1958); Chem. Abstr. *53*, 20527 (1959).

23. H. Ogawa, T. Ito, S. Inoue, and S. Kondo, J. Antibiotics (Tokyo) *11*, 169 (1958); Chem. Abstr. *53*, 18877 (1959).

24. M. J. Cron, O. B. Fardig, D. L. Johnson, D. F. Whitehead, I. R. Hooper, and R. U. Lemieux, J. Am. Chem. Soc. *80*, 4115 (1958).

25. S. Umezawa, Y. Ito, and S. Fukatsu, Bull. Chem. Soc. Japan *32*, 81 (1959).

26. H. Ogawa, T. Ito, S. Kondo, and S. Inoue, Bull. Agr. Chem. Soc. Japan *23*, 289 (1959); Chem. Abstr. *53*, 22230 (1959).

27. S. Umezawa and Y. Ito, Bull. Chem. Soc. Japan *34*, 1540 (1961).

28. E. Vilkas, Compt. rend. *245*, 588 (1957); Chem. Abstr. *52*, 1362 (1958).

29. E. Vilkas and E. Lederer, Bull. soc. chim. biol. *38*, 111 (1956).

30. E. Vilkas, Bull. soc. chim. biol. *42*, 1005 (1960).

31. E. Vilkas and E. Lederer, Bull. soc. chim. biol. *42*, 1013 (1960).

32. R. J. Anderson, W. C. Lothrop, and M. M. Creighton, J. Biol. Chem. *125*, 299 (1938).

33. S. J. Angyal and B. Shelton, Proc. Chem. Soc. *1963*, 57.

# XXXVI

## Analysis of Oligosaccharides

### 1. QUALITATIVE ANALYSIS

The presence of a free carbonyl group in the saccharide molecule imparts to such a compound characteristic properties manifesting themselves for example by reduction of Fehling solution, formation of phenylosazones and many other reactions.[1] Reducing oligosaccharides, however, reduce a solution of complex cupric ions much less intensely than does the corresponding amount of monosaccharides. By appropriate adjustment of the reaction conditions, Barfoed has even succeeded[2] in preparing a reagent that oxidizes monosaccharides only. In this way, monosaccharides may be qualitatively differentiated from reducing oligosaccharides, such as lactose or maltose. A modification of the Barfoed reagent, consisting in principle of a cupric acetate solution in acetic acid, has been the subject of further studies.[3] It must be borne in mind, however, that even so-called non-reducing oligosaccharides, such as sucrose, reduce complex cupric ion solutions to a certain degree and that this reducing power, due to partial hydrolysis, increases strongly with the alkalinity of the solution. It is also for this reason that, for instance in the quantitative determinations of monosaccharides apart from sucrose with Fehling solution, the sodium hydroxide is replaced by sodium carbonate.[4] Sucrose[5] as well as raffinose reduce Tollens reagent.[1]

The number of colour reactions specific for oligosaccharides in general or at least for some of them is very small. Many reagents employed in the monosaccharide series and producing intense coloration of the reaction mixture are also used for oligosaccharides. This is possible because these reactions are for the greater part carried out in a strongly acid solution causing splitting of the glycosidic linkage and rapid hydrolysis of the oligosaccharide with the formation of one or more monosaccharides, which then give further reactions. For example, the violet coloration with chromotropic acid in 15M sulphuric acid, based on the formation of $\omega$-hydroxymethylfurfural and the removal of the hydroxymethyl group in the form of formaldehyde, is given not only by hexoses but also by the disaccharides lactose, maltose and others.[6] Similarly, sucrose, too, gives the Molisch reaction with $\alpha$-naphthol. It is not surprising, therefore, that oligosaccharides containing D-fructose in their molecules exhibit positive colour reactions with a number of reagents specific for ketoses. Thus, sucrose shows a positive Seliwanoff reaction with resorcinol[7,8] and a positive Foulger reaction with urea;[9,10] with the Folin-Denis reagent in the presence of trisodium phosphate it gives a blue coloration,[11] while its colour reaction in the presence of aminoguanidine is red-violet.[12] All these reactions are characteristic of ketohexoses; however, as they are always carried out in acid solution, the sucrose is split into D-glucose and D-fructose. The intense blue coloration of ketohexoses with diphenylamine, the Ihl-Pechmann reaction, is also usable for the proof of 4-O-β-D-galactopyranosyl-D-fructose.[13]

The enumeration of characteristic derivatives of some oligosaccharides, as given below, is in all cases limited to nitrogen-containing compounds, mainly substituted hydrazones, osazones and osotriazoles. Later investigations are concerned with 1-phenylflavazoles of oligosaccharides[14] and with per-O-p,p'-nitrophenylazobenzoyl derivatives.[15]

Attention has also been paid to the possibility of identifying some monosaccharides and oligosaccharides by fermentation procedures, either by means of yeast,[16] bacteria,[17-20] or other micro-organisms.[21,22] In this respect it is interesting to note that, for example, all sucrose-fermenting yeast types also ferment raffinose, while those fermenting lactose do not attack maltose. The presence of trehalose can be indirectly proved in oligosaccharide mixtures after enzymic hydrolysis to D-glucose.[23]

### Lactose

Qualitative tests characteristic of lactose are not described in the literature. Lactose conceivably reduces Fehling solution, and the oxidation of lactose with nitric acid gives rise to the sparingly water-soluble galactaric (mucic) acid. This reaction is significant for the characterization of lactose, although it is a qualitative specific test for galactose and some of its derivatives. Another important compound for the identification of lactose is its phenylosazone which, due to its good solubility in hot water, can be separated from a mixture of phenylosazones of monosaccharides. By boiling with dilute sulphuric acid it is split into phenyl-D-glucosazone and D-galactose, which can be identified after extraction of the phenyl-D-glucosazone with ether.

Important derivatives of lactose are:
Lactose
benzylphenylhydrazone, m. p. 128°C, $[\alpha]_D$ —25·7°
    (MeOH)[24,25]
β-naphthylhydrazone, m. p. 203°C, brown needles[25]
allylphenylhydrazone, m. p. 132°C, $[\alpha]_D$ —14·6° (MeOH),
    light yellow needles[25]

*References see p. 514*

phenylosazone, m. p. 210—212°C, $[\alpha]_D$ —25·4°→ —7·8 (MeOH),
agglomerates of fine yellow prisms[26—29]
phenylosotriazole, m. p. 180—181°C, $[\alpha]_D$ —43·6° $(H_2O)$[30]
p-nitrophenylosazone, m. p. 258°C, red powder, soluble in sodium hydroxide
solution with blue coloration[31]
octa-O-p,p'-nitrophenylazobenzoyl derivative, m. p. 238°C, $[\alpha]_D$ +350°
$(CHCl_3)$[15]

## Maltose

Maltose reduces Fehling solution and, like lactose, gives no characteristic
colour reactions. The formation of its phenylhydrazone, apart from paper
chromatography, is one of the most frequently employed methods for the
identification of maltose. The higher solubility of phenylmaltosazone in warm
water permits its separation from phenylosazones of monosaccharides. The
action of a nitration mixture on maltose may be utilized for preparing maltose
octa-O-nitrate.

Important maltose derivatives are:

Maltose

$\beta$-naphthylhydrazone, m. p. 176°C, $[\alpha]_D$ +10·6° (MeOH)[25]
phenylosazone, m. p. 206°C, $[\alpha]_D$ +82·6° (EtOH/$C_5H_5N$), light yellow crystals;
      [26,27,32,33] separable from phenyl-D-glucosazone by extraction with acetone
p-nitrophenylosazone, m. p. 261°C, red powder[31]
p-bromophenylosazone, m. p. 198°C, light yellow needles[34,35]
p-iodophenylosazone, m. p. 208°C, $[\alpha]_D$ +82·9°→ +66·1° $(C_5H_5N)$[36]
octa-O-nitrate, m. p. 163—164°C, $[\alpha]_D$ +128·6° (AcOH)[37]
octa-O-p,p'-nitrophenylazobenzoyl derivative, m. p. 272°C, $[\alpha]_D$ +35° $(CHCl_3)$[15]

## Melibiose

This reducing disaccharide likewise gives no specific colour reactions. It
may be converted into its phenylosazone, which reacts with benzaldehyde to
form the corresponding osone; the latter is hydrolysed by the action of emulsin
into D-galactose and D-glucosone. In a similar manner to the case of lactose, the
oxidation of melibiose or its osone leads to galactaric (mucic) acid.

Important melibiose derivatives are:

Melibiose

phenylhydrazone, m. p. 145°C, light yellow crystals[38]
$\beta$-naphthylhydrazone, m. p. 135°C, $[\alpha]_D$ +15·9° (MeOH)[25]
allylphenylhydrazone, m. p. 197°C, $[\alpha]_D$ +21·2° (MeOH), light yellow crystals[25]
phenylosazone, m. p. 177°C, $[\alpha]_D$ +43·2° $(C_5H_5N)$[39,44]

phenylosotriazole, m. p. 153—154°C, $[\alpha]_D$ +61° (EtOH)[40]
p-bromophenylosazone, m. p. 182°C[34,41]

### Other reducing oligosaccharides

Some more important derivatives suitable for identifying reducing oligo-saccharides are:

Primeverose phenylosazone, m. p. 220°C, $[\alpha]_D$ —109·7° ($C_5H_5N$)[42]

Cellobiose phenylosazone, m. p. 198—200°C, $[\alpha]_D$ —6·5° ($C_5H_5N$/EtOH),[43,45]
    phenylosotriazole, m. p. 164—165°C, $[\alpha]_D$ —50·8° ($H_2O$)[30]

Gentiobiose phenylosazone, m. p. 170—173°C, $[\alpha]_D$ —74°→ —44·4° ($C_5H_5N$
    and EtOH)[46-48]

Laminaribiose phenylosazone, m. p. 195°C, $[\alpha]_D$ —79·6° (EtOH)[49]

Turanose phenylosazone, m. p. 200—205°C (dec.), $[\alpha]_D$ +24·5° → +33°
    ($C_5H_5N$/EtOH)[50]
    phenylosotriazole, m. p. 193—194°C, $[\alpha]_D$ +74·5° ($H_2O$)[50,51]

For nitrogen-containing derivatives of other reducing oligosaccharides see Chapter XXVI.

### Sucrose

Sucrose is a non-reducing disaccharide which, however, is readily split in acid solution into D-glucose and D-fructose, and thus gives a large number of colour reactions characteristic of monosaccharides. With regard to its high practical importance, great attention has been paid to the analysis of sucrose; nevertheless, only few qualitative proofs of sucrose have been worked out which, moreover, are not always quite specific.

## Raybin's proof[52,53]

40 to 50 mg of sucrose are dissolved in a few millilitres of a 0·95N potassium hydroxide solution and shaken at about 10°C with 7 to 10 mg of diazouracil in a stoppered test tube. A bluish green coloration appears within a few minutes. In the presence of soluble magnesium salts, a permanent blue precipitation is formed. This reaction is given neither by glucose nor by fructose or other sugars, with the exception of those characterized by a glycosidic D-fructofuranose-D-glucose linkage, such as raffinose, gentianose and stachyose.

## Pictet's proof[54]

Pictet has found that concentrated solutions of sucrose and copper sulphate, when standing for several hours in the cold, form microscopic needles of the double salt $C_{11}H_{22}O_{12}$ . $CuSO_4$ . $H_2O$. This reaction is actually specific of sucrose. For achieving a positive reaction, however, the concentration of the sucrose solution must be at least 10%.

*References see p. 514*

## Hadi's proof[55]

This writer has recently described a reaction of sucrose with a solution of camphor in sulphuric acid, whereby a red coloration is produced. A 1% solution of camphor in sulphuric acid is added to approximately the equal volume of the sugar solution. The maximum intensity of the coloration is attained 5 minutes after the mixing of both solutions.

## Schlemmer's proof of sucrose in the presence of invert sugar[56]

This test is based upon the removal of reducing sugars by boiling with milk of lime and on the proof of sucrose by means of α-naphthol or thymol.

In a recent paper, the octa-$O$-$p,p'$-nitrophenylazobenzoyl derivative, m. p. 155°C, $[\alpha]_D$ $+40°$ ($CHCl_3$), has been recommended for identifying sucrose.[15]


## 2. QUANTITATIVE ANALYSIS*

The methods of quantitative determination of oligosaccharides are in principle analogous to those employed for monosaccharides. Besides the possibility of using physico-chemical procedures, reducing oligosaccharides can be determined directly by conventional methods of monosaccharide analysis, while non-reducing oligosaccharides must be hydrolysed for this purpose.[1] For this reason, the chapter on oligosaccharide analysis will not present a survey of all applicable methods but deal with only some of them.


### A. REDUCING OLIGOSACCHARIDES

Of greatest importance from the practical viewpoint are the determinations of lactose and maltose. Both these compounds can be estimated from the course of the reduction of a copper ion complex by the sugar; suitable methods for this purpose are, for example, those of Munson-Walker,[57] Quisumbing-Thomas,[58] Bertrand,[59] Lane-Eynon,[60] Somogyi,[61,62] and others. To this group also belong methods recently described, namely complexometric determination of the precipitated cuprous oxide[63,64] and a modification of the Bertrand method using a copper complex of trihydroxyglutarate,[65] or the use of cuprithiosalicylate.[66]

Colorimetric determinations of reducing oligosaccharides are based on their reactions with 3,5-dinitrosalicylate ions,[67] with phenol and sulphuric acid,[68] with $o$-aminodiphenyl,[69] with benzidine in glacial acetic acid,[70] and with

---

* The analysis of oligosaccharides from the viewpoint of food technology has been dealt with in hundreds of original papers. Since the treatment of such an extensive and special field surpasses the scope of this book, the reader must be referred to special monographs.

many other reagents. Lactose, for example, has been determined colorimetrically on the basis of the green coloration produced by the action of orcinol and ferric chloride in hydrochloric acid,[71] by the action of triphenyltetrazolium salts,[72,73,] etc. In milk and in powdered milk, lactose can be determined by means of 3,6-dinitrophthalic acid[74] even in the presence of sucrose, which reacts with this acid only after inversion.

Just as in the case of monosaccharides, a very suitable reagent for the colorimetric determination of oligosaccharides is anthrone,[75–77] mainly in connection with paper chromatography. The problem of determining reducing oligosaccharides besides monosaccharides by means of anthrone was solved in a very interesting way.[78] The principle of the method is an oxidation of the sugar mixture to the corresponding aldonic and aldobionic acids. The aldonic acid does not give any colour reaction when heated with anthrone in sulphuric acid, whereas the aldobionic acid, due to hydrolysis, will react with the anthrone giving a blue-green colour reaction.

A recent paper describes the determination of reducing oligosaccharides with an aldehydic terminal unit by oxidation with iodine in alkaline solution and spectrophotometric determination of the excess of the reagent.[79]

## B. NON-REDUCING OLIGOSACCHARIDES

The most important non-reducing oligosaccharide is sucrose. Its determination is carried out either by physico-chemical methods, such as measurement of the density, viscosity, refractive index, or optical rotation of solutions of pure sucrose, or spectophotometrically in the ultra-violet region after heating of the sample with dilute sulphuric acid.[80] The determination of sucrose is often carried out, especially in the presence of other optically active compounds, on the basis of the difference of the values of optical rotations before and after inversion.[81] Sucrose may also be determined cerimetrically,[82] by oxidation with dichromate,[83] colorimetrically with phenol and sulphuric acid,[84] or with anthrone.[77,85,86]

Other non-reducing oligosaccharides are determined mostly after acid or enzymic hydrolysis.

### Identification and determination of oligosaccharides by means of infra-red spectra

As far as physico-chemical methods are concerned, infra-red spectroscopy is of steadily growing importance.* For instance, in paper chromatography, when only a small quantity of the sugar is at disposal, and rarely in crystalline form, neither melting point, X-ray diffraction nor crystallographic data can be

---

\* For a review see W. B. Neely, Advances in Carbohydrate Chem. *12*, 13 (1957).

*References see p. 514*

utilized as criteria for identification. Although the determination of the optical rotation does not require crystals, it is rather inexact with a sample of a few milligrams. Consequently, identification by means of infra-red spectra is assuming great significance and has been dealt with in a number of papers published in the last years.[87-90] The problem of identifying disaccharides by means of this method was investigated by White and co-workers,[91] who demonstrated its suitability for amorphous disaccharides and their acetyl derivatives. They described the spectra of 10 disaccharides derived either from D-glucose or from D-glucose and D-fructose. The infra-red spectra of trisaccharides were studied by Whiffen.[92] A recent paper is concerned with the quantitative determination of lactose by infra-red spectroscopy.[93]

### Enzymic determination of oligosaccharides

The enzymic determination of oligosaccharides, too, has been investigated, in particular from the viewpoint of the analysis of sugar mixtures.[94-97] This method is especially advantageous for determining maltose in the presence of D-glucose.

### REFERENCES

1. J. Staněk, M. Černý, J. Kocourek, and J. Pacák, *The Monosaccharides*, Acad. Press, New York 1963.
2. C. T. Barfoed, Z. anal. Chem. *12*, 27 (1873).
3. H. Tauber, Mikrochemie *14*, 167 (1934).
4. J. Urban, Listy cukrovar. *28*, 97 (1909/1910; Chem. Zentr. *1010*, I, 1057.
5. E. Salkowski, Hoppe-Seyler's Z. physiol. Chem. *4*, 133 (1880).
6. B. Klein and M. Weissman, Anal. Chem. *25*, 771 (1953).
7. T. Seliwanoff, Ber. *20*, 181 (1887).
8. E. Pinoff, Ber. *38*, 3308 (1905).
9. J. H. Foulger, J. Biol. Chem. *99*, 207 (1932).
10. W. R. Fearon and J. A. Drum, Analyst *75*, 56 (1950).
11. F. J. Harris, Analyst *78* 287 (1953).
12. H. Tauber, Anal. Chem. *25,* 826 (1953).
13. N.Gallo, Atti e relaz. accad. pugliese sci., Pt II 13, 8 (1955); Chem. Abstr. *53*, 18873 (1959).
14. T. Kobayashi, T. Haneishi, and M. Saito, J. Agr. Chem. Soc. Japan *36*, 189 (1962).
15. El S. Amin, J. Chem. Soc. *1961*, 5544.
16. E. Fischer and H. Thierfelder, Ber. *27*, 2031 (1894).
17. A. I. Kendall and S. Yoshida, J. Infectious Diseases *32*, 355 (1923); Chem. Abstr. *17*, 2593 (1923).
18. A. I. Kendall, J. Infectious Diseases *32*, 362 (1923); Chem. Abstr. *17*, 2723 (1923).
19. A. I. Kendall and S. Yoshida, J. Infectious Diseases *32*, 369 (1923); Chem. Abstr. *17*, 2723 (1923).
20. A. I. Kendall, R. Bly, and R. C. Haner, J. Infectious Diseases *32*, 377 (1923); Chem. Abstr. *17*, 2724 (1923).
21. A. Castellani and F. E. Taylor, Biochem. J. *16*, 655 (1922).
22. V. J. Harding and T. F. Nicholson, Biochem. J. *27*, 1082 (1933).

23. M. Wyss-Huber, H. Jäger, and E. Weiss, Helv. Chim. Acta *43*, 1010 (1960).
24. A. Hofmann, Ann. *366*, 277 (1904).
25. A. W. van Ekenstein and C. Lobry de Bruyn, Rec. trav. chim. *15*, 225 (1896).
26. E. Fischer, Ber. *17*, 579 (1884).
27. E. Fischer, Ber. *20*, 821 (1887).
28. E. Fischer, Ber. *41*, 73 (1908).
29. E. Votoček and F. Valentin, Collection Czech Chem. Communs *3*, 432 (1931).
30. W. T. Haskins, R. M. Hann, and C. S. Hudson, J. Am. Chem. Soc. *67*, 939 (1945).
31. E. Hyde, Ber. *32*, 1810 (1899).
32. C. Neuberg, Ber. *32*, 3384 (1899).
33. H. Ost, Chem. Ztg. *19*, 1501 (1895).
34. E. Fischer, Ber. *44*, 1898 (1911).
35. E. Fischer and E. F. Armstrong, Ber. *35*, 3141 (1902).
36. E. Fischer and K. Freudenberg, Ber. *46*, 1116 (1913).
37. W. Will and F. Lenze, Ber. *31*, 68 (1898).
38. C. Scheibler and H. Mittelmeier, Ber. *23*, 1438 (1890).
39. B. Helferich and H. Rauch, Ber. *59*, 2655 (1926).
40. W. T. Haskins, R. M. Hann, and C. S. Hudson, J. Am. Chem. Soc. *69*, 1461 (1947).
41. E. O. Lippmann, Ber. *53*, 2069 (1920).
42. B. Helferich and H. Rauch, Ann. *455*, 168 (1927).
43. Z. Skraup and J. König, Monatsh. Chem. *22*, 1011 (1901).
44. C. Scheibler and H. Mittelmeier, Ber. *22*, 1678 (1889).
45. G. Zemplén, Z. Csürös, and Z. Bruckner, Ber. *61*, 927 (1928).
46. G. Zemplén, Ber. *48*, 233 (1915).
47. B. Helferich, K. Bäuerlein, and F. Wiegand, Ann. *447*, 27 (1926).
48. G. Zemplén, Hoppe-Seyler's Z. physiol. Chem. *85*, 395 (1913).
49. V. C. Barry, Sci. Proc. Roy. Dublin Soc. *22*, 423 (1941), Chem. Abstr. *35*, 7985 (1941).
50. C. S. Hudson, J. Org. Chem. *9*, 470 (1944).
51. S. A. Barker, E. J. Bourne, and M. Stacey, J. Chem. Soc. *1953*, 3084.
52. H. W. Raybin, J. Am. Chem. Soc. *55*, 2603 (1933).
53. H. W. Raybin, J. Am. Chem. Soc. *59*, 1402 (1937).
54. A. Pictet, Helv. Chim. Acta *16*, 144 (1933).
55. J. Hadi, Cukoripar *11*, 225 (1958); Chem. Abstr. *53*, 2655 (1959).
56. J. Schlemmer, Listy cukrovar. *45*, 243 (1926/1927); Chem. Abstr. *22*, 180 (1928).
57. L. S. Munson and P. H. Walker, J. Am. Chem. Soc. *28*, 663 (1906).
58. F. A. Quisumbing and A. W. Thomas, J. Am. Chem. Soc. *43*, 1503 (1921).
59. G. Bertrand, Bull. soc. chim. France *35*, 1285 (1906).
60. J. H. Lane and L. Eynon, J. Soc. Chem. Ind. *42*, 32 (1923).
61. M. Somogyi, J. Biol. Chem. *160*, 61 (1945).
62. M. Somogyi, J. Biol. Chem. *195*, 19 (1952).
63. H. Eschmann, Chemist Analyst *45*, 5 (1956).
64. M. Potterat and H. Eschmann, Mitt. Gebiete Lebensm. u. Hyg. (Bern) *45*, 312 (1954); Chem. Abstr. *49*, 784 (1955).
65. A. V. Ablov and D. G. Batyr, Zhur. analyt. Khim. *12*, 749 (1957); Chem. Abstr. *52*, 8853 (1958).
66. C. Rabega, R. Stănescu, M. Rabega, and T. Osorhan, An. Univ. "C. P. Parhon", Bucuresti, Ser. Ştiinţ. Nat. (12) 65 (1956); Chem. Abstr. *52*, 19718 (1958).
67. R. T. Bottle and G. A. Gilbert, Analyst *83*, 403 (1958).
68. M. Dubois, K. A. Gilles, J. K. Hamilton, P. A. Rebers, and F. Smith, Anal. Chem. *28*, 350 (1956).

69. T. E. Timell and C. P. Glaudemans, Anal. Chem. *28*, 1916 (1956).

70. J. K. N. Jones and J. B. Pridham, Biochem. J. *58*, 288 (1954).

71. T. F. Slater, Analyst *82*, 818 (1957).

72. R. A. Fairbridge, K. J. Willis, and R. G. Booth, Biochem. J. *49*, 423 (1951).

73. A. M. Mattson and C. O. Jensen, Anal. Chem. *22*, 182 (1950).

74. T. Momose and Y. Mukai, J. Pharm. Soc. Japan (Yakugaku Zasshi) *81*, 227 (1961); Chem. Abstr. *55*, 27682 (1961).

75. R. J. Dimler, W. C. Schaefer, C. S. Wise, and C. E. Rist, Anal. Chem. *24*, 1411 (1952).

76. E. L. Richards, J. Dairy Res. *26*, 53 (1959); Chem. Abstr. *53*, 13437 (1959).

77. T. Nakata, Tokyo Jikeikai Ika Daigaku Zasshi *72*, 464 (1957); Chem. Abstr. *52*, 15835 (1958).

78. B. B. Jørgensen and O. B. Jørgensen, Acta Chem. Scand. *15*, 710 (1961).

79. G. L. Miller and A. L. Burton, Anal. Chem. *31*, 1790 (1959).

80. I. H. Bath, Analyst *83*, 451 (1958).

81. E. C. Wood, Analyst *79*, 779 (1954).

82. N. N. Sharma, Z. anal. Chem. *154*, 340 (1957).

83. G. Halliwell, Biochem. J. *74*, 457 (1960).

84. A. Lemaitre, Sucr. franç. *99*, 250 (1958); Chem. Abstr. *53*, 7636 (1959).

85. L. Pausz and J. Hadi, Cukoripar *11*, 259 (1958); Chem. Abstr. *53*, 3746 (1959).

86. N. J. Fairbairn, Chem. & Ind. (London) *1953*, 86.

87. S. A. Barker, E. J. Bourne, M. Stacey, and D. H. Whiffen, J. Chem. Soc. *1954*, 171.

88. R. L. Whistler and L. R. House, Anal. Chem. *25*, 1463 (1953).

89. L. P. Kuhn, Anal. Chem. *22*, 276 (1950).

90. H. S. Isbell, F. A. Smith, C. Creitz, H. L. Frush, J. D. Moyer, and J. E. Stewart, J. Research Natl. Bur. Standards *59*, 41 (1957).

91. J. W. White, C. R. Eddy, J. Petty, and N. Hoban, Anal. Chem. *30*, 506 (1958).

92. D. H. Whiffen, Chem. & Ind. (London) *1957*, 129.

93. J. D. S. Goulden, J. Dairy Res. *26*, 151 (1959); Anal. Abstr. *1960*, No. 265.

94. S. C. Pan, L. W. Nicholson, and P. Kolachov, Anal. Chem. *25*, 231 (1953).

95. W. Kempf and E. Lindemann, Stärke *6*, 217 (1954); Chem. Abstr. *49*, 785 (1955).

96. K. Beran and M. Burger, Chem. listy *49*, 1693 (1955); Chem. Abstr. *50*, 1529 (1956).

97. S. Böttger and W. Steinmetzer, Z. Zuckerind. *9*, 16 (1959); Chem. Abstr. *53*, 7637 (1959).

## 3. CHROMATOGRAPHIC ANALYSIS*

The introduction of chromatographic methods was of decisive significance for the study of oligosaccharides and polysaccharides, because it brought the possibility of separating complicated oligosaccharide mixtures, which are formed by partial hydrolysis of polysaccharides, enzymic conversion of saccha-

---

* For reviews see: J. Staněk, M. Černý, J. Kocourek, and J. Pacák, *The Monosaccharides*, Academic Press, New York 1963; G. N. Kowkabany, Advances in Carbohydrate Chem. *9*, 303 (1954); Y. Matsuo, Hakko Kogaku Zasshi *37*, 114, 156 (1959); K. Macek and I. M. Hais, *Bibliografie papírové chromatografie a přehled použití* (1943—1956) [*Bibliography of Paper Chromatography and Survey of Its Application* (1943—1956)], Czechoslovak Academy of Sciences, Prague 1960; I. M. Hais and K. Macek, *Papírová chromatografie* (*Paper Chromatography*), Czechoslovak Academy of Sciences, Prague 1959; E. Lederer, *Chromatographie en chimie organique et biologique*, Vol. 2, Masson et Cie, Paris 1960; F. Cramer, *Papierchromatographie*, Weinheim (1958); H. F. Linskens, *Papierchromatographie in der Botanik*, Berlin (1955).

rides, metabolic processes, etc. At present, almost every work concerned with oligosaccharides or polysaccharides, undertaken for purposes of pure synthesis, isolation or analysis, utilizes some chromatographic method.

## A. PAPER CHROMATOGRAPHY

Chromatography of oligosaccharides on paper is carried out on the same principles as that of monosaccharides. The developing techniques and the types of paper employed are the same, and most of the detecting reagents used for monosaccharides are also suitable for oligosaccharides. Moreover, the quantitative determination of oligosaccharides is effected in principle by the same procedures as in the case of monosaccharides.

The general rules of sugar chromatography on paper will be dealt with here only very briefly, because they have been treated in more detail in the book *The Monosaccharides*. Furthermore, they are also the subject of a number of reviews and monographs.[1-11]

### a) Preparation of the sample

Prior to its application to the paper, the saccharide solution must be freed from the greater part of inorganic salts because they affect the development and sometimes also the detection. Desalting is most frequently performed by means of ion exchangers[12-14] which, however, must not be strongly basic to prevent decomposition of reducing saccharides.[15-19] A low concentration of sulphuric acid ($1N$)[20] and $0.1M$ salt concentration[9] cause no disturbance. Simple and advantageous methods of desalting on paper[21,22] and on special carbon[23-25] have been described. Various procedures for preparing plant extracts for chromatography are given in monographs.[5,26]

In the chromatographic investigation of the structure of oligosaccharides and polysaccharides, great care must be devoted to their hydrolysis. Incorrectly selected conditions of chemical or enzymic hydrolysis may cause a resynthesis of oligosaccharides with a changed structure. These artefacts, detected on paper together with the actual hydrolysis products, may then lead to erroneous conclusions as to the structure of the original oligosaccharide or polysaccharide. On the basis of numerous papers,[27-34] of which the studies by Hadorn[27] and Peat[32] are especially exhaustive, it may be summarized that reversion (Chapter VI) in hydrolysis by acids (usually $0.3N$ to $1N$ sulphuric acid) is enhanced by higher concentrations of the saccharide or the acid and by a prolonged time of hydrolysis. Müller[31] recommends hydrolysis of 1% solutions of saccharides. Other writers replace sulphuric acid by 85% formic acid[29] or $0.1N$ hydrochloric or acetic acid.[33]

*References see p. 521*

Hydrolysis on ion exchangers according to Glegg[30] seems to be advantageous. Peat[32] recommends simultaneous control hydrolysis of an appropriate model disaccharide; he states that the reversion of D-glucose leads predominantly to isomaltose and gentiobiose.

Enzymic hydrolysis,[28,35-39] which may be carried out either directly on paper[36-38] or by a micromethod worked out for paper chromatography by Porter and Hoban,[39] may also lead to transglycosylation; consequently, caution is required in the interpretation of the results.

### b) Developing technique

The development is usually carried out in a descending or ascending,[41] circular[40-42] (less frequently horizontal,[43,44] and exceptionally two-dimensional [38,45,46]) arrangement. Matthias[47] chromatographs on wedge-shaped paper strips; a similar technique is employed by other investigators.[48] Separation is accelerated and improved at higher temperatures.[43,44]

Suitable paper types are Whatman and Schleicher-Schüll; for preparative purposes thick papers are employed.[49-53] Detection is facilitated by chromatography on glass-fibre papers.[54-56]

### c) Developing solvent systems

The separation of oligosaccharides is in the majority of cases carried out with systems that have already given good results in the separation of monosaccharides. These are, for example, the classical system n-butanol–acetic acid–water $(4 : 1 : 5)$[12,14,32,33,59-63] or $(20 : 7 : 10)$,[40] the frequently employed system n-butanol–pyridine–water in various ratios,[43,57,58,64-70] in particular $(6 : 4 : 3)$[50,57,64] or $(10 : 3 : 3)$,[65-68] the systems propanol–ethyl acetate–water $(7 : 1 : 2)$[71-73] or $(6 : 1 : 3)$,[74-76] ethyl acetate–pyridine–water $(10 : 4 : 3)$,[77] acetic acid–ethyl acetate–water $(2 : 4 : 6)$,[48] n-butanol–ethyl acetate–ethylene glycol–water $(6 : 1 : 1{\cdot}5 : 1{\cdot}5)$,[78] isopropyl alcohol–acetic acid–pyridine–water $(8 : 1 : : 8 : 4)$.[41]

Thoma[70] has thoroughly studied the separating properties of various systems for homologous series of oligosaccharides and recommends the systems pyridine–n-butanol–water $(34 : 50 : 16)$, water–acetic acid–ethyl acetate $(20 : : 20 : 60)$ and water–ethyl alcohol–nitromethane $(15 : 35 : 50)$. These systems are well suited for separating hydrolysates of maltodextrin, inulin and dextran.

### d) Detecting reagents

Of the large number of detecting agents suitable for oligosaccharides (see *The Monosaccharides*), the most frequently employed are anilinium phthalate[41,69,77,79] and anilinium oxalate,[14,33,60,61] mixtures of aniline and diphenylamine with phosphoric acid,[40,74,80,81] salts of benzidine[43,61] and anisidine,[66,67,76,78] further silver nitrate,[64] ethanolic sodium hydroxide for systems with picric acid.[82] Reagents of later date are ammonium molybdate,[83] acido–basic indicators,[84] and the reagent very common for saccharides and their derivatives, namely dimethyl-$p$-phenylenediamine with stannous chloride.[63]

Specific reagents for detecting keto-oligosaccharides are urea salts,[14,58,85] naphthoresorcinol with trichloroacetic acid,[33,86] and $\beta$-indolylacetic acid.[87] The differentiation between raffinose and kestose has been effected with $p$-diethylaminoanilinium sulphite.[88] A mixture of diphenylamine, aniline and orthophosphoric acid is suitable for distinguishing the 1→4 linkage from the 1→6 linkage in oligosaccharides.[80,81,89] A specific reagent for the glycosidic linkage contained in sucrose is diazouracil,[90] which permits the detection of sucrose, kestose, raffinose and stachyose. The Kiliani reagent is suited to detecting oligosaccharides containing 2-deoxy-D-glucose,[53] and the Elson-Morgan reagent for detecting amino-oligosaccharides.[91]

### e) R$_F$ value and structure

While the relation between $R_F$ value and monosaccharide structure has been the subject of many successful papers, little is known in this respect as far as oligosaccharides are concerned.

French and other writers[57,70,77,92–94] have found that to homologous series of oligosaccharides applies the linear relationship between log $[R_F/(1-R_F)]$ and the number of monosaccharide units contained in the oligosaccharide. Since the slope of the straight line expressing this relationship varies according to the type of the linkages in the oligosaccharides and according to the monosaccharides of which they are composed, it permits a comparatively rapid identification of some polysaccharides, such as dextran, amylose, inulin, galactan, fructan. This relation between the $R_F$ values and the number of monosaccharide units in an oligosaccharide holds true also for homologous series of oligosaccharide $N$-glycosides.[95]

### f) Quantitative determination

The introduction of paper chromatography for quantitative determination of saccharides has made possible a rapid and, in comparison with other methods, very exact analysis of complicated saccharide mixtures,[96,97] such as obtained by isolation from plants, foodstuffs and other sources.[98] An inestimable advantage is the fact that the entire analysis may usually be carried out with a very small amount of sample (10 μg to 1 mg).

The determination is carried out either directly on the paper or after elution of the distributed spots, in the solution obtained. Direct determination on

*References see p. 521*

paper is less accurate, but steadily employed for its rapidity and simplicity,[43,72,] [99–104] in particular in cases where the $R_F$ values of the separated oligosaccharides exhibit small differences and thus render separate elution impossible. The detected spots may be evaluated either visually[105,106] or photometrically.[98,99,103] The detection is effected by means of silver nitrate,[99,100,102,104] aniline,[103] benzidine,[43] α-naphthol,[107] and diethyl-$p$-phenylenediamine.[72]

This method has been utilized, for instance, for determining the ratio of the oligosaccharides, produced by the hydrolysis of polysaccharides,[99–101] then for the determination of lactose,[43,106] raffinose[106,107] and a mixture of raffinose and melibiose.[72]

The quantitative determination of oligosaccharides is more frequently carried out after elution from the paper. It is effected by present-day analytical methods, whose suitability for paper chromatography was critically evaluated by Fischer[108] and Quick.[109]

This method has been employed, for example, for determining the oligosaccharides obtained by the hydrolysis of polysaccharides,[61,64,77,101] and for determining lactose,[113] lactose and sucrose,[75] and raffinose.[115]

Errors in this method may be due to insufficient elution of the spots from the paper.[77,98] Various elution procedures are critically judged by Schallenberger;[98] Reith recommends chromatographic elution of oligosaccharides.[110] Kowkabany has proved radiometrically that small losses ($0.2—0.5\%$) occur during migration of the saccharide in the paper owing to adsorption.[111,112]

### g) Examples of application

Paper chromatography is at present the most frequently employed physicochemical method in saccharide chemistry. Of the large number of papers on this subject, only a few, concerned with the identification of oligosaccharides in natural material, will be mentioned here as examples.

Paper chromatography has been employed for investigating the formation of sucrose in photosynthesis,[114–117] for determining sucrose in milk[118] and in glucose[60] and for proving the presence of amino-oligosaccharides in human milk,[14,52,119–122] of maltose and its homologues in liver,[123] of lactose in mammary glands[113] and in blood,[104] of lactose, sucrose and raffinose in urine,[124] of trehalose and other oligosaccharides in the haemolymph of insects.[125,126] A number of oligosaccharides has been determined in honey,[73,78] in sugar,[127–129] in beer,[130,131] in malt extracts,[132] in various foodstuffs,[3,133,134] in plants,[26,48,53,98,135,136] in hydrolysates of plant gums and mucilages,[65,66,137–142] and in hydrolysates of hemicelluloses[143–145] and laminarin.[146]

Chromatography was utilized for studying the composition of hydrol,[97,] [147–149] the course and products of the reversion of D-glucose,[32,34,50,150–152] the reversion of L-arabinose, D-mannose,[68] D-galactose,[153] and D-fructose;[34] this method was also employed for the investigation of enzymic reactions, such as dextran synthesis,[58] conversion of lactose[102] and D-glucose,[154–156] transglucosylation,[157–162] transfructosylation[163–168] and transgalactosylation.[169,170]

## REFERENCES

1. S. M. Partridge, Biochem. Soc. Symposia (Cambridge, Engl.) *3*, 52 (1949).
2. V. V. Ratchinskiĭ, Uspekhi Khim. *19*, 445 (1950).
3. K. Täufel, Chem. Tech. *5*, 365 (1953).
4. G. N. Kowkabany, Advances in Carbohydrate Chem. *9*, 303 (1954).
5. D. J. Bell, *Modern Methods of Plant Analysis*, Berlin 1955.
6. R. J. Block and Coll., *A Manual of Paper Chromatography and Paper Electrophoresis*, New York 1955.
7. H. F. Linskens, *Papierchromatographie in der Botanik*, Springer Verlag, Berlin 1955.
8. I. M. Hais and K. Macek, *Papírová chromatografie*, Czechoslovak Academy of Sciences, Prague 1959.
9. Y. Matsuo, Hakko Kogaku Zasshi *37*, 114, 156 (1959).
10. E. Lederer, *Chromatographie en chimie organique et biologique,* Vol. 2, Masson et Cie., Paris 1960.
11. K. Macek and I. M. Hais, *Bibliography of Paper Chromatography* (1943—1956), Czechoslovak Academy of Sciences, Prague 1960.
12. S. M. Partridge and R. G. Westall, Biochem. J. *42*, 238 (1948).
13. K. T. Williams, A. Bevenue, and B. Washauer, J. Assoc. Offic. Agr. Chemists *33*, 986 (1950).
14. J. Montreuil, Bull. soc. chim. biol. *39*, 395 (1957).
15. S. Roseman, R. H. Abeles, and A. Dorfman, Arch. Biochem. Biophys. *36*, 232 (1952).
16. J. D. Phillips and A. Pollard, Nature *171*, 41 (1953).
17. A. C. Hulme, Nature *171*, 610 (1953).
18. L. I. Woolf, Nature *171*, 841 (1953).
19. L. Rebenfeld and E. Pacsu, J. Am. Chem. Soc. *75*, 4370 (1953).
20. B. D. E. Gaillard, Nature *171*, 1160 (1953).
21. G. Högström, Acta Chem. Scand. *11*, 743 (1957).
22. R. M. Smillie, J. Chromatog. *4*, 494 (1960).
23. R. C. Hughes and W. J. Whelan, Chem. & Ind. (London) *1958*, 884.
24. W. J. Whelan and K. Morgan, Chem. & Ind. (London) *1954*, 78.
25. R. L. Whistler and D. F. Durso, J. Am. Chem. Soc. *72*, 677 (1950).
26. C. J. Morris, Bot. Rev. *25*, 121 (1959).
27. H. Hadorn, Mitt. Gebiete, Lebensm. u. Hyg. (Bern) *43*, 211 (1952).
28. A. I. Oparin and M. S. Bardinskaya, Doklady Akad. Nauk S.S.S.R. *94*, 305 (1954).
29. D. B. Das, M. K. Mitra, and J. Wareham, Nature *174*, 1058 (1954).
30. R. E. Glegg and D. Eidinger, Anal. Chem. *26*, 1365 (1954).
31. K. Müller and K. Täufel, Z. Lebensmittelunters. Forsch. *100*, 437 (1955).
32. S. Peat, W. J. Whelan, T. E. Edwards, and O. Owen, J. Chem. Soc. *1958*, 586.
33. S. Goldschmidt and H. Burkert, Hoppe-Seyler's Z. physiol. Chem. *300*, 188 (1955).
34. H. C. Silberman, J. Org. Chem. *26*, 1967 (1961).
35. P. H. Blanchard and N. Albon, Arch. Biochem. *29*, 220 (1950).
36. K. T. Williams and A. Bevenue, Science *113*, 582 (1951).
37. J. S. D. Bacon and J. Edelman, Arch. Biochem. *28*, 467 (1950).

38. J. S. D. Bacon and J. Edelman, Biochem. J. *48*, 114 (1951).
39. W. L. Porter and N. Hoban, Anal. Chem. *26*, 1846 (1954).
40. K. V. Giri and V. N. Nigam, Naturwissenschaften *40*, 343 (1953).
41. H. T. Gordon, W. Thornburg, and L. N. Werum, Anal. Chem. *28*, 849 (1956).
42. M. Potterat, Mitt. Gebiete, Lebensm. u. Hyg. (Bern) *47*, 66 (1956).
43. H. R. Roberts, Anal. Chem. *29*, 1443 (1957).
44. J. B. Himes, L. D. Metcalfe, and H. Ralston, Anal. Chem. *33*, 364 (1961).
45. D. Hamerman, K. W. Bartz, and A. Reife, Anal. Chem. *27*, 1524 (1955).
46. A. A. Benson, J. A. Baasham, and M. Calvin, J. Am. Chem. Soc. *73*, 2970 (1951).
47. V. Matthias, Naturwissenschaften *43*, 351 (1956).
48. F. Scheffer, E. Welte, and K. Müller, Z. anal. Chem. *165*, 321 (1959).
49. S. Peat, W. J. Whelan, and J. G. Roberts, J. Chem. Soc. *1957*, 3916.
50. J. H. Pazur and T. Budovich, J. Am. Chem. Soc. *78*, 1885 (1956).
51. S. Peat, W. J. Whelan, and H. G. Lawley, J. Chem. Soc. *1958*, 729.
52. F. H. Malpress and F. E. Hytten, Biochem. J. *68*, 708 (1958).
53. G. A. Barber, J. Am. Chem. Soc. *81*, 3722 (1959).
54. G. Jayme and H. Knolle, Angew. Chem. *68*, 243 (1956).
55. J. W. Dieckert and N. J. Morris, Anal. Chem. *29*, 31 (1957).
56. E. J. McDonald, Anal. Chem. *29*, 32 (1957).
57. A. Jeanes, C. S. Wise, and R. J. Dimler, Anal. Chem. *23*, 415 (1951).
58. H. J. Koepsell, H. M. Tsuchiya, N. N. Hellman, A. Kazenko, C. A. Hoffman, E. S. Sharpe, and R. W. Jackson, J. Biol. Chem. *200*, 793 (1953).
59. V. Jiráček, J. Netušil, and R. Ivšinová, J. Chromatog. *2*, 659 (1959).
60. S. Vach and F. Horák, Československ. farm. *4*, 310 (1955).
61. J. Büchi and R. Gräub, Pharm. Acta Helv. *33*, 547 (1958).
62. S. M. Partridge, Biochem. J. *42*, 238 (1948).
63. F. Schneider and A. Emerich, Stärke *11*, 1 (1959).
64. R. J. Dimler and W. C. Schaefer, Anal. Chem. *24*, 1411 (1952).
65. J. K. N. Jones and W. W. Reid, J. Chem. Soc. *1954*, 1361.
66. P. Andrews and J. K. N. Jones, J. Chem. Soc. *1954*, 4134.
67. P. Andrews and J. K. N. Jones, J. Chem. Soc. *1955*, 583.
68. J. K. N. Jones and W. H. Nicholson, J. Chem. Soc. *1958*, 27.
69. E. Becker, Z. Lebensmittelunters. Forsch. *104*, 122 (1956).
70. J. A. Thoma and D. French, Anal. Chem. *29*, 1645 (1957).
71. N. Hoban and J. W. White, Anal. Chem. *30*, 1294 (1958).
72. A. Bevenue and K. T. Williams, Arch. Biochem. Biophys. *73*, 291 (1958).
73. J. W. White and N. Hoban, Arch. Biochem. Biophys. *80*, 386 (1959).
74. J. L. Buchan and R. I. Savage, Analyst *77*, 401 (1952).
75. K. J. Gardner, Nature *176*, 929 (1955).
76. H. Thaler, Z. Lebensmittelunters. Forsch. *100*, 359 (1955).
77. R. L. Whistler and J. T. Hickson, Anal. Chem. *27*, 1514 (1955).
78. J. P. Wolf and W. H. Ewart, Arch. Biochem. Biophys. *58*, 365 (1955).
79. H. Venner, Naturwissenschaften *42*, 180 (1955).
80. S. Schwimmer and A. Bevenue, Science *123*, 543 (1956).
81. R. W. Bailey and E. J. Bourne, J. Chromatog. *4*, 206 (1960).
82. H. S. Loring, L. W. Levy, and L. K. Moss, Anal. Chem. *28*, 539 (1956).
83. H. El Khadem and S. Hanessian, Anal. Chem. *30*, 1965 (1958).
84. G. Cerutti and W. Vezzini, Chim. e Ind. *43*, 789 (1961); Anal. Abstr. *9*, 1091 (1962).
85. R. Dedonder, Compt. rend. *230*, 997 (1950).
86. W. G. C. Forsyth, Nature *161*, 239 (1948).

87. A. Heyrovský, Biochim. et Biophys. Acta *21*, 180 (1956).

88. H. C. S. De Whalley, Intern. Sugar J. *54*, 158 (1952).

89. J. S. D. Bacon and B. Dickinson, Biochem. J. *66*, 289 (1957).

90. H. J. Breuer and J. S. D. Bacon, Biochem. J. *66*, 462 (1957).

91. B. Weissmann, K. Meyer, P. Sampson, and A. Linker, J. Biol. Chem. *208*, 417 (1954).

92. D. French and G. M. Wild, J. Am. Chem. Soc. *75*, 2612 (1953).

93. L. M. White and G. E. Secor, Arch. Biochem. Biophys. *43*, 60 (1953).

94. D. S. Feingold, G. Avigad, and S. Hestrin, Biochem. J. *48*, 515 (1951).

95. R. J. Bayly and E. J. Bourne, Nature *171*, 385 (1953).

96. H. Wanner, Helv. Chim. Acta *35*, 460 (1952).

97. R. L. Görnhardt, Stärke *7*, 305 (1955).

98. R. S. Schallenberger and R. G. Moores, Anal. Chem. *29*, 27 (1957).

99. S. M. Martin, Chem. & Ind. (London) *1957*, 823.

100. E. F. McFarren, K. Brand, and H. R. Rutkowski, Anal. Chem. *23*, 1146 (1951).

101. W. H. Wadman, G. J. Thomas, and A. B. Pardee, Anal. Chem. *26*, 1192 (1954).

102. K. Wallenfels, E. Bernt, and G. Limberg, Ann. *579*, 113 (1953).

103. R. M. McCready and E. A. McComb, Anal. Chem. *26*, 1645 (1954).

104. K. Wallenfels, E. Bernt, and G. Limberg, Angew. Chem. *65*, 581 (1953).

105. G. C. Gibbons and R. A. Boissonnas, Helv. Chim. Acta *33*, 1477 (1950).

106. K. Kanomata and F. Ikawa, J. Chem. Soc. Japan, Pure Chem. Sect. *82*, 638 (1961).

107. N. Albon and D. Gross, Analyst *77*, 410 (1952).

108. F. G. Fischer and H. Dörfel, Hoppe-Seyler's Z. physiol. Chem. *297*, 164 (1954).

109. R. H. Quick, Anal. Chem. *29*, 1439 (1957).

110. W. S. Reith, Nature *179*, 580 (1957).

111. C. K. Hordis and G. N. Kowkabany, Anal. Chem. *30*, 1210 (1958).

112. R. A. Schwane and G. N. Kowkabany, Anal. Chem. *34*, 325 (1962).

113. R. Heyworth and J. S. D. Bacon, Biochem. J. *61*, 224 (1955).

114. K. Täufel, H. Ruttloff, and A. Täufel, Nahrung *5*, 353 (1961).

115. A. A. Benson, J. A. Bassham, M. Calvin, T. C. Goodale, V. A. Haas, and W. Stepka, J. Am. Chem. Soc. *72*, 1710 (1950).

116. E. W. Putman and W. Z. Hassid, J. Biol. Chem. *207*, 885 (1954).

117. J. F. Turner, Biochem. J. *67*, 450 (1957).

118. A. Castiglioni and R. Pilleri, Z. anal. Chem. *154*, 187 (1957).

119. J. Montreuil, Compt. rend. *239*, 510 (1954).

120. R. Kuhn, A. Gauhe, and H. H. Baer, Chem. Ber. *86*, 827 (1953).

121. R. Kuhn, A. Gauhe, and H. H. Baer, Chem. Ber. *87*, 289 (1954).

122. A. Gauhe, P. György, J. R. E. Hoover, R. Kuhn, C. S. Rose, H. W. Ruelmes, and F. Zilliken, Arch. Biochem. Biophys. *48*, 214 (1954).

123. W. H. Fishman and H. G. Sie, J. Am. Chem. Soc. *80*, 121 (1958).

124. S. N. Tewari, Z. anal. Chem. *176*, 406 (1960).

125. D. R. Evans and V. G. Dethier, J. Insect. Physiol. *1*, 3 (1957).

126. M. Wyss-Huber, H. Jäger, and E. Weiss, Helv. Chim. Acta *43*, 1010 (1960).

127. D. Gross, F. J. Gardiner, and R. W. Butters, Intern. Sugar J. *64*, 69 (1962).

128. N. Albon and D. Gross, Intern. Sugar J. *53*, 12 (1951).

129. D. H. Foster and G. H. Marsh, Intern. Sugar J. *60*, 8 (1958).

130. A. Stöckli, Schweiz. Brauerei Rdsch. *69*, [4] 59 (1958).

131. H. R. Stocker, Schweiz. Brauerei Rdsch. *69*, [4] 167 (1958); Anal. Abstr. *6*, 3211 (1959).

132. L. Acker, W. Diemar, and D. Pfeil, Stärke *6*, 241 (1954).

133. A. Motquin, Ann. Falsif. *54*, 281 (1961); Anal. Abstr. *9*, 364 (1962).
134. S. David, I. Izvernariu, and G. Ciue, Ind. Aliment., Produce Vegetale *13*, 71 (1962); Chem. Abstr. *57*, 11437 (1962).
135. A. Archambault, J. E. Courtois, A. Wickström, and P. Le Dizet, Bull. soc. chim. biol. *38*, 1133 (1956).
136. J. E. Courtois, A. Wickström, and P. Le Dizet, Bull. soc. chim. biol. *38*, 1117 (1956).
137. E. L. Hirst, E. G. Percival, and C. B. Wylam, J. Chem. Soc. *1954*, 189.
138. R. L. Whistler and H. E. Conrad, J. Am. Chem. Soc. *76*, 3544 (1954).
139. P. Andrews and J. K. N. Jones, J. Chem. Soc. *1954*, 1724.
140. J. K. N. Jones and J. R. Nunn, J. Chem. Soc. *1955*, 3001.
141. A. M. Stephen, J. Chem. Soc. *1957*, 1919.
142. J. K. Hamilton, D. Spriestersbach, and F. Smith, J. Am. Chem. Soc. *79*, 443 (1957).
143. J. K. N. Jones and T. J. Painter, J. Chem. Soc. *1957*, 669.
144. H. C. Srivastava and F. Smith, J. Am. Chem. Soc. *79*, 982 (1957).
145. R. Montgomery, F. Smith, and H. C. Srivastava, J. Am. Chem. Soc. *79*, 698 (1957).
146. K. Fujimoto, K. Matsuda, and K. Aso, Tôhoku J. Agr. Res. *13*, 55 (1962).
147. K. Aso and K. Shibasaki, Tôhoku J. Agr. Res. *7*, 159 (1956).
148. K. Matsuda, Nature *180*, 985 (1957).
149. A. Sato and K. Aso, Nature *180*, 984 (1957).
150. K. Myrbäck, M. Hammarstand, and H. Gelinder, Arkiv Kemi *1*, 235 (1949); Chem. Abstr. *44*, 1913 (1950).
151. K. Täufel and R. Reiss, Z. anal. Chem. *134*, 252 (1951).
152. K. Anno, N. Seno, E. Nakamura, H. Saito, and R. Hoshii, Bull. Agr. Chem. Soc. Japan *23*, 67 (1959).
153. K. Müller and K. Täufel, Naturwissenschaften *40*, 140 (1953).
154. S. Peat, W. J. Whelan, and K. A. Hinson, Chem. & Ind. (London) *1955*, 385.
155. K. Saroja, R. Venkataraman, and K. V. Giri, Biochem. J. *60*, 399 (1955).
156. T. K. Walker and H. B. Wright, Arch. Biochem. Biophys. *69*, 362 (1957).
157. J. H. Pazur and D. French, J. Biol. Chem. *196*, 265 (1952).
158. S. C. Pan, L. W. Nicholson, and P. Kolachov, Arch. Biochem. Biophys. *42*, 406 (1953).
159. H. E. Gray and G. Fraenkel, Science *118*, 304 (1953).
160. J. W. White and J. Maher, Arch. Biochem. Biophys. *42*, 360 (1953).
161. J. H. Pazur, T. Budowich, and C. L. Tipton, J. Am. Chem. Soc. *79*, 625 (1957).
162. S. A. Barker, E. J. Bourne, G. C. Hewitt, and M. Stacey, J. Chem. Soc. *1957*, 3541.
163. J. Edelman and J. S. D. Bacon, Biochem. J. *49*, 529 (1951).
164. K. Wallenfels and E. Bernt, Angew, Chem. *64*, 28 (1952).
165. J. H. Pazur, J. Biol. Chem. *199*, 217 (1952).
166. F. J. Bealing and J. S. D. Bacon, Biochem J. *53*, 277 (1953).
167. S. Hestrin, D. S. Feingold, and G. Avigad, Biochem. J. *64*, 340 (1956).
168. C. Péaud-Lenoël, Bull. soc. chim. biol. *39*, 747 (1957).
169. M. Aronson, Arch. Biochem. Biophys. *39*, 370 (1952).
170. J. H. Pazur, Science *117*, 355 (1953).

## B. ELECTROPHORESIS ON PAPER

Electrophoresis, because of its good separating effect, is being increasingly employed in the study of saccharides[1-4] in conjunction with chromatography, both column and paper.

The separation of saccharides is carried out on chromatographic[5-10] or on glass-fibre paper.[11,12] The advantages of glass-fibre paper are easier detection, less adsorption and better separation of oligosaccharides of similar mobility. Better and faster separation with restricted diffusion of the spots is also attained by using a high potential gradient,[7,10,11,13] which, however, requires a more complicated apparatus.

The commonest electrolyte is borate buffer;[1-9] Frahn[10] recommends also sodium arsenite, sodium hydroxide and basic lead acetate. Advantageous separating properties are exhibited by molybdate[14] and germanate[15] buffers.

The relationship between mobility and structure is not as simple as in partition chromatography on paper; the mobility depends much more on the structure than on the molecular weight. Some oligosaccharides, such as raffinose and stachyose, migrate faster than sucrose;[7] melibiose migrates faster than rhamnose[16] and isomaltose faster than fructose.[13] The $N$-benzylglycosylammonium ions of oligosaccharides are separated in a formate buffer in strict dependence on their molecular weight;[17] the mobility decreases with rising molecular weight.

For determining the type of the glycosidic linkage in oligosaccharides, Bourne[14] recommends a method based on the separation of the corresponding glycitols prepared by reduction.

Electrophoresis has been employed for investigating the course of D-glucose reversion,[18] for separating oligosaccharide mixtures produced by partial hydrolysis of glycogen[19,20] and of fucoidin,[21] in identifying oligosaccharides in honey,[22] and for determining lactose in blood.[23] The method has been successfully used for separating oligosaccharide mixtures whose separation by chromatography on paper is difficult or not feasible at all, such as mixtures of isomaltose and gentiobiose,[24] and of maltose and cellobiose.[9]

## REFERENCES

1. A. B. Foster, Advances in Carbohydrate Chem. *12*, 81 (1957).
2. M. Lederer, *Introduction to Paper Electrophoresis and Related Methods*, Elsevier, Amsterdam 1955.
3. R. J. Block, E. L. Durrum, and G. Zweig, *A Manual of Paper Chromatography and Paper Electrophoresis*, Acad. Press, New York 1955.
4. J. Staněk, M. Černý, J. Pacák, and J. Kocourek, *The Monosaccharides*, Acad. Press, New York 1963.
5. F. Micheel and F. P. van der Kamp, Angew. Chem. *64*, 607 (1952).
6. R. Consden and W. M. Stanier, Nature *169*, 783 (1952).
7. D. Gross, Nature *172*, 908 (1953).
8. A. B. Foster and M. Stacey, J. Appl. Chem. (London) *3*, 19 (1953).
9. A. B. Foster, J. Chem. Soc. *1953*, 982.
10. J. L. Frahn and J. A. Mills, Australian J. Chem. *12*, 65 (1959).

11. E. J. Bourne, A. B. Foster, and P. M. Grant, J. Chem. Soc. *1956*, 4311.
12. D. R. Briggs, E. F. Garner, and F. Smith, Nature *178*, 154 (1956).
13. E. J. Bourne, D. H. Hutson, and H. Weigel, Chem. & Ind. (London) *1960*, 1111.
14. E. J. Bourne, D. H. Hutson, and H. Weigel, J. Chem. Soc. *1960*, 4252.
15. B. Lindberg and B. Swan, Acta. Chem. Scand. *14*, 1043 (1960).
16. B. Galos and W. Ostrowski, Bull. Acad. Sci. Polon. *2*, 61 (1954).
17. S. A. Barker, E. J. Bourne, P. M. Grant, and M. Stacey, Nature *177*, 1125 (1956).
18. S. Peat, W. J. Whelan, T. E. Edwards, and O. Owen, J. Chem. Soc. *1958*, 586.
19. S. Peat, W. J. Whelan, and T. E. Edwards, J. Chem. Soc. *1955*, 355.
20. M. L. Wolfrom and A. Thompson, J. Am. Chem. Soc. *79*, 4212 (1957).
21. R. H. Côté, J. Chem. Soc. *1959*, 2248.
22. J. W. White and N. J. Hoban, Arch. Biochem. Biophys. *80*, 386 (1959).
23. H. M. C. Robinson and J. C. Rathbun, Science *127*, 1501 (1958).
24. N. Seno, Nat. Sci. Rep. Ochanomizu Univ. *9*, 57 (1958); Anal. Abstr. *6*, 4459 (1959).

## C. COLUMN CHROMATOGRAPHY*

Column chromatography has become the most important method for purifying and separating saccharides for preparative purposes. The most frequently employed methods are adsorption on activated carbon, Fuller's earth or Magnesol and partition on cellulose; ion exchangers have also given satisfactory results. Separation has mainly been applied to free oligosaccharides or to their acylated derivatives, most frequently acetic acid esters.

Column chromatography of saccharides is dealt with in special reviews and monographs.[1-5]

### a) Activated carbon

The good separating effect of activated carbon on saccharides was discovered by Tiselius.[6-9] The properties of carbon with regard to chromatography were exhaustively studied by Jermyn.[10]

Carbon as an adsorbent has a very high capacity and separates saccharides excellently, mainly according to their molecular weights. The affinity to carbon rises with the molecular weight so that, in the series D-glucose, sucrose and raffinose, the adsorption of D-glucose is lowest and that of raffinose highest. The flow rate of the solvents through the column is increased by an admixture of a suitable porous material, such as Celite, although this somewhat lowers the capacity.

---

* For reviews see: J. Staněk, M. Černý, J. Kocourek, and J. Pacák, *The Monosaccharides*, Acad. Press, New York 1963; W. W. Binkley, Advances in Carbohydrate Chem. *10*, 55 (1955); E. Lederer, *Chromatographie en chimie organique et biologique,* Vol. 2, Paris 1960; L. Hough, *Analysis of Mixtures of Sugars by Paper and Cellulose Column Chromatography*, Vol. I of „Methods of Biochemical Analysis", D. Glick, Interscience Publishers, Inc., New York 1954.

Separation of the saccharides may be brought about by three methods:[7,8,11] the elution, the frontal and the displacement methods. The elution method worked out by Whistler and Durso[12,13] is the most widely used.

The adsorbent consists of a mixture of activated carbon, for example Darco G 60 and Celite in the ratio 1 : 1. On the column is placed an approximately 10% solution of the saccharides, whereupon the monosaccharides are successively washed out with water, the disaccharides with 5% aqueous ethyl alcohol, the trisaccharides with 15% aqueous ethyl alcohol, and the higher oligosaccharides with a more concentrated alcohol. In this way, the above investigators separated a mixture of 1 g of D-glucose, 1 g of maltose and 1 g of raffinose on a column of 3·4 cm in width and 17 cm in height. For washing out the D-glucose, they required 800 ml of water, for maltose 1500 ml of 5% ethyl alcohol, and for raffinose 700 ml of 15% ethyl alcohol.

A further improvement of the separating effect of the carbon column was achieved by gradual increase of the ethyl alcohol content in the developing system[14-17] and the use of automatic fraction collectors.[18,19] Moreover, it was found that it is advantageous to wash the carbon with ethyl alcohol[20,21] prior to use or to impregnate it with stearic acid,[14-17] as more regular separation and more complete elution of the saccharides from the column are thus attained. In some cases, where the method of successive elution failed (maltose and melibiose), good results were obtained with a column[22,23] impregnated with borate buffer of pH 10 or with ammonium molybdate.[24] Excellent separation[25] of pairs of disaccharides with a small difference in $R_F$ value was attained on a column of carbon and Celite heated up to $50-70°C$. 3% aqueous ethyl alcohol was used for separating mixtures of cellobiose with lactose, melibiose, gentiobiose and maltose. Hoban[16] employs for the same purpose a carbon column without Celite, impregnated with stearic acid. He thus separated pairs of disaccharides which by paper chromatography could not be separated at all, or not sharply enough; these pairs are: turanose and sucrose, isomaltose and gentiobiose, maltulose and nigerose, lactose and melibiose, maltulose and maltose, maltulose and sucrose, turanose and isomaltose, sucrose and maltose. Other modifications of the original method are the use of several columns and another ratio of carbon and Celite (2 : 1),[26] and replacement of Celite by deactivated alumina.[27]

Barker[28] has ingeniously separated some disaccharide pairs (for example, maltose and nigerose, cellobiose and laminaribiose) by converting them into a mixture of pyranosides and furanosides by means of methanolic hydrogen chloride. Nigerose, for instance, under these conditions forms a furanoside, whereas maltose can give rise only to a pyranoside. This mixture of glycosides is then separated on carbon by the conventional method. Hughes[29] employs a special activated carbon for rapid removal of salts from the oligosaccharide solution.

*References see p. 530*

A quantitative method for separating oligosaccharides on a microscale (0·2 mg) on a column of carbon and Celite, impregnated with stearic acid, has been described by Miller.[17]

The method of Whistler and Durso[12] has been employed in the isolation of oligosaccharides produced by hydrolysis of starch (from maltose up to malto-octaose),[24,30–34] and Schardinger dextrin,[14,15] by hydrolysis of xylans,[35,36] glycogen,[37] pectin,[38,39] hemicelluloses,[40] laminarin[41] and fucoidin;[42] this procedure was further utilized in the analysis of hydrol,[23,43,44] human milk,[45–50] and honey.[51] It was also employed in the study of the enzymic conversion of saccharides,[52–60] such as D-glucose,[52,53] maltose,[54] lactose,[55] and sucrose,[56–60] as well as for investigating the reversion of D-glucose,[61–63] D-xylose,[64] D-galactose,[26] L-arabinose and D-mannose;[65] moreover, it was utilized for isolating oligosaccharides from lucerne[66] and for studying the biological synthesis of lactose.[67,68]

### b) Siliceous earths (Fuller's earths)

The significance of siliceous earths for separating oligosaccharides is negligible in comparison with that of activated carbon.[5,69–72] The adsorption of saccharides is here opposite to that on carbon, which means that the elution of oligosaccharides requires a higher water content in the developing system. The developers employed are aqueous ethyl alcohol and aqueous isopropyl alcohol.

This method has been employed, for instance, for separating sucrose from the unfermentable component of molasses.[71]

### c) Cellulose

Partition chromatography on cellulose was first employed for saccharides by Hough.[73,74] Separation on a cellulose column proceeds in a similar way to that on paper, which facilitates the prediction of the course of the elution. Developing is effected by similar solvent mixtures as in paper chromatography, for example, by isopropyl alcohol–n-butanol–water (7 : 1 : 2),[75] ethyl acetate–pyridine–water (10 : 4 : 3),[32] n-butanol–pyridine–water (6 : 1 : 1),[50] and others.

The small amount of impurities washed out from the cellulose columns can be removed from the eluate by filtration through carbon with Celite.[76] Whistler [77] therefore recommends that the column be washed with water prior to chromatography.

Chromatography on cellulose has been utilized for quantitative determination of raffinose besides sucrose and stachyose in raw beet sugar,[75] for isolating kestose[78] formed by transfructosylation from sucrose and further for isolating a tetrasaccharide from human milk;[49,50] maltulose, lactulose and melibiulose after the action of alkalis on maltose, lactose and melibiose;[79,80] a mixture of oligosaccharides from Jerusalem artichoke;[81] a mixture of oligosaccharides from pectin hydrolysate.[38]

Following separation on carbon, panose[32] and maltohexaose[33] have been isolated from starch hydrolysate. Maltose homologues have been separated on a heated cellulose column into as many as 20 units.[82]

### d) Ion exchangers

A general method for separating saccharides in the form of borate complexes on ion exchangers has been worked out by Khym and Zill.[83],[85] Elution from the column is performed with a 0·001M—0·02M sodium tetraborate solution. Non-reducing oligosaccharides are less adsorbed than reducing ones and washed out more rapidly; for example, stachyose before D-fructose; sucrose and trehalose before cellobiose, maltose and lactose.[84],[85] A shortcoming of ion exchangers is the fact that elution of saccharides requires large volumes of washing solutions (100 ml and even more for 1 mg).

This method has been successfully employed for separating a complicated mixture of monosaccharides and oligosaccharides,[86] as well as for separating oligouronic acids.[88—91]

A significant improvement[87] has been achieved by the use of Dowex 50 W (200—400 mesh) in the Li$^+$ cycle, on which sugar mixtures have been separated, such as raffinose, sucrose and D-glucose, or raffinose and melibiose, by elution with water. The method is rapid and is a suitable supplement to separation on a carbon or cellulose column for, in contrast to them, the affinity of oligosaccharides to Dowex 50 W decreases with rising molecular weight.

### e) Chromatography of acylated derivatives

Acetylated saccharide derivatives are often employed for their good crystallizing properties and easy preparation. McNeely[92] has worked out a method for their separation on Magnesol and thus further enhanced their significance as intermediates in the isolation and synthesis of saccharides.[31,43,44,61,93—102] The adsorbing power of Magnesol varies considerably with moisture; a higher water content lowers adsorption and worsens separation.[93] Usual developers are mixtures of benzene with ethyl alcohol and of benzene with $t$-butyl alcohol.

On Magnesol have been separated, for instance, acetylated derivatives of sucrose and isosucrose,[94] of gentiobiose and maltose,[93] of isomaltose and 5-$O$-$\beta$-D-glucopyranosyl-D-glucose,[44] and further a mixture of acetylated oligosaccharides after the acetylation of cellulose[99] and after reversion of D-glucose.[61] Sucrose,[101,102] isomaltose,[97] maltotriose[31] and panose[100] have been isolated by this method.

*References see p. 530*

34 — The Oligosaccharides

Better results in the separation of acetylated oligosaccharides with a higher number of glucose units have been obtained with Silene EF.[96,103]

$\beta$-Cellobiose octa-O-acetate and $\beta$-maltose octa-O-acetate may be separated on a mixture of silicic acid and calcium carbonate (1 : 1).[104] Aluminium oxide is not suited for such a separation because partial deacetylation may take place on its surface.

Azoylated derivatives of oligosaccharides, prepared by the action of $p$-phenylazobenzoyl chloride, have been separated on silica-gel[105,106] and on Magnesol.[107]

### REFERENCES

1. J. Staněk, M. Černý, J. Kocourek, and J. Pacák, *The Monosaccharides*, Acad. Press, New York 1963.
2. W. W. Binkley, Advances in Carbohydrate Chem. *10*, 55 (1955).
3. E. Lederer, *Chromatographie en chimie organique et biologique*, Masson et Cie, Paris 1960.
4. L. Hough, *Analysis of Mixtures of Sugars by Paper and Cellulose Column Chromatography*, Vol. I of *Methods of Biochemical Analysis,* D. Glick, Interscience Publishers, Inc., New York 1954.
5. W. W. Binkley and M. L. Wolfrom, *Chromatography of Sugars and Related Substances*, Sugar Research Foundation N. Y., Sci. Rept. Ser. No. 10, 1948.
6. A. Tiselius, Science *94*, 145 (1941).
7. A. Tiselius, Arkiv Kemi, Mineral. Geol. *16*, A, 1 (1943).
8. A. Tiselius, Kolloid-Z. *105*, 101 (1943).
9. R. J. P. Williams, L. Hagdahl, and A. Tiselius, Arkiv Kemi *7*, 1 (1954).
10. M. A. Jermyn, Australian J. Chem. *10*, 55 (1957).
11. L. Hagdahl, Acta Chem. Scand. *2*, 574 (1948).
12. R. L. Whistler and D. F. Durso, J. Am. Chem. Soc. *72*, 677 (1950).
13. R. L. Whistler and D. F. Durso, J. Am. Chem. Soc. *74*, 5140 (1952).
14. R. S. Alm, R. J. P. Williams, and A. Tiselius, Acta Chem. Scand. *6*, 836 (1952).
15. R. S. Alm, Acta Chem. Scand. *6*, 1186 (1952).
16. N. Hoban and J. W. White, Anal. Chem. *30*, 1294 (1958).
17. G. L. Miller, Anal. Biochem. *1*, 133 (1960).
18. D. F. Durso, E. D. Schall, and R. L. Whistler, Anal. Chem. *23*, 425 (1951).
19. J. L. Hickson and R. L. Whistler, Anal. Chem. *25*, 1425 (1953).
20. B. Lindberg and B. Wickberg, Acta Chem. Scand. *8*, 569 (1954).
21. H. J. Breuer and J. S. D. Bacon, Biochem. J. *66*, 462 (1957).
22. S. A. Barker, E. J. Bourne, and O. Theander, J. Chem. Soc. *1955*, 4276.
23. A. Sato, K. Watanabe, and K. Aso, Chem. & Ind. (London) *1958*, 887.
24. S. A. Barker, E. J. Bourne, A. B. Foster, and R. B. Ward, Nature *179*, 262 (1957).
25. C. C. Tu and K. Ward, J. Am. Chem. Soc. *77*, 4938 (1955).
26. C. N. Turton, A. Bebbington, S. Dixon, and E. Pacsu, J. Am. Chem. Soc. *77*, 2565 (1955).
27. V. Dj. Stefanović, J. Chromatog. *5*, 453 (1961).
28. S. A. Barker, E. J. Bourne, and D. M. O'Mant, Chem. & Ind. (London) *1955*, 425.
29. R. C. Hughes and W. J. Whelan, Chem. & Ind. (London) *1958*, 884.

30. W. J. Whelan, J. M. Bailey, and P. J. P. Roberts, J. Chem. Soc. *1953*, 1293.
31. A. Thompson and M. L. Wolfrom, J. Am. Chem. Soc. *74*, 3612 (1952).
32. R. L. Whistler and J. L. Hickson, J. Am. Chem. Soc. *76*, 1671 (1954).
33. R. L. Whistler and B. F. Moy, J. Am. Chem. Soc. *77*, 5761 (1955).
34. S. J. Patterson and J. L. Buchan, Analyst *86*, 160 (1961).
35. R. L. Whistler and C.-C. Tu, J. Am. Chem. Soc. *75*, 645 (1953).
36. R. L. Whistler and C.-C. Tu, J. Am. Chem. Soc. *74*, 3609 (1952).
37. M. L. Wolfrom and A. Thompson, J. Am. Chem. Soc. *79*, 4213 (1957).
38. H. Deuel and E. Stutz, Advances in Enzymology *20*, 3416 (1958).
39. J. K. N. Jones and W. W. Reid, J. Chem. Soc. *1954*, 1361.
40. A. R. N. Gorrod and J. K. N. Jones, J. Chem. Soc. *1954*, 2522.
41. S. Peat, W. J. Whelan, and H. G. Lawley, J. Chem. Soc. *1958*, 729.
42. R. H. Côté, J. Chem. Soc. *1959*, 2248.
43. M. L. Wolfrom, A. Thompson, A. N. O'Neill, and T. T. Galkowski, J. Am. Chem. Soc. *74*, 1062 (1952).
44. J. C. Sowden and A. S. Spriggs, J. Am. Chem. Soc. *78*, 2503 (1956).
45. R. Kuhn, A. Gauhe, and H. H. Baer, Chem. Ber. *86*, 827 (1953).
46. R. Kuhn, A. Gauhe, and H. H. Baer, Chem. Ber. *87*, 289 (1954).
47. R. Kuhn, H. H. Baer, and A. Gauhe, Chem. Ber. *88*, 1135 (1955).
48. R. Kuhn and W. Kirschenlohr, Chem. Ber. *87*, 1547 (1954).
49. R. Kuhn and A. Gauhe, Ann. *611*, 249 (1958).
50. F. H. Malpress and F. E. Hytten, Biochem. J. *68*, 708 (1958).
51. J. W. White and N. Hoban, Arch. Biochem. Biophys. *80*, 386 (1959).
52. T. K. Walker and H. B. Wright, Arch. Biochem. Biophys. *69*, 362 (1957).
53. K. V. Giri, K. Saroja, R. Venkataraman, and P. L. Narasimha Rao, Arch. Biochem. Biophys. *51*, 62 (1954).
54. S. A. Barker and E. J. Bourne, J. Chem. Soc. *1952*, 209.
55. K. Wallenfels, E. Bernt, and G. Limberg, Ann. *579*, 113 (1953).
56. N. Albon, D. J. Bell, P. H. Blanchard, D. Gross, and J. T. Rundell, J. Chem. Soc. *1953*, 24.
57. J. S. D. Bacon and D. J. Bell, J. Chem. Soc. *1953*, 2528.
58. D. J. Bell and J. Edelman, J. Chem. Soc. *1954*, 4652.
59. D. Gross, P. H. Blanchard, and D. J. Bell, J. Chem. Soc. *1954*, 1727.
60. S. A. Barker, E. J. Bourne, P. M. Grant, and M. Stacey, J. Chem. Soc. *1958*, 601.
61. A. Thompson, K. Anno, M. L. Wolfrom, and M. Inatome, J. Am. Chem. Soc. *76*, 1309 (1954).
62. S. Peat, W. J. Whelan, T. E. Edwards, and O. Owen, J. Chem. Soc. *1958*, 586.
63. M. L. Wolfrom, A. Thompson, and A. M. Brownstein, J. Am. Chem. Soc. *80*, 2015 (1958).
64. D. H. Ball and J. K. N. Jones, J. Chem. Soc. *1958*, 33.
65. J. K. N. Jones and W. H. Nicholson, J. Chem. Soc. *1958*, 27.
66. H. Hérissey, P. Fleury, A. Wickström, J. E. Courtois, and P. Le Dizet, Bull. soc. chim. biol. *36*, 1507 (1954).
67. H. G. Wood, P. Sin, and P. Schambye, Arch. Biochem. Biophys. *69*, 390 (1957).
68. P. Schambye, H. G. Wood, and M. Kleiber, J. Biol. Chem. *226*, 1011 (1957).
69. B. W. Lew, M. L. Wolfrom, and R. M. Goepp, J. Am. Chem. Soc. *68*, 1449 (1946).
70. B. W. Lew, M. L. Wolfrom, and R. M. Goepp, J. Am. Chem. Soc. *67*, 1865 (1945).
71. W. W. Binkley and M. L. Wolfrom, J. Am. Chem. Soc. *69*, 664 (1947).
72. M. L. Wolfrom and G. M. Blair, J. Am. Chem. Soc. *70*, 2046 (1948).
73. L. Hough, J. K. N. Jones, and W. H. Wadman, Nature *162*, 448 (1948).

74. L. Hough, J. K. N. Jones, and W. H. Wadman, J. Chem. Soc. *1949*, 2511.
75. D. Gross and N. Albon, Analyst *78*, 191 (1953).
76. J. S. D. Bacon, Biochem J. *57*, 320 (1954).
77. P. L. Whistler, Science *120*, 899 (1954).
78. N. Albon, D. J. Bell, P. H. Blanchard, D. Gross, and J. T. Rundell, J. Chem. Soc. *1953*, 24.
79. L. Hough, J. K. N. Jones, and E. L. Richards, J. Chem. Soc. *1953*, 2005.
80. L. Hough, J. K. N. Jones, and E. L. Richards, J. Chem. Soc. *1954*, 295.
81. R. Dedonder, Bull. soc. chim. biol. *34*, 144 (1952).
82. J. A. Thoma, H. B. Wright, and D. French, Arch. Biochem. Biophys. *85*, 452 (1959).
83. J. X. Khym and L. P. Zill, J. Am. Chem. Soc. *73*, 2399 (1951).
84. G. R. Noggle and L. P. Zill, Arch. Biochem, Biophys. *41*, 21 (1952).
85. J. X. Khym and L. P. Zill, J. Am. Chem. Soc. *74*, 2090 (1952).
86. L. P. Zill, J. X. Khym, and G. M. Cheniae, J. Am. Chem. Soc. *75*, 1339 (1953).
87. J. K. N. Jones, R. A. Wall, and A. O. Pittet, Can. J. Chem. *38*, 2285 (1960).
88. R. Derungs and H. Deuel, Helv. Chim. Acta *37*, 657 (1954).
89. P. Andrews and J. K. N. Jones, J. Chem. Soc. *1954*, 1724.
90. A. Roudier and L. Ebenhard, Compt. rend. *240*, 2012 (1955).
91. J. K. N. Jones and T. J. Painter, J. Chem. Soc. *1957*, 669.
92. W. H. McNeely, W. W. Binkley, and M. L. Wolfrom, J. Am. Chem. Soc. *67*, 527 (1945).
93. M. L. Wolfrom, A. Thompson, T. T. Galkowski, and E. J. Quinn, Anal. Chem. *24*, 1670 (1952).
94. W. W. Binkley and M. L. Wolfrom, J. Am. Chem. Soc. *68*, 2171 (1946).
95. M. L. Wolfrom, L. W. Georges, and I. L. Miller, J. Am. Chem. Soc. *71*, 125 (1949).
96. E. E. Dickey and M. L. Wolfrom, J. Am. Chem. Soc. *71*, 825 (1949).
97. M. L. Wolfrom, J. T. Tyree, T. T. Galkowski, and A. N. O'Neill, J. Am. Chem. Soc. *73*, 4927 (1951).
98. M. L. Wolfrom, E. N. Lassettre, and A. N. O'Neill, J. Am. Chem. Soc. *73*, 595 (1951).
99. M. L. Wolfrom and J. C. Dacons, J. Am. Chem. Soc. *74*, 5331 (1952).
100. A. Thompson and M. L. Wolfrom, J. Am. Chem. Soc. *73*, 5849 (1951).
101. R. U. Lemieux and G. Huber, J. Am. Chem. Soc. *75*, 4118 (1953).
102. R. U. Lemieux and G. Huber, J. Am. Chem. Soc. *78*, 4117 (1956).
103. L. W. Georges, R. S. Bower, and M. L. Wolfrom, J. Am. Chem. Soc. *68*, 2169 (1946).
104. H. Bredereck, H. Dürr, and K. Ruck, Chem. Ber. *87*, 526 (1954).
105. G. H. Coleman and C. M. McCloskey, J. Am. Chem. Soc. *65*, 1588 (1943).
106. C. D. Hurd and R. P. Zelinski, J. Am. Chem. Soc. *69*, 243 (1947).
107. G. H. Coleman, A. G. Farnham, and A. Miller, J. Am. Chem. Soc. *64*, 1501 (1942).

## D. THIN-LAYER CHROMATOGRAPHY

Chromatography on thin layers[1,2] is a rapid method applicable to both analytical and preparative purposes on a semimicroscale. Separation is most frequently performed on silica-gel,[3–6,9] on kieselguhr,[7–9] which may be impregnated with sodium acetate[7] or boric acid,[8] or on cellulose.[10] Arrangement of the adsorption layer in wedge form improves the separating effect.

Detection is carried out with reagents that are also currently employed in paper chromatography. For hydrophobic substances (for example peracetylated oligosaccharide derivatives), water is suitable when silica-gel is used.[3]

The method is utilized for separating free sugars,[6-10] for example, for identification of raffinose and sucrose in molasses,[8] for separating malto-oligosaccharides after starch hydrolysis,[9] and mainly for separating acylated sugar derivatives,[3-5] where paper chromatography is difficult. For example, a mixture of acetates of β-laminaribiose, -triose, -tetraose and -pentaose has been separated on silica-gel with 4% of methanol in benzene as developer.[3]

### REFERENCES

1. E. G. Woolish, M. Schmall, and M. Hawrylyshin, Anal. Chem. *33*, 1138 (1961).
2. E. Stahl, Angew. Chem. *73*, 646 (1961).
3. M. E. Tate and C. T. Bishop, Can. J. Chem. *40*, 1043 (1962).
4. J. O. Deferrari, R. Muchnik de Lederkremer, B. Matsuhiro, and J. F. Sproviero, J. Chromatog. *9*, 283 (1962).
5. M. Gee, J. Chromatog. *9*, 278 (1962).
6. G. Pastuska, Z. anal. Chem. *179*, 427 (1961).
7. E. Stahl, and V. Kaltenbach, J. Chromatog. *5*, 351 (1961).
8. V. Prey, H. Berbalk, and M. Kausz, Mikrochim. Acta *1961*, 968.
9. C. E. Weill and P. Hanke, Anal. Chem. *34*, 1736 (1962).
10. A. Schweiger, J. Chromatog. *9*, 374 (1962).

## E. GAS-LIQUID PARTITION CHROMATOGRAPHY

This method has so far been utilized mainly in the analysis of monosaccharides;[1] however, as demonstrated by Jones,[2] it is also a suitable analytical method for separating oligosaccharides.

Acetates of non-reducing disaccharides and acetylated sugar alcohols, prepared by reduction, such as a mixture of per-O-acetyl derivatives of α-D-xylopyranosyl α-D-xylopyranoside, 5-O-β-D-xylopyranosyl-L-arabitol, sucrose and maltitol have been separated at a temperature of 236°C on glass beads impregnated with methyl silicone rubber gum. The separation of acetates of reducing disaccharides is unsatisfactory, because they form broad peaks.

### REFERENCES

1. J. Staněk, M. Černý, J. Kocourek, and J. Pacák, *The Monosaccharides*, Acad. Press, New York 1963.
2. H. G. Jones and M. B. Perry, Can. J. Chem. *40*, 1339 (1962).

# Index of authors cited in the text

# Biological subject index